RECENT DEVELOPMENTS IN THE CHEMISTRY OF
NATURAL CARBON COMPOUNDS

RECENT DEVELOPMENTS IN THE CHEMISTRY OF NATURAL CARBON COMPOUNDS

VOLUME IX

Editors of the Series:

R. BOGNÁR, V. BRUCKNER, CS. SZÁNTAY

Consultant Editors:

S. J. ANGYAL (Sydney), Z. CSŰRÖS (Budapest), Z. FÖLDI (Budapest),
Á. GERECS (Budapest), D. IVANOV (Sofia), N. K. KOCHETKOV (Moscow),
K. MOTHES (Halle), YU. A. OVCHINNIKOV (Moscow), F. ŠORM (Prague),
W. TREIBS (Heidelberg), B. C. L. WEEDON (London), I. WROBEL (Warsaw)

AKADÉMIAI KIADÓ

PUBLISHING HOUSE OF THE HUNGARIAN ACADEMY OF SCIENCES

BUDAPEST 1979

SYNTHETIC CHEMISTRY OF INSECT PHEROMONES AND JUVENILE HORMONES

by

K. MORI

Department of Agricultural Chemistry, University of Tokyo
Tokyo, Japan

COMPOSITION OF BULGARIAN ROSE FLOWER CONCRETE THE STRUCTURE AND BIOGENESIS OF ITS COMPONENTS

by

B. STOIANOVA-IVANOVA

Department of Organic Chemistry, University of Sofia
Sofia, Bulgaria

CHALCONE EPOXIDES IN FLAVONOID CHEMISTRY

by

GY. LITKEI

Institute of Organic Chemistry, Kossuth Lajos University
Debrecen, Hungary

AKADÉMIAI KIADÓ

PUBLISHING HOUSE OF THE HUNGARIAN ACADEMY OF SCIENCES

BUDAPEST 1979

Series ISBN 963 05 0702 1
Vol. 9 ISBN 963 05 1632 2

CONTENTS

K. MORI

Synthetic chemistry of insect pheromones and juvenile hormones

B. STOIANOVA–IVANOVA

Composition of Bulgarian rose flower concrete
The structure and biogenesis of its components

Gy. Litkei

Chalcone epoxides in flavonoid chemistry

K. MORI

SYNTHETIC CHEMISTRY
OF INSECT PHEROMONES AND JUVENILE
HORMONES

I. GENERAL INTRODUCTION

For many years scientists wondered at the spectacular scenes of metamorphosis, aggregation and mating of insects. During the past two decades it has gradually become clear that these biological phenomena are regulated by chemical substances known as insect hormones and pheromones. Insect chemistry, the study of natural products of insect origin, is now regarded as an established branch of natural products chemistry. Butenandt and his associates were the pioneers. It was about fifteen years ago when they established the structure of α-ecdysone (1) [1], the moulting hormone, and bombykol (2) [2], the sex pheromone of the silkworm moth, *Bombyx mori*. In 1967 Röller and his co-workers completed the structure elucidation of the juvenile hormone of the *Cecropia* moth, *Hyalophora cecropia*, now known as JH I (**3**) [3].

The presentations of these unique structures were indeed challenges to synthetic organic chemists, which were answered by a flood of syntheses. This provided ample supplies of otherwise inaccessible natural products and opened the way to the practical uses of these hormones and pheromones to improve the welfare of mankind.

There are many monographs both on insect hormones and pheromones [4-7]. However, none of them is written with a special emphasis on synthetic aspects and therefore they are inadequate as a reference material for those who want to synthesize insect hormones or pheromones. The aim of the present article is to provide a compilation of synthetic works in insect chemistry. As the major synthetic problem in this field is the stereoselective construction of an olefinic linkage, the chapter entitled "synthetic methods useful in insect chemistry" mainly deals with the methods of olefin formation. Then "synthesis of insect pheromones" is detailed according to the classification of pheromones mainly based on the type of compounds. The chapter on the "synthesis of insect juvenile hormones" describes the syntheses of the *Cecropia* juvenile hormone, juvabione and related compounds. As the trend in modern synthetic organic chemistry is to develop new methods for providing optically active compounds in stereocontrolled manners, syntheses of optically active compounds are treated comprehensively. It is hoped that the present review will be useful not only to synthetic organic chemists, but also to entomologists who wish to prepare by themselves compounds of their own interests by the established methods. The style employed in the present article is the rapid visual retrieval of information, which is particularly satisfactory in describing organic syntheses.

The syntheses of moulting hormones are excluded from the present article, for there is an excellent short review on this subject [8].

REFERENCES

1. HUBER, R., HOPPE, W., *Chem. Ber.*, **98**, 2403 (1965).
2. BUTENANDT, A., HECKER, E., HOPP, M., KOCH, W., *Liebigs Ann. Chem.*, **658**, 39 (1962).
3. RÖLLER, H., DAHM, K. H., SWEELY, C. C., TROST, B. M., *Angew. Chem. intern. Ed.*, **6**, 179 (1967).
4. WIGGLESWORTH, V. B., "Insect Hormones", Oliver & Boyd, R. & R. Clark Ltd., Edinburgh (1970).
5. SLÁMA, K., ROMAŇUK, M., ŠORM, F., "Insect Hormones and Bioanalogues", Springer-Verlag, Wien and New York (1974).

6. JACOBSON, M., "Insect Sex Pheromones", Academic Press, New York and London (1972).
7. BIRCH, M. C., (Ed.), "Pheromones", North-Holland Publ. Co, Amsterdam (1974).
8. NAKANISHI, K., GOTO, T., ITO, S., NATORI, S., NOZOE, S., (Eds), "Natural Products Chemistry", Vol. 1, pp. 525–532, Kodansha, Ltd., Tokyo (1974).

II. SYNTHETIC METHODS USEFUL IN INSECT CHEMISTRY

1. INTRODUCTION

Before the advent of pheromone and juvenile hormone chemistry, the stereoselective construction of di- and trisubstituted olefins was of only limited interest to terpene and oil chemists. During the past decade the situation has changed and we now have many ingenious new methods as well as modifications of older methods for olefin syntheses. Two excellent reviews are available concerning the stereoselective synthesis of olefins [1, 2]. In the following section, reactions are collected which have been used, or may be useful, in insect chemistry.

2. STEREOSELECTIVE ROUTES TO DISUBSTITUTED OLEFINS

A. Synthesis of E-olefins

(i) *Metal–ammonia reduction of acetylenes.* The reduction of acetylenets with sodium in liquid ammonia is the standard method [Equation (1)] [3].

$$R-C\equiv C-(CH_2)_nOTHP \xrightarrow{\ Na/NH_3\ } \begin{matrix} H & (CH_2)_nOTHP \\ & C=C \\ R & H \end{matrix} \qquad (1)$$

Warthen and Jacobson recommend the use of a large volume of liquid ammonia to minimize the recovery of the starting acetylenes [4].

(ii) *Lithium aluminium hydride reduction of acetylenes.* The reduction of propargylic alcohols to allylic alcohols with lithium aluminium hydride usually proceeds in an excellent yield [Equation (2)] [5].

$$R-C\equiv C-CH_2OH \xrightarrow{\ LiAlH_4\ } \begin{matrix} >Al\overset{O}{\diagdown}CH_2 \\ C=C \\ R \qquad H \end{matrix} \xrightarrow{\ H_2O\ } \begin{matrix} H & CH_2OH \\ & C=C \\ R & H \end{matrix} \qquad (2)$$

(iii) *Reductive elimination of allylic substituents.* E-Homoallylic alcohols can be prepared from acetylenes by the route shown in Equation (3). The key stereoselective step (97% E-isomer) is the reductive elimination of the allylic t-butoxy group [6]. A highly stereoselective synthesis of E-olefins employs the reduction of a phosphonate ester as the key step [Equation (4)] [7]. The yields are moderate to excellent.

$$
\begin{array}{c}
\underset{\displaystyle C_3H_7CH-C\equiv C-CH_2OH}{\overset{Bu^t O}{}} \xrightarrow{\text{H}_2/\text{Lindlar–Pd}} \underset{\displaystyle C_3H_7CH-C=C-CH_2OH}{\overset{Bu^t O\ \ H\ H}{}} \longrightarrow
\end{array}
$$

$$
\xrightarrow[68\%]{\text{LiAlH}_4/\text{Dioxan}} \underset{\displaystyle C_3H_7C=C-CH_2CH_2OH}{\overset{H}{}\ \underset{H}{}} \tag{3}
$$

$$
\underset{R}{\overset{Me}{}}C=CHCH_2\underset{O}{\overset{}{P}}(OEt)_2 \xrightarrow[R'X]{\text{n–BuLi}} \underset{R}{\overset{Me}{}}C=CHCH-\underset{R'\ \ O}{P}(OEt)_2 \longrightarrow
$$

$$
\xrightarrow[\text{Ether, 0°C}]{\text{LiAlH}_4} \underset{H}{\overset{MeCHR\ \ H}{C=C}}_{R'} \tag{4}
$$

(iv) *Rearrangement of allylic dithiocarbamates.* This method is applicable to the synthesis of various alkenol sex pheromones [Equation (5)] [8]. The yield is excellent.

$$
\overset{S}{\underset{\displaystyle \diagup\!\!\diagup\!\!\diagup\, S-C-NMe_2}{\|}} \xrightarrow[2.\ Me(CH_2)_mI]{1.\ LiNPr^i_2} \underset{\underset{NMe_2}{\displaystyle S\diagdown S}}{\overset{H\ (CH_2)_m Me}{\diagup\!\!\diagup}} \xrightarrow{\Delta}
$$

$$
\longrightarrow Me(CH_2)_m\underset{H}{\overset{H}{C}}=C\!CH_2S\overset{S}{\overset{\|}{C}}NMe_2 \xrightarrow[2.\ I(CH_2)_{n-1}OTHP]{1.\ LiN\diagdown Pr^i} Me(CH_2)_m\underset{H}{\overset{H}{C}}=C\!\!\underset{\underset{S}{\overset{S-C-NMe_2}{\|}}}{C}(CH_2)_{n-1}OTHP \longrightarrow
$$

$$
\tag{5}
$$

$$
\xrightarrow{\text{Li/EtNH}_2} Me(CH_2)_m\underset{H}{\overset{H}{C}}=C(CH_2)_nOTHP \xrightarrow[\text{AcOH}]{\text{AcCl}} Me(CH_2)_m\underset{H}{\overset{H}{C}}=C(CH_2)_nOAc
$$

(v) *The Wittig olefin synthesis.* The Schlosser modification of the Wittig reaction as shown in Equation (6) gives E-olefins in 60–72% yield with 96–99% stereoselectivity [9, 10].

$$
\left[Ph_3\overset{\oplus}{P}\!\!\underset{Li}{-}\!\!CHR \right] X^{\ominus} \xrightarrow{R'-CHO} \left[Ph_3\overset{\oplus}{P}\!-\!\underset{}{CH}\!-\!\underset{OLi}{\overset{R'}{CH}} \right] X^{\ominus} \xrightarrow[\text{ether, THF (1:1), } -30°C]{\text{PhLi or n-BuLi·}}
$$

$$
\xrightarrow{\quad} X^{\ominus} \left[\underset{Li}{\overset{Ph_3\overset{\oplus}{P}}{\diagup}}\!\!\overset{OLi}{\underset{H}{\diagdown}}\!\!\overset{}{\underset{R}{\diagup}} R' \right] \quad \rightleftharpoons \quad \left[\underset{R}{\overset{Ph_3\overset{\oplus}{P}}{\diagup}}\!\!\overset{OLi}{\underset{H}{\diagdown}}\!\!\overset{}{\underset{Li}{\diagup}} R' \right] X^{\ominus} \xrightarrow{\quad} \qquad (6)
$$

$$
\xrightarrow[\text{or Bu}^t\text{OH}]{\text{HCl-ether}} \quad \textit{threo}-\text{Betaine} \xrightarrow[\text{r.t., 2h}]{\text{KOBu}^t} \quad \overset{R}{\underset{H}{\diagup}}C\!=\!C\overset{H}{\underset{R'}{\diagdown}}
$$

(vi) Utilization of organoaluminium compounds. Disubstituted *E*-alkenes can be prepared by the reaction of *E*-alkenyl trialkylaluminates with alkyl halides and sulfonates [Equation (7)] [11]. The yield is good (44–79%) for allylic halides and moderate (41–44%) for primary halides. Secondary and tertiary halides gave poor results. *E*-Vinyl iodides are obtainable in 94% stereoselectivity as shown in Equation (8) [12]. Reaction with dialkyl lithium cuprate (R_2CuLi) converts the iodide to *E*-olefin. A vinylalane is converted to *E*-homoallylic alcohol in a yield of 81–88% [Equation (9)] [13].

$$
RC\!\equiv\!CH \xrightarrow[\text{2. Bu}^n\text{Li}]{\text{1. Bu}_2^i\text{AlH}} \left[\overset{R}{\underset{H}{\diagup}}C\!=\!C\overset{H}{\underset{AlBu_2^iBu^n}{\diagdown}} \right]^{\ominus} Li^{\oplus} \xrightarrow{R'X} \overset{R}{\underset{H}{\diagup}}C\!=\!C\overset{H}{\underset{R'}{\diagdown}} \qquad (7)
$$

$$
C_4H_9C\!\equiv\!CH + Bu_2^i\text{AlH} \xrightarrow{\quad} \overset{C_4H_9}{\underset{H}{\diagup}}C\!=\!C\overset{H}{\underset{AlBu_2^i}{\diagdown}} \xrightarrow{I_2} \overset{C_4H_9}{\underset{H}{\diagup}}C\!=\!C\overset{H}{\underset{I}{\diagdown}} \qquad (8)
$$

$$
RC\!\equiv\!CH + Bu_2^i\text{AlH} \xrightarrow{\quad} \overset{R}{\underset{H}{\diagup}}C\!=\!C\overset{H}{\underset{AlBu_2^i}{\diagdown}} \xrightarrow{\text{MeLi/ether}}
$$

$$
\xrightarrow{\quad} \left[\overset{R}{\underset{H}{\diagup}}C\!=\!C\overset{H}{\underset{\underset{Me}{\overset{}{Al}}\diagdown Bu^i}{\diagdown}}\!\!\!^{\ominus}Bu^i \right] Li^{\oplus} \xrightarrow[\text{2. 10\% HCl}]{\substack{\text{1. } \triangleright\!O, -15°C \\ \text{Bu}_3\text{N}}} \overset{R}{\underset{H}{\diagup}}C\!=\!C\overset{H}{\underset{CH_2CH_2OH}{\diagdown}} \qquad (9)
$$

(vii) *Utilization of organotin compounds.* E-Allylic alcohols can be prepared from propargyl alcohol *via* an organotin compound [Equation (10)] [14].

$$HC{\equiv}CCH_2OTHP \quad + \quad Bu_3^nSnH \quad \longrightarrow$$

(structure: $C=C$ with H, CH_2OTHP, Bu_3^nSn, H) $\xrightarrow{Bu^nLi}$

(structure: $C=C$ with H, CH_2OTHP, Li, H) $\xrightarrow{Br(CH_2)_8Br}$

(structure: diene with $(CH_2)_8$, H, H, $THPOCH_2$, H, H, CH_2OTHP)   (10)

(viii) *Utilization of organoboranes.* E,E-Conjugated dienes are obtainable *via* hydroboration [Equation (11)] [15].

$$RC{\equiv}CCl \quad + \quad \text{(} \vert\vert\text{—}BH_2\text{)} \quad \longrightarrow$$

(structure with B, $C=C$, Cl, R) $\xrightarrow{HC{\equiv}CR'}$ (structure with B, $C=C$, R', H, Cl, R) $\longrightarrow$ (11)

$\xrightarrow{NaOMe}$ (structure: R', H, $C=C$, $C=C$, H, B, R, OMe) $\xrightarrow{Pr^iCO_2H}$ (structure: R', H, $C=C$, H, $C=C$, H, R)

B. Synthesis of Z-olefins

(i) *Hydrogenation of acetylenes.* This is the standard method for the preparation of a Z-olefin [Equation (12)]. Lindlar's palladium catalyst is widely used for this purpose [16]. However, 5% palladium on barium sulfate in methanol containing a small amount of quinoline [17] or P-2 nickel in ethanol containing a small amount of ethylenediamine [18] are two alternatives whose use is gradually prevailing. P-2 nickel seems to be the best catalyst for stereoselective reduction with a Z : E ratio as high as 200 : 1.

$$R{-}C{\equiv}C{-}R' \quad \xrightarrow{\text{H}_2/\text{Lindlar–Pd or Pd–BaSO}_4 \text{ or P-2 Ni}} \quad R{-}\overset{H}{C}{=}\overset{H}{C}{-}R' \quad (12)$$

(ii) *The Wittig olefin synthesis.* The Wittig olefination carried out in DMSO is known to give a Z-disubstituted olefin as the major product

[Equation (13)] [19, 20]. The use of salt-free ylid solution is recommended for the preparation of Z-olefins [Equation (14)] [21]. The ylid solution is prepared by treating a phosphonium salt with sodium bis-trimethylsilyl-amide in THF. The formation of a Z-olefin is favoured by a low reaction temperature (98% Z at $-78°C$; 84% at $+100°C$). The use of potassium in HMPA as the base also favours the Z-olefination [Equation (15)] [22]. The stereochemistry of the Wittig reaction is discussed by Schlosser [23] and by House [24].

$$R—CH=PPh_3 \quad + \quad R'CHO \xrightarrow{\text{DMSO}} \overset{H}{R}C=\overset{H}{C}R' \quad (\sim 90\% Z) \tag{13}$$

$$\left[R—CH_2—\overset{\oplus}{P}Ph_3\right]X^{\ominus} + NaN(SiMe_3)_2 \xrightarrow[-78°C]{\text{THF}} RCH=PPh_3 \longrightarrow$$
$$\text{(salt free)} \tag{14}$$

$$\xrightarrow[-78°C]{R'CHO} \overset{H}{R}C=\overset{H}{C}R' \quad (98\% Z, 2\% E)$$

$$\left[R—CH_2\overset{\oplus}{P}Ph_3\right]X^{\ominus} \xrightarrow[\text{HMPA}]{K} RCH=PPh_3 \xrightarrow{R'CHO} \overset{H}{R}C=\overset{H}{C}R' \tag{15}$$

(*iii*) *Utilization of organoboranes.* Z-Olefins (98–99% Z) can be prepared from disubstituted acetylenes by hydroboration-protonolysis [Equation(16)] [25]. Z-Vinyl iodides are obtainable from iodoacetylenes by the same process [Equation (17)] [26]. They are convertible to Z-olefins by treatment with organocopper reagents.

$$R—C\equiv C—R' \xrightarrow{\left(\text{H}\right)_2 BH} \underset{R}{\overset{H}{}}C=C\underset{R'}{\overset{B(\text{H})_2}{}} \xrightarrow{\text{AcOH}} \underset{R}{\overset{H}{}}C=C\underset{R'}{\overset{H}{}} \tag{16}$$

$$C_4H_9C\equiv CI \xrightarrow{\left(\text{H}\right)_2 BH} \underset{H}{\overset{C_4H_9}{}}C=C\underset{B(\text{H})_2}{\overset{I}{}} \xrightarrow{\text{AcOH}} \underset{H}{\overset{C_4H_9}{}}C=C\underset{H}{\overset{I}{}} \tag{17}$$

C. Carbon–carbon Linking Reactions

(*i*) *Alkylation of acetylenes.* Alkylation of acetylenes gives disubstituted acetylenes which are the starting materials for both *E*- and Z-olefins. The traditional procedures are listed in a monograph [27]. Recently a convenient and efficient procedure for the alkylation was proposed independently by two groups [Equation (18)] [3, 28]. The procedure is particularly convenient for a small scale preparation. The yield is excellent if the alkylating agent is a primary, unbranched halide. An interesting 1,3-disubstitution reaction of 1,3-dilithiopropyne may be useful in pheromone synthesis [Equation (19)] [29].

$$HC \equiv C-(CH_2)_n \, OTHP \xrightarrow[\substack{2. \, Me(CH_2)_m X/HMPA \\ <25°C, \, a \, few \, min.}]{1. \, Bu^nLi/hexane/THF} Me(CH_2)_m C \equiv C(CH_2)_n OTHP$$

$$Me(CH_2)_m C \equiv CH \xrightarrow[\substack{2. \, Cl(CH_2)_n OTHP/HMPA}]{1. \, Bu^nLi/hexane/THF} Me(CH_2)_m C \equiv C(CH_2)_n OTHP \qquad (18)$$

$$MeC \equiv CH \xrightarrow{2 \, Bu^nLi/Me_2N(CH_2)_2NMe_2} LiCH_2C \equiv CLi \xrightarrow{Bu^nBr/hexane}$$

$$\longrightarrow Bu^n CH_2C \equiv CLi \xrightarrow{CH_2O} Bu^nCH_2C \equiv CCH_2OH \qquad (19)$$

(ii) *Grignard coupling with allylic acetates.* An acetoxyl group occupying allylic position can be replaced by the hydrocarbon moiety of a Grignard reagent. The replacement is regio- and stereoselective [Equation (20)] [30].

$$(20)$$

3. STEREOSELECTIVE ROUTES TO TRISUBSTITUTED OLEFINS

A. Olefins from Acetylenes

(i) *Lithium aluminium hydride reduction followed by iodination.* This method is based on the iodination of the vinylalane intermediates of lithium aluminium hydride reduction of propargylic alcohols [Equations (21) and (22)] [31, 32]. The resulting iodo alcohol may be transformed into various isoprenoids such as farnesol [31] and santalol [32] by treatment with organocopper reagents. An interesting double iodination procedure has also been reported [Equation (23)] [33].

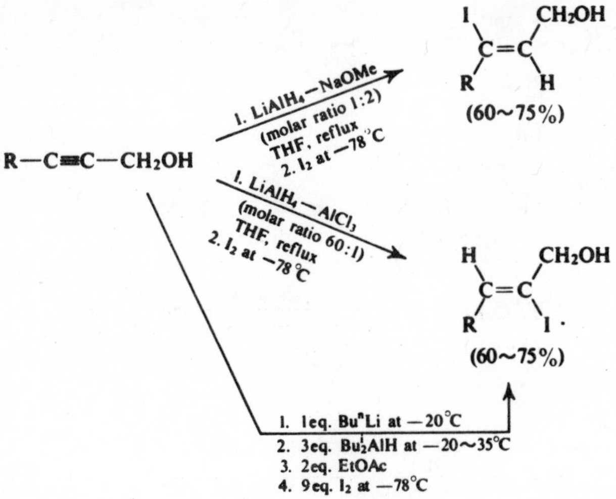

$$R-C\equiv C-CH_2OH$$

1. LiAlH$_4$—NaOMe
(molar ratio 1:2)
THF, reflux
2. I$_2$ at —78 °C

$$\underset{R}{\overset{I}{>}}C=C\underset{H}{\overset{CH_2OH}{<}}$$

(21)

(60~75%)

1. LiAlH$_4$ — AlCl$_3$
(molar ratio 60:1)
THF, reflux
2. I$_2$ at —78 °C

$$\underset{R}{\overset{H}{>}}C=C\underset{I}{\overset{CH_2OH}{<}}\cdot$$

(22)

(60~75%)

1. 1 eq. Bu^{n}Li at —20 °C
2. 3 eq. Bu$_2^i$AlH at —20~35 °C
3. 2 eq. EtOAc
4. 9 eq. I$_2$ at —78 °C

LiAlH$_4$—
NaOMe

$\xrightarrow{\text{I}_2}$

Et$_2$CuLi

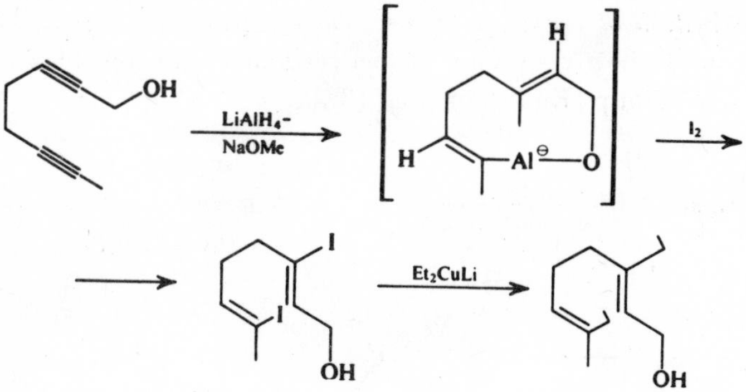

(23)

(ii) Addition of organocopper reagents to acetylenic esters. This method involves the conjugate addition of organocopper reagents to α,β-acetylenic esters at low temperatures [Equation (24)] [34, 35]. The improvement and modification of this reaction are reported with full experimental details [Equations (25) and (26)] [36]. In order to obtain high stereochemical purity in the olefinic product, it is important that the reaction temperature is maintained near —78 °C during the addition of the acetylenic ester to the reagent and during protonation of the vinylcopper intermediate. Conjugate addition of the organocopper reagent is reviewed by Posner [37].

2*

$$R-C\equiv C\cdot CO_2Me \ + \ R'_2CuLi \ \xrightarrow[-100^\circ C]{-78\sim} \ \underset{R'}{\overset{R}{C}}=\underset{Cu}{\overset{CO_2Me}{C}} \ \xrightarrow[-100^\circ C]{H_2O}$$

(24)

$$\longrightarrow \ \underset{R'}{\overset{R}{C}}=\underset{H}{\overset{CO_2Me}{C}} \ + \ \underset{R'}{\overset{R}{C}}=\underset{CO_2Me}{\overset{H}{C}}$$

(97~99.8%)   (0.2~3%)

$$MeC\equiv CCO_2Me \ + \ Bu_2^nCuLi \ \xrightarrow[\substack{Me_2NCH_2CH_2NMe_2 \\ 82\sim84\%}]{-78^\circ C,\ THF\ or\ ether} \ \underset{Bu^n}{\overset{Me}{C}}=\underset{H}{\overset{CO_2Me}{C}}$$

(0.6 eq.)

(25)

$$\xrightarrow[\substack{2.\ EtC\equiv CCO_2R \\ 70.7\%}]{\substack{1.\ CuI,\ Me_2NCH_2CH_2NMe_2,\ ether \\ -78^\circ C}}$$

(26)

$Z:E=5:95$

(*iii*) *Utilization of vinylcopper reagents.* Addition of an organocopper reagent to an acetylene gives a vinylcopper reagent whose copper can be replaced by an alkyl group [Equation (27)] [38].

$$EtCu\cdot MgBr_2 \ \xrightarrow[\substack{2.\ CH_2OCH_2CH_2Cl \\ |\ \\ Br \quad 82\%}]{1.\ MeC\equiv CH} \ \underset{Et}{\overset{Me}{C}}=\underset{CH_2O(CH_2)_2Cl}{\overset{H}{C}} \ \xrightarrow[85\%]{Bu^sLi}$$

(27)

$$\longrightarrow \ \underset{Et}{\overset{Me}{C}}=\underset{CH_2OH}{\overset{H}{C}}$$

(*iv*) *Stereoselective addition of hydrogen halides to acetylenes through intramolecular processes.* Methyl 6-iodo-2-hexynoate undergoes 1,4-iodide shift in refluxing trifluoroacetic acid [Equation (28)] [39]. This process is useful in preparing the key intermediate for juvenile hormone synthesis [39].

$$\xrightarrow[reflux,\ 50h,\ 100\%]{CF_3CO_2H}$$

(28)

$$\xrightarrow[\substack{THF \\ -70^\circ C \\ 95\%}]{Me_2CuLi}$$

$Z:E=5:95$

B. Substitution with Organocopper and Related Reagents

(*i*) *Reaction of organocopper reagents with β-phenylthio-α,β-unsaturated esters.* The phenylthio group can be replaced by an alkyl group of an organocopper reagent with retention of the original olefin geometry [Equation (29)] [40] and [Equations (30) and (31)] [41].

$$
\begin{array}{c}
\text{PhS} \\
\diagdown \\
\diagup \diagdown \text{CO}_2\text{Et}
\end{array}
\quad
\xrightarrow[\text{0°C, 1h, 80\%}]{\text{Me}_2\text{CuLi}}
\quad
\diagup \diagdown \text{CO}_2\text{Et}
\tag{29}
$$

$$
\begin{array}{c}
\text{PhS} \\
\diagdown \\
\diagup \diagdown \text{CO}_2\text{Et}
\end{array}
\quad
\xrightarrow[\text{THF, }-78°\text{C, 79\%}]{\text{Bu}^n\text{MgBr, CuI}}
\quad
\begin{array}{c}
\text{Bu}^n \\
\diagdown \\
\diagup \diagdown \text{CO}_2\text{Et}
\end{array}
\tag{30}
$$

$$
\text{PhS} \diagup \diagdown \text{CO}_2\text{Et}
\quad
\xrightarrow[\text{THF, }-78°\text{C, 94\%}]{\text{Bu}^n\text{MgBr, CuI}}
\quad
\text{Bu}^n \diagup \diagdown \text{CO}_2\text{Et}
\tag{31}
$$

(*ii*) *Reaction of organocopper reagents with β-acyloxy-α,β-unsaturated esters.* The acyloxy group can also be replaced by an alkyl group [Equation (32)] [42].

$$
\begin{array}{c}
\text{O} \\
\parallel \\
\diagup \diagdown \text{CO}_2\text{Me}
\end{array}
\xrightarrow[\text{H}^+]{\diagup\diagdown\text{OAc}}
\begin{array}{c}
\text{OAc} \\
\diagdown \\
\diagup \diagdown \text{CO}_2\text{Me} \\
Z:E = 18:1
\end{array}
\xrightarrow[\substack{\text{excess EtI} \\ -100°\text{C, 97\%}}]{\text{Et}_2\text{CuLi}-\text{PBu}_3^n}
\begin{array}{c}
\diagup \diagdown \text{CO}_2\text{Me} \\
Z:E = 4.9:1
\end{array}
\tag{32}
$$

(*iii*) *Reaction of organocopper reagents with alkenyl halides.* The coupling between organocopper reagents and alkenyl halides proceeds stereospecifically with retention of configuration in the substrate [Equation (33)] [43]. This is used in several syntheses of juvenile hormones [*cf.* Equation (23)].

$$
\begin{array}{c}
\text{H} \quad\; \text{Br} \\
\diagdown \text{C}=\text{C} \diagup \\
\text{Ph} \quad\; \text{H}
\end{array}
\xrightarrow[\substack{\text{0°C, 2.5h,} \\ \text{81\%}}]{\text{Me}_2\text{CuLi}}
\begin{array}{c}
\text{H} \quad\; \text{Me} \\
\diagdown \text{C}=\text{C} \diagup \\
\text{Ph} \quad\; \text{H}
\end{array}
$$

$$
\begin{array}{c}
\text{H} \quad\; \text{H} \\
\diagdown \text{C}=\text{C} \diagup \\
\text{Ph} \quad\; \text{Br}
\end{array}
\xrightarrow{\text{Me}_2\text{CuLi}}
\begin{array}{c}
\text{H} \quad\; \text{H} \\
\diagdown \text{C}=\text{C} \diagup \\
\text{Ph} \quad\; \text{Me}
\end{array}
\tag{33}
$$

(iv) Reaction of organocopper reagents with allylic acetates. Reaction of
lithium dialkylcuprate with acyclic allylic acetates leads to displacement of
the acetoxyl group with allylic rearrangement to give *E*-trisubstituted
olefins [Equations (34) and (35)] [44].

(v) Reaction of organocopper reagents with allylic epoxides. Lithium dialkylcuprate reacts with allylic epoxides to give allylic alcohols with moderate
stereoselectivity [Equations (36) and (37)] [45, 46]. Incidentally, this type of
α,β-unsaturated epoxides is known to be reduced stereoselectively [Equation
(38)] [47]. Substitution reactions using organocopper reagents have been
reviewed recently [48].

$$(38)$$

C. Claisen and Related Thermal Rearrangements

(i) *The Claisen rearrangement.* The stereoselectivity of this rearrangement was carefully studied by Faulkner [Equation (39)] [49, 50], who suggested the chair form of cyclohexane as a model for the transition state. The transition state shown in Equation (40) with an *equatorial* R_2 is more stable than that with an *axial* R_2. This results in the formation of 99% E-olefin [Equation (40)] [49, 50].

$$(39)$$

E		Z		
90	:	10	$R_1 = Me$	$R_2 = Et$
93	:	7	Me	$CHMe_2$
90	:	10	Et	Et

$$(40)$$

$$> 99\% E$$

(ii) *The Claisen ortho ester rearrangement.* This version of the Claisen rearrangement is simpler to perform (one instead of two operations) and the overall yield, as well as stereoselectivity is satisfactory [Equation (41)] [51]. The Claisen rearrangement has been reviewed recently [52].

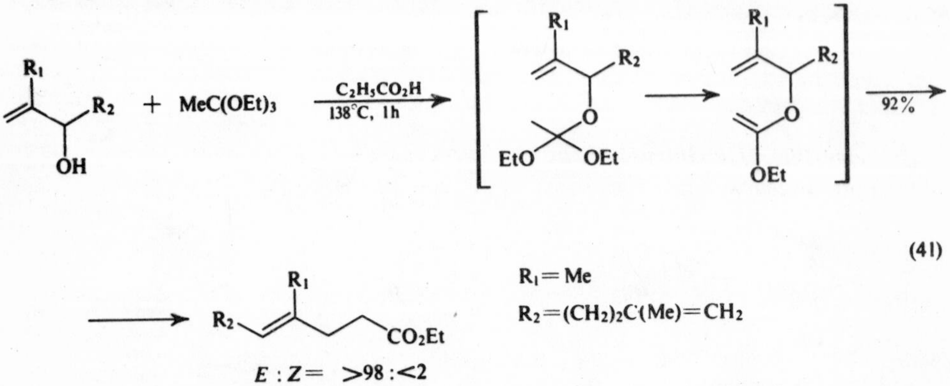

$$R_1 = Me$$
$$R_2 = (CH_2)_2C(Me) = CH_2$$

$$E : Z = >98 : <2$$

(41)

(iii) *Thermal 1,5-prototropic shift.* This reaction is used in a synthesis of juvenile hormone [Equation (42)] [53].

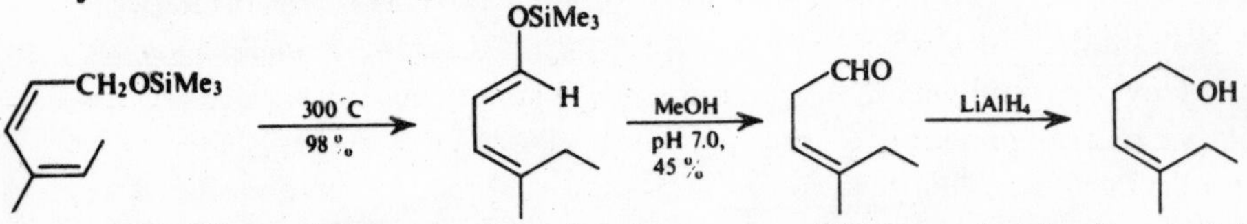

(42)

(iv) *Thermal cleavage of vinylcyclopropanes.* This reaction is also used in a synthesis of juvenile hormone [Equation (43)] [54].

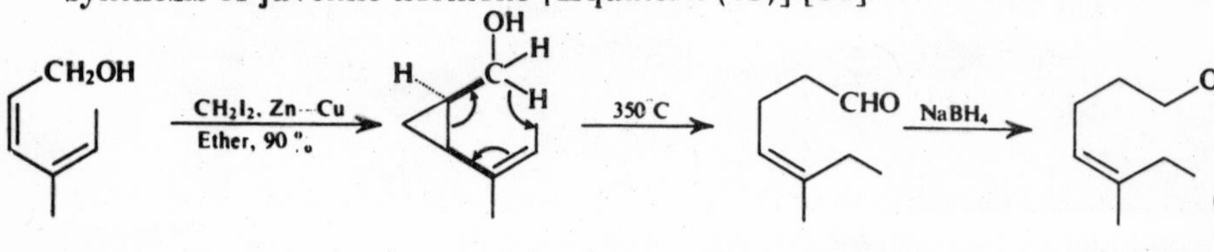

(43)

D. Cleavage of Cyclopropyl Carbinols

(i) *Cleavage of secondary cyclopropyl carbinols.* Julia synthesized homoallylic bromides by the treatment of cyclopropyl carbinols with 48% hydrobromic acid. The reaction is stereoselective in the case of secondary cyclopropyl carbinols giving *E*-disubstituted olefins [Equation (44)] [55], although its application in pheromone syntheses is still scarce.

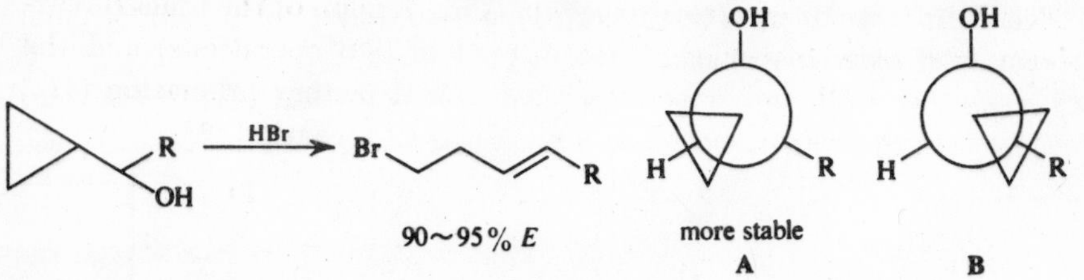

(44)

90~95% E

more stable
A   B

(ii) *Cleavage of tertiary cyclopropyl carbinols.* A tertiary cyclopropyl carbinol rearranges to a mixture of E- and Z-olefins [Equation (45)] [55].

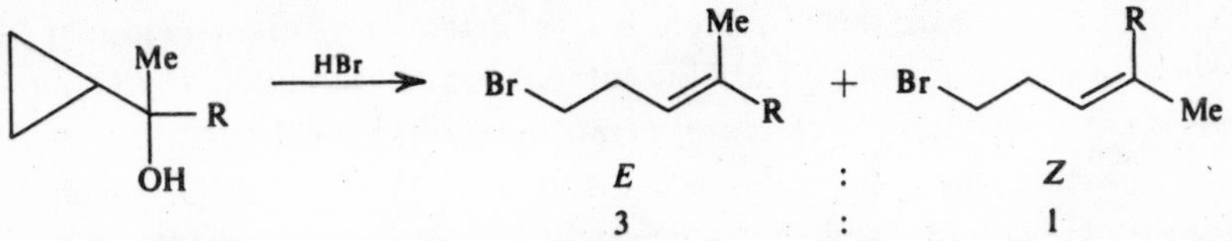

(45)

E   :   Z
3   :   1

(iii) *Cleavage of tertiary cyclopropyl carbinols with an ethynyl substituent.* The stereoselectivity in the case depicted in Equation (44) is attributed to the relative stability of the transition state **A**. It is therefore natural that the tertiary cyclopropyl carbinol with an ethynyl substituent undergoes stereoselective rearrangement [56, 57, 58], since the ethynyl group is less bulky than alkyl groups. This reaction is used in a synthesis of juvenile hormone [Equation (46)] [59].

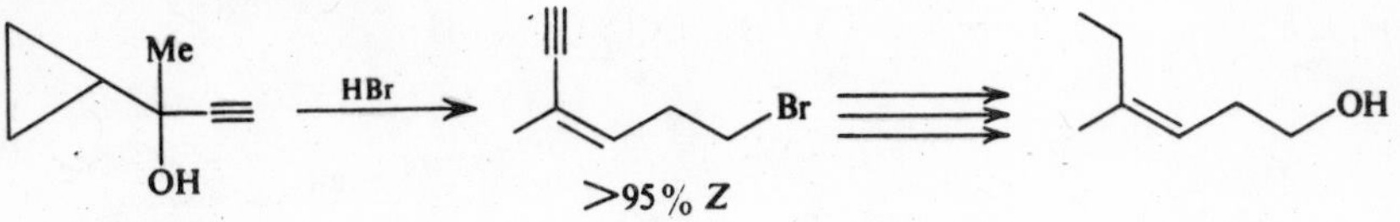

(46)

>95% Z

(iv) *Johnson's modification.* The stereoselectivity in the synthesis of trisubstituted olefins was improved by employing secondary carbinols as starting materials [Equation (47)] [60].

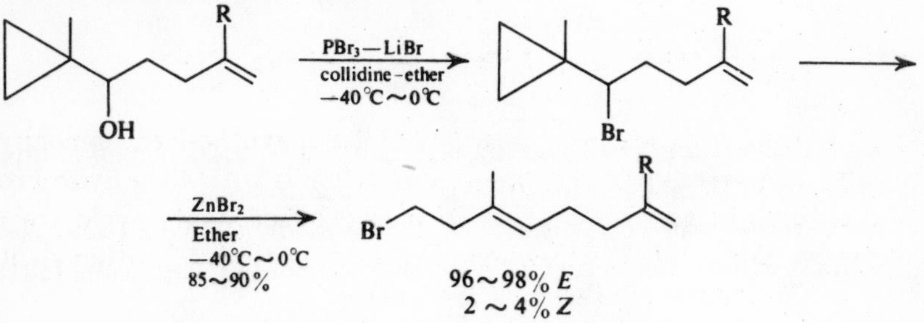

(47)

96~98% E
2 ~ 4% Z

(v) *Cleavage of cyclopropyl epoxides.* This reaction affords bifunctional trisubstituted *E*-olefins [Equation (48)] [61].

$$\qquad\qquad\qquad\qquad\qquad\xrightarrow{\text{HBr}}\qquad\qquad\qquad\qquad\qquad (48)$$

E. Other Methods in Olefin Synthesis

(i) *Grignard addition to α-chloroketones.* At low temperatures (from $-75°C$ to $-95°C$), an α-chloroketone prefers anti-parallel conformation of the chlorine and oxygen atoms. Addition of a Grignard reagent to the least hindered side is favoured, yielding a mixture of chlorohydrins in which one of the diastereomers predominates (80–85%) [Equation (49)] [62, 63]. The chlorohydrin can be converted to *E*-olefin *via* an epoxide [Equation (50)] [62, 63].

$$ (49) $$

$$ (50) $$

(ii) *The Wittig olefin synthesis.* The alkylation of a β-oxido-phosphonium ylid gives an *E*-olefin [Equation (51)] [64]. This reaction was further modified to provide stereoselective syntheses of allylic alcohols [Equation (52)] [65], which proved useful in juvenile hormone synthesis [Equation (53)] [54].

$$EtCH = PPh_3 \quad + \quad PhCHO \longrightarrow PhCH-CHEt \xrightarrow{BuLi} PhCH-CEt \longrightarrow$$

$$\xrightarrow{MeI} \quad H-C-C-Et \longrightarrow \quad \begin{array}{c} H \\ C=C \\ Ph \end{array} \begin{array}{c} Et \\ Me \end{array} \tag{51}$$

$$97\% E \quad (3\% Z)$$

$$RCHO \quad + \quad Ph_3P=CHMe \xrightarrow[-78^\circ C]{THF} R-CH-CH-PPh_3 \xrightarrow[-78^\circ C]{BuLi} R-CH-C-Me \longrightarrow$$

$$\xrightarrow{R'CHO} \quad R=alkyl,\ R'=H \longrightarrow \begin{array}{c} R \\ C=C \\ H \end{array} \begin{array}{c} CH_2OH \\ Me \end{array}$$

$$R, R' \neq H \longrightarrow \tag{52}$$

$$\tag{53}$$

(iii) *Inversion of olefin geometry.* An olefin can be converted to its geometrical isomer *via* an epoxide by the phosphorus betaine method [Equation (54)] [66]. This is also applicable in juvenile hormone synthesis [Equation (55)] [66]. Trimethylsilylpotassium deoxygenation of epoxides is reported to proceed with the inversion of stereochemistry [67].

$$\xrightarrow{Ph_2PLi} \tag{54}$$

$$\xrightarrow{MeI} \tag{55}$$

F. Carbon–carbon Linking Reactions

(i) *Alkylation of a sulfur-stabilized carbanion followed by reductive cleavage
of the carbon–sulfur bond.* A carbanion stabilized by a phenyl thioether
[Equation (56)] [68] or a phenylsulfone [Equation (57)] [69] group can be
alkylated in a good yield. The activating groups can be removed by reduction. This method is useful in isoprenoid synthesis in general.

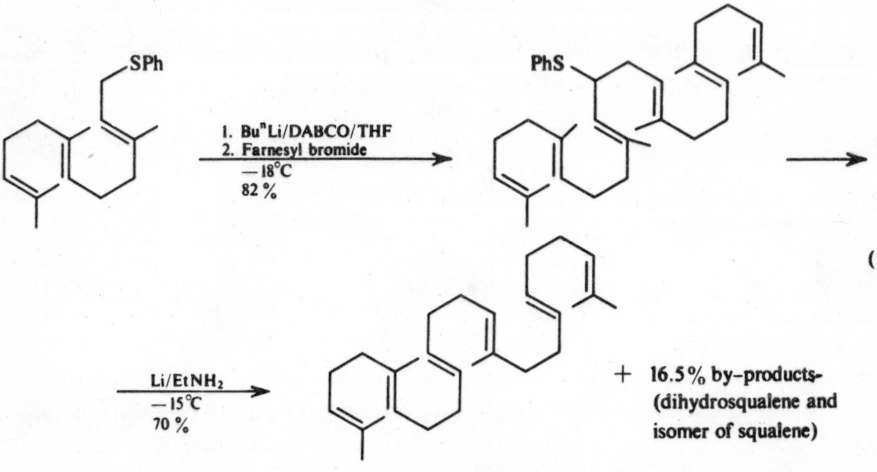

(56)

+ 16.5% by-products-
(dihydrosqualene and
isomer of squalene)

Squalene

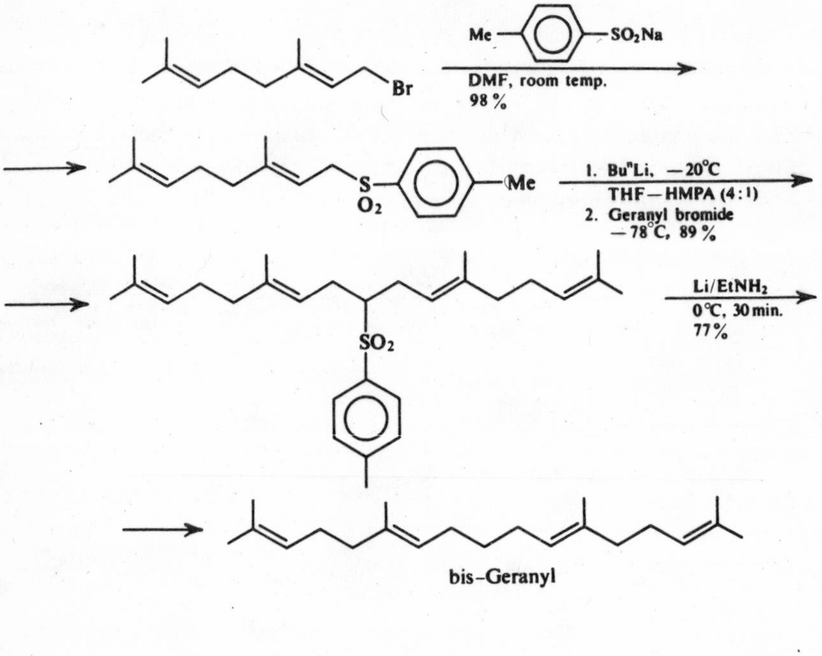

(57)

bis-Geranyl

(*ii*) *Use of sulfoxide rearrangement.* E-Olefins can be prepared by alkylation of a sulfoxide-stabilized carbanion with alkyl halides followed by rearrangement [Equations (58) and (59)] [70].

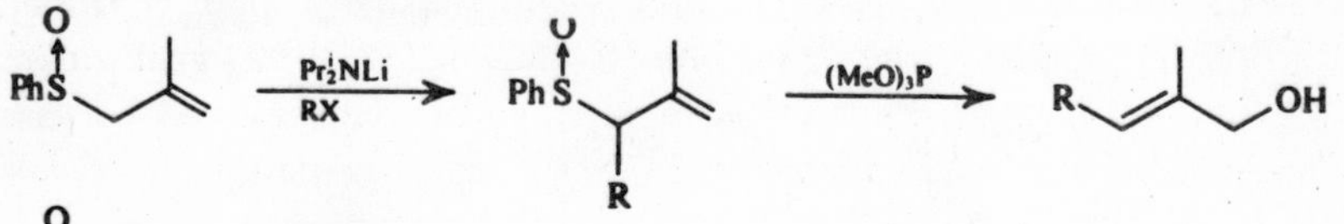

(58)

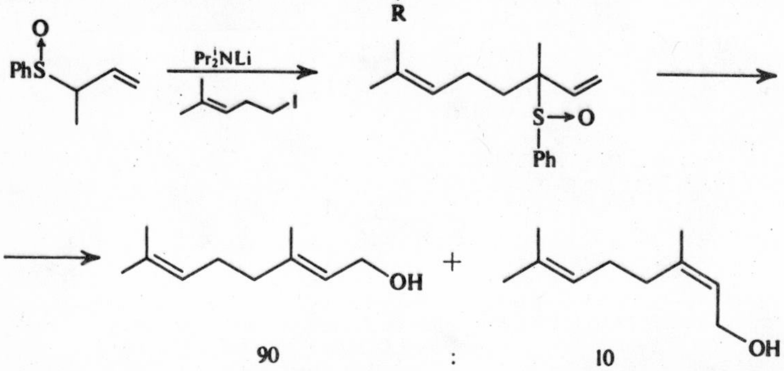

(59)

90   :   10

(*iii*) *Utilization of sulfones and organopalladium compounds.* Farnesol has been synthesized by this interesting method devised by Trost [Equation (60)] [71].

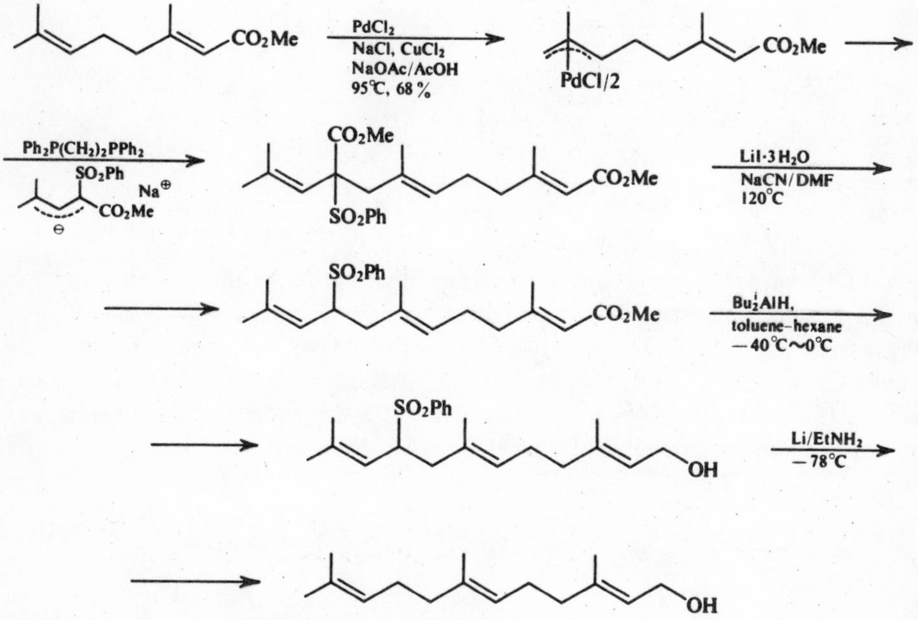

(60)

(iv) γ-Alkylation of α,β-unsaturated acids. α,β-Acetylenic and olefinic acids can be alkylated to effect chain lengthening. The operation is simple, but regio- and stereoselectivities are only moderate [Equations (61) and (62)] [72].

$$(61)$$

3   :   1

$$(62)$$

1   :   2.2   1.5

(v) Utilization of organocopper reagents. Substitution of the bromine atom in *E*-4-bromo-3-methyl-2-buten-1-ol by organocopper reagents gives *E*-olefins [Equation (63)] [73]. Isoprene can be converted to the required bromo-alcohol in a good yield [73]. Conventional carbon–carbon linking reactions are not included in this review. Alkylation of π-allyl nickel complexes is a versatile carbon–carbon linking reaction with moderate stereoselectivity [74].

$$(63)$$

$R = Bu^n$: 98% E

4. OTHER USEFUL METHODS

A. *Methods for Pheromone Synthesis*

(*i*) *Conversion of alkyl chlorides to bromides.* For the alkylation of acety-lenes [see Equations (18) and (19), (p. 18) alkyl chlorides are not so reac-tive, in general. Therefore an efficient method is desirable for the conver-sion of chlorides to bromides. A new procedure employs ethyl bromide as the source of bromine [Equation (64)] [75]. The high volatility of ethyl chloride, the by-product, is the drivingf orce for the completion of the reac-tion.

$$Cl(CH_2)_6OTHP \xrightarrow[\substack{\text{1 eq. NaBr, 30 eq. EtBr}}]{} Br(CH_2)_6OTHP \qquad (64)$$

60∼70°C, 5 days
84 %

(*ii*) *Conversion of tetrahydropyranyl ethers to acetates.* Many pheromones are acetates of long chain alcohols. The tetrahydropyranyl (THP) group is the most commonly employed protecting group in the course of pheromone synthesis. The direct conversion of THP ethers into acetates can be achieved in 85–92% yield [Equation (65)] [3].

$$ROTHP \xrightarrow[\substack{35\sim40°C, \text{ overnight} \\ 85\sim92\%}]{AcCl-AcOH\ (1:10)} ROAc \qquad (65)$$

(*iii*) *Conversion of THP ethers to bromides.* It is possible to carry out the direct conversion of THP ethers to halides [Equation (66)] [76].

$$(66)$$

R = n–C$_{16}$H$_{33}$,　　X = Br,　87% yield

(*iv*) *Carbonyl–olefin metathesis.* Photochemical cycloaddition and thermal rearrangement are coupled to yield *E*-olefinic aldehydes [Equation (67)] [77].

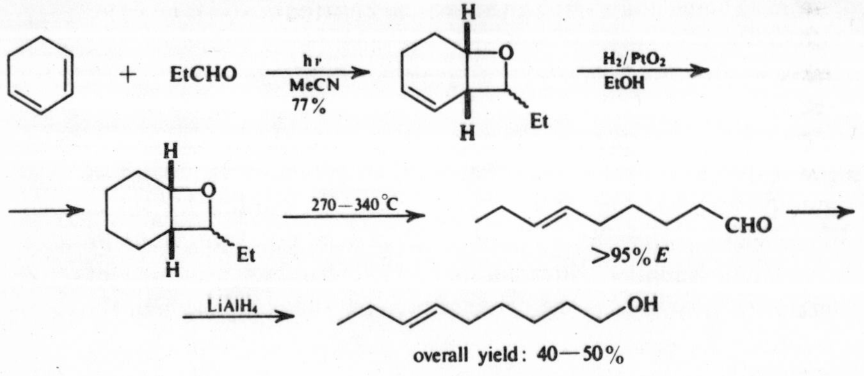

(67)

overall yield: 40—50%

(v) *Solid phase synthesis*. The first application of solid phase synthesis in the pheromone field has recently been reported [Equation (68)] [78]. The solid phase synthesis gives comparable or better overall yields than previous methods, uses inexpensive symmetrical diols as starting materials, and has

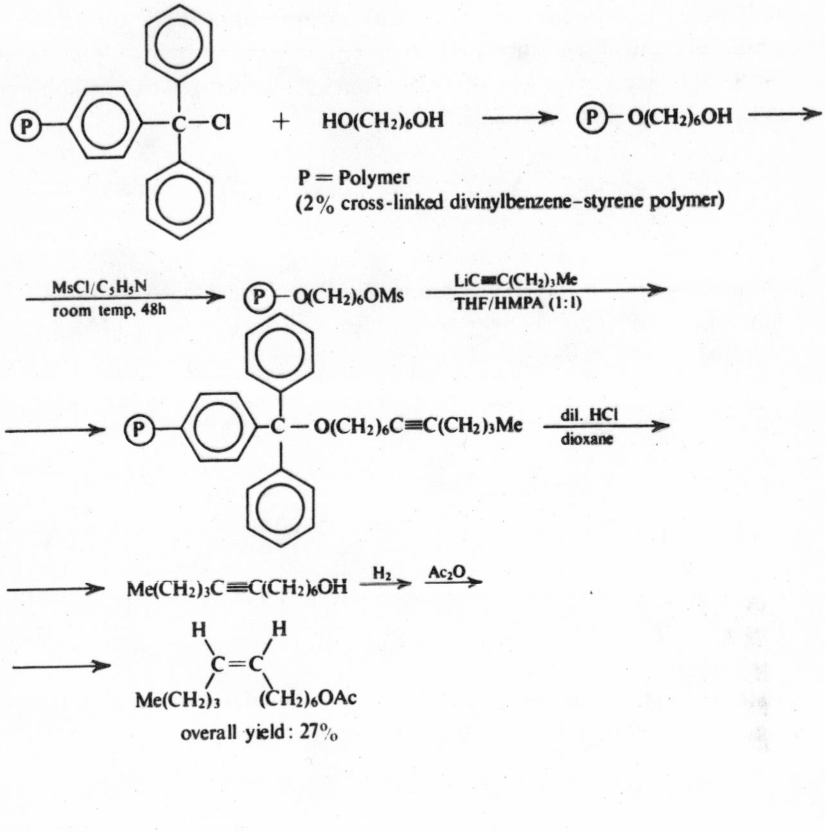

P = Polymer
(2% cross-linked divinylbenzene–styrene polymer)

(68)

overall yield: 27%

the potential of being adapted to an automated procedure. It is questionable, however, whether this method is applicable for a large scale preparation of pheromones required in field tests.

B. Methods for Juvenile Hormone Synthesis

(i) *Oxidative esterification of allylic alcohols.* Farnesol and its homologues are popular intermediates in juvenile hormone syntheses. Transformation of these compounds to methyl farnesoate and homologues needs a very mild method to avoid isomerization at the C-2 double bond. Corey's oxidative esterification method is particularly suited for this purpose [Equation (69)] [79].

$$(69)$$

51 mg >99% pure

(ii) *Selective formation of terminal bromohydrin.* The terminal epoxide function is a common feature in naturally occurring juvenile hormones. Selective oxidation of polyolefins was studied by van Tamelen [80, 81]. The highly selective formation of a terminal bromohydrin was observed during the attack of N-bromosuccinimide to squalene in aqueous ethylene glycol dimethyl ether (DME). The solvent can be substituted by aqueous *t*-butanol or aqueous tetrahydrofuran (THF). An example is shown in Equation (70) [82].

$$(70)$$

REFERENCES

1. FAULKNER, D. J., *Synthesis, 1971*, 175.
2. REUCROFT, J., SAMMES P. J., *Quart. Rev. Chem. Soc.*, 25, 135 (1971).
3. SCHWARZ, M., WATERS, R. M., *Synthesis, 1972*, 567.
4. WARTHERN, JR., J. D., JACOBSON, M., *Synthesis, 1973*, 616.
5. ATTENBURROW, J., CAMERON, A. F. B., CHAPMAN, J. H., EVANS, R. M., HEMS, B. A., JANSEN, A. B. A., WALKER, T., *J. Chem. Soc.*, 1952, 1094.
6. CLAESSON, A., BOGENTOFT, C., *Synthesis, 1973*, 539.
7. KONDO, K., NEGISHI, A., TUNEMOTO, D., *Angew. Chem. intern. Ed.*, 13, 407 (1974).
8. HAYASHI, T., MIDORIKAWA, H., *Synthesis, 1975*, 100.
9. SCHLOSSER, M., CHRISTMANN, K. F., *Angew. Chem. intern. Ed.*, 5, 126 (1966).
10. SCHLOSSER, M., CHRISTMANN, K. F., *Liebigs Ann. Chem.*, 708, 1 (1967).
11. BABA, S., VAN HORN, D. E., NEGISHI, E., *Tetrahedron Letters, 1976*, 1927.
12. ZWEIFEL, G., WHITNEY, C. C., *J. Am. Chem. Soc.*, 89, 2753 (1967).
13. WARWEL, S., SCHMITT, G., AHLFAENGER, B., *Synthesis, 1975*, 632.
14. COREY, E. J., WALLENBERG, R. H., *J. Org. Chem.*, 40, 2265 (1975).
15. NEGISHI, E., YOSHIDA, T., *J. C. S. Chem. Commun.*, 1973, 606.
16. LINDLAR, H., *Helv. Chim. Acta*, 35, 446 (1952).
17. CRAM, D. J., ALLINGER, N. L., *J. Am. Chem. Soc.*, 78, 2518 (1956).
18. BROWN, C. A., AHUJA, V. K., *J. C. S. Chem. Commun.*, 1973, 553.
19. GOTO, G., SHIMA, T., MASUYA, H., MASUOKA, Y, HIRAGA, K., *Chemistry Letters, 1975*, 103.
20. HALL, D. R., BEEVOR, P. S., LESTER, R., POPPI, R. G., NESBITT, B. F., *Chem. and Ind., 1975*, 216.
21. BESTMANN, H. J., STRANSKY, W., VOSTROWSKY, O., *Chem. Ber.*, 109, 1694 (1976).
22. BESTMANN, H. J., VOSTROWSKY, O., PLATZ, H., *Chem. Zeitung*, 98, 161 (1974).
23. SCHLOSSER, M., *Topics in Stereochemistry*, 5, 1 (1970).
24. HOUSE, H. O., "Modern Synthetic Reactions", Second Edition, pp. 704—709, W. A. Benjamin, Inc., Menlo Park (1972).
25. BROWN, H. C., ZWEIFEL, G., *J. Am. Chem. Soc.*, 83, 3834 (1961).
26. ZWEIFEL, G., ARZOUMANIAN, H., *J. Am. Chem. Soc.*, 89, 5086 (1967).
27. BRANDSMA, L., "Preparative Acetylenic Chemistry", Elsevier, Amsterdam (1971).
28. BRATTESANI, D. N., HEATHCOCK, C. H., *Synth. Commun.*, 3, 245 (1973).
29. BHANU, S., SCHEINMANN, F., *J. C. S. Chem. Commun.*, 1975, 817.
30. FOUQUET, G., SCHLOSSER, M., *Angew. Chem. Internat. Ed.*, 13, 82 (1974).
31. COREY, E. J., KATZENELLENBOGEN, J. A., POSNER, G. H., *J. Am. Chem. Soc.*, 89, 4245 (1967).
32. COREY, E. J., KIRST, H. A., KATZENELLENBOGEN, J. A., *J. Am. Chem. Soc.*, 92, 6314 (1970).
33. COREY, E. J., KATZENELLENBOGEN, J. A., ROMAN, S. A., GILMAN, N. W., *Tetrahedron Letters, 1971*, 1821.
34. COREY, E. J., KATZENELLENBOGEN, J. A., *J. Am. Chem. Soc.*, 91, 1851 (1969).
35. SIDDALL, J. B., BISKUP, M., FRIED, J. H., *J. Am. Chem. Soc.*, 91, 1853 (1969).
36. ANDERSON, R. J., CORBIN, V. L., COTTERRELL, G., COX, G. R., HENRICK, C. A., SCHAUB, F., SIDDALL, J. B., *J. Am. Chem. Soc.*, 97, 1197 (1975).
37. POSNER, G. H., *Organic Reactions*, 19, 1 (1972).
38. NORMANT, J. F., CAHIEZ, G., CHUIT, C., VILLIERAS, J., *Tetrahedron Letters, 1973*, 2407.
39. BRYSON, T. A., *Tetrahedron Letters, 1973*, 4923.
40. POSNER, G. H., BRUNELLE, D. J., *J. C. S. Chem. Commun.*, 1973, 907.
41. KOBAYASHI, S., TAKEI, H., MUKAIYAMA, T., *Chemistry Letters, 1973*, 1097.
42. CASEY, C. P., MARTEN, D. F., *Tetrahedron Letters, 1974*, 925.
43. COREY, E. J., POSNER, G. H., *J. Am. Chem. Soc.*, 89, 3911 (1967).
44. ANDERSON, R. J., HENRICK, C. A., SIDDALL, J. B., *J. Am. Chem. Soc.*, 92, 735 (1970).
45. ANDERSON, R. J., *J. Am. Chem. Soc.*, 92, 4978 (1970).

46. HERR, R. W., JOHNSON, C. R., *J. Am. Chem. Soc.*, *92*, 4979 (1970).
47. LENOX, R. S., KATZENELLENBOGEN, J. A., *J. Am. Chem. Soc.*, *95*, 958 (1973).
48. POSNER, G. H., *Organic Reactions*, *22*, 253 (1975).
49. FAULKNER, D. J., PETERSEN, M. R., *Tetrahedron Letters*, *1969*, 3243.
50. FAULKNER, D. J., PETERSEN, M. R., *J. Am. Chem. Soc.*, *95*, 553 (1973).
51. JOHNSON, W. S., WERTHEMANN, L., BARTLETT, W. R., BROCKSOM, T. J., LI, T., FAULKNER, D. J., PETERSEN, M. R., *J. Am. Chem. Soc.*, *92*, 741 (1970).
52. RHOADS, S. J., RAULINS, N. R., *Organic Reactions*, *22*, 1 (1975).
53. COREY, E. J., HERRON, D. K., *Tetrahedron Letters*, *1971*, 1641.
54. COREY, E. J., YAMAMOTO, H., HERRON, D. K., ACHIWA, K., *J. Am. Chem. Soc.*, *92*, 6635 (1970).
55. JULIA, M., JULIA, S., GUÉGAN, R., *Bull. Soc. Chim. France*, *1960*, 1072.
56. JULIA, M., DESCOINS, C., *Bull. Soc. Chim. France*, *1962*, 1933.
57. JULIA, M., JULIA, S., STALLA-BOURDILLON, B., DESCOINS, C., *Bull. Soc. Chim. France*, *1964*, 2533.
58. JULIA, M., DESCOINS, C., RISSE, C., *Tetrahedron Suppl.*, *8*, Part II, 443 (1966).
59. MORI, K., OHKI, M., SATO, A., MATSUI, M. *Tetrahedron*, *28*, 3739 (1972).
60. BRADY, S. F., ILTON, M. A., JOHNSON, W. S., *J. Am. Chem. Soc.*, *90*, 2882 (1968).
61. NAKAMURA, H., YAMAMOTO, H., NOZAKI, H., *Tetrahedron Letters*, *1973*, 111.
62. CORNFORTH, J. W., CORNFORTH, R. H., MATHEW, K. K., *J. Chem. Soc.*, *1959*, 112.
63. CORNFORTH, J. W., CORNFORTH, R. H., MATHEW, K. K., *J. Chem. Soc.*, *1959*, 2539.
64. SCHLOSSER, M., CHRISTMANN, K. F., *Synthesis*, *1969*, 38.
65. COREY, E. J., YAMAMOTO, H., *J. Am. Chem. Soc.*, *92*, 226 (1970).
66. VEDEJS, E., FUCHS, P. L., *J. Am. Chem. Soc.*, *95*, 822 (1973).
67. DERVAN, P. B., SHIPPEY, M. A., *J. Am. Chem. Soc.*, *98*, 1266 (1976).
68. BIELLMANN, J. F., DUCEP, J. B., *Tetrahedron*, *27*, 5861 (1971).
69. GRIECO, P. A., MASAKI, Y., *J. Org. Chem.*, *39*, 2135 (1974).
70. EVANS, D. A., *Tetrahedron Letters*, *1973*, 1389.
71. TROST, B. M., WEBER, L., *J. Org. Chem.*, *40*, 3617 (1975).
72. PITZELE, B. S., BARAN, J. S., STEINMAN, D. H., *Tetrahedron*, *32*, 1347 (1976).
73. BABLER, J. H., BUTTNER, W. J., *Tetrahedron Letters*, *1976*, 239.
74. SAMMELHACK, M. F., *Organic Reactions*, *19*, 115 (1972).
75. WILLY, W. E., McKEAN, D. R., GARCIA, B. A., *Bull. Chem. Soc. Japan*, *49*, 1989 (1976).
76. SONNET, P. E., *Synth. Commun.*, *6*, 21 (1976).
77. JONES II, G., ACQUADRO, M. A., CARMODY, M. A., *J. C. S. Chem. Commun.*, *1975*, 206.
78. LEZNOFF, C. C., FYLES, T. M., *J. C. S. Chem. Commun.*, *1976*, 251.
79. COREY, E. J., GILMAN, N. W., GANEM, B. E., *J. Am. Chem. Soc.*, *90*, 5616 (1968).
80. VAN TAMELEN, E. E., CURPHEY, T. J., *Tetrahedron Letters*, *1962*, 121.
81. VAN TAMELEN, E. E., SHARPLESS, K. B., *Tetrahedron Letters*, *1967*, 2655.
82. ANDERSON, R. J., HENRICK, C. A., SIDDALL, J. B., ZURFLÜH, R., *J. Am. Chem. Soc.*, *94*, 5379 (1972).

III. SYNTHESIS OF INSECT PHEROMONES

1. INTRODUCTION

Fifteen years have passed since the first synthesis of bombykol, the sex pheromone of the silkworm moth, *Bombyx mori*, was published by Butenandt and his co-workers. From the beginning, synthetic approach was very important in pheromone researches because of the limited availability of natural pheromones from insects (usually no more than a few milligrams).

3*

The roles of synthesis in insect pheromone researches may be classified as
follows [1]. (*i*) A synthesis can give the final proof of the proposed structure
including the olefin geometry and the relative as well as absolute stereochemistry. (*ii*) A simple and efficient synthesis can provide sufficient material for biological study, including field tests. (*iii*) The synthesis of a number
of analogues and stereoisomers clarifies the structure–activity relationship.
Analogues of practical importance may be created by this approach.

The number of pheromones isolated from insects is rapidly increasing.
Four recent reviews are useful to a novice in pheromone chemistry [2–5].
Pheromones are scattered among various types of volatile compounds
ranging from alkanes to nitrogen heterocycles. The present review deals
with the synthesis of pheromones having a certain novel structural feature.
For example, the synthesis of alkanes is not treated.

The stereochemical aspects of pheromone synthesis are discussed in full
depth. Recent studies on structure–activity relationships have revealed the
importance of stereochemistry in pheromone perception by insects. Indeed,
three types of isomerism, geometrical, stereo- and optical isomerisms, have
all been shown to affect the biological activity as described below.

A. Biological Activity of Bombykol and its Geometrical Isomers

Butenandt *et al.* [6, 7] and Truscheit and Eiter [8] synthesized all of the
four possible geometrical isomers of bombykol (1) and compared their
attractancy to male silkworm moth, *Bombyx mori*. The results are shown in
Table I.

Table 1
Biological Activity of Natural Bombykol and Synthetic Geometrical Isomers of 10, 12-Hexadecadien-1-ol

	Butenandt [6]	Activity (μg/ml)* Butenandt [7]	Eiter [8]
10Z, 12Z	1	1	--
10Z, 12E	10^{-3}	10^{-2}	10^{-5}
10E, 12Z	10^{-12}	10^{-12}	10^{-12}
10E, 12E	10	100	10
Natural bombykol	10^{-10}	10^{-10}	10^{-10}

* The activity is expressed by "die Lockstoffeinheit (LE)." This is the lower limit
of the pheromone concentration (μg/ml) to which 50% of the test insects show reaction.

The biological activity as well as physical properties of $(10\,E : 12\,Z) - 10,12$-
hexadecadien-1-ol were almost identical with that of natural bombykol.
The geometry of the diene system in bombykol was thus established as

$10E : 12Z$ by these synthetic works. It should be noted that the other three geometrical isomers possess only moderate or weak biological activities. A highly stereoselective synthesis of the most active isomer is therefore of paramount importance both scientifically and practically.

$$Bu^nC\underset{12}{=}C-C\underset{10}{=}C-(CH_2)_9OH$$ with H, H, H, H

$$Bu^nC=C-C=C-(CH_2)_9OH$$ with H, H, H, H

$$Bu^nC=C-C=C-(CH_2)_9OH$$ with H, H, H, H

Bombykol **1**

$$Bu^nC=C-C=C-(CH_2)_9OH$$ with H, H, H, H

$$Et-C-C=C-(CH_2)_{10}OAc$$ with H, H

2

$$Et-C-C=C-(CH_2)_{10}OAc$$ with H, H

3

$$Bu^nC=C(CH_2)_2C=C(CH_2)_6OAc$$ with H, H, H, H

4

$$Bu^nC=C(CH_2)_2C=C(CH_2)_6OAc$$ with H, H, H, H

5

B. The Pheromone of Red-banded Leaf Roller (Argyrotaenia velutinana) and its Geometrical Isomer

Roelofs' et al. identified *(Z)*-11-tetradecenyl acetate (**2**) as the sex phero-mone of red-banded leaf roller moths *(Argyrotaenia velutinana)* [9]. They then demonstrated that a large amount of the (11E)-isomer (**3**) is inhibitory to the pheromone action [10]. Here again the stereochemistry was shown to be important. Roelofs's argument on this subject was based on his bioassay results with many pheromone analogues, some of them acting inhibitory, while others synergistically [10]. Subsequently Klun et al. [11] and Beroza et al. [12] reported a very interesting observation that a small amount of the opposite geometrical isomer was critical to pheromone attraction. Klun found that a geometrically pure preparation of **2** was very weakly attractive to the moth and that the presence of 7% of the (11E)-isomer (**3**) was neces-sary for maximum activity [11]. Previous syntheses of **2** employed either the Wittig reaction or the Lindlar semi-hydrogenation, and neither of them was 100% stereoselective. It is therefore obvious that a highly pure geomet-rical isomer is required to discover this kind of very subtle biological phenom-ena. Beroza's relevant work was on the pheromone of the oriental fruit moths, *Grapholitha molesta*. The biological activity of the synthetic phero-mone, *(Z)*-8-dodecenyl acetate increased twenty-five times by the addition of a small amount of the (8E)-isomer [12].

C. Gossyplure, the Pheromone of Pink Bollworm Moth
(Pectinophora gossypiella)

In this case the pheromone consists of a mixture of two geometrical isomers in an equal amount: (7Z : 11Z)-7,11-hexadecadienyl acetate (4) and
its (7Z : 11Z)-isomer (5) [13]. Neither of them is biologically active by itself
alone. This suggests the existence of two different receptor sites on the
pheromone receptor of the pink bollworm moth.

D. The Pheromone of Dendroctonus Bark Beetles

Two stereoisomers of 7-methyl-5-methyl-6,8-dioxabicyclo[3.2.1]octa n
were isolated from the frass of the western pine beetle (Dendroctonus brevicomis) [14]. Only one of them, exo-brevicomin (6), is biologically active as a
component of the aggregation pheromone of the western pine beetle. The
other isomer, endo-brevicomin (7), is inactive to the western pine beetle and
even inhibits the olfactory response of flying male and female southern pine
beetles (Dendroctonus frontalis) to the female-produced pheromone, frontalin (8) [15]. In this case the endo-exo stereoisomerism was of utmost
importance for biological activity. This necessitated the stereoselective
synthesis of these pheromones.

6   7   H   8

9 (S)—(+)   10 (R)—(−)

E. Biological Activities of the Optical Isomers of Pheromones

exo-Brevicomin (6) and frontalin (8) are chiral molecules. They, therefore,
can exist in two enantiomeric forms. Very recently both enantiomers of
these pheromones were synthesized enabling the biological evaluation of the
isomers [16, 17]. The biologically active isomers were (1R : 5S : 7R)-(+)-
exo-brevicomin (6) and (1S : 5R)-(−)-frontalin (8) [18]. In these cases only
one enantiomer of the two optical isomers possesses pheromone activity.

Sulcatol is the aggregation pheromone produced by males of *Gnathotrichus sulcatus* [19]. Both *(S)*-(+)-sulcatol (**9**) and the *(R)*-(−) isomer (**10**) were synthesized [20]. Surprisingly, neither of them was biologically active. However, when combined to give a racemic mixture, synthetic sulcatol was more active than the natural pheromone which consisted of a mixture of 65% of **9** and 35% of **10** [21]. This situation is somewhat similar to that encountered in the case of gossyplure, and suggested the presence of enantiomer-specific active sites on the receptor proteins in the same or different cells of *Gnathotrichus sulcatus*.

The above examples well illustrate how important is the concept of stereochemistry in pheromone synthesis, which is undoubtedly one of the frontiers in applying the modern methodology of synthetic organic chemistry.

A very readable review on the sex-attractant receptor of moths is to be referred to [22] before going into the individual treatise of the pheromones.

2. PHEROMONES WITH *E*-OLEFINIC LINKAGE

A. *(E)-2-Hexenyl Acetate* (**11**)

This is the sex pheromone of Indian water bug *(Lethocerus indicus)* and serves to excite the female immediately before or during mating. Its synthesis is shown in Scheme 1 [23]. Pattenden, however, states that **11** is neither sex- nor species-specific [24].

$$Pr^nCHO \quad + \quad CH_2(CO_2Et)_2 \quad \xrightarrow{\text{N}} \quad Pr^nC\overset{H}{=}CCO_2Et \quad \xrightarrow{\text{LiAlH}_4}$$

$$\longrightarrow \quad Pr^nC\overset{H}{=}\underset{H}{C}-CH_2OH \quad \xrightarrow{\text{AcCl}} \quad Pr^nC\overset{H}{=}\underset{H}{C}-CH_2OAc$$

11

Scheme 1

B. *(E)-7-Dodecenyl Acetate* (**12**)

This is the sex pheromone of false codling moth *(Cryptophlebia leucotreta)* [25]. Syntheses by Berger *et al.* [25] and Henderson *et al.* [26] are shown in Schemes 2 and 3, respectively.

$$Cl(CH_2)_6OTHP \xrightarrow[Me_2CO]{NaI} I(CH_2)_6OTHP \xrightarrow{Bu^nC\equiv CLi}$$

$$Bu^nC\equiv C(CH_2)_6OTHP \xrightarrow[EtOH]{HCl} Bu^nC\equiv C(CH_2)_6OH \xrightarrow[NH_3]{Na}$$

$$\underset{H}{\overset{H}{Bu^nC=C(CH_2)_6OH}} \xrightarrow{AcCl} \underset{H}{\overset{H}{Bu^nC=C(CH_2)_6OAc}}$$
                                                                    12

Scheme 2

$$Br(CH_2)_6OTHP \xrightarrow{Bu^nC\equiv CLi} Bu^nC\equiv C(CH_2)_6OTHP \xrightarrow[NH_3]{Na}$$

$$\underset{H}{\overset{H}{Bu^nC=C(CH_2)_6OTHP}} \xrightarrow[AcOH]{AcCl} \underset{H}{\overset{H}{Bu^nC=C(CH_2)_6OAc}}$$
                                                                    12

Scheme 3

C. (E)-11-Tetradecenal (13)

Eastern spruce budworm *(Choristoneura fumiferana)* uses this compound as its sex pheromone [27]. Two syntheses are reported as shown in Schemes 4 [27] and 5 [28]. The latter employs the highly stereoselective phosphonate method (Equation 4).

$$EtC\equiv C(CH_2)_{10}OH \xrightarrow[NH_3]{Na} \underset{H}{\overset{H}{EtC=C(CH_2)_{10}OH}} \xrightarrow[2.\ DMSO]{1.\ MsCl}$$

$$\underset{H}{\overset{H}{EtC=C(CH_2)_9CHO}}$$
       13

Scheme 4

$$\underset{O}{\overset{\|}{MeCH=CHCH_2P(OEt)_2}} \xrightarrow[2.\ Br(CH_2)_{10}OTHP]{1.\ Bu^nLi} \underset{O=P(OEt)_2}{MeCH=CHCH(CH_2)_{10}OTHP}$$

$$\xrightarrow{LiAlH_4} \underset{H}{\overset{H}{EtC=C(CH_2)_{10}OTHP}} \xrightarrow{H^+} \underset{H}{\overset{H}{EtC=C(CH_2)_{10}OH}} \xrightarrow{CrO_3}$$
                                                                    73% overall yield

$$\underset{H}{\overset{H}{EtC=C(CH_2)_9CHO}}$$
       13

Scheme 5

3. PHEROMONES WITH Z-OLEFINIC LINKAGE

A. Muscalure, (Z)-9-Tricosene (14)

This is a sex pheromone isolated from the cuticle and faeces of the female house fly *(Musca domestica)* and attracts the male fly [29]. The first synthesis was carried out by the Wittig reaction to give 85% of *(Z)*- and 15% of *(E)*-isomers (Scheme 6) [29]. This Wittig synthesis was later modified by using potassium in HMPA as the base, to give 94% of *(Z)*-olefin plus 6% of the *(E)*-isomer (Scheme 7) [30]. The second type of synthesis employs Lindlar semi-hydrogenation of the acetylene (Scheme 8) [31]. The use of the naturally occurring erucic acid as the starting material yields the pheromone only in two steps (Scheme 9) [32]. This strategy was further modified by using the cheap oleic acid as the starting material (Scheme 10) [33]. The mixed Kolbe electrolysis of oleic and *n*-heptanoic acids gives muscalure in 14% yield. (Scheme 11) [34].

$$Ph_3\overset{\oplus}{P}(CH_2)_{13}Me \quad Br^{\ominus} \xrightarrow[\text{2. } Me(CH_2)_{12}CHO]{\text{1. } Bu^nLi/DMSO} Me(CH_2)_{12}\overset{H}{C}=\overset{H}{C}(CH_2)_7Me$$

$$E:Z = 15:85$$

14

Scheme 6

$$Ph_3\overset{\oplus}{P}(CH_2)_8Me \quad Br^{\ominus} \xrightarrow[\text{2. } Me(CH_2)_{12}CHO]{\text{1. } K/HMPA} Me(CH_2)_{12}\overset{H}{C}=\overset{H}{C}(CH_2)_7Me$$

$$E:Z = 6:94$$

Scheme 7

$$Me(CH_2)_{12}C\equiv CH \xrightarrow[\text{2. } Me(CH_2)_7Br]{\text{1. } Bu^nLi/diglyme} Me(CH_2)_{12}C\equiv C(CH_2)_7Me$$

$$\xrightarrow{H_2/Lindlar-Pd} Me(CH_2)_{12}\overset{H}{C}=\overset{H}{C}(CH_2)_7Me$$

14

Scheme 8

$$Me(CH_2)_7\overset{H}{C}=\overset{H}{C}(CH_2)_{11}CO_2H \xrightarrow{MeLi} Me(CH_2)_7\overset{H}{C}=\overset{H}{C}(CH_2)_{11}\overset{O}{\overset{\|}{C}}Me$$

$$\xrightarrow{N_2H_4-KOH} Me(CH_2)_7\overset{H}{C}=\overset{H}{C}(CH_2)_{12}Me$$

Scheme 9

$$Me(CH_2)_7\overset{H}{C}=\overset{H}{C}(CH_2)_7CO_2H \quad \xrightarrow{Me(CH_2)_4Li} \quad Me(CH_2)_7\overset{H}{C}=\overset{H}{C}(CH_2)_7\overset{O}{\overset{\|}{C}}(CH_2)_4Me$$

$$\xrightarrow{N_2H_4-KOH} \quad Me(CH_2)_7\overset{H}{C}=\overset{H}{C}(CH_2)_{12}Me$$

Scheme 10

$$Me(CH_2)_7\overset{H}{C}=\overset{H}{C}(CH_2)_7CO_2H \quad + \quad Me(CH_2)_5CO_2H \quad \xrightarrow[14\%]{\text{Kolbe electrolysis}}$$

$$Me(CH_2)_7\overset{H}{C}=\overset{H}{C}(CH_2)_{12}Me$$

Scheme 11

B. Disparlure, (Z)-7,8-Epoxy-2-methyloctadecane (15)

The gypsy moth, *Porthetria, dispar* is a serious despoiler of forest. The sex pheromone was extracted from 78 000 tips of the last two abdominal segments of female moths and shown to be an epoxide **15** [35]. The first synthesis employed the Wittig reaction (Scheme 12) [35]. As small as 2 pg of *(Z)*-epoxide (**15**) was active in laboratory bioassay. A highly stereoselective version of this Wittig synthesis is reported by Bestmann (Scheme 13) [36]. Two syntheses *via* acetylenic intermediates are recorded (Scheme 14) [37, 38]. A synthesis by Chan and Chang employs organosilicon compounds, but the stereoselectivity is low (Scheme 15) [39]. The olefinic precursor, *(Z)*-2-methyl-7-octadecene, is present in the female sex pheromone gland of the gypsy moth and inhibits male attraction to disparlure [40]. The synthesis of optically active disparlure will be discussed later (see Schemes **133** and **134**, p. 104 – 106).

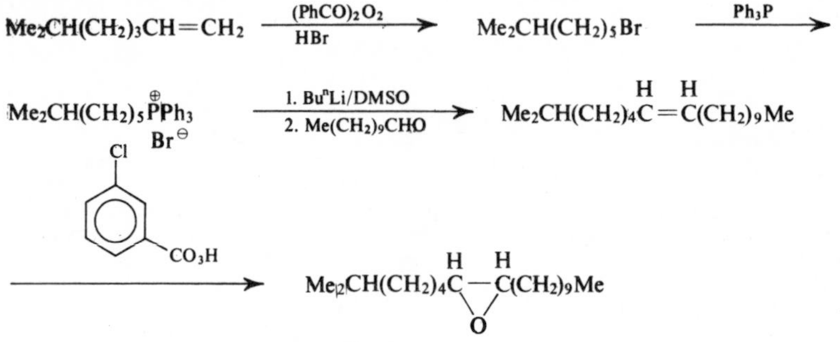

$$Me_2CH(CH_2)_3CH=CH_2 \quad \xrightarrow[HBr]{(PhCO)_2O_2} \quad Me_2CH(CH_2)_5Br \quad \xrightarrow{Ph_3P}$$

$$Me_2CH(CH_2)_5\overset{\oplus}{P}Ph_3 \quad Br^{\ominus} \quad \xrightarrow[\text{2. } Me(CH_2)_9CHO]{\text{1. } Bu^nLi/DMSO} \quad Me_2CH(CH_2)_4\overset{H}{C}=\overset{H}{C}(CH_2)_9Me$$

$$\xrightarrow{} \quad Me_2CH(CH_2)_4\overset{H}{C}\overset{}{\underset{O}{\diagdown\diagup}}\overset{H}{C}(CH_2)_9Me$$

15   *E : Z* = 15 : 85

Scheme 12

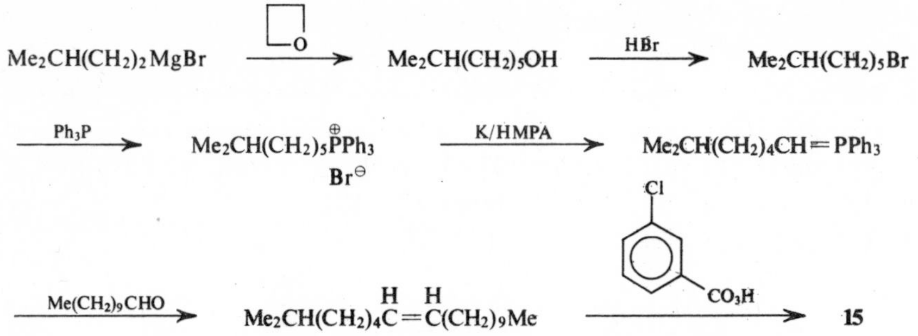

Me₂CH(CH₂)₂MgBr → [O] → Me₂CH(CH₂)₅OH → HBr → Me₂CH(CH₂)₅Br

→ Ph₃P → Me₂CH(CH₂)₅P⁺Ph₃ Br⁻ → K/HMPA → Me₂CH(CH₂)₄CH=PPh₃

→ Me(CH₂)₉CHO → Me₂CH(CH₂)₄C(H)=C(H)(CH₂)₉Me → [3-Cl-C₆H₄CO₃H] → **15**

Scheme 13

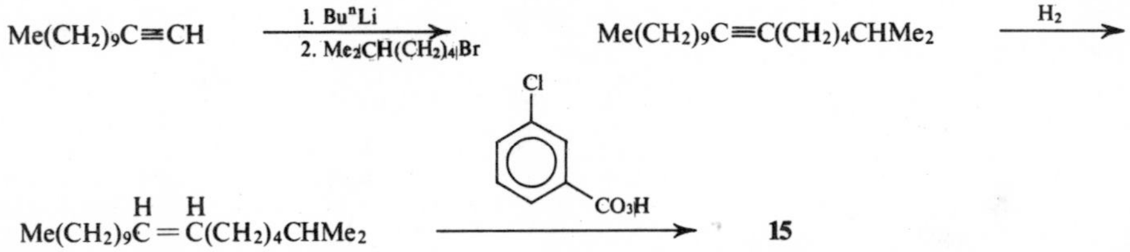

Me(CH₂)₉C≡CH → 1. BuⁿLi / 2. Me₂CH(CH₂)₄Br → Me(CH₂)₉C≡C(CH₂)₄CHMe₂ → H₂ →

Me(CH₂)₉C(H)=C(H)(CH₂)₄CHMe₂ → [3-Cl-C₆H₄CO₃H] → **15**

Scheme 14

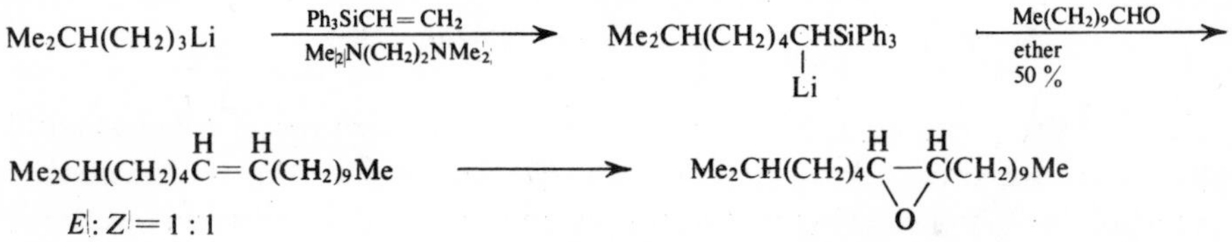

Me₂CH(CH₂)₃Li → Ph₃SiCH=CH₂ / Me₂N(CH₂)₂NMe₂ → Me₂CH(CH₂)₄CHSiPh₃ (Li) → Me(CH₂)₉CHO / ether / 50 % →

Me₂CH(CH₂)₄C(H)=C(H)(CH₂)₉Me → Me₂CH(CH₂)₄C—C(CH₂)₉Me (O)
E:Z=1:1   **15**

Scheme 15

C. (Z)-7-Dodecenyl Acetate (**16**)

This is the sex pheromone of the cabbage looper *(Trichoplusia ni)* [41]. The synthesis is straightforward *via* acetylenic intermediates (Scheme 16) [41]

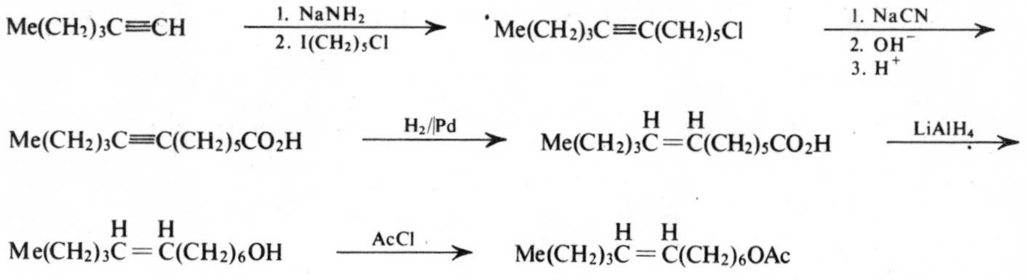

Me(CH₂)₃C≡CH → 1. NaNH₂ / 2. I(CH₂)₅Cl → Me(CH₂)₃C≡C(CH₂)₅Cl → 1. NaCN / 2. OH⁻ / 3. H⁺ →

Me(CH₂)₃C≡C(CH₂)₅CO₂H → H₂/Pd → Me(CH₂)₃C(H)=C(H)(CH₂)₅CO₂H → LiAlH₄ →

Me(CH₂)₃C(H)=C(H)(CH₂)₆OH → AcCl → Me(CH₂)₃C(H)=C(H)(CH₂)₆OAc

Scheme 16   **16**

D. (Z)-8-Dodecenyl Acetate (17)

Oriental fruit moth, *Grapholitha molesta*, uses this compound as the sex pheromone [42]. The structure was confirmed by syntheses *via* both the Wittig and the acetylenic routes [42]. A recent synthesis employs cyclohexane-1,3-dione as a C_6-synthon (Scheme 17) [43].

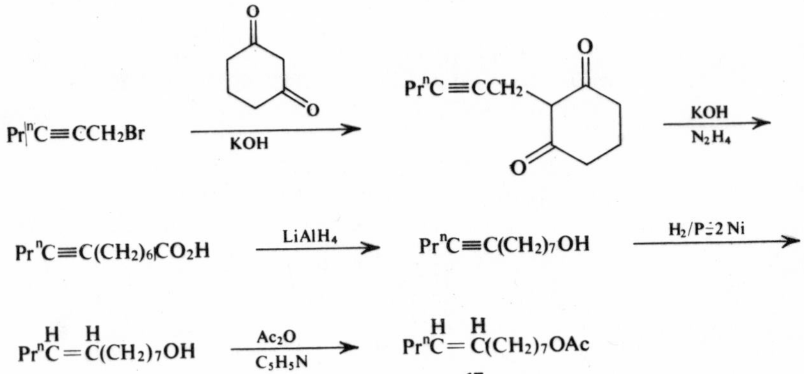

$$Pr^nC\equiv CCH_2Br \xrightarrow{KOH}$$

$$Pr^nC\equiv CCH_2 \quad \xrightarrow[N_2H_4]{KOH}$$

$$Pr^nC\equiv C(CH_2)_6CO_2H \xrightarrow{LiAlH_4} Pr^nC\equiv C(CH_2)_7OH \xrightarrow{H_2/P\div 2\,Ni}$$

$$\underset{H}{Pr^n}C=\underset{H}{C}(CH_2)_7OH \xrightarrow[C_5H_5N]{Ac_2O} \underset{H}{Pr^n}C=\underset{H}{C}(CH_2)_7OAc$$

17

Scheme 17

E. (Z)-9-Tetradecenyl Acetate (18)

This is the pheromone of fall armyworm, *Spodoptera frugiperda* [44] and smaller tea tortorix, *Adoxophyes fasciata* [45]. The first synthesis used methyl myristolate as the starting material (Scheme 18) [44]. The second synthesis was based on the conventional acetylene chemistry (Scheme 19) [46], and the third one was a partial synthesis from **16** (Scheme 20) [47]. A Wittig synthesis is also recorded (Scheme 21) [48].

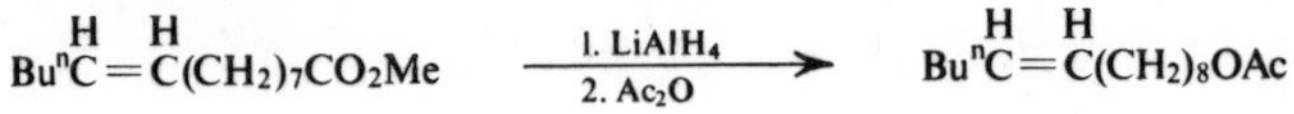

$$\underset{H}{Bu^n}C=\underset{H}{C}(CH_2)_7CO_2Me \xrightarrow[2.\ Ac_2O]{1.\ LiAlH_4} \underset{H}{Bu^n}C=\underset{H}{C}(CH_2)_8OAc$$

18

Scheme 18

$$Cl(CH_2)_8OTHP \xrightarrow[DMSO]{LiC\equiv CH} HC\equiv C(CH_2)_8OTHP \xrightarrow[2.\ Bu^nBr]{1.\ LiNH_2}$$

$$Bu^nC\equiv C(CH_2)_8OTHP \xrightarrow{H_2/Pd-CaCO_3} \underset{H}{Bu^n}C=\underset{H}{C}(CH_2)_8OTHP$$

$$\xrightarrow[AcOH]{AcCl} \underset{H}{Bu^n}C=\underset{H}{C}(CH_2)_8OAc$$

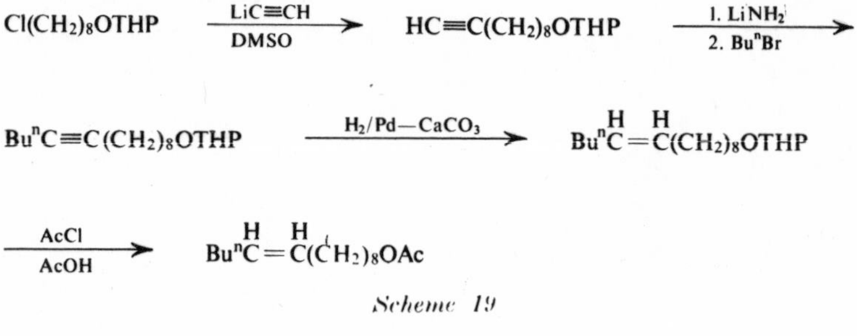

Scheme 19

$$Bu^nC \overset{H}{=} \overset{H}{C}(CH_2)_6OH \xrightarrow[\text{2. NaCH(CO_2Et)_2}]{\text{1. PBr_3}} Bu^nC \overset{H}{=} \overset{H}{C}(CH_2)_6CH(CO_2Et)_2$$

$$\xrightarrow[\substack{\text{2. H^+} \\ \text{3. heat}}]{\text{1. OH^-}} Bu^nC \overset{H}{=} \overset{H}{C}(CH_2)_7CO_2H \xrightarrow[\text{2. AcCl}]{\text{1. LiAlH_4}} Bu^nC \overset{H}{=} \overset{H}{C}(CH_2)_8OAc$$

Scheme 20

$$Bu^nCH = PPh_3 \quad + \quad OHC(CH_2)_8OAc \xrightarrow[\text{salt-free}]{C_6H_6} Bu^nC \overset{H}{=} \overset{H}{C}(CH_2)_8OAc$$
18

Scheme 21

F. (Z)-11-Tetradecenyl Acetate (2)

Red-banded leaf roller, *Argyrotaenia velutinana* [9], and the smaller tea tortorix [45] use this compound as the pheromone. The synthesis was carried out either through acetylenic intermediates [9] or by employing the Wittig reaction (Scheme 22) [9, 45].

$$EtCHO \quad + \quad Ph_3\overset{\oplus}{P}(CH_2)_{11}OAc \xrightarrow[\text{DMF}]{\text{NaOMe}} EtC \overset{H}{=} \overset{H}{C}(CH_2)_{10}OAc$$
$$Br^{\ominus}$$
2

Scheme 22

G. (Z)-11-Hexadecenal (19) and (Z)-Octadecenal (20)

The striped rice borer, *Chilo suppressalis*, is a serious pest of rice in Asian countries. Its female sex pheromone is a 5 : 1 mixture of 19 and 20 [49]. They were obtained by the conventional acetylene route (Scheme 23) [49].

$$Bu^nC \equiv CH \quad + \quad Br(CH_2)_{10}OTHP \xrightarrow[\text{2. H^+}]{\text{1. LiNH_2}} Bu^nC \equiv C(CH_2)_{10}OH$$

$$\xrightarrow{\text{H_2/Lindlar–Pd}} Bu^nC \overset{H}{=} \overset{H}{C}(CH_2)_{10}OH \xrightarrow{CrO_3 \cdot 2 C_5H_5N} Bu^nC \overset{H}{=} \overset{H}{C}(CH_2)_9CHO$$
21 (as the acetate)
19

$$Bu^nC \equiv CH \quad + \quad Br(CH_2)_{12}OTHP \xrightarrow[\text{2. H^+}]{\text{1. LiNH_2}} Bu^nC \equiv C(CH_2)_{12}OH$$

$$\xrightarrow{\text{H_2/Lindlar–Pd}} Bu^nC \overset{H}{=} \overset{H}{C}(CH_2)_{12}OH \xrightarrow{CrO_3 \cdot 2 C_5H_5N} Bu^nC \overset{H}{=} \overset{H}{C}(CH_2)_{11}CHO$$
20

Scheme 23

H. (Z)-11-Hexadecenyl Acetate (21)

This is the pheromone of the purple stem borer, *Sesamia inferens*, a noctuid moth whose larvae attack a wide range of graminaceous crops [50]. The pheromone is the acetate of *(Z)*-11-hexadecenol as depicted in Scheme 23.

I. (Z)-3-Decenoic Acid (22)

The sex pheromone of the furniture carpet beetle, *Anthrenus flavipes*, was identified as **22** (Scheme 24) [51].

$$Me(CH_2)_5C \equiv CCH_2CH_2OH \xrightarrow{CrO_3} Me(CH_2)_5C \equiv CCH_2CO_2H$$

$$\xrightarrow[C_5H_5N-EtOH]{H_2/Pd-C} Me(CH_2)_5\overset{H}{C} = \overset{H}{C}CH_2CO_2H$$

22

Scheme 24

J. (Z)-14-Methyl-8-hexadecen-1-ol (23) and Methyl (Z)-14-Methyl-8-hexadecenoate (24)

These are the sex pheromones produced by female dermestid beetles, *Trogoderma inclusum* [52]. The first [52] and the second [53] syntheses employed the Wittig reaction (Schemes 25 and 26). The third synthesis utilized an interesting Cope rearrangement reaction (Scheme 27) [54]. The synthesis of optically active pheromones will be described later (see Scheme 130, p. 100).

$$MeCH = CHMe \xrightarrow[2.\ CH_2=CHCHO]{1.\ B_2H_6} \underset{Et}{\overset{Me}{\diagdown}}CH(CH_2)_2CHO \xrightarrow{Ph_3P = CHCHO}$$

$$\underset{Et}{\overset{Me}{\diagdown}}CH(CH_2)_2CH = CHCHO \xrightarrow[\substack{2.\ HBr \\ 3.\ Ph_3P}]{1.\ Reduction} \underset{Et}{\overset{Me}{\diagdown}}CH(CH_2)_5\overset{\oplus}{P}Ph_3 \underset{Br^{\ominus}}{} \xrightarrow[\substack{TLC\ (SiO_2-Ag^+) \\ Separation}]{OHC(CH_2)_6CO_2Me}$$

$$\underset{Et}{\overset{Me}{\diagdown}}CH(CH_2)_4\overset{H}{C} = \overset{H}{C}(CH_2)_6CO_2Me \xrightarrow{LiAlH_4} \underset{Et}{\overset{Me}{\diagdown}}CH(CH_2)_4\overset{H}{C} = \overset{H}{C}(CH_2)_7OH$$

24   **23**

Scheme 25

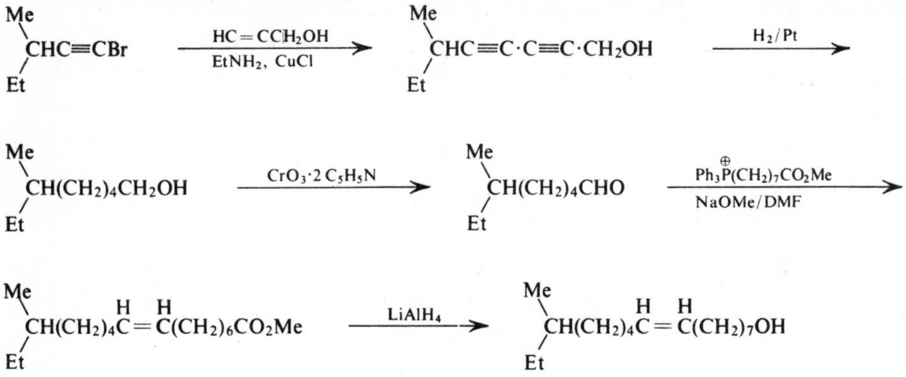

$$\underset{\text{Et}}{\overset{\text{Me}}{\diagdown}}\text{CHC}\equiv\text{CBr} \xrightarrow[\text{EtNH}_2,\ \text{CuCl}]{\text{HC}=\text{CCH}_2\text{OH}} \underset{\text{Et}}{\overset{\text{Me}}{\diagdown}}\text{CHC}\equiv\text{C}\cdot\text{C}\equiv\text{C}\cdot\text{CH}_2\text{OH} \xrightarrow{\text{H}_2/\text{Pt}}$$

$$\underset{\text{Et}}{\overset{\text{Me}}{\diagdown}}\text{CH(CH}_2)_4\text{CH}_2\text{OH} \xrightarrow{\text{CrO}_3\cdot 2\,\text{C}_5\text{H}_5\text{N}} \underset{\text{Et}}{\overset{\text{Me}}{\diagdown}}\text{CH(CH}_2)_4\text{CHO} \xrightarrow[\text{NaOMe/DMF}]{\overset{\oplus}{\text{Ph}_3\text{P(CH}_2)_7\text{CO}_2\text{Me}}}$$

$$\underset{\text{Et}}{\overset{\text{Me}}{\diagdown}}\text{CH(CH}_2)_4\overset{\text{H}}{\text{C}}=\overset{\text{H}}{\text{C}}\text{(CH}_2)_6\text{CO}_2\text{Me} \xrightarrow{\text{LiAlH}_4} \underset{\text{Et}}{\overset{\text{Me}}{\diagdown}}\text{CH(CH}_2)_4\overset{\text{H}}{\text{C}}=\overset{\text{H}}{\text{C}}\text{(CH}_2)_7\text{OH}$$

Scheme 26

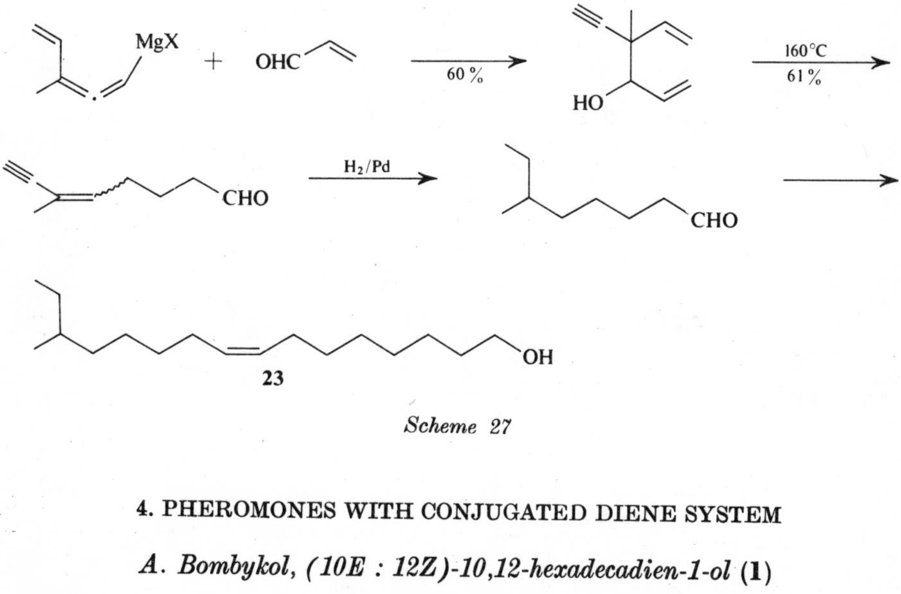

Scheme 27

4. PHEROMONES WITH CONJUGATED DIENE SYSTEM

A. Bombykol, (10E : 12Z)-10,12-hexadecadien-1-ol (1)

Bombykol was the first pheromone isolated from insects. Its isolation [55] and structure elucidation [56] were fully described in 1961. Neither the Butenandt [6,7] nor the Eiter [8] synthesis was stereoselective. Separations of the intermediates were required as shown in Schemes 28 [7], 29 [7], 30 [8], 31 [8] and 32 [8]. Borane chemistry was successfully applied in a recently reported stereoselective synthesis (Scheme 33) [57]. Another stereoselective route was an application of organocopper and related carbanion chemistry

(Scheme 34) [58]. Thus various syntheses of bombykol are the reflexion of the synthetic methodology available at the time of their achievements. The recent two syntheses are remarkable on account of their high stereo-selectivities.

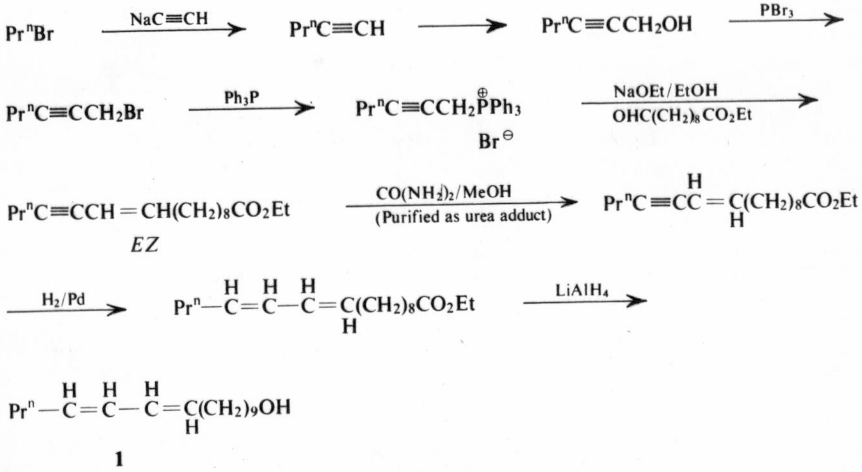

$$Pr^nBr \xrightarrow{NaC\equiv CH} Pr^nC\equiv CH \longrightarrow Pr^nC\equiv CCH_2OH \xrightarrow{PBr_3}$$

$$Pr^nC\equiv CCH_2Br \xrightarrow{Ph_3P} Pr^nC\equiv CCH_2\overset{\oplus}{P}Ph_3 \xrightarrow[OHC(CH_2)_8CO_2Et]{NaOEt/EtOH}$$
$$Br^\ominus$$

$$Pr^nC\equiv CCH=CH(CH_2)_8CO_2Et \xrightarrow[\text{(Purified as urea adduct)}]{CO(NH_2)_2/MeOH} Pr^nC\equiv CC\overset{H}{=}\underset{H}{C}(CH_2)_8CO_2Et$$
$$EZ$$

$$\xrightarrow{H_2/Pd} Pr^n-\overset{H}{C}=\overset{H}{C}-\overset{H}{C}=\underset{H}{C}(CH_2)_8CO_2Et \xrightarrow{LiAlH_4}$$

$$Pr^n-\overset{H}{C}=\overset{H}{C}-\overset{H}{C}=\underset{H}{C}(CH_2)_9OH$$
$$\mathbf{1}$$

Scheme 28

$$CH_2=CH(CH_2)_8CO_2Et \xrightarrow{LiAlH_4} CH_2=CH(CH_2)_9OH \longrightarrow$$

(benzene ring with CO₃H and CO₂H substituents)

$$\underset{O}{CH_2-CH(CH_2)_9OH} \longrightarrow \underset{O}{CH_2-CH(CH_2)_9OTHP} \xrightarrow[dioxane]{Pr^nC\equiv CLi}$$

$$Pr^nC\equiv CCH_2CH(OH)(CH_2)_9OTHP \xrightarrow[\text{2. H}^+]{\text{1. TsCl}} Pr^nC\equiv CCH=CH(CH_2)_9OH$$
$$\text{base}$$

$$\xrightarrow[\text{urea adduct}]{\text{Purified as}} Pr^nC\equiv CC\overset{H}{=}\underset{H}{C}(CH_2)_9OH \xrightarrow{H_2/Pd} Pr^nC\overset{H}{=}\overset{H}{C}-\overset{H}{C}=\underset{H}{C}(CH_2)_9OH$$

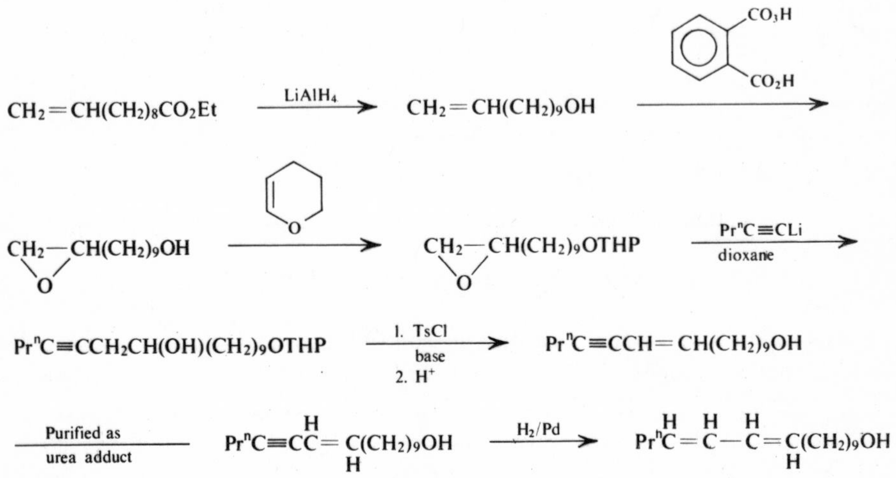

Scheme 29

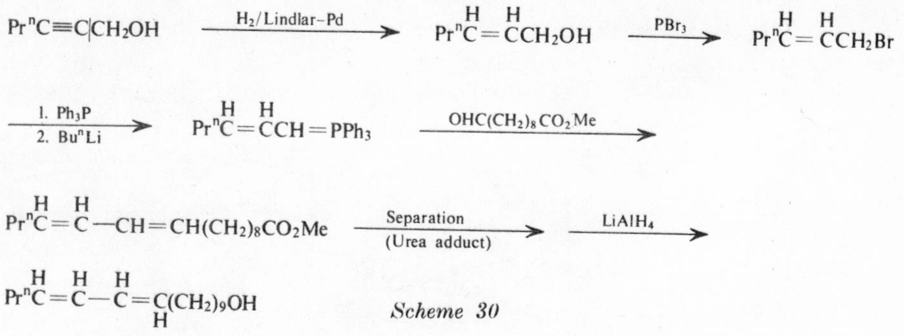

$$Pr^nC\equiv C|CH_2OH \xrightarrow{H_2/Lindlar-Pd} Pr^nC\overset{H}{=}\overset{H}{C}CH_2OH \xrightarrow{PBr_3} Pr^nC\overset{H}{=}\overset{H}{C}CH_2Br$$

$$\xrightarrow[\text{2. }Bu^nLi]{\text{1. }Ph_3P} Pr^nC\overset{H}{=}\overset{H}{C}CH=PPh_3 \xrightarrow{OHC(CH_2)_8CO_2Me}$$

$$Pr^nC\overset{H}{=}\overset{H}{C}-CH=CH(CH_2)_8CO_2Me \xrightarrow[\text{(Urea adduct)}]{\text{Separation}} \xrightarrow{LiAlH_4}$$

$$Pr^nC\overset{H}{=}\overset{H}{C}-\overset{H}{C}=\underset{H}{C}(CH_2)_9OH$$

Scheme 30

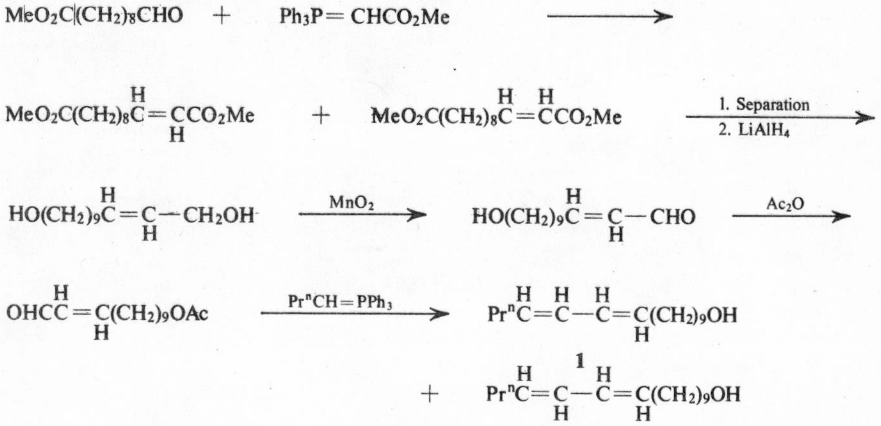

$$MeO_2C(CH_2)_8CHO \quad + \quad Ph_3P=CHCO_2Me \xrightarrow{\hspace{2cm}}$$

$$MeO_2C(CH_2)_8\overset{H}{\underset{H}{C}}=CCO_2Me \quad + \quad MeO_2C(CH_2)_8\overset{H}{C}=\overset{H}{C}CO_2Me \xrightarrow[\text{2. }LiAlH_4]{\text{1. Separation}}$$

$$HO(CH_2)_9\overset{H}{\underset{H}{C}}=C-CH_2OH \xrightarrow{MnO_2} HO(CH_2)_9\overset{H}{C}=\underset{H}{C}-CHO \xrightarrow{Ac_2O}$$

$$OHC\overset{H}{C}=\underset{H}{C}(CH_2)_9OAc \xrightarrow{Pr^nCH=PPh_3} Pr^nC\overset{H}{=}\overset{H}{C}-\overset{H}{C}=\underset{H}{C}(CH_2)_9OH$$

$$+ \quad Pr^n\overset{H}{C}=\overset{\mathbf{1}}{\underset{H}{C}}-\overset{H}{C}=\underset{H}{C}(CH_2)_9OH$$

Scheme 31

$$HC\equiv CCH_2\underset{OH}{CH}(CH_2)_8CO_2Me \xrightarrow[C_5H_5N]{POCl_3} HC\equiv CCH_2\underset{Cl}{CH}(CH_2)_8CO_2Me$$

$$\xrightarrow[85\%]{} HC\equiv CCH=CH(CH_2)_8CO_2Me \xrightarrow[\text{2.}]{\text{1. }LiAlH_4} HC\equiv CCH=CH(CH_2)_9OTHP$$

$$E:Z = 7:3$$

$$\xrightarrow[\substack{\text{2. }Pr^nBr \\ \text{3. }H^+}]{\text{1. }LiNH_2} Pr^nC\equiv CCH=CH(CH_2)_9OH \xrightarrow[\text{2. Sepn}]{\text{1. }H_2/Pd}$$

$$Pr^nC\overset{H}{=}\overset{H}{C}-\overset{H}{C}=C-(CH_2)_9OH$$

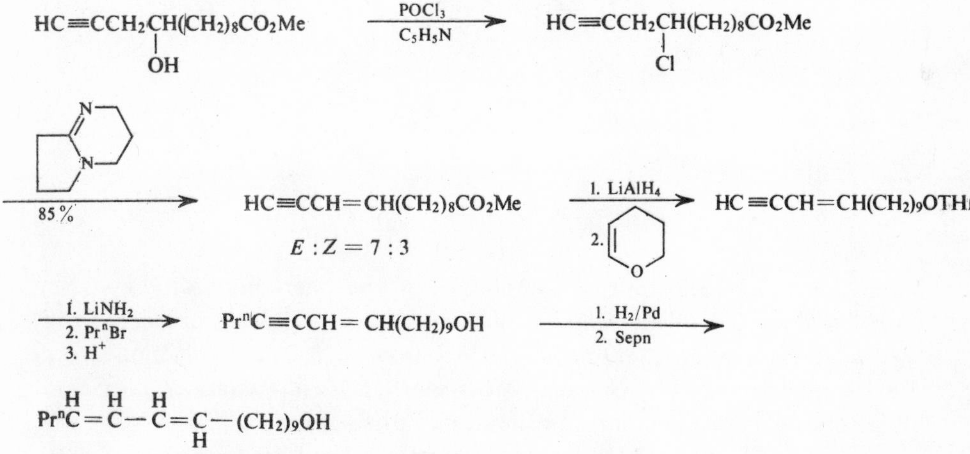

1   (Urea adduct and recrystallization)

Scheme 32

$HC{\equiv}C(CH_2)_9OSiMe_3$ $\xrightarrow[\text{THF}]{(\!|\!+\!|\!)_2\text{BH}}$ $(\!|\!+\!|\!)_2\text{B}$ ... $\underset{H}{\overset{H}{C}}=\underset{(CH_2)_9OSiMe_3}{\overset{}{C}}$

$\xrightarrow[\substack{\text{THF-hexane}\\-50°C,\ 1h}]{Pr^nC{\equiv}CLi}$ $\underset{\substack{C\equiv CPr^n\\ \\ \underset{H}{C}=\underset{(CH_2)_9OSiMe_3}{C}}}{\overset{H}{|\!+\!|}B\overset{H}{}}$ $\xrightarrow[\text{2. 3N NaOH, 25°C, 63\%}]{\text{1. } I_2/\text{THF, }-78{\sim}25°C}$

$Pr^nC{\equiv}C{-}\underset{H}{\overset{H}{C}}{=}C(CH_2)_9OSiMe_3$ $\xrightarrow[\substack{\text{CO}_2H,\ \text{THF}\\\text{reflux}}]{(\!|\!+\!|\!)_2\text{BH, 0°C, 1h}}$ $\xrightarrow{LiAlH_4}$

$Pr^nC\underset{H}{\overset{H\ \ H}{=}}C{-}\underset{H}{\overset{H}{C}}{=}C(CH_2)_9OH$

1

Scheme 33

Pr^nMgBr $\xrightarrow[\substack{\text{3. BrC}{\equiv}CCH_2OSiMe_3\\\text{4. H}_3O^+\quad 65\%}]{\substack{\text{1. CuBr}\\\text{2. CH}{\equiv}CH}}$ $Pr^nC\overset{H\ \ H}{=}C{-}C{\equiv}C{-}CH_2OH$ $\xrightarrow[\substack{\text{2. Ac}_2O\\93\%}]{\text{1. LiAlH}_4}$

$Pr^nC\underset{H}{\overset{H\ \ H}{=}}C{-}\overset{H}{C}{=}C{-}CH_2OAc$ $\xrightarrow[\substack{\text{2. BrMg(CH}_2)_8OCHOEt\\\text{3. H}_3O^+\qquad Me\\75\%}]{\text{1. Cu(I), THF, }-30°C}$ $Pr^nC\underset{H}{\overset{H\ \ H}{=}}C{-}\underset{H}{\overset{H}{C}}{=}C(CH_2)_9OH$

1

Scheme 34

B. (8E : 10E)-8,10-Dodecadien-1-ol (25)

Roelofs *et al.* isolated this compound as the pheromone of the codling moth, *Laspeyresia pomonella*, a notorious pest of apple orchards [59]. Although there is a dispute between Roelofs *et al.* [59] and McDonough *et al.* [60] concerning the pheromone of this moth, **25** is now commercially available as an effective agent for "the insect monitoring system." The first synthesis (Scheme 35) [59] used the Wittig reaction and the later syntheses (Schemes 36 [61], 37 [62] and 38 [63]) utilized the Grignard reaction for the construction of the carbon chain.

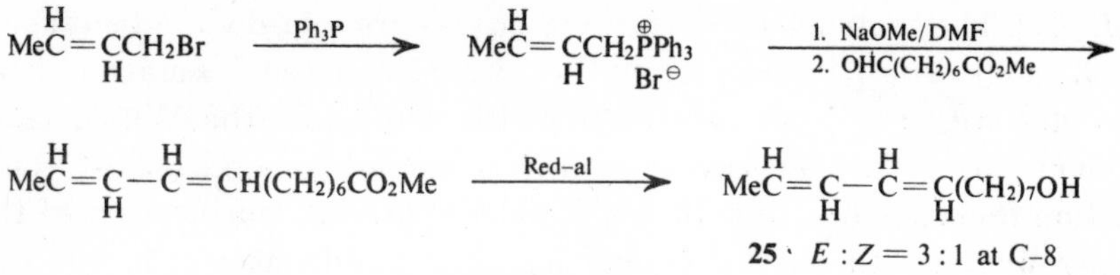

$$MeC{=}CCH_2Br \xrightarrow{Ph_3P} MeC{=}CCH_2\overset{\oplus}{P}Ph_3 \;\; Br^{\ominus} \xrightarrow[\text{2. OHC(CH}_2)_6CO_2Me]{\text{1. NaOMe/DMF}}$$

$$MeC{=}C{-}C{=}CH(CH_2)_6CO_2Me \xrightarrow{Red\text{--}al} MeC{=}C{-}C{=}C(CH_2)_7OH$$

25 · $E : Z = 3 : 1$ at C–8

Scheme 35

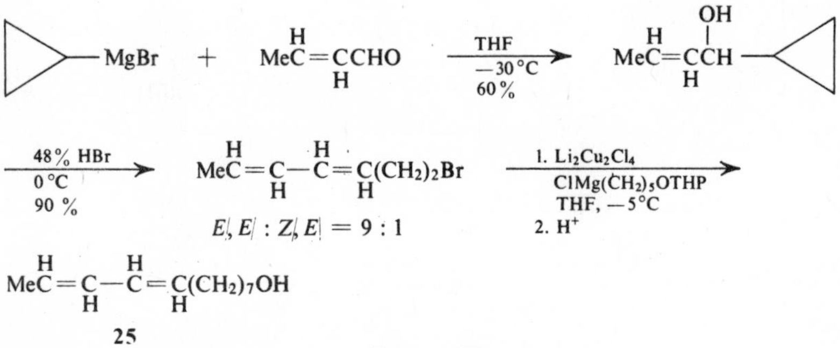

$$\triangleright{-}MgBr \;\; + \;\; MeC{=}CCHO \xrightarrow[\substack{-30\,^\circ C \\ 60\%}]{THF} MeC{=}\overset{OH}{\underset{}{C}}CH{-}\triangleleft$$

$$\xrightarrow[\substack{0\,^\circ C \\ 90\%}]{48\%\ HBr} MeC{=}C{-}C{=}C(CH_2)_2Br \xrightarrow[\substack{ClMg(CH_2)_5OTHP \\ THF, -5\,^\circ C \\ \text{2. } H^+}]{\text{1. Li}_2Cu_2Cl_4}$$

$E,E : Z,E = 9 : 1$

$$MeC{=}C{-}C{=}C(CH_2)_7OH$$

25

Scheme 36

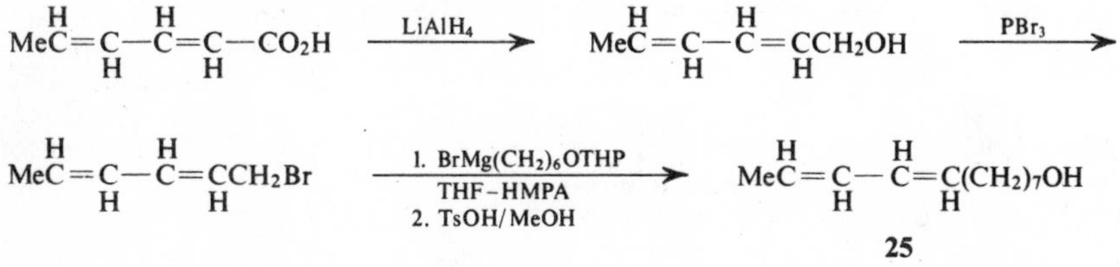

$$MeC{=}C{-}C{=}C{-}CO_2H \xrightarrow{LiAlH_4} MeC{=}C{-}C{=}CCH_2OH \xrightarrow{PBr_3}$$

$$MeC{=}C{-}C{=}CCH_2Br \xrightarrow[\substack{THF\text{--}HMPA \\ \text{2. TsOH/MeOH}}]{\text{1. BrMg(CH}_2)_6OTHP} MeC{=}C{-}C{=}C(CH_2)_7OH$$

25

Scheme 37

$$MeC{=}C{\rightarrow}C{=}CCHO \xrightarrow[\text{2. MsCl}]{\text{1. ClMg(CH}_2)_6OTHP} MeC{=}C{-}C{=}\overset{OMs}{\underset{}{C}}{-}CH(CH_2)_6OTHP$$

$$\xrightarrow[\text{2. } H^+]{\text{1. LiAlH}_4} MeC{=}C{-}C{=}C(CH_2)_7OH$$

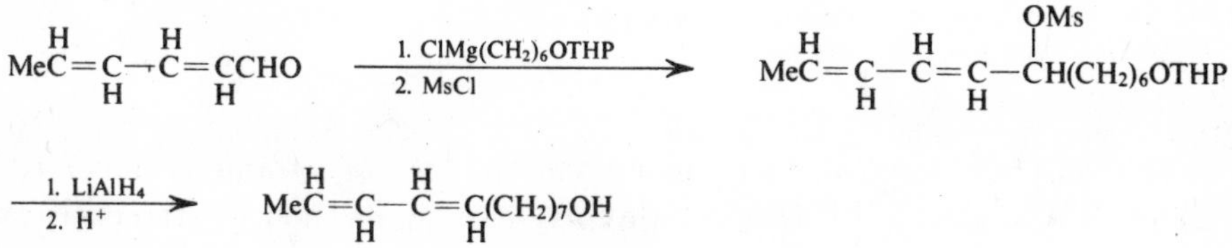

Scheme 38

C. (E)-Dodecadienyl Acetate (26)

The red-bollworm moth, *Diparopsis castanea*, is a major cotton pest in south-eastern Africa. The most potent of the sex pheromones produced by the virgin female was shown to be (E)-9,11-dodecadienyl acetate (26) by Nesbitt *et al.* [64]. The components of the pheromones are 9,11-dodecadienyl acetate ($E : Z = 80 : 20$), *(E)*-9-dodecenyl acetate, 11-dodecenyl acetate and dodecanyl acetate. The synthesis by Nesbitt *et al.* uses the Wittig reaction (Scheme 39) [65]. The second synthesis employs the Grignard coupling reaction (Scheme 40) [62]. In the Nesbitt synthesis, purification of the *E*-isomer was carried out by converting it to sulfolane, which was readily separated from the unchanged *Z*-isomer. The *E*-olefin was regenerated by thermal decomposition.

$$CH_2{=}CHCH_2\overset{\oplus}{P}Ph_3 \;\;\; \overset{\text{1. Bu}^n\text{Li/ether}}{\underset{70\%}{\xrightarrow{\text{2. OHC(CH}_2)_8\text{OAc}}}} \;\;\; CH_2{=}CHCH{=}CH(CH_2)_8OAc \;\;\; \overset{\text{liq. SO}_2}{\underset{\text{2 days}}{\xrightarrow{-20^\circ C}}}$$

$$\overset{\text{Br}^\ominus}{} \qquad\qquad\qquad\qquad E : Z = 60 : 40$$

(sulfolane ring)$(CH_2)_8OAc$ $\overset{n-\text{Octane}}{\xrightarrow{\text{reflux}}}$ $CH_2{=}CH{-}\overset{H}{\underset{H}{C}}{=}C(CH_2)_8OAc$

26

Scheme 39

$$CH_2{=}CH\overset{H}{\underset{H}{C}}{=}CCO_2H \;\;\xrightarrow{\text{LiAlH}_4}\;\; CH_2{=}CH\overset{H}{\underset{H}{C}}{=}CCH_2OH \;\;\xrightarrow{\text{PBr}_3}\;\;$$

$$CH_2{=}CH\overset{H}{\underset{H}{C}}{=}CCH_2Br \;\;\overset{\text{1. BrMg(CH}_2)_7\text{OTHP}}{\underset{\substack{\text{2. TsOH/MeOH}\\ \text{3. Ac}_2\text{O/C}_5\text{H}_5\text{N}}}{\xrightarrow{\text{THF-HMPA}}}}\;\; CH_2{=}CH{-}\overset{H}{\underset{H}{C}}{=}C(CH_2)_8OAc$$

26

Scheme 40

D. *(7E : 9Z)-7,9-Dodecadienyl Acetate* (**27**)

The sex pheromone of the grape vine moth, *Lobesia botrana*, is shown to be **27** [66]. A synthesis by Descoins involves a new method of stereoselective synthesis of a conjugated diene with *E*, *Z*-geometry. Dicobalt octacarbonyl was used as the protecting group for the triple bond [67]. The bulkiness of this protecting group makes the Julia cleavage of the cyclopropane ring stereoselective (Scheme 41) (*cf.* Equations (44) and (45), p. 25) [68]. The synthesis is shown in Scheme 42 [69]. Another synthesis employed the ortho ester Claisen rearrangement as the key step, although it was only 80% stereoselective (Scheme 43) [70]. The triple bond was reduced by hydroboration (*cf.* Equation (16), p. 17).

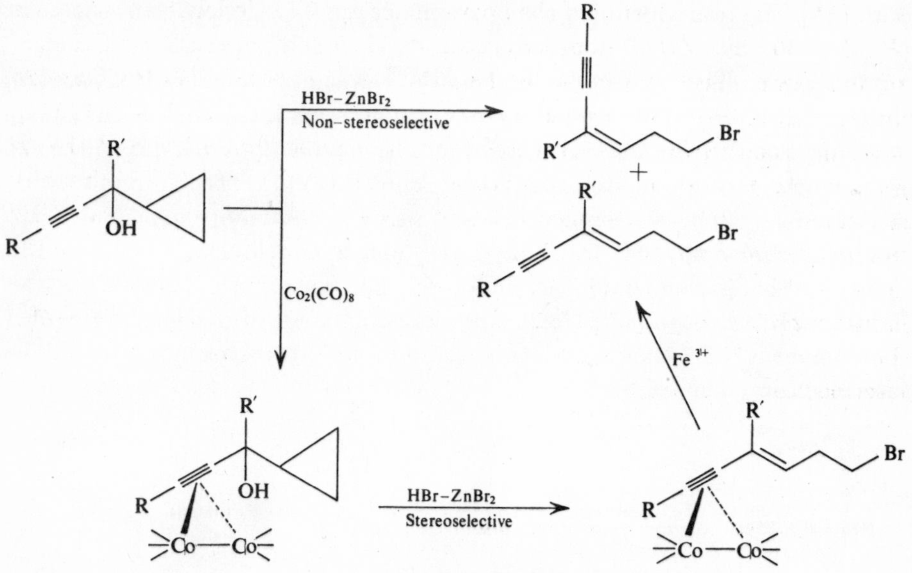

Scheme 41

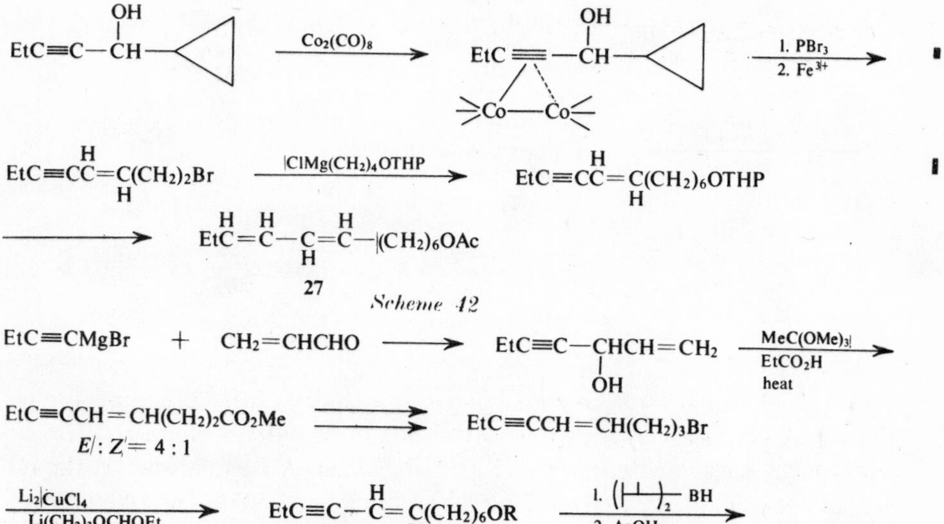

Scheme 42

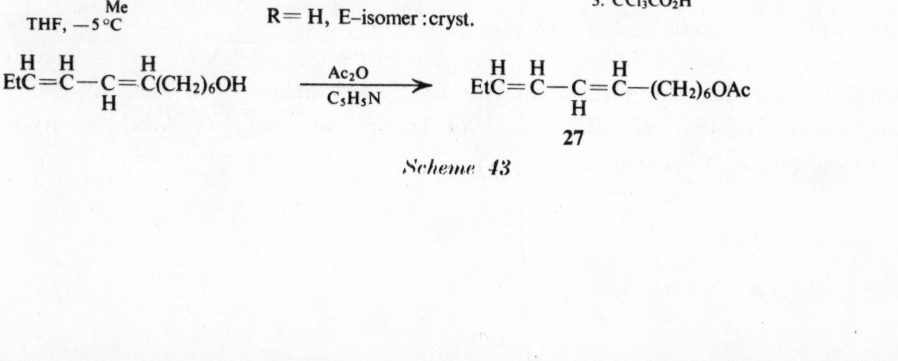

$$EtC\equiv CMgBr \quad + \quad CH_2=CHCHO \longrightarrow EtC\equiv C-CHCH=CH_2 \xrightarrow[\text{heat}]{\substack{MeC(OMe)_3\\EtCO_2H}}$$

$$EtC\equiv CCH=CH(CH_2)_2CO_2Me \quad\Longrightarrow\quad EtC\equiv CCH=CH(CH_2)_3Br$$
$$E/:Z'= 4:1$$

$$\xrightarrow[\substack{Li(CH_2)_3OCHOEt\\ \quad \quad Me\\THF,\ -5\,^\circ C}]{Li_2CuCl_4} \quad EtC\equiv C-C=C(CH_2)_6OR \xrightarrow[\substack{2.\ AcOH\\3.\ CCl_3CO_2H}]{1.\ (\ )_2 BH}$$

$$R = H,\ E\text{–isomer}:\text{cryst.}$$

$$EtC=C-C=C(CH_2)_6OH \xrightarrow[C_5H_5N]{Ac_2O} EtC=C-C=C-(CH_2)_6OAc$$

27

Scheme 43

E. (9Z : 11E)-9,11-Tetradecadienyl Acetate (28)

This compound is a major component of the sex pheromone of *Spodoptera litura*, a serious pest of vegetable crops in Japan [71]. It has also been isolated from the Egyptian cotton leafworm, *Spodoptera littoralis* [72, 73]. The first synthesis was non-stereoselective (Scheme 44) [71]. The second synthesis was 80 – 90% stereoselective and carried out independently by two groups (Scheme 45) [74, 75]. The Wittig olefination in DMSO was used to generate the Z-olefin and the undesired *E,E*-diene was removed as an adduct with tetracyanoethylene. Another component of *Spodoptera littoralis* pheromone is (9Z : 12E)-9,12-tetradecadienyl acetate whose synthesis will be described in Schemes 51–53.

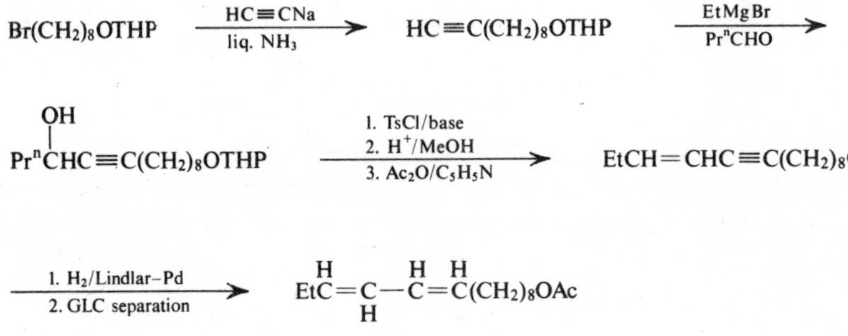

$$Br(CH_2)_8OTHP \xrightarrow[\text{liq. NH}_3]{HC\equiv CNa} HC\equiv C(CH_2)_8OTHP \xrightarrow[\text{Pr}^n\text{CHO}]{EtMgBr}$$

$$\underset{OH}{Pr^nCHC}\equiv C(CH_2)_8OTHP \xrightarrow[\substack{\text{1. TsCl/base} \\ \text{2. H}^+/\text{MeOH} \\ \text{3. Ac}_2\text{O}/\text{C}_5\text{H}_5\text{N}}]{} EtCH=CHC\equiv C(CH_2)_8OAc$$

$$\xrightarrow[\substack{\text{1. H}_2/\text{Lindlar–Pd} \\ \text{2. GLC separation}}]{} \underset{H}{EtC}=\underset{H}{C}-\underset{H}{C}=C(CH_2)_8OAc$$

28

Scheme 44

$$\underset{H}{EtC}=\underset{H}{CCHO} + \underset{Br^\ominus}{Ph_3\overset{\oplus}{P}(CH_2)_9OAc} \xrightarrow[\text{DMSO}]{NaH} \underset{H}{EtC}=\underset{H}{C}-\underset{H}{C}=C(CH_2)_8OAc +$$

28 (80~90%)

$$+ \underset{H}{EtC}=\underset{H}{C}-\underset{H}{C}=C(CH_2)_8OAc \xrightarrow{} Et\text{~~~}\bigcirc(CH_2)_8OAc$$

10~20%

(NC)₂ (CN)₂

Removed by chromatography

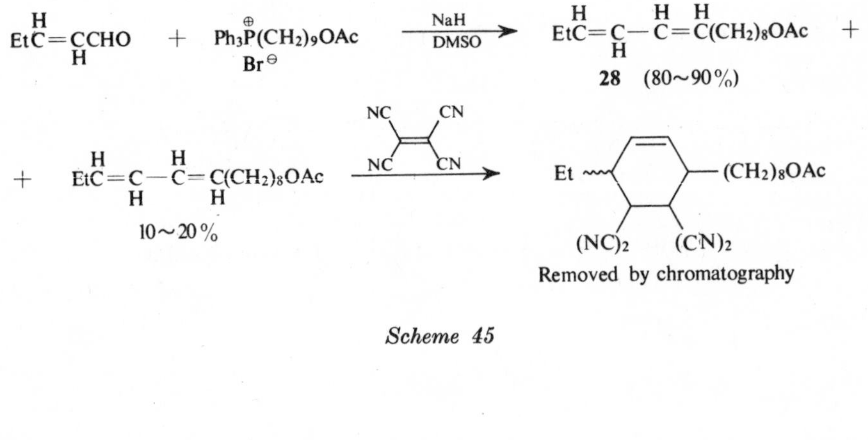

Scheme 45

F. (3E : 5Z)-3,5-Tetradecadienoic Acid (29)

This is the pheromone of black carpet beetle, *Attagenus megatoma*, and synthesized as shown in Scheme 46 [76].

$$Me(CH_2)_7C\equiv CH \xrightarrow[CH_2=CHCHO]{EtMgBr} Me(CH_2)_7C\equiv C-\underset{\underset{OH}{|}}{C}HCH=CH_2 \xrightarrow{PBr_3}$$

$$Me(CH_2)_7C\equiv C-\underset{H}{\overset{H}{C}}=CCH_2Br \xrightarrow[\substack{2. MeOH-HCl \\ 3. KOH \\ 4. H_2/Lindlar-Pd}]{1. CuCN} Me(CH_2)_7\overset{H}{C}=\overset{H}{C}-\overset{H}{C}=\overset{H}{C}-CH_2CO_2H$$

29

Scheme 46

5. PHEROMONES WITH NON-CONJUGATED DIENE SYSTEM

A. Gossyplure, a Mixture of (7Z : 11Z)-7,11-Hexadecadienyl Acetate (4) and its (7Z : 11E)-Isomer (5)

The pheromone produced by female pink bollworm moth *(Pectinophora gossypiella)*, a severe cotton pest in the United States, was studied for many years. In 1973 Hummel *et al.* identified it to be a 1 : 1 mixture of 4 and 5 and named it gossyplure [13]. Their synthetic procedure was not disclosed, although they mentioned the bioassay of synthetic compounds. A synthesis reported by Bierl *et al.* [77] was rather complicated and based on the coupling of two allylic halides to construct the carbon chain, which proved to be unsatisfactory. Their paper, however, contains a lot of biological data. The second synthesis by Sonnet was stereoselective in synthesizing 4 but not so in preparing 5 as shown in Scheme 47 [78]. The stereoselective Z-Wittig olefination was achieved by the use of *n*-butyllithium in HMPA–THF mixture as the base. The third synthesis by Mori *et al.* was based on a Grignard coupling reaction and it is highly stereoselective in preparing both isomers (Scheme 48) [79]. The next two examples illustrate the two different strategies in employing the Wittig reaction. Bestmann *et al.* synthesized the two isomers separately by the stereoselective Z-olefination method developed by them (Scheme 49) [80]. Anderson and Henrick, however, obtained gossyplure by controlling the reaction conditions to give the two isomers in 1 : 1 ratio (Scheme 50) [81]. This is convenient for practical purpose. It is also interesting to note their utilization of 1,5-cyclooctadiene as a precursor of a Z-olefinic aldo ester.

$Cl(CH_2)_6OTHP$ $\xrightarrow{LiC\equiv CH}$ $HC\equiv C(CH_2)_6OTHP$ $\xrightarrow[\text{2. } Cl(CH_2)_3Br]{\text{1. } Bu^nLi}$

$Cl(CH_2)_3C\equiv C(CH_2)_6OTHP$ $\xrightarrow[\begin{array}{l}\text{1. } Ph_3P \\ \text{2. } Bu^nLi/HMPA\text{-}THF \\ \text{3. } Bu^nCHO \\ \text{4. } AcCl\end{array}]{}$

$\overset{\text{H}\quad\text{H}}{Bu^nC=C(CH_2)_2C}\equiv C(CH_2)_6OAc$ $\xrightarrow[\text{Lindlar-Pd}]{H_2}$ $\overset{\text{H}\quad\text{H}\quad\quad\text{H}\quad\text{H}}{Bu^nC=C(CH_2)_2C=C(CH_2)_6OAc}$

4

$\downarrow$ $HNO_2,\ 70\sim75\ °C$

$\overset{\text{H}}{Bu^nC}=\underset{\text{H}}{C}(CH_2)_2C\equiv C(CH_2)_6OAc$ $\xrightarrow[\text{Lindlar-Pd}]{H_2}$ $\overset{\text{H}}{Bu^nC}=\underset{\text{H}}{C}(CH_2)_2\overset{\text{H}}{C}=\overset{|\text{H}}{C}(CH_2)_6OAc$

75 % E

5

Scheme 47

$Bu^nC\equiv CCH_2OH$ $\xrightarrow{PBr_3}$ $Bu^nC\equiv CCH_2Br$ $\xrightarrow[\text{THF, 79 \%}]{HC\equiv CCH_2MgBr}$

$Bu^nC\equiv C(CH_2)_2C\equiv CH$ $\xrightarrow[\begin{array}{l}\text{1. } Bu^nLi/THF\text{-}HMPA \\ \text{2. } Br(CH_2)_6OTHP \\ \text{3. } TsOH/MeOH\end{array}]{}$

$Bu^nC\equiv C(CH_2)_2C\equiv C(CH_2)_6OH$ $\xrightarrow[\text{2. } Ac_2O/C_5H_5N]{\text{1. } H_2/P\text{-}2\ Ni}$ $\overset{\text{H}\quad\text{H}\quad\quad\text{H}\quad\text{H}}{Bu^nC=C(CH_2)_2C=C(CH_2)_6OAc}$

4

$Bu^nC\equiv CCH_2OH$ $\xrightarrow{LiAlH_4}$ $\overset{\text{H}}{Bu^nC}=\underset{\text{H}}{C}CH_2OH$ $\xrightarrow{PBr_3}$ $\overset{\text{H}}{Bu^nC}=\underset{\text{H}}{C}CH_2Br$

$\xrightarrow[\text{THF, 63 \%}]{HC\equiv CCH_2MgBr}$ $\overset{\text{H}}{Bu^nC}=\underset{\text{H}}{C}(CH_2)_2C\equiv CH$ $\xrightarrow[\begin{array}{l}\text{1. } Bu^nLi/THF\text{-}HMPA \\ \text{2. } Br(CH_2)_6OTHP \\ \text{3. } TsOH/MeOH\end{array}]{}$

$\overset{\text{H}}{Bu^nC}=\underset{\text{H}}{C}(CH_2)_2C=C(CH_2)_6OH$ $\xrightarrow[\text{2. } Ac_2O/C_5H_5N]{\text{1. } H_2/P\text{-}2\ Ni}$ $\overset{\text{H}\quad\quad\text{H}\quad\text{H}}{Bu^nC}=\underset{\text{H}}{C}(CH_2)_2C=C(CH_2)_6OAc$

5

Scheme 48

B. (9Z : 12E)-9,12-Tetradecadienyl Acetate (30)

This was first isolated and synthesized by Jacobson *et al.* as a pheromone of the southern armyworm moth *(Spodoptera eridiana)* [82]. This insect also uses *(Z)*-9-tetradecenyl acetate (18) as the pheromone. Later 30 was found

Ph₃$\overset{\oplus}{P}$(CH₂)₃CO₂Et $\xrightarrow[\substack{-78\,°C \\ 2.\ Bu^nCHO}]{1.\ NaN(SiMe_3)_2}$ Bu$^n\overset{H}{C}$=$\overset{H}{C}$(CH₂)₂CO₂Et $\xrightarrow{LiAlH_4}$

Br$^\ominus$

Bu$^n\overset{H}{C}$=$\overset{H}{C}$(CH₂)₃OH $\xrightarrow{PBr_3}$ Bu$^n\overset{H}{C}$=$\overset{H}{C}$(CH₂)₃Br $\xrightarrow[\substack{1.\ Ph_3P \\ 2.\ NaN(SiMe_3)_2 \\ 3.\ OHC(CH_2)_5CO_2Et}]{}$

Bu$^n\overset{H}{C}$=$\overset{H}{C}$(CH₂)₂$\overset{H}{C}$=$\overset{H}{C}$(CH₂)₅CO₂Et $\xrightarrow[\substack{2.\ Ac_2O}]{1.\ LiAlH_4}$ Bu$^n\overset{H}{C}$=$\overset{H}{C}$(CH₂)₂$\overset{H}{C}$=$\overset{H}{C}$(CH₂)₆OAc

4

Bu$^n\overset{H}{\underset{H}{C}}$=C(CH₂)₃$\overset{\oplus}{P}$Ph₃ $\Longrightarrow$ Bu$^n\overset{H}{C}$=$\overset{H}{\underset{H}{C}}$(CH₂)₂$\overset{H}{C}$=C(CH₂)₆OAc

Br$^\ominus$

5

Scheme 49

OHC(CH₂)₂$\overset{H}{C}$=$\overset{H}{C}$(CH₂)₂ $\xrightarrow[\substack{ether \\ -40\,°C,\ 1\sim1.5\ h, \\ then\ add\ EtOH \\ -40\,°C,\ 10\ min.}]{Bu^nCH=PPh_3}$ Bu$^n\overset{H}{C}$=$\overset{H}{C}$(CH₂)₂$\overset{H}{C}$=$\overset{H}{C}$(CH₂)₂CO₂Et

|
CO₂Et

1 :

+ Bu$^n\overset{H}{\underset{H}{C}}$=C(CH₂)₂$\overset{H}{C}$=$\overset{H}{C}$(CH₂)₂CO₂Et $\Longrightarrow$ Bu$^n\overset{H}{C}$=$\overset{H}{\underset{H}{C}}$(CH₂)₂$\overset{H}{C}$=C(CH₂)₃I +

: 1

+ Bu$^n\overset{H}{\underset{H}{C}}$=C(CH₂)₂$\overset{H}{C}$=$\overset{H}{C}$(CH₂)₃I $\xrightarrow[Li_2CuCl_2,\ THF-ether]{[EtOCHO(CH_2)_3]_2-CuLi}$ $\xrightarrow{H^+}$ $\xrightarrow[C_5H_5N]{Ac_2O}$

Me
|

Gossyplure (**4**+**5**, 1:1)

Scheme 50

to be the pheromone of the almond moth *(Cedra cautella)* and the Indian meal moth *(Plodia interpunctella)* [83, 84]. Jacobson's synthesis is shown in Scheme 51 [82]. Brady's synthesis started from 1,9-decadiyne as shown in Scheme 52 [85]. Bestmann's synthesis is a combination of the Julia cyclopropane cleavage and the Wittig reaction (Scheme 53) [86].

$Cl(CH_2)_8OTHP$ $\xrightarrow[\text{DMSO}]{LiC\equiv CH}$ $HC\equiv C(CH_2)_8OTHP$ $\xrightarrow[\underset{H}{MeC}=CCH_2\overset{|}{Br}]{\underset{H}{LiNH_2}}$

$\underset{H}{MeC}=\overset{H}{C}CH_2C\equiv C(CH_2)_8OTHP$ $\xrightarrow[\text{AcCl/AcOH}]{H_2/\text{Lindlar–Pd}}$

$\underset{H}{MeC}=\overset{H}{C}CH_2\overset{H}{C}=\overset{H}{C}(CH_2)_8OAc$

30

Scheme 51

$HC\equiv C(CH_2)_6C\equiv CH$ $\Longrightarrow$ $HC\equiv C(CH_2)_7\overset{H}{C}\!\!\begin{array}{c}O\!-\!\\O\!-\!\end{array}$ $\xrightarrow[\text{2. }\underset{H}{MeC}=CCH_2Br]{\text{1. }LiNH_2/\text{dioxane}}$

$\underset{H}{MeC}=\overset{H}{C}CH_2C\equiv C(CH_2)_7\overset{H}{C}\!\!\begin{array}{c}O\!-\!\\O\!-\!\end{array}$ $\xrightarrow{H_3O^+}$ $\underset{H}{MeC}=\overset{H}{C}CH_2C\equiv C(CH_2)_7CHO$

$\xrightarrow{LiAlH_4}$ $\underset{H}{MeC}=\overset{H}{C}CH_2C\equiv C(CH_2)_8OH$ $\xrightarrow[\text{MeOH, quinoline}]{H_2/\text{Pd–BaSO}_4}$

$\underset{H}{MeC}=\overset{H}{C}CH_2\overset{H}{C}=\overset{H}{C}(CH_2)_8OH$ $\xrightarrow{AcCl/C_5H_5N}$ $\underset{H}{MeC}=\overset{H}{C}CH_2\overset{H}{C}=\overset{H}{C}(CH_2)_8OAc$

30

Scheme 52

$\underset{OH}{\overset{|}{MeCH}}\!\!-\!\!\triangleleft$ $\xrightarrow{48\% \text{ HBr}}$ $\underset{H}{MeC}=\overset{H}{C}(CH_2)_2Br$ $\xrightarrow{Ph_3P}$ $\underset{H}{MeC}=\overset{H}{C}(CH_2)_2\overset{\oplus}{P}Ph_3\;\;Br^\ominus$ $\xrightarrow[\text{HMPA}]{K}$

$\underset{H}{MeC}=\overset{H}{C}CH_2CH=PPh_3$ $\xrightarrow{OHC(CH_2)_8OAc}$ $\underset{H}{MeC}=\overset{H}{C}CH_2\overset{H}{C}=\overset{H}{C}(CH_2)_8OAc$.

30

Scheme 53

C. *(6E : 11Z)-6,11-Hexadecadienyl Acetate* (**31**) *and (6E : 11Z)-6,11-Hexadecadienal* (**32**)

These were isolated and synthesized by Kochansky *et al.* as the sex pheromone of the wild silk moth, *Antheraea polyphemus* [87]. The pheromone is a 90 : 10 mixture of **31** and **32**. The synthesis is shown in Scheme 54.

$$HC \equiv C(CH_2)_3OTHP \xrightarrow[\text{2. } Bu^nBr]{\text{1. } LiNH_2} Bu^nC \equiv C(CH_2)_3OTHP \xrightarrow{H_2/Pd}$$

$$\underset{Bu^n}{H}\overset{H}{C} = \overset{H}{C}(CH_2)_3OTHP \Longrightarrow \underset{Bu^n}{H}\overset{H}{C} = \overset{H}{C}(CH_2)_3Br \xrightarrow{HC \equiv C(CH_2)_5OTHP}$$

$$\underset{Bu^n}{H}\overset{H}{C} = \overset{H}{C}(CH_2)_3C \equiv C(CH_2)_5OTHP \xrightarrow[\text{2. } AcCl/AcOH]{\text{1. } Na/NH_3}$$

$$\underset{Bu^n}{H}\overset{H}{C} = \overset{H}{C}(CH_2)_3\underset{H}{\overset{H}{C}} = \overset{H}{C}(CH_2)_5OAc \xrightarrow[\substack{\text{2. } CrO_3^- \\ C_5H_5N}]{\text{1. } OH^-} \underset{Bu^n}{H}\overset{H}{C} = \overset{H}{C}(CH_2)_3\overset{H}{C} = \overset{H}{C}(CH_2)_4CHO$$

31   32

Scheme 54

D. (3Z : 13Z)-3,13-Octadecadienyl Acetate (33) and (3E : 13Z)-3,13 Octadecadienyl Acetate (34)

The female peach tree borer, *Sanninoidea exitiosa*, uses (3Z : 13Z)-3,13-octadecadienyl acetate (33) and the female lesser peach tree borer, *Synanthedon pictipes*, uses its (3E : 13Z)-isomer (34) as sex pheromones [88]. These compounds are the largest pheromones isolated thus far from a lepidopterous species. *S. exitiosa* males did not respond to the (3E : 13Z)-isomer and low concentrations of it in the (3Z : 13Z)-isomer did not interfere with their response to the (3Z : 13Z)-isomer. In contrast, even very low concentrations of the (3Z : 13Z)-isomer (1%) in the (3E : 13Z)-isomer significantly inhibited the response of *S. pictipes* males. The synthesis is shown in Scheme 55 [88].

$$Cl(CH_2)_8I \xrightarrow[\text{liq. } NH_3]{Bu^nC \equiv CNa} Bu^nC \equiv C(CH_2)_8Cl \xrightarrow[\substack{\text{2. } NaC \equiv C(CH_2)_2OTHP \\ \text{liq. } NH_3 \\ \text{3. } H^+, MeOH}]{\text{1. } NaI/acetone}$$

$$Bu^nC \equiv C(CH_2)_8C \equiv C(CH_2)_2OH \xrightarrow[\text{2. } Ac_2O]{\text{1. } H_2/Pd} \underset{Bu^n}{H}\overset{H}{C} = \overset{H}{C}(CH_2)_8\underset{H}{\overset{H}{C}} = \overset{H}{C}(CH_2)_2OAc$$

33

$$Bu^nC \equiv C(CH_2)_8Cl \xrightarrow{H_2/Pd} \underset{Bu^n}{H}\overset{H}{C} = \overset{H}{C}(CH_2)_8Cl \xrightarrow[\text{2. } \triangle_O]{\text{1. } LiC \equiv CH, H_2N(CH_2)_2NH_2}$$

$$\underset{Bu^n}{H}\overset{H}{C} = \overset{H}{C}(CH_2)_8C \equiv C(CH_2)_2OH \xrightarrow[\text{2. } Ac_2O]{\text{1. } Na/NH_3} \underset{Bu^n}{H}\overset{H}{C} = \overset{H}{C}(CH_2)_8\overset{H}{C} = \overset{H}{C}(CH_2)_2OAc$$

Scheme 55   34

6. PHEROMONES WITH TRIENE SYSTEM

A. (3Z : 6Z : 8E)-3,6,8-Dodecatrien-1-ol (35)

This is the trail-following pheromone for a southern subterranean termite. Termite trail-following substance is secreted by the sternal gland of various species of termite workers to mark the source of suitable wood to other workers of the same species. The synthesis was non-stereoselective and carried out as shown in Scheme 56 [89]. The minimum amount of the pheromone required to stimulate the worker termites to follow was 0.01 pg.

$$Pr^nCHO \ + \ BrCH_2C\equiv CH \ \xrightarrow[THF]{Zn} \ \underset{OH}{Pr^nCHCH_2C\equiv CH} \ \xrightarrow[2.\ KOH/EtOH]{1.\ TsCl}$$

$$Pr^nCH=CHC\equiv CH \ \xrightarrow[\substack{2.\ BrCH_2C\equiv CH \\ 3.\ CuCl}]{1.\ EtMgBr} \ Pr^nCH=CHC\equiv CCH_2C\equiv CH \ \xrightarrow[2.]{1.\ EtMgBr}$$

$$Pr^nCH=CHC\equiv CCH_2C\equiv CCH_2CH_2OH \ \xrightarrow[\substack{2.\ GLC\ separation}]{1.\ H_2/Lindlar-Pd}$$

$$\underset{H}{Pr^nC}=\overset{H}{C}-\overset{H}{C}=\overset{H}{C}-CH_2-\overset{H}{C}=\overset{H}{C}-CH_2CH_2OH$$

35

Scheme 56

B. Methyl (2E)-(−)-2,4,5-Tetradecatrienoate (36)

Horler isolated this (−)-allenic ester from the male dried bean bettle, *Acanthoscelides obtectus*, as a sex pheromone [90]. This unique structure attracted the attention of many chemists and four different syntheses have been reported. The key features of the syntheses are, of course, in the formation of the allenic linkage. The first synthesis was achieved by Landor employing a reductive elimination reaction (Scheme 57) [91]. The second synthesis used the addition of an organocopper reagent to an acetoxyacetylene as the key step (Scheme 58) [92]. The third synthesis employed the coupling of two acetylenic units with concomitant elimination of a mesyloxy group (Scheme 59) [93]. The latest synthesis was the simplest one, using the new organocopper chemistry (Scheme 60) [94]. The synthesis of the optically active pheromone remains to be accomplished.

$$n-C_8H_{17}CHC \equiv CH$$
$$\overset{|}{OH}$$
→
$$n-C_8H_{17}CHC \equiv CH$$
$$\overset{|}{OTHP}$$
$$\xrightarrow[\text{2. } CH_2O \text{ gas}]{\text{1. EtMgBr}}$$

$$n-C_8H_{17}CHC \equiv CCH_2OH$$
$$\overset{|}{OTHP}$$
$$\xrightarrow{LiAlH_4}$$
$$n-C_8H_{17}CH = C = CHCH_2OH$$
$$\xrightarrow{MnO_2}$$

$$n-C_8H_{17}CH = C = CHCHO$$
$$\xrightarrow[\text{base, } MeOCH_2CH_2OMe]{\overset{\overset{O}{\|}}{(MeO)_2PCH_2CO_2Me}}$$

$$n-C_8H_{17}CH = C = CH - \overset{H}{\underset{H}{C}} = C - CO_2Me$$

36

Scheme 57

⇒
$$OHC \overset{OMe}{\underset{OMe}{\diagup}}$$
$$\xrightarrow[-30\,°C]{\overset{HC \equiv CMgCl}{THF}}$$
(alkyne- OH-diene-OMe OMe structure)

$$\xrightarrow{\overset{Ac_2O}{C_5H_5N}}$$
(alkyne OAc diene OMe OMe)
$$\xrightarrow[\substack{\text{ether, } -30\,°C \\ 25\,\%}]{(n-C_8H_{17})_2CuLi}$$

(long chain = = diene OMe OMe)
$$\xrightarrow[60\,\%]{H^+}$$

(long chain = = diene CHO)
$$\xrightarrow[60\,\%]{\substack{MnO_2 \\ MeOH- HCN}}$$

(long chain = = diene CO_2Me)

36

Scheme 58

$$n-C_8H_{17}CH - C \equiv CH$$
$$\overset{|}{OMs}$$
$$\xrightarrow[\substack{Bu^t NH_2 \\ CuCl-DMF \\ 50\,\%}]{HC \equiv CCH_2OH}$$
$$n-C_8H_{17}CH = C = CH - C \equiv C - CH_2OH$$

$$\xrightarrow[\text{2. } H_2O, \ 80\,\%]{\text{1. } LiAl(OMe)_3H/THF, \ 70\,°C}$$
$$n-C_8H_{17}CH = C = CH\overset{H}{C} = CCH_2OH$$
$$\xrightarrow[\substack{\text{hexane} \\ 70\,\%}]{MnO_2}$$

$$n-C_8H_{17}CH = C = CH\overset{H}{\underset{H}{C}} = CCHO$$
$$\xrightarrow[\substack{HCN \\ MeOH}]{MnO_2}$$
$$n-C_8H_{17}CH = C = CH\overset{H}{C} = CCO_2Me$$

36

Scheme 59

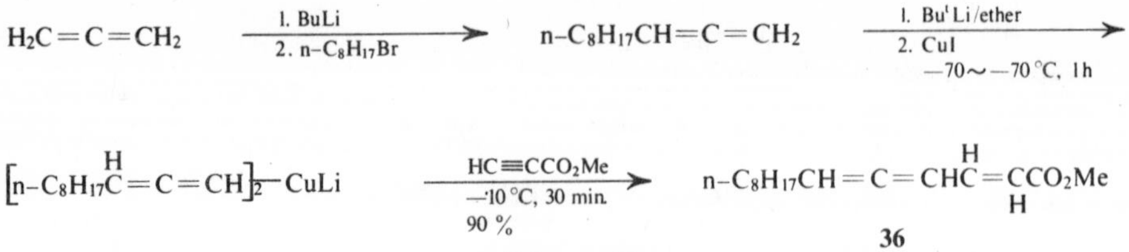

$$H_2C=C=CH_2 \xrightarrow[\text{2. n-C}_8\text{H}_{17}\text{Br}]{\text{1. BuLi}} \text{n-C}_8\text{H}_{17}\text{CH}=C=CH_2 \xrightarrow[\substack{\text{2. CuI} \\ -70 \sim -70\,^\circ\text{C, 1h}}]{\text{1. Bu}^t\text{Li/ether}}$$

$$\left[\text{n-C}_8\text{H}_{17}\overset{H}{C}=C=CH\right]_2\text{—CuLi} \xrightarrow[\substack{-10\,^\circ\text{C, 30 min.} \\ 90\,\%}]{HC\equiv CCO_2Me} \text{n-C}_8\text{H}_{17}\text{CH}=C=\overset{H}{\underset{H}{CHC}}=CCO_2Me$$

36

Scheme 60

7. PHEROMONES WITH A CARBONYL GROUP

A. Undecanal (37)

There are some aldehydes among insect pheromones; they are commercially available or easy to prepare. A synthesis of undecanal (37) is shown in Scheme 61 [95]. It is the pheromone produced by the male greater wax moth, *Galleria mellonella* [96].

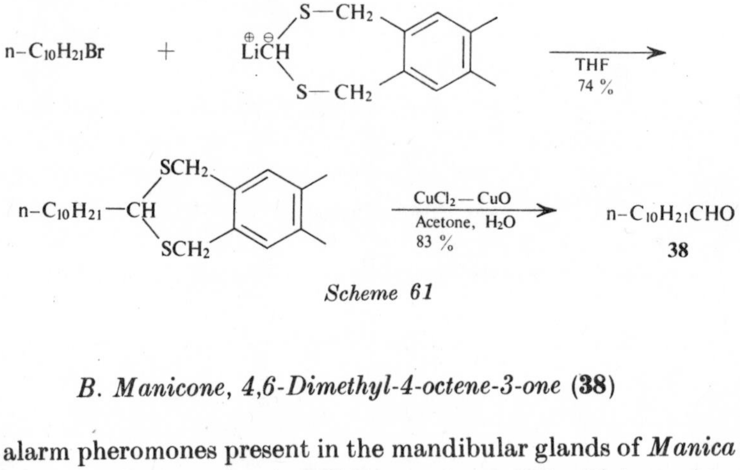

Scheme 61

B. Manicone, 4,6-Dimethyl-4-octene-3-one (38)

The alarm pheromones present in the mandibular glands of *Manica mutica* and *Manica bradleyi* are dominated by manicone (38) with two minor ketones, 4-methyl-3-hexanone and 3-decanone [97]. The first synthesis was achieved by conventional aldol condensation (Scheme 62) [97]. The second synthesis employed an organocopper reagent (Scheme 63) [98].

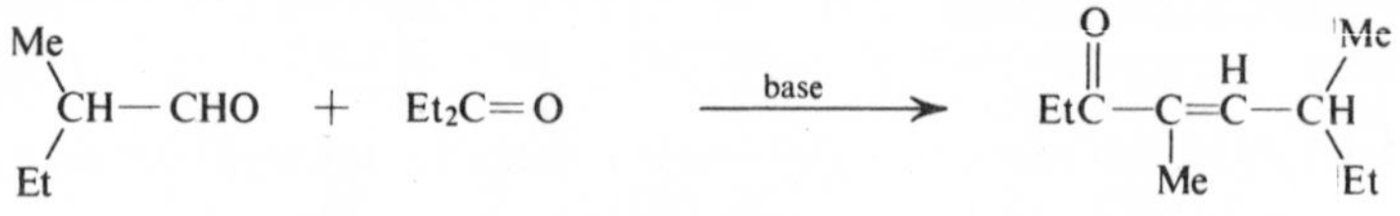

97 % E 38

Scheme 62

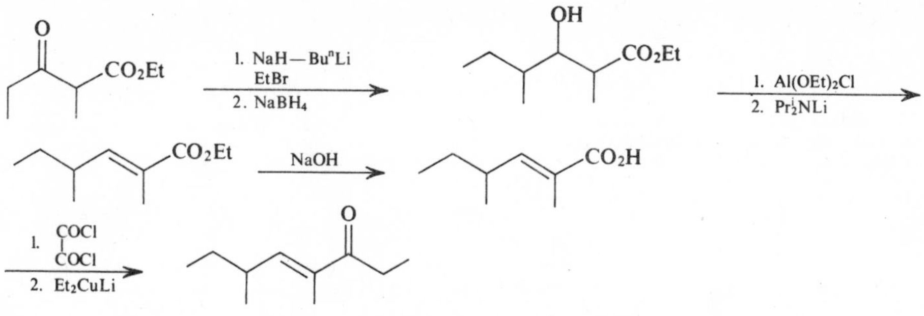

Scheme 63

C. 3,11-Dimethylnonacosan-2-one (39)
and 29-Hydroxy-3,11-dimethylnonacosan-2-one (40)

From the cuticular wax of sexually mature females of the German cockroach, *Blattella germanica*, Nishida *et al.* isolated **39** and **40** as the sex pheromone which elicited wing-raising and direction-turning response from the male adults at the first stage of their sequential courtship behaviour [99, 100]. The stereochemistry of **39** and **40** is unknown. The first synthesis of **39** by Nishida *et al.* is shown in Scheme 64 [99, 101]. Scheme 65 illustrates the synthesis by Schwarz *et al.* [102] whose clever use of the stabilized ylid and conversion of a THP ether to a bromide are noteworthy. The third synthesis by Burgstahler *et al.* is summarized in Scheme 66 [103]. The latest Zoecon synthesis is an application of organocopper chemistry (Scheme 67) [104]. The synthesis of **40** was achieved by Nishida *et al.*, in close analogy with the synthesis of **39**, as shown in Scheme 68 [200].

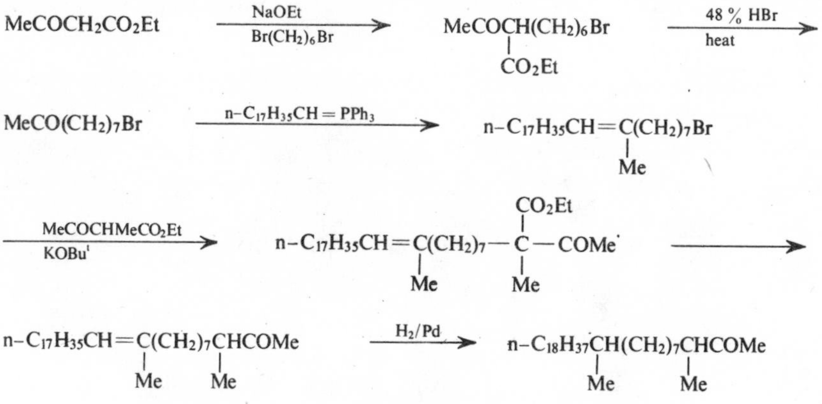

Scheme 64   39

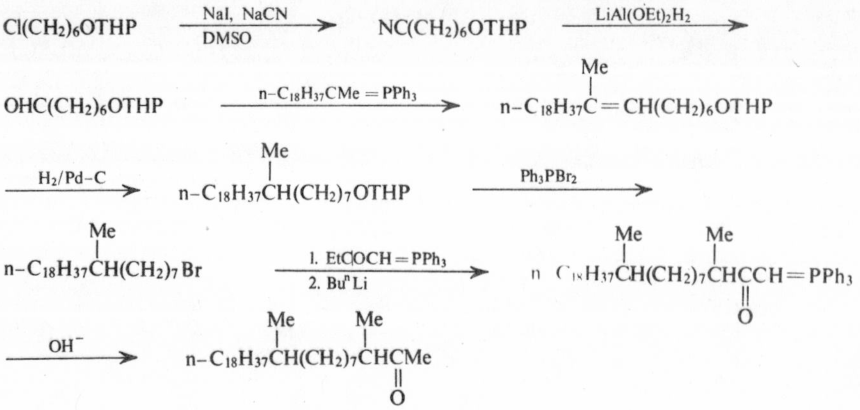

$$Cl(CH_2)_6OTHP \xrightarrow[\text{DMSO}]{\text{NaI, NaCN}} NC(CH_2)_6OTHP \xrightarrow{LiAl(OEt)_2H_2}$$

$$OHC(CH_2)_6OTHP \xrightarrow{n-C_{18}H_{37}CMe=PPh_3} n-C_{18}H_{37}\overset{\overset{\displaystyle Me}{|}}{C}=CH(CH_2)_6OTHP$$

$$\xrightarrow{H_2/Pd-C} n-C_{18}H_{37}\overset{\overset{\displaystyle Me}{|}}{CH}(CH_2)_7OTHP \xrightarrow{Ph_3PBr_2}$$

$$n-C_{18}H_{37}\overset{\overset{\displaystyle Me}{|}}{CH}(CH_2)_7Br \xrightarrow[\text{2. Bu}^n\text{Li}]{\text{1. EtClOCH}=PPh_3} n-C_{18}H_{37}\overset{\overset{\displaystyle Me}{|}}{CH}(CH_2)_7\overset{\overset{\displaystyle Me}{|}}{CH}\underset{\underset{\displaystyle O}{\|}}{C}CH=PPh_3$$

$$\xrightarrow{OH^-} n-C_{18}H_{37}\overset{\overset{\displaystyle Me}{|}}{CH}(CH_2)_7\overset{\overset{\displaystyle Me}{|}}{CH}\underset{\underset{\displaystyle O}{\|}}{C}Me$$

39 *Scheme 65*

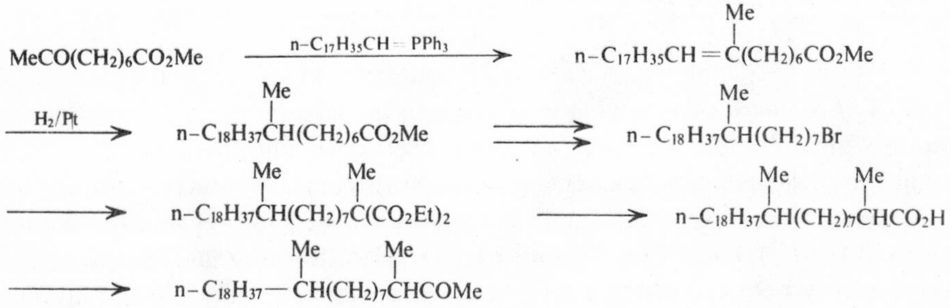

$$MeCO(CH_2)_6CO_2Me \xrightarrow{n-C_{17}H_{35}CH=PPh_3} n-C_{17}H_{35}CH=\overset{\overset{\displaystyle Me}{|}}{C}(CH_2)_6CO_2Me$$

$$\xrightarrow{H_2/Pt} n-C_{18}H_{37}\overset{\overset{\displaystyle Me}{|}}{CH}(CH_2)_6CO_2Me \Longrightarrow n-C_{18}H_{37}\overset{\overset{\displaystyle Me}{|}}{CH}(CH_2)_7Br$$

$$\longrightarrow n-C_{18}H_{37}\overset{\overset{\displaystyle Me}{|}}{CH}(CH_2)_7\overset{\overset{\displaystyle Me}{|}}{C}(CO_2Et)_2 \longrightarrow n-C_{18}H_{37}\overset{\overset{\displaystyle Me}{|}}{CH}(CH_2)_7\overset{\overset{\displaystyle Me}{|}}{CH}CO_2H$$

$$\longrightarrow n-C_{18}H_{37}-\overset{\overset{\displaystyle Me}{|}}{CH}(CH_2)_7\overset{\overset{\displaystyle Me}{|}}{CH}COMe$$

39 *Scheme 66*

$$n-C_{18}H_{37}\overset{\overset{\displaystyle O}{\|}}{C}SPh \quad + \quad \left[EtOCHO(CH_2)_6\right]_2-CuLi \xrightarrow{\hspace{3cm}}$$

$$n-C_{18}H_{37}\overset{\overset{\displaystyle O}{\|}}{C}(CH_2)_6OCHOEt \xrightarrow{\hspace{3cm}} n-C_{18}H_{37}\overset{\overset{\displaystyle CH_2}{\|}}{C}(CH_2)_6O\overset{\overset{\displaystyle Me}{|}}{CH}OEt$$

$$\xrightarrow{H_2/Pd} n-C_{18}H_{37}\overset{\overset{\displaystyle Me}{|}}{CH}(CH_2)_6OCHOEt \Longrightarrow n-C_{18}H_{37}\overset{\overset{\displaystyle Me}{|}}{CH}(CH_2)_6Br$$

$$\xrightarrow[\text{Li}_2\text{CuCl}_4]{LiCH_2\overset{\overset{\displaystyle Me}{|}}{CH}\overset{\overset{\displaystyle Me}{|}}{CH}\overset{\overset{\displaystyle Me}{|}}{CH}OCHOEt} n-C_{18}H_{37}\overset{\overset{\displaystyle Me}{|}}{CH}(CH_2)_7\overset{\overset{\displaystyle Me}{|}}{CH}=\overset{\overset{\displaystyle Me}{|}}{CH}\overset{\overset{\displaystyle Me}{|}}{CH}OCHOEt \xrightarrow[\text{2. CrO}_3]{\text{1. H}^+}$$

$$n-C_{18}H_{37}\overset{\overset{\displaystyle Me}{|}}{CH}(CH_2)_7\overset{\overset{\displaystyle Me}{|}}{CH}COMe$$

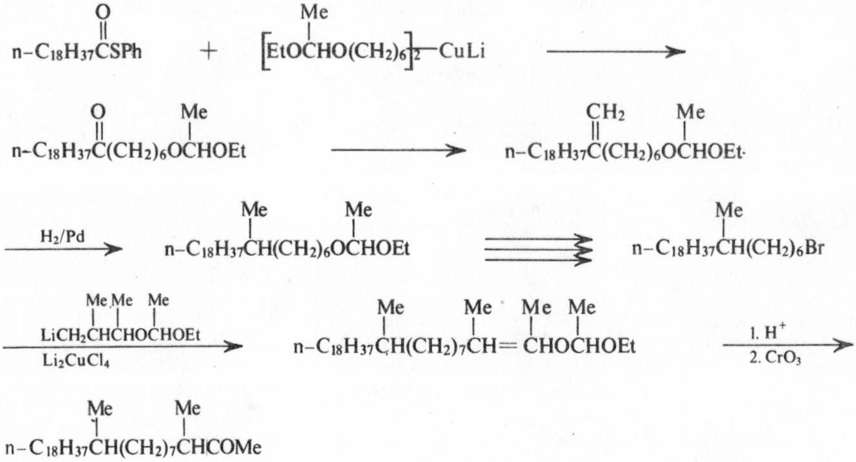

39 *Scheme 67*

Me
|
MeCOCHCO₂Et $\xrightarrow[\text{KOBu}^t/\text{Bu}^t\text{OH}]{\text{excess Br(CH}_2)_6\text{Br}}$

$$\text{Br(CH}_2)_6\overset{\overset{\displaystyle CO_2Me}{|}}{\underset{\underset{\displaystyle Me}{|}}{C}}\text{COMe} \xrightarrow{\text{HBr/AcOH}}$$

$$\text{Br(CH}_2)_6\overset{|}{\underset{\underset{\displaystyle Me}{|}}{CH}}\text{COMe} \xrightarrow[\text{p–TsOH, C}_6\text{H}_6]{\substack{\text{OH} \\ \text{OH}}}$$

$$\text{Br(CH}_2)_6\overset{|}{\underset{\underset{\displaystyle Me}{|}}{CH}}\overset{\overset{\displaystyle O\diagup\diagdown O}{}}{C}\text{Me} \xrightarrow{\text{THPO(CH}_2)_{18}\text{MgBr}} \blacksquare$$

$$\text{THPO(CH}_2)_{18}\overset{\overset{\displaystyle OH}{|}}{\underset{\underset{\displaystyle Me}{|}}{C}}(\text{CH}_2)_7\overset{|}{\underset{\underset{\displaystyle Me}{|}}{CH}} \;\; C\text{Me} \xrightarrow[\text{2. TsOH/MeOH}]{\text{1. TsOH/MeCO}_2\text{Et}} \text{HO(CH}_2)_{17}\text{CH}=\overset{|}{\underset{\underset{\displaystyle Me}{|}}{C}}(\text{CH}_2)_7\overset{|}{\underset{\underset{\displaystyle Me}{|}}{CH}}\text{COMe}$$

$$\xrightarrow[\text{EtOH–hexane}]{\text{H}_2/\text{Pt}} \text{HO(CH}_2)_{18}\overset{|}{\underset{\underset{\displaystyle Me}{|}}{CH}}(\text{CH}_2)_7\overset{|}{\underset{\underset{\displaystyle Me}{|}}{CH}}\text{COMe}$$

40

Scheme 68

D. (Z)-6-Heneicosen-11-one (41)

This is the sex pheromone of Douglas fir tussock moth *(Orgyia pseudotsugata)*, which is a severe defoliator of fir forests in western North America [105]. The synthesis by Smith *et al.* was based on the alkylation of a 1,3-dithiane (Scheme 69) [106], while Mori *et al.* employed the Eschenmoser ring cleavage of an epoxyketone as the key reaction (Scheme 70) [107].

$$\xrightarrow[\text{2. n–C}_5\text{H}_{11}\text{C}\equiv\text{C(CH}_2)_3\text{Cl}]{\text{1. Bu}^n\text{Li/THF}}$$

$$\xrightarrow[\substack{\text{Acetone–H}_2\text{O} \\ 90\%}]{\text{CuO, CuCl}_2\cdot2\,\text{H}_2\text{O}} \;\; \text{n–C}_{10}\text{H}_{21}\overset{\overset{\displaystyle O}{\|}}{C}(\text{CH}_2)_3\text{C}\equiv\text{CC}_5\text{H}_{11} \xrightarrow[67\%]{\text{NaBH}_4}$$

$$\text{n–C}_{10}\text{H}_{21}\overset{\overset{\displaystyle OH}{|}}{C}\text{H}(\text{CH}_2)_3\text{C}\equiv\text{CC}_5\text{H}_{11} \xrightarrow[89\%]{\text{H}_2/\text{P–2 Ni}} \text{n–C}_{10}\text{H}_{21}\overset{\overset{\displaystyle OH}{|}}{C}\text{H}(\text{CH}_2)_3\text{C}\overset{\displaystyle H}{=}\overset{\displaystyle H}{C}\text{C}_5\text{H}_{11}$$

$$\xrightarrow[\substack{\text{CH}_2\text{Cl}_2 \\ 86\%}]{\text{CrO}_3\cdot\text{C}_5\text{H}_5\text{N}} \text{n–C}_{10}\text{H}_{21}\overset{\overset{\displaystyle O}{\|}}{C}(\text{CH}_2)_3\text{C}\overset{\displaystyle H}{=}\overset{\displaystyle H}{C}\text{C}_5\text{H}_{11}$$

41

Scheme 69

EtOH
C_6H_6–TsOH

1. Li, n-$C_{10}H_{21}Br$/THF
2. dil. H_2SO_4
65 %

$C_{10}H_{21}$

H_2O_2/NaOH
80 %

$C_{10}H_{21}$

TsNHNH₂
CH_2Cl_2–AcOH
70 %

$n-C_{10}H_{21}C(CH_2)_3C\equiv CH$

OH
OH
C_6H_6/TsOH
83 %

$n\text{-}C_{10}H_{21}C(CH_2)_3C\equiv CH$

Bu^{n}Li/THF–HMPA
n-$C_5H_{11}Br$
80 %

$n-C_{10}H_{21}C(CH_2)_3C\equiv CC_5H_{11}$

$HClO_4$
THF–H_2O
89 %

$n-C_{10}H_{21}C(CH_2)_3C\equiv CC_5H_{11}$

H_2/Pd–BaSO₄
MeOH–quinoline
86 %

$n-C_{10}H_{21}C(CH_2)_3C \overset{H}{=}\overset{H}{C}C_5H_{11}$

41

Scheme 70

8. PHEROMONES WITH INTRAMOLECULAR ACETAL LINKAGE

These acetal pheromones are asymmetric. In this section the discussion is restricted to the synthesis of racemates. For the synthesis of optically active compounds, see Section III. 13.

A. exo-Brevicomin,
exo-7-Ethyl-3-methyl-6,8-dioxabicyclo[3.2.1]Octane (6)

Silverstein *et al.* isolated *exo*-brevicomin (6) as the principal aggregation pheromone in the frass of the female western pine beetle, *Dendroctonus brevicomis* [14]. They achieved two different syntheses of its racemate (Schemes 71 and 72) [108]. One of them (Scheme 72) was stereoselective. The second synthesis employed thermal rearrangement of an epoxyketone as the key step (Scheme 73) [109]. A synthesis by Mundy *et al.* used a Diels–Alder reaction (Scheme 74) [110]. A unique electrochemical synthesis gave *exo*-brevicomin in moderate yield (Scheme 75) [111]. A recent synthesis used the Eschenmoser fragmentation as the key step (Scheme 76) [112]. This synthesis is stereoselective, although somewhat lengthy.

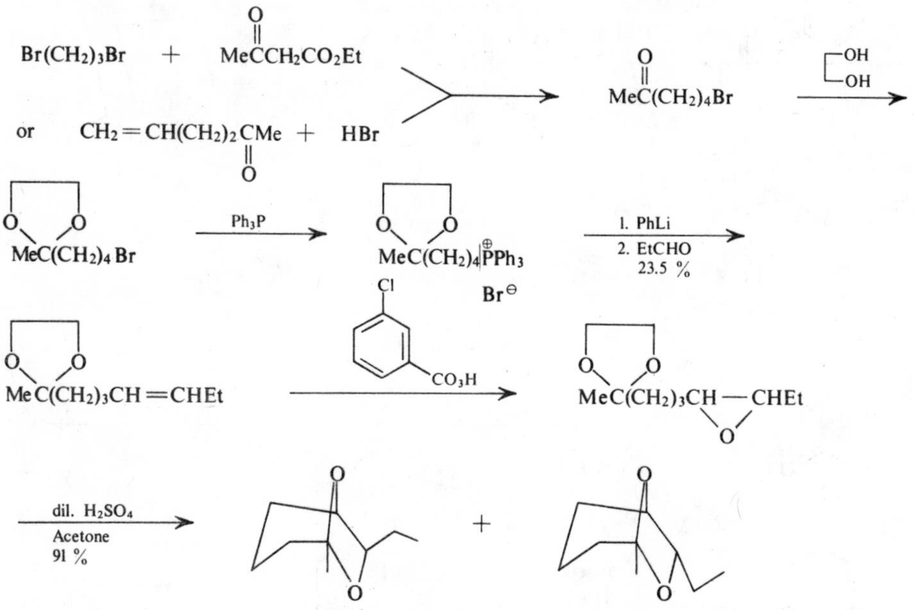

6 (*exo*)   **7** (*endo*)

4   :   1

Scheme 71

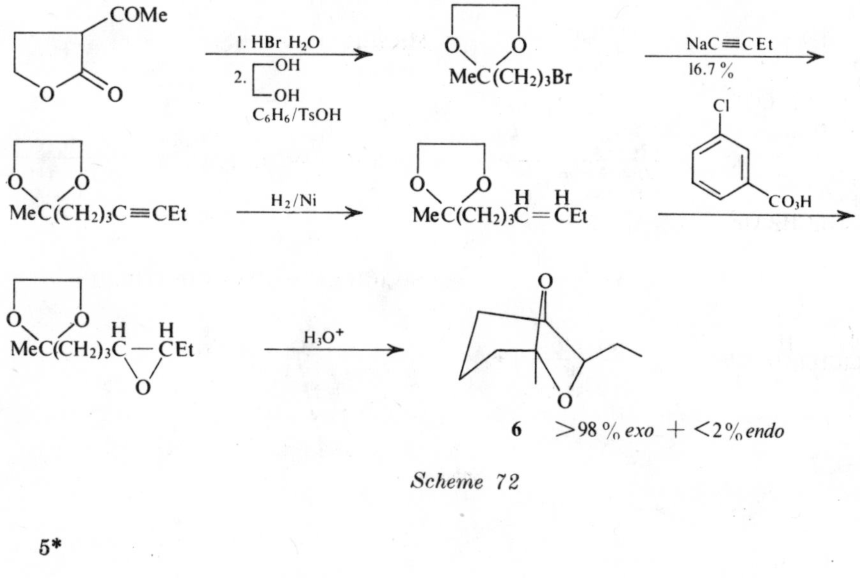

6 $>98\%\,exo\,+\,<2\%\,endo$

Scheme 72

5*

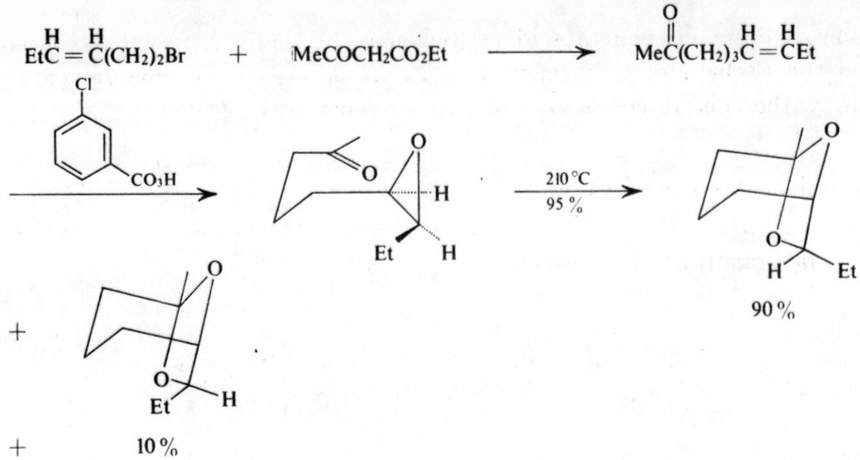

$$\text{EtC} \overset{H}{=} \overset{H}{\text{C}}(\text{CH}_2)_2\text{Br} \;+\; \text{MeCOCH}_2\text{CO}_2\text{Et} \longrightarrow \text{MeC}(\text{CH}_2)_3\overset{H}{\text{C}} \overset{H}{=} \text{CEt}$$

Scheme 73

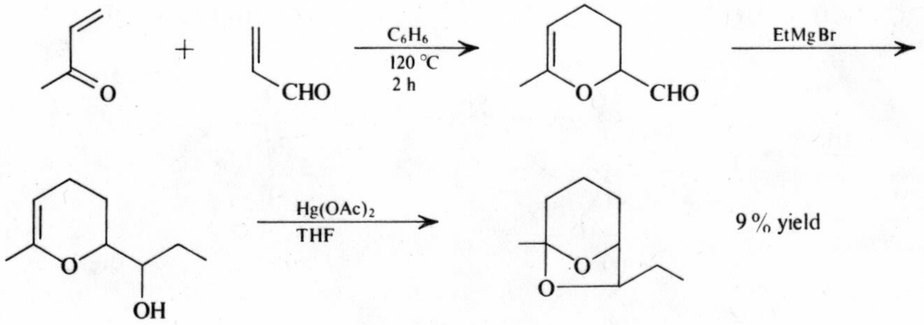

9 % yield

Scheme 74

$$\text{MeC}(\text{CH}_2)_4\text{CMe}$$
$$+$$
$$\text{MeC}(\text{CH}_2)_3\overset{H}{\text{C}} \overset{}{=} \text{CEt} \quad (33\%)$$
$$+$$
$$\text{MeC}(\text{CH}_2)_2\overset{Et}{\text{CH}}-\text{CH}=\text{CH}_2 \;(12\%)$$

$$\text{EtC} \overset{H}{=} \text{CCH}_2\text{CO}_2^{\ominus}$$
$$+$$
$$\text{MeCCH}_2\text{CH}_2\text{CO}_2^{\ominus}$$

−2e, − 2CO₂ / NaOMe/MeOH / Pt−electrode

GLC separation

$$\text{MeC}(\text{CH}_2)_3\overset{H}{\text{C}} \overset{H}{=} \text{CEt}$$

1. OsO₄ 2. H⁺ 42 %

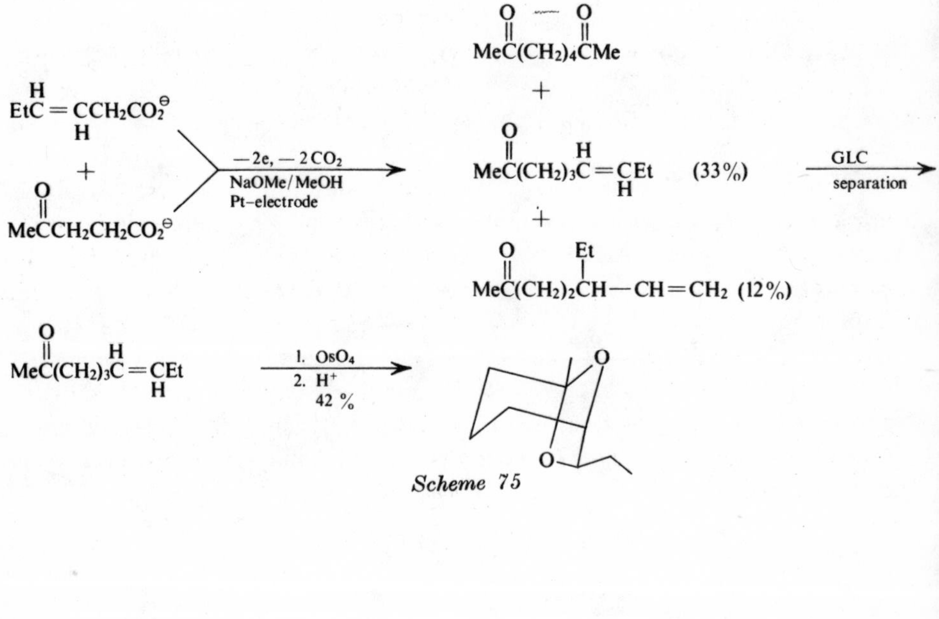

Scheme 75

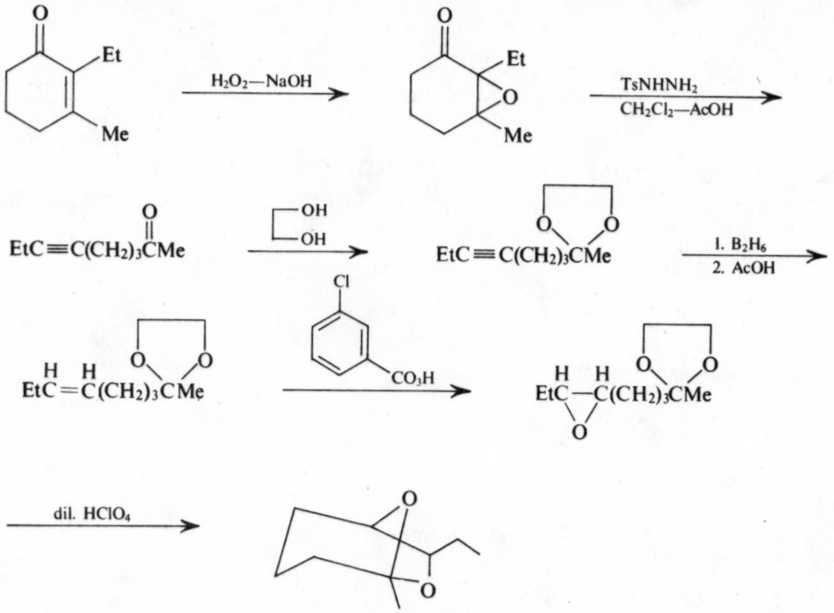

Scheme 76

B. *endo-Brevicomin*,
endo-7-Ethyl-3-methyl-6,8-dioxabicyclo[3.2.1]Octane (**7**)

This stereoisomer was also isolated by Silverstein *et al.* as a biologically inactive component of the frass [14]. Later work showed it to be a pheromone inhibitor to the southern pine beetle, *Dendroctonus frontalis* (see Section III. 1) [15]. This *endo*-isomer was a by-product of non-stereoselective syntheses of *exo*-brevicomin [108, 110]. Wasserman's epoxy ketone rearrangement was about 90% stereoselective to give **7** (Scheme 77) [109]. The recognition of this substance as a pheromone inhibitor, which may be useful as an agrochemical, prompted synthetic works and four stereoselective syntheses were reported. All of them employ the epoxidation of pure *E*-olefins as the key step. Kocienski and Ostrow generated the *E*-olefin by the Birch reduction (Scheme 78) [112]. Look's synthesis employed a preformed *E*-olefinic alcohol as the starting material (Scheme 79) [113]. An interesting catalytic synthesis was reported by Byrom *et al.* in which the *E*-olefin was generated by the dimerization of butadiene (Scheme 80) [114]. Kondo's phosphonate method [see Equation (4), p. 14] was applied to prepare an *E*-olefin (Scheme 81) [115].

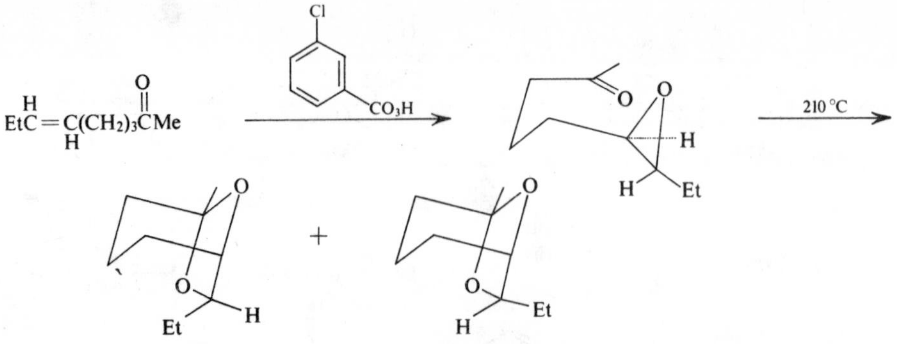

$$H\atop EtC=C(CH_2)_3\overset{O}{\overset{\|}{C}}Me\atop H$$

91 %

7

+

9 %

6

Scheme 77

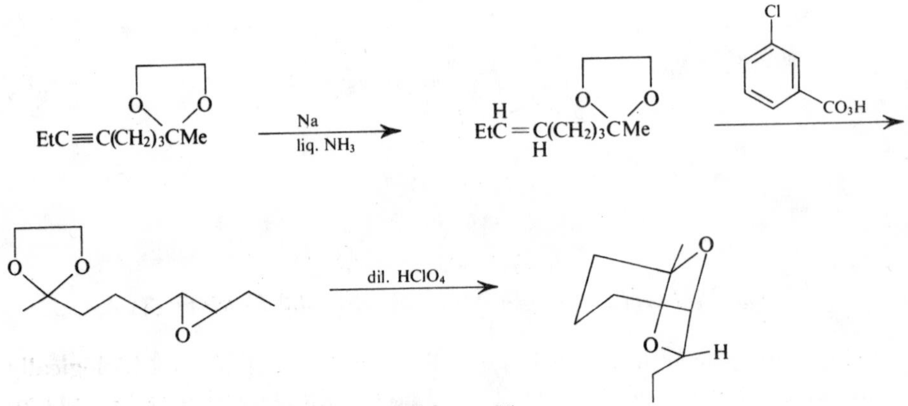

$$EtC\equiv C(CH_2)_3CMe$$

$$\xrightarrow[\text{liq. NH}_3]{\text{Na}}$$

$$H\atop EtC=C(CH_2)_3CMe\atop H$$

dil. HClO₄

Scheme 78   **7**

$$H\atop EtC=C(CH_2)_2OH\atop H$$

1. TsCl/C₅H₅N
2. MeCOCH₂CO₂Et
3. OH⁻, —CO₂

$$H\atop EtC=C(CH_2)_3COMe\atop H$$

Scheme 79   **7**

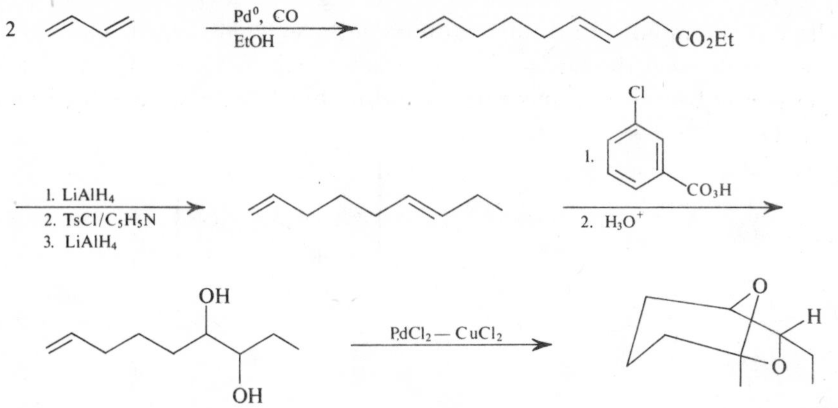

Scheme 80

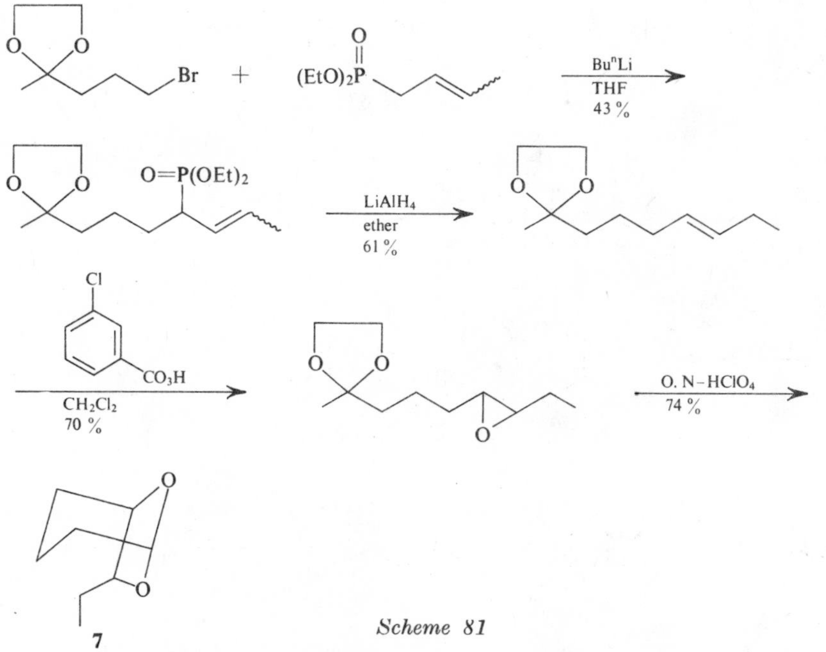

Scheme 81

C. Frontalin, 5,5-Dimethyl-6,8-dioxabicyclo[3.2.1]Octane (8)

Extraction of about 6500 hindguts of male western pine beetle, *Dendroctonus brevicomis*, led to the isolation of frontalin (**8**). Kinzer *et al.* synthesized this compound by the Diels–Alder reaction (Scheme 82) [116]. D'Silva's

72 K. MORI

synthesis also employed a similar approach (Scheme 83) [117]. The Mundy
synthesis, too, used the Diels–Alder reaction (Scheme 84) [110]. The fourth
synthesis was based on a linear and building-block type approach (Scheme
85) [118].

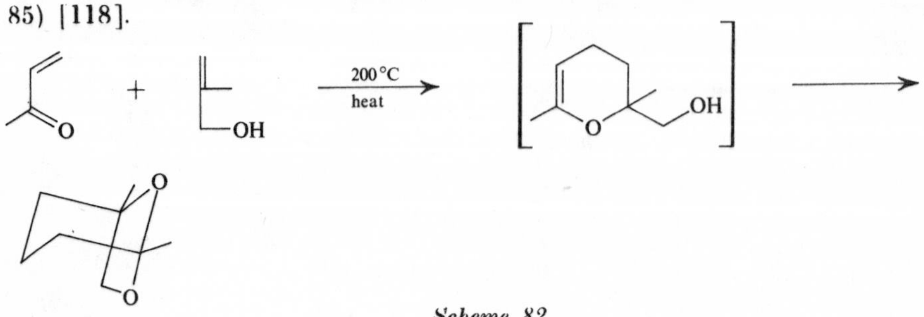

8

Scheme 82

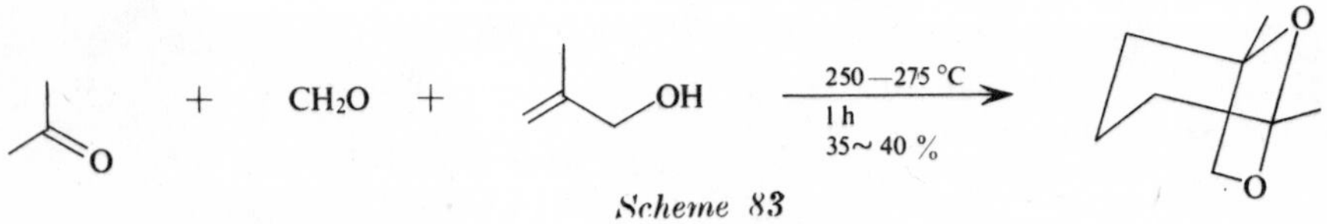

Scheme 83

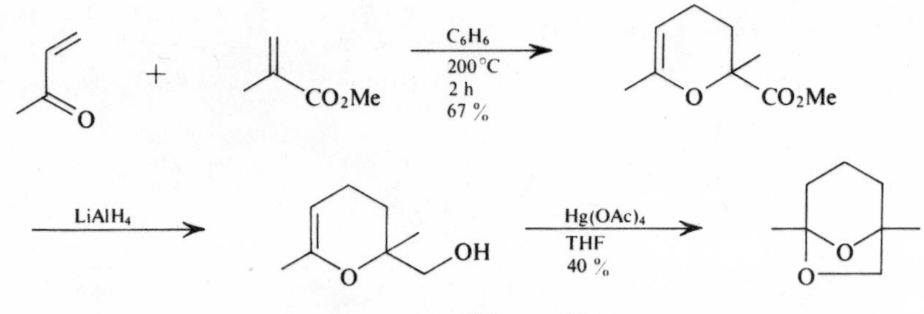

Scheme 84

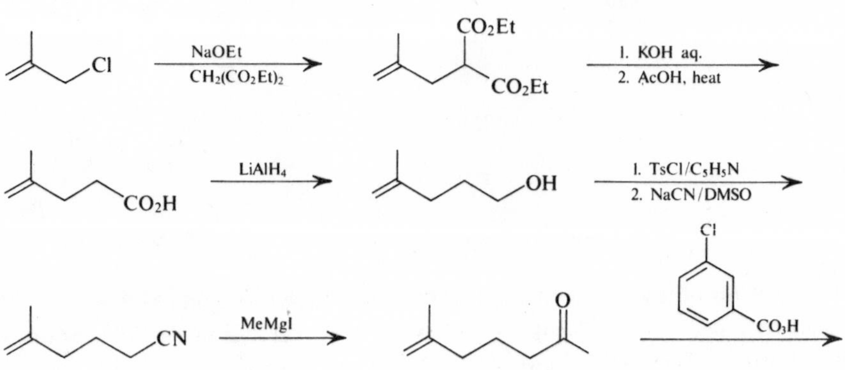

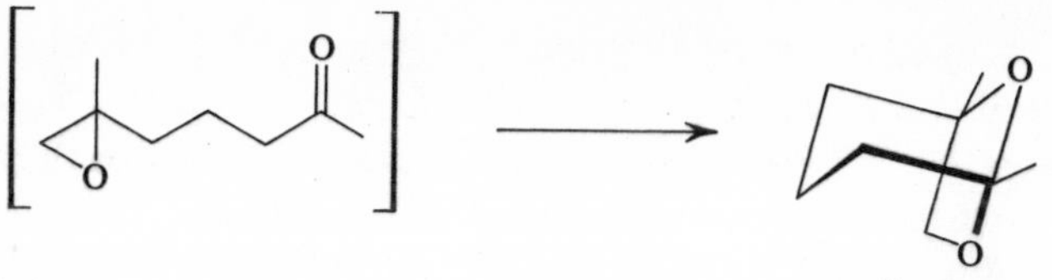

Scheme 85 (cont'd)

D. α-Multistriatin,
2,4-Dimethyl-5-ethyl-6,8-dioxabicyclo[3.2.1]Octane (42)

Pearce *et al.* showed that the attractant for the smaller European elm bark beetle *(Scolytus multistriatus)* was a mixture of ( )-4-methyl-3-heptanol, (−)-α-multistriatin (42) and a sesquiterpene, ( )-α-cubebene [119]. All three compounds were isolated from the volatile mixture collected by aerating elm bolts infested with virgin female beetles. Individually each compound was inactive in the laboratory bioassay, but a mixture of all three showed activity nearly equivalent to that of the original extract. The synthesis was carried out by Pearce *et al.* in two different ways: Scheme 86 [119]

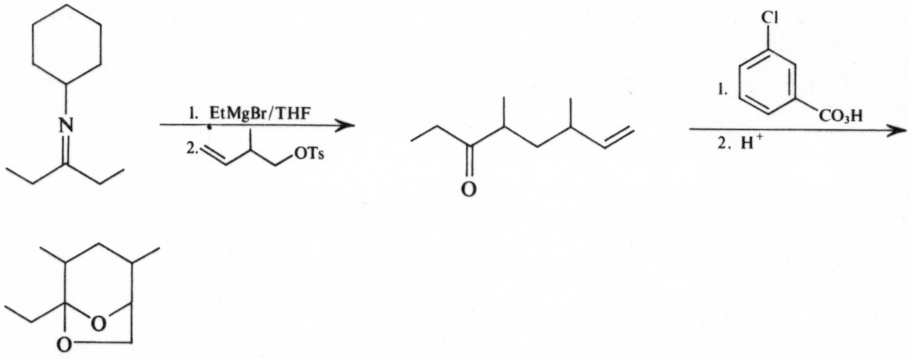

Scheme 86

and Scheme 87 [120]; the latter Diels–Alder approach coupled with a detailed NMR analysis [121] enabled them to assign formula 42 to the biologically active α-isomer of 2,4-dimethyl-5-ethyl-6,8-dioxabicyclo[3.2.1]octane.

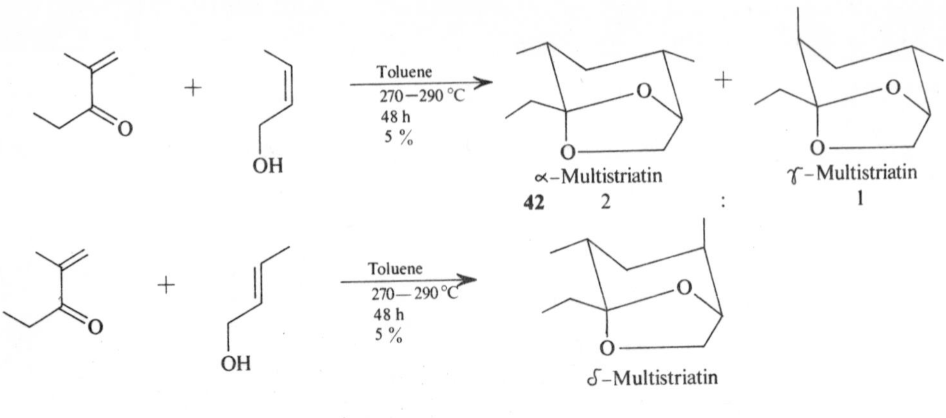

Scheme 87

9. MONOTERPENOID PHEROMONES

A. Ipsenol, 2-Methyl-6-methylene-7-octen-4-ol (43)

Ipsenol (**43**), ipsdienol (**44**) and *cis*-verbenol (**61**) are the monoterpene aggregation pheromones isolated from the frass produced by male California five-spined Ips *(Ips paraconfusus)* [122]. The first synthesis of ipsenol was carried out by the dithiane alkylation as shown in Scheme 88 to give 0.45 g of

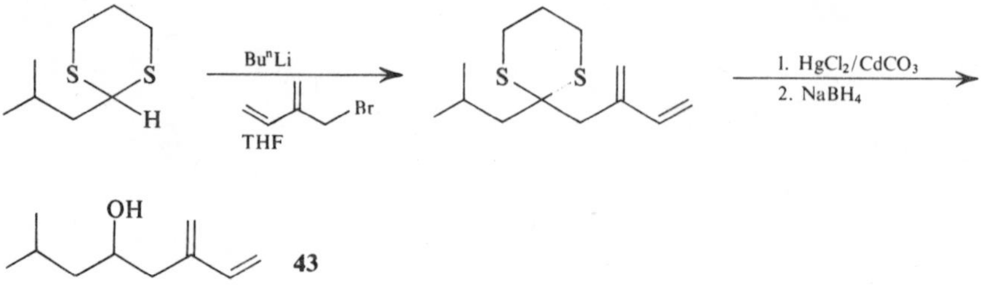

Scheme 88

80% pure **43** [123]. Vig's synthesis was based on a building block-type approach (Scheme 89) [124]. Katzenellenbogen and Lenox devised a simple synthesis, although it was not so easy to prepare the required bromide (Scheme 90) [125]. The latest synthesis was based on an interesting application of cyclobutane chemistry (Scheme 91) [126]. The synthesis of optically active ipsenol will be described in Section III. 13.

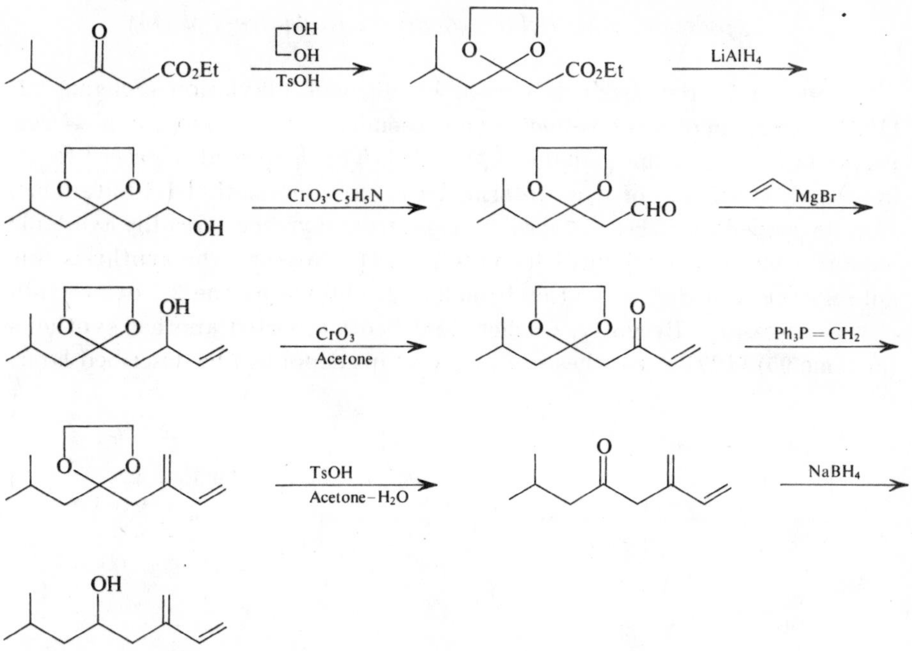

Scheme 89

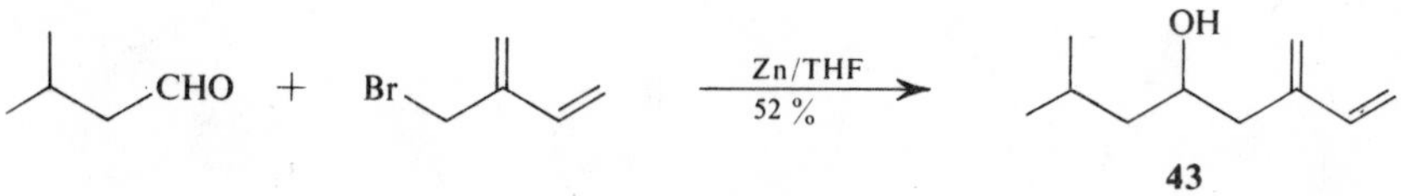

Scheme 90

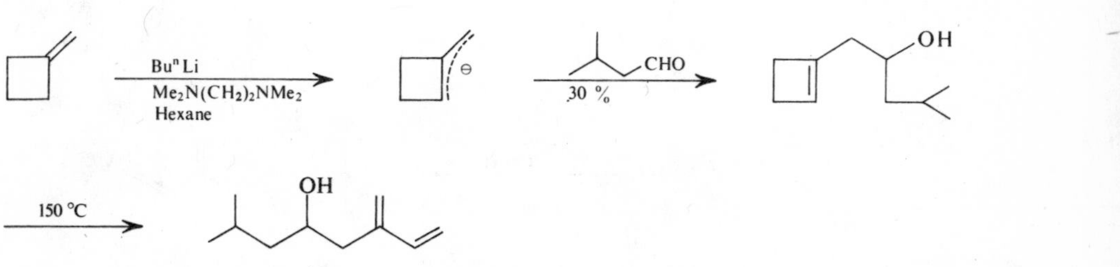

Scheme 91

B. Ipsdienol, 2-Methyl-6-methylene-2,7-octadien-4-ol (44)

Silverstein synthesized this trienol by dithiane alkylation (Scheme 92) [123]. Extension of Katzenellenbogen's ipsenol synthesis to ipsdienol **44** was particularly successful (Scheme 93) [127]. This paper also describes an improved synthesis of the intermediate, 2-bromomethyl-1,3-butadiene. Mori developed a synthesis of ipsdienol (**44**) from myrcene, a readily available monoterpene hydrocarbon (Scheme 94) [128]. However, the synthesis was not regioselective and separation from 2-methyl-6-methylene-3,7-octadien-2-ol was necessary. Recently, Garbers and Scott reported another synthesis (Scheme 95) [129]. A synthesis of (R)-(−)-ipsdienol will be described later.

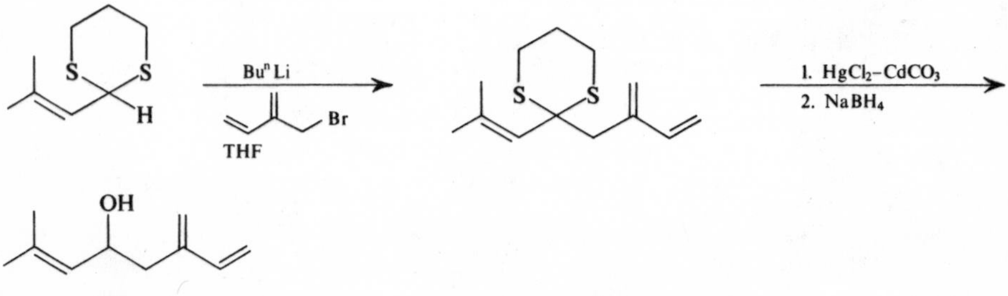

Scheme 92

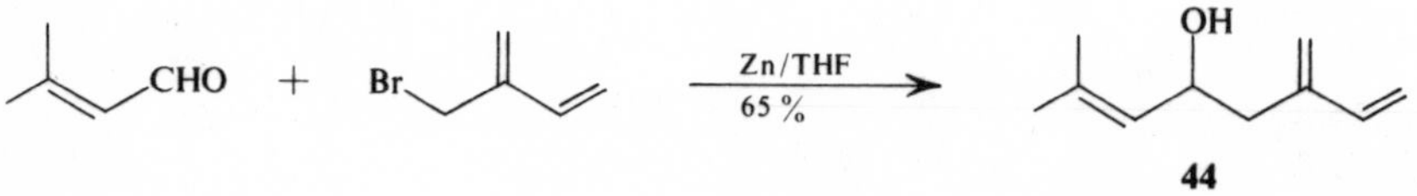

Scheme 93

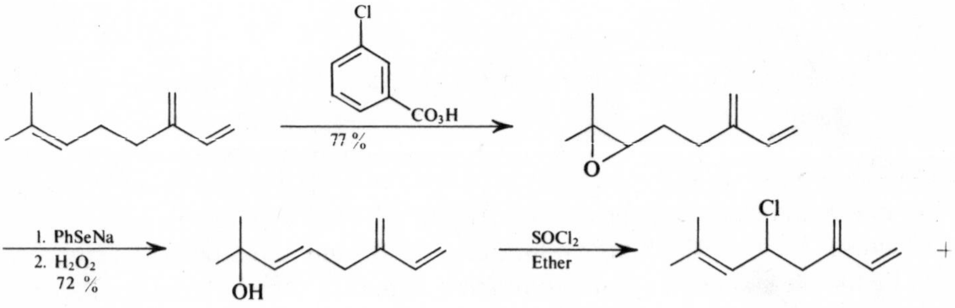

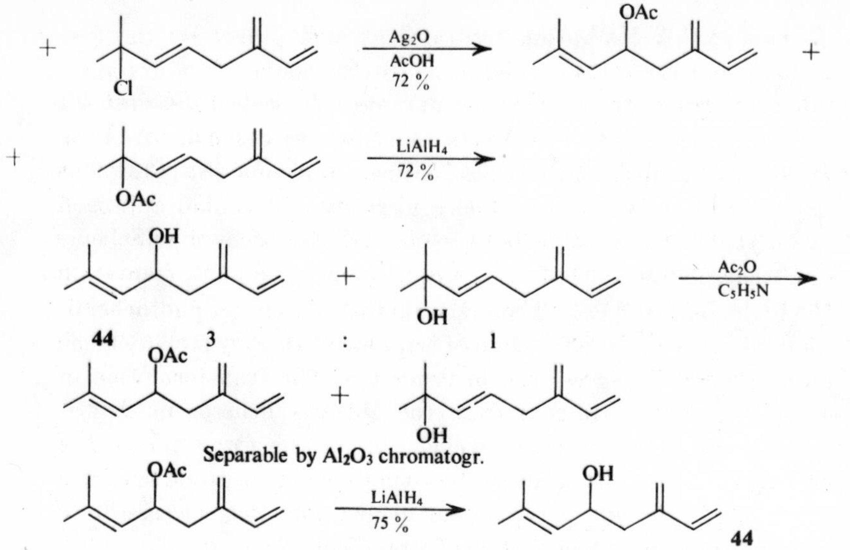

Scheme 94 (cont'd)

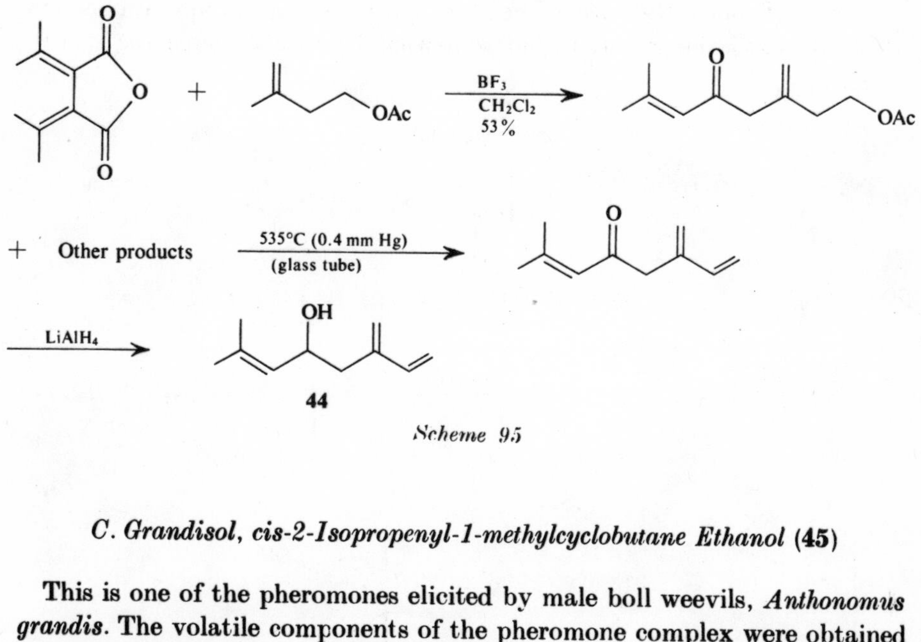

Scheme 95

C. Grandisol, cis-2-Isopropenyl-1-methylcyclobutane Ethanol (45)

This is one of the pheromones elicited by male boll weevils, *Anthonomus grandis*. The volatile components of the pheromone complex were obtained by steam distillation of the crude extracts of 4 500 000 weevils and 54.7 kg of weevil faeces [130]. This cyclobutane compound attracted the attention of many chemists and several syntheses appeared. The popular approaches

utilize photochemical cycloaddition reactions as exemplified by the first
synthesis (Scheme 96) [130, 131]. The relative stereochemistry of grandisol
was established by this synthesis. The second and stereoselective synthesis
was carried out by the Zoecon chemists as shown in Scheme 97 [132].
Gueldner *et al.* then published a shorter synthesis (Scheme 98) [133]. The
final dehydration step, however, was not regioselective. A similar approach
has been recently reported which is both regio- and stereoselective (Scheme
99) [134]. Another photochemical synthesis involves a new fragmentation
of an ozonide (Scheme 100) [135]. The first example of the non-photochemi-
cal approach used catalytic dimerization of isoprene as the key step (Scheme
101) [136] and yielded (±)-grandisol in two steps. The transformation of
carvone into (±)-grandisol differed from the above syntheses in that it
employed an efficient intramolecular cyclization for the formation of the
cyclobutane ring (Scheme 102) [137]. The overall yield of grandisol from
eucarvone was 20%. Stork's epoxynitrile cyclization was successful in
generating the correct stereochemistry of grandisol (Scheme 103) [138].
An intramolecular cyclization of a chloro ester was also reported to yield the
pheromone (Scheme 104) [139]. The Trost synthesis was a unique application
of his secoalkylation reaction, but somewhat lengthy (Scheme 105) [140].

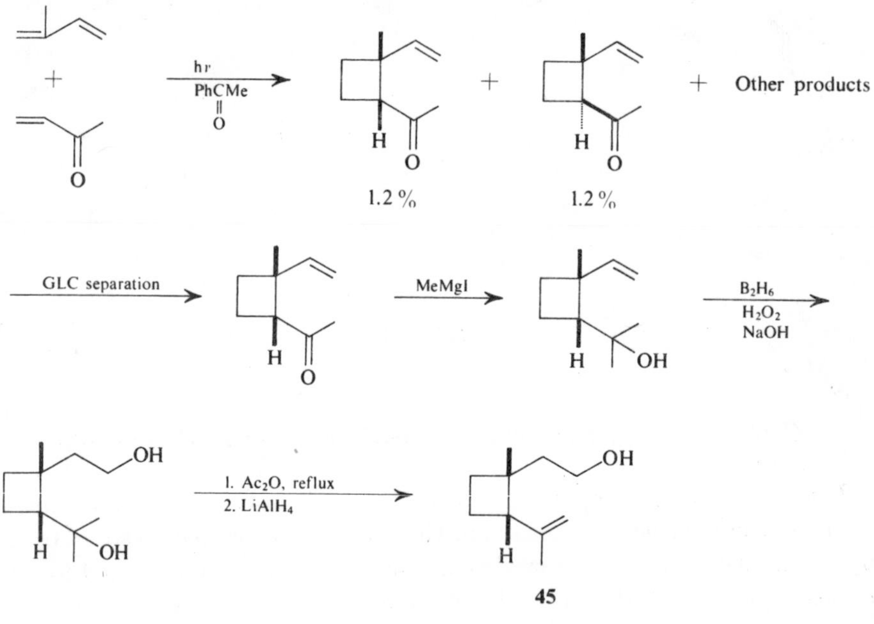

Scheme 96

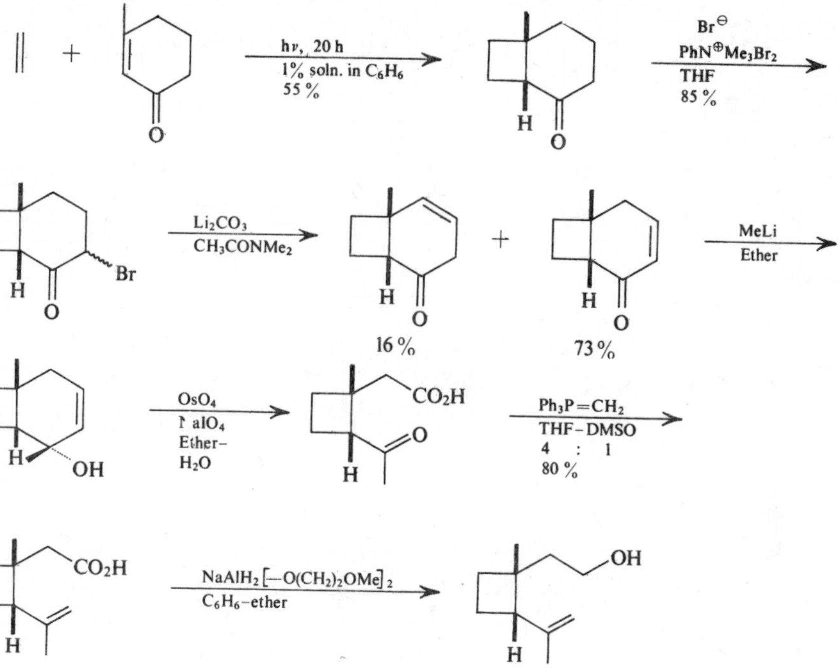

Scheme 97

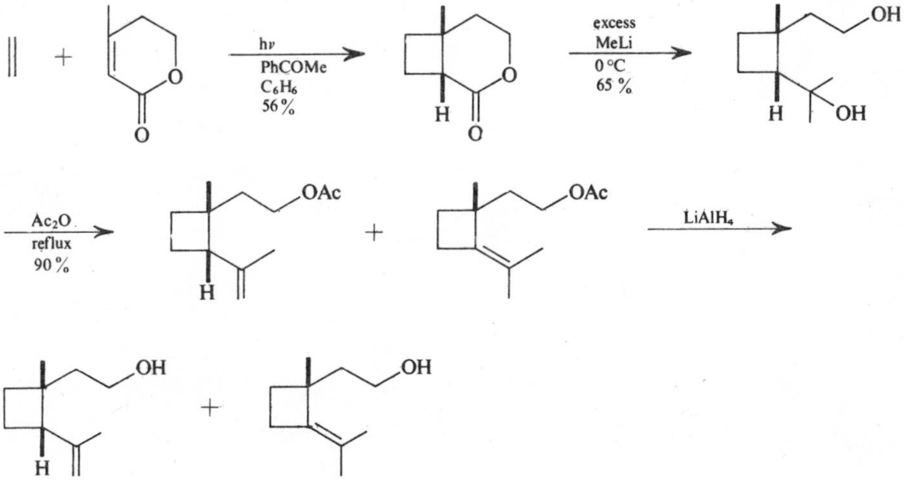

Scheme 98

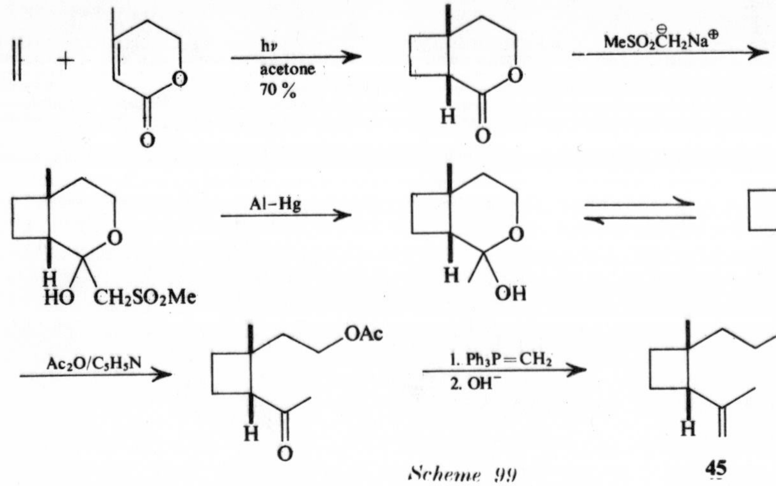

Scheme 99

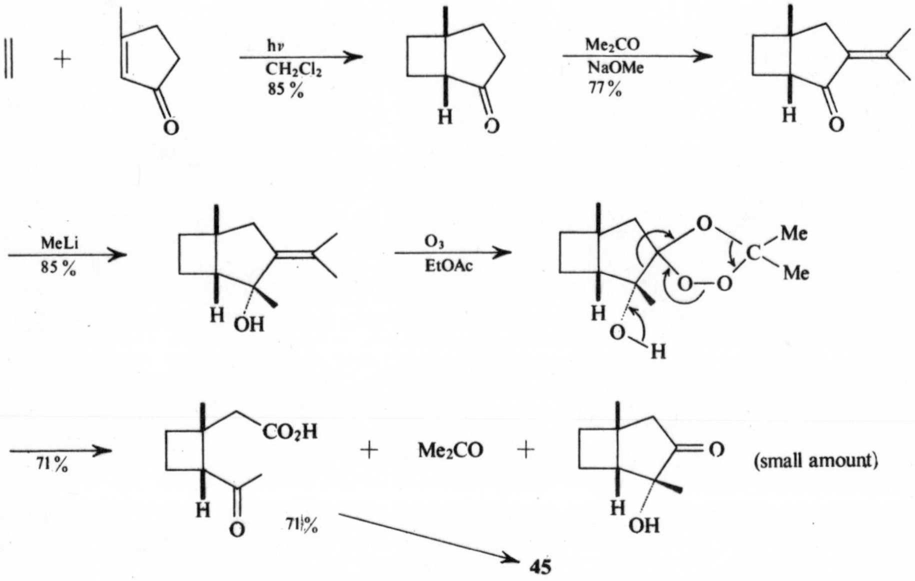

45

Scheme 100

45

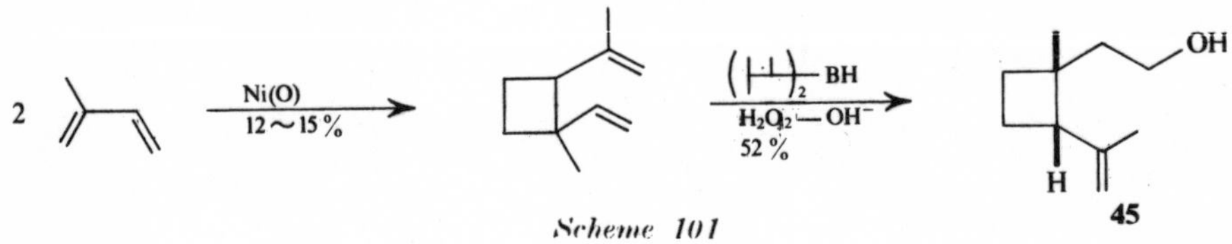

Scheme 101

45

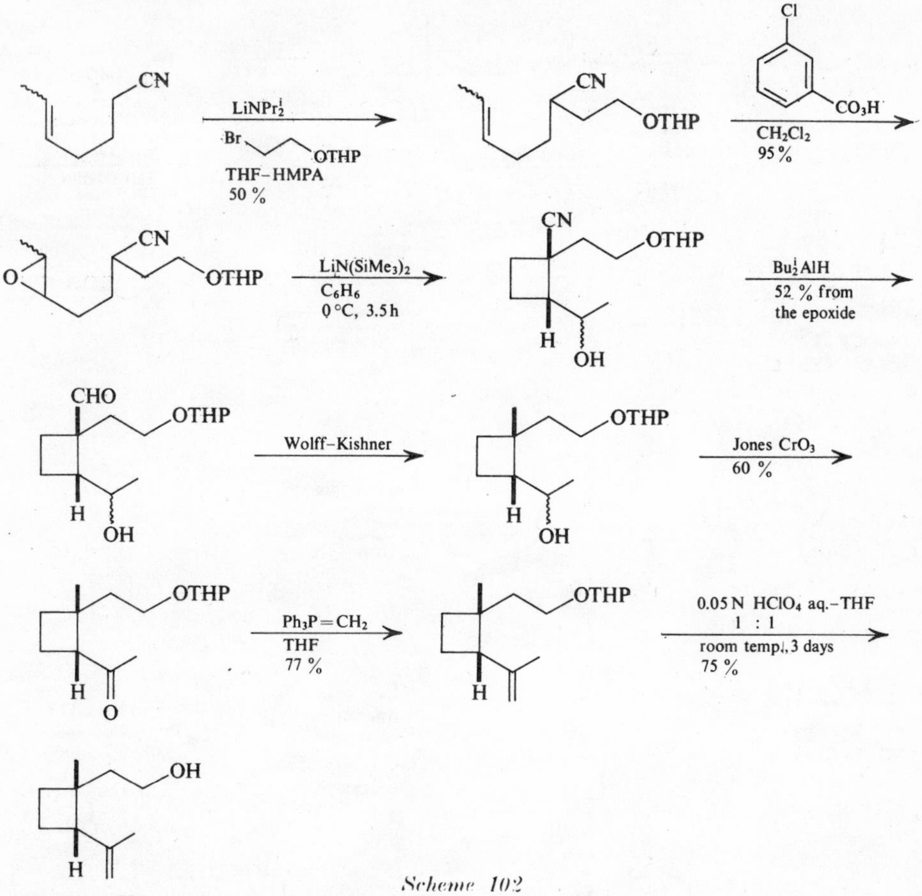

Scheme 102

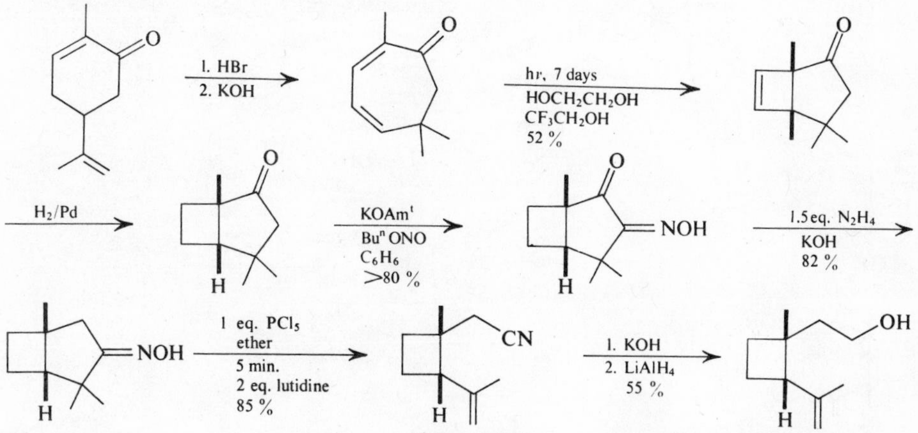

Scheme 103

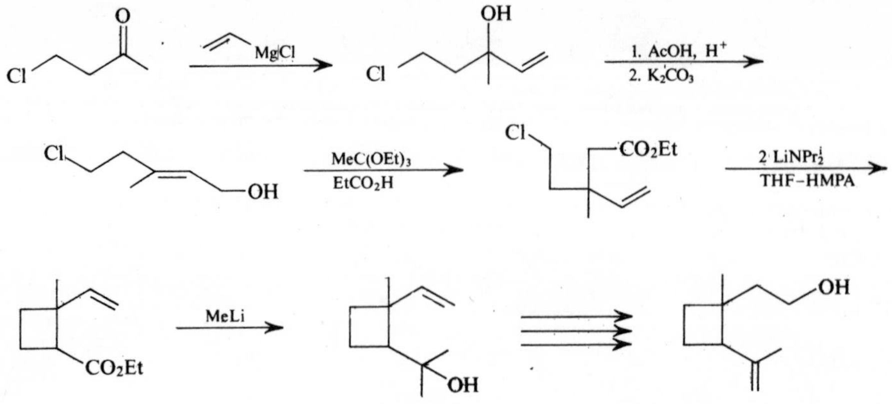

Scheme 104

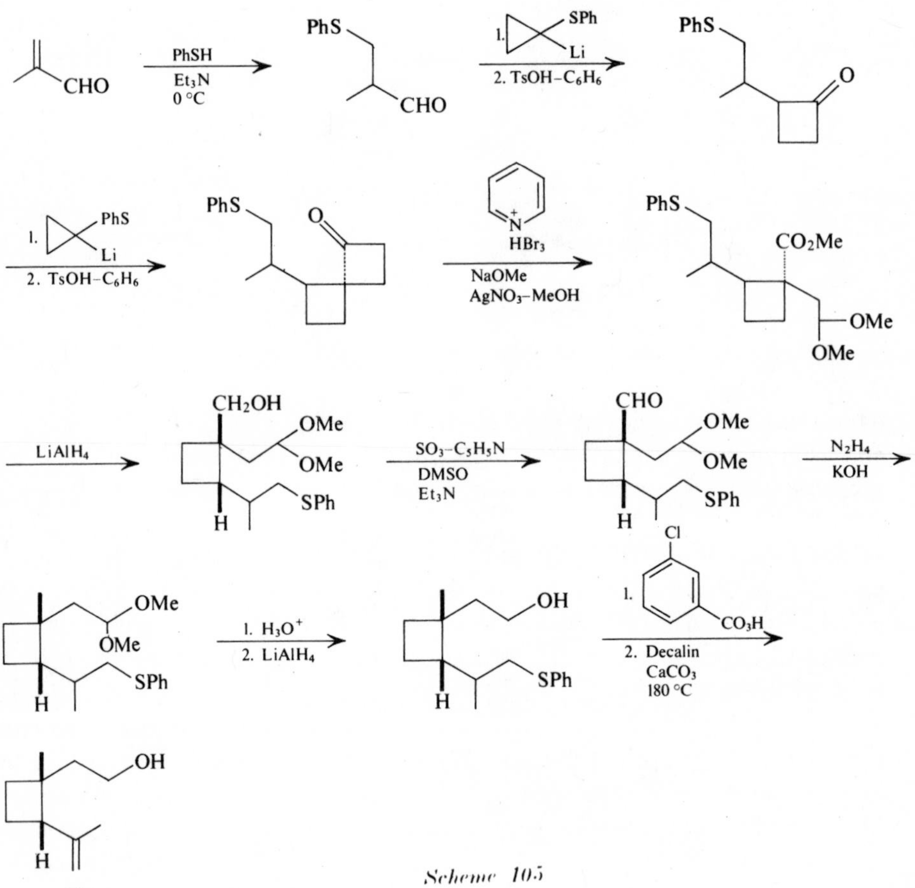

Scheme 105

45

D. (E)-3,3-Dimethyl-$\Delta^{1,\alpha}$-cyclohexaneacetaldehyde (46),
(Z)-3,3-Dimethyl-$\Delta^{1,\alpha}$-cyclohexaneacetaldehyde (47)
and (Z)-3,3-Dimethyl-$\Delta^{1,\beta}$-cyclohexaneethanol (48)

These monoterpenes are also the components of the pheromone produced by male boll weevils [130, 131]. Tumlinson *et al.* synthesized them as shown in Scheme 106, [131]. Babler's synthesis employed the modified Wittig

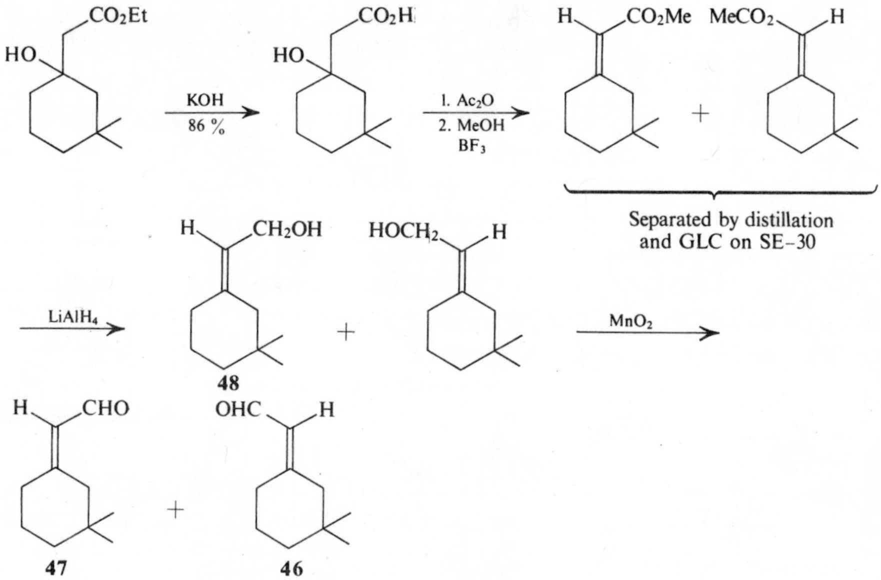

Scheme 106

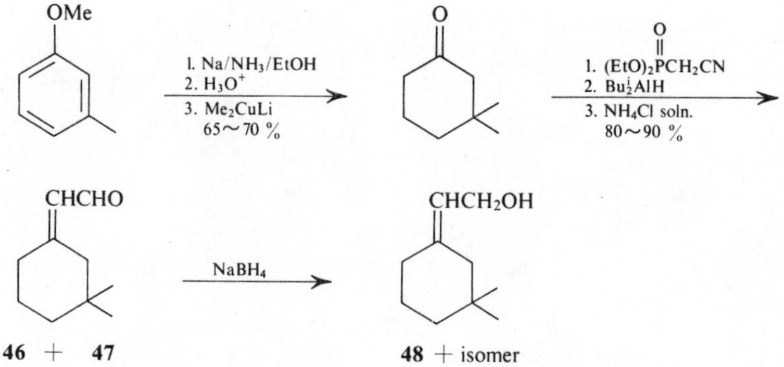

Scheme 107

6*

reaction to attach the side chain (Scheme 107) [141]. For that purpose
Pelletier used acetylene (Scheme 108) [142]. A biogenetic-type synthesis of
these monoterpenes was reported by Bedoukian and Wolinsky (Scheme 109)
[143].

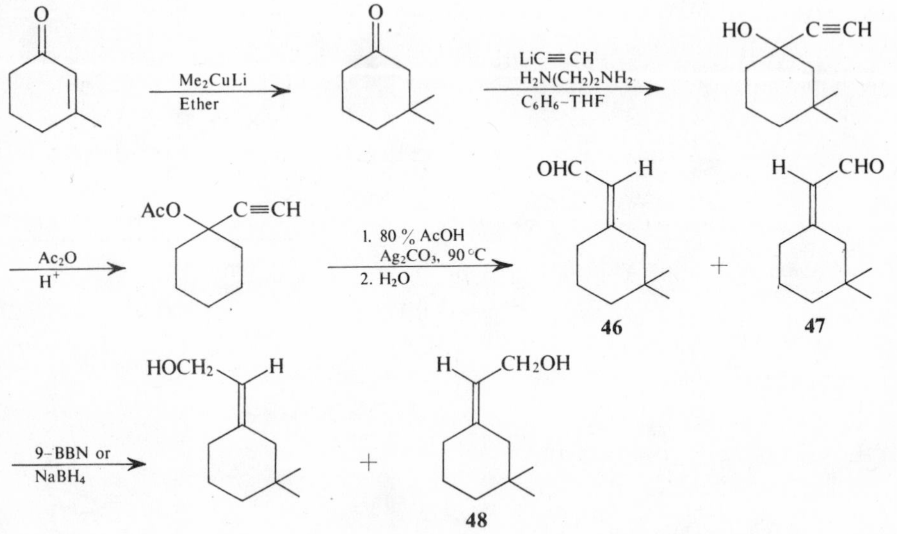

Scheme 108

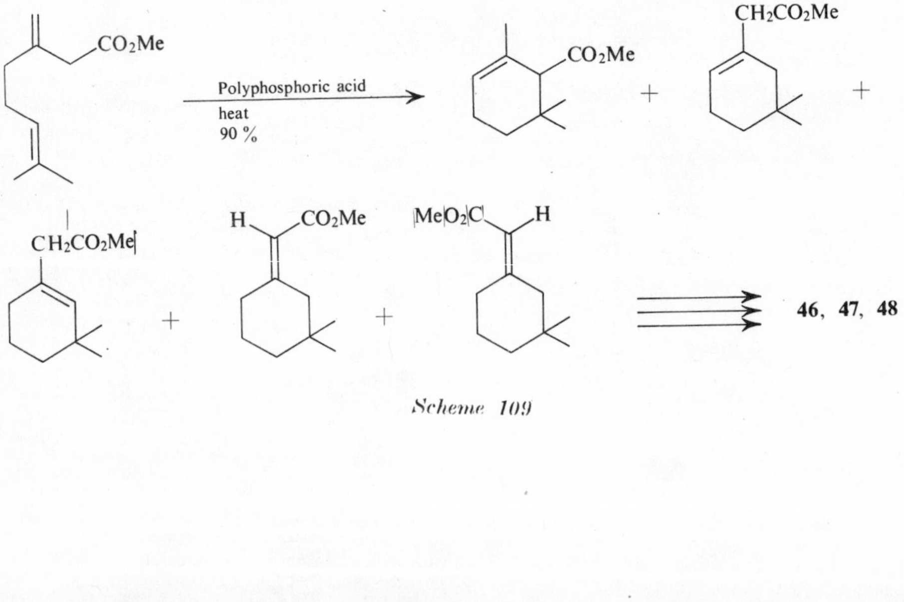

Scheme 109

10. PHEROMONES BELONGING TO HOMOMONOTERPENOIDS, DEGRADED SESQUITERPENOIDS AND DITERPENOIDS

A. (2Z : 6Z)-7-Methyl-3-n-propyl-2,6-decadien-1-ol (49)

This is said to be the sex pheromone of the codling moth [60]. Apart from this claim, the interesting tetrahomoterpene structure of **49** attracted the attention of chemists and several syntheses have been reported. The synthetic strategies used for this compound were similar to those used for juvenile hormones. Cooke's synthesis is shown in Scheme 110 [144]. The final stage of the synthesis was the application of Vedejs's new method for the inversion of olefin geometry [see Equation (54), p. 27]. Another synthesis

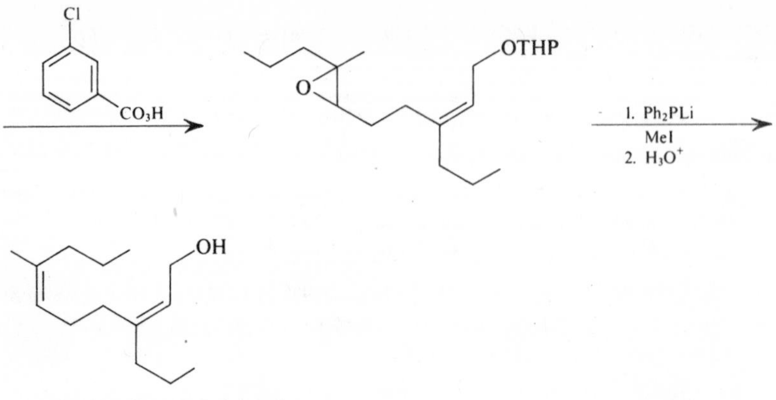

49 (53% from Z E–isomer)

Scheme 110 (cont'd)

was reported simultaneously by Katzenellenbogen (Scheme 111) [145, 146].
The reaction with di-n-propylcopper lithium had to be carried out at low temperature, otherwise the 2E-isomer was generated. The third synthesis used
the photorearrangement as the key step (Scheme 112) [147]. This synthesis
was not stereoselective and the desired (Z, Z)-product was obtained by GLC
separation. An additional stereoselective synthesis was reported using an
organocopper reagent and dianion alkylation (Scheme 113) [148].

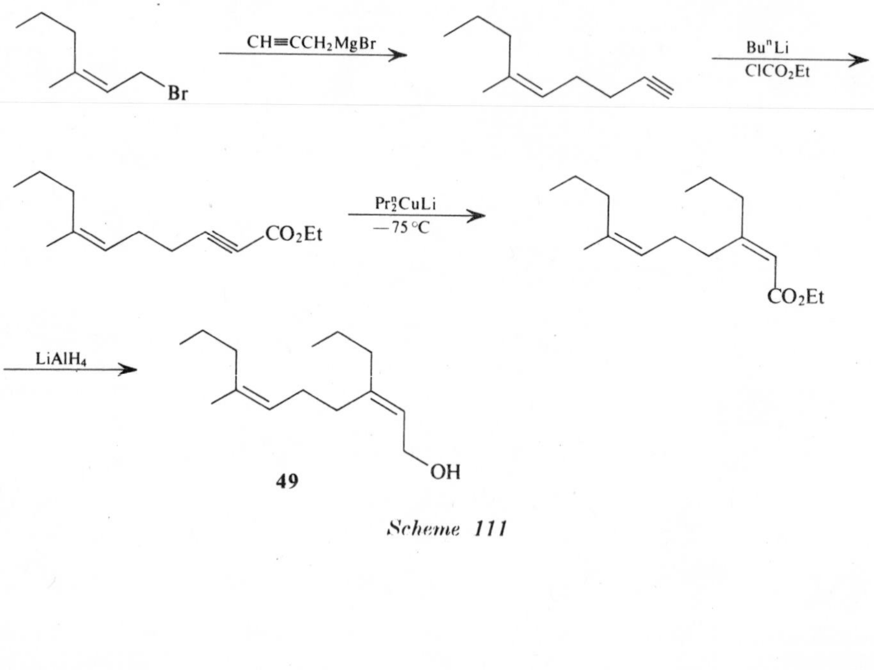

49

Scheme 111

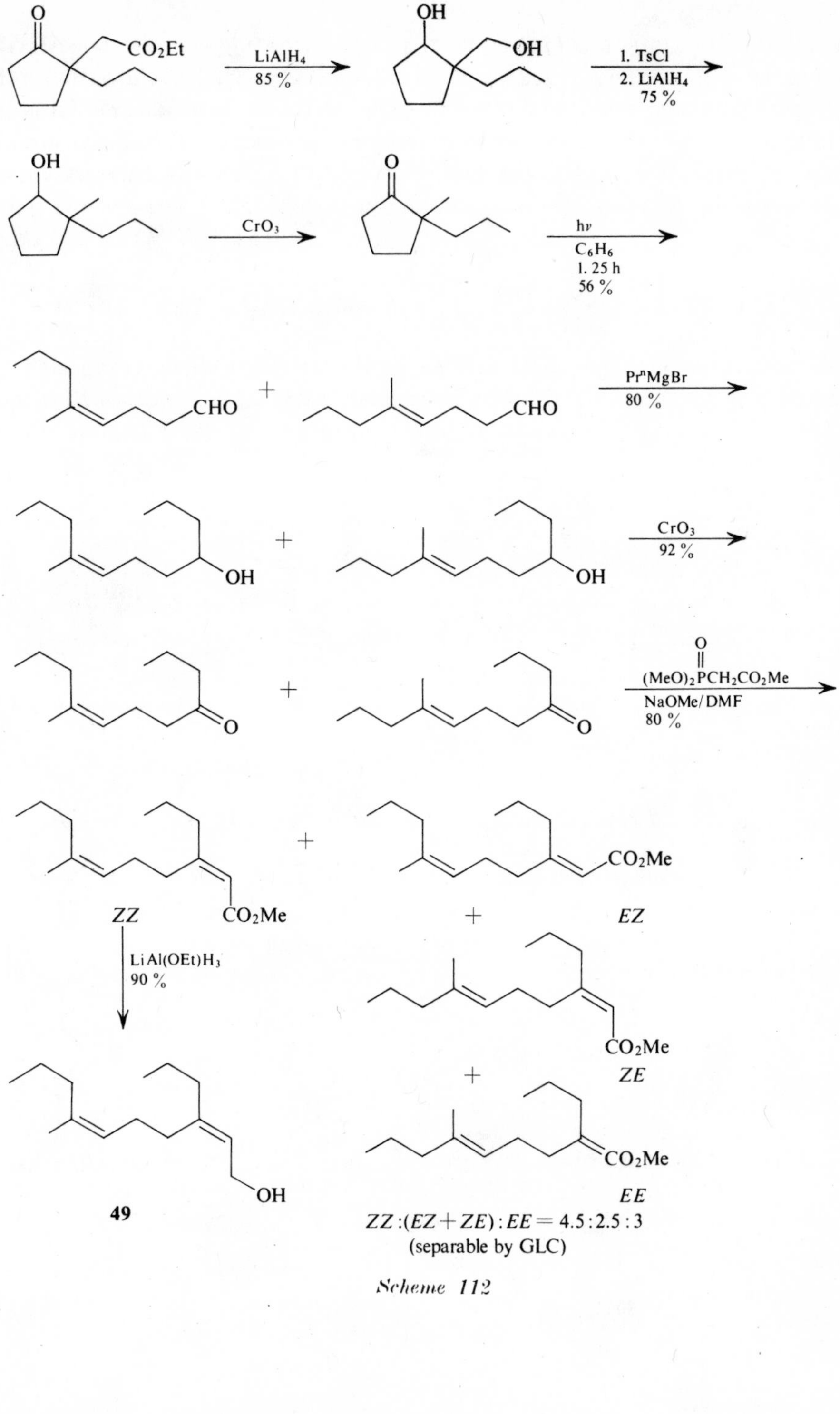

$$ZZ:(EZ+ZE):EE = 4.5:2.5:3$$
(separable by GLC)

Scheme 112

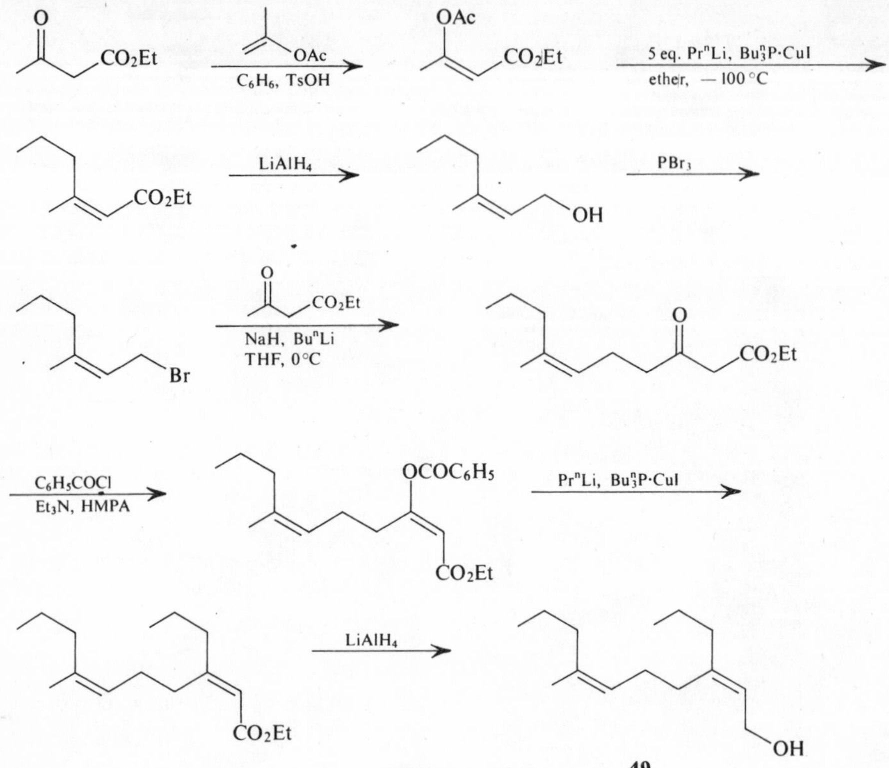

Scheme 113   **49**

B. (2E : 6E)-10-Hydroxy-3,7-dimethyl-2,6-decadienoic Acid (50)

Meinwald isolated this compound as a major component in the "hairpencil" secretion of the male monarch butterfly *(Danaus plexippus)* [149]. Its methyl ester acetate (**50′**) was prepared by degradation of racemic JH III (Scheme 114) [149].

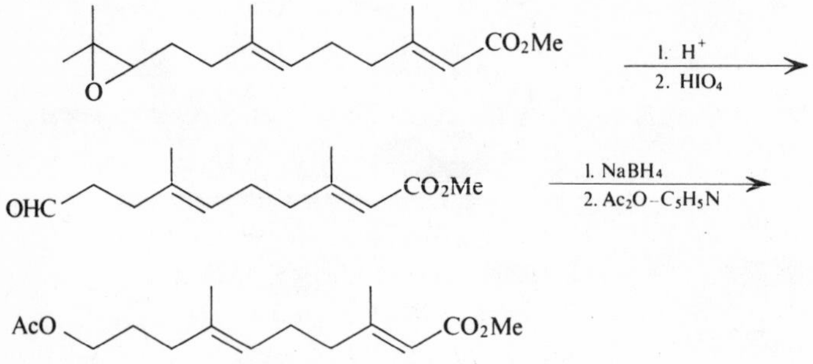

50′

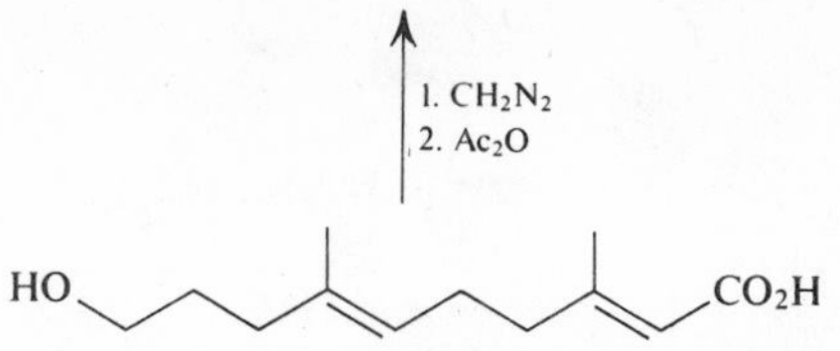

SYNTHESIS OF INSECT PHEROMONES AND JUVENILE HORMONES

Scheme 114 (cont'd)

C. (2E : 6E)-3,7-Dimethyl-2,6-decadien-1,10-diol (51)

This is one of the components of the hairpencil secretion of the male queen butterfly *(Danaus gilippus berenice)* and was prepared from farnesol as shown in Scheme 115 [150].

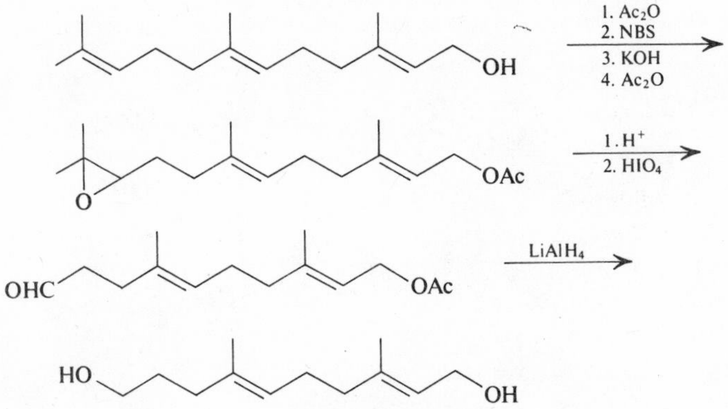

Scheme 115

D. (E)-3,7-Dimethyl-2-octene-1,8-diol (52)

Meinwald isolated this compound as one of the components of the hairpencil secretion of the African monarch butterfly, *Danaus chrysippus* [151]. It was synthesized from geranyl acetate (Scheme 116) [151]. The configuration of the asymmetric carbon is unknown. Johnson devised a short, stereoselective synthesis of these degraded terpenes utilizing a modification of the Claisen ortho ester rearrangement (Scheme 117) [152]. Another synthesis of 52 used the Norrish type I photorearrangement (Scheme 118) [153].

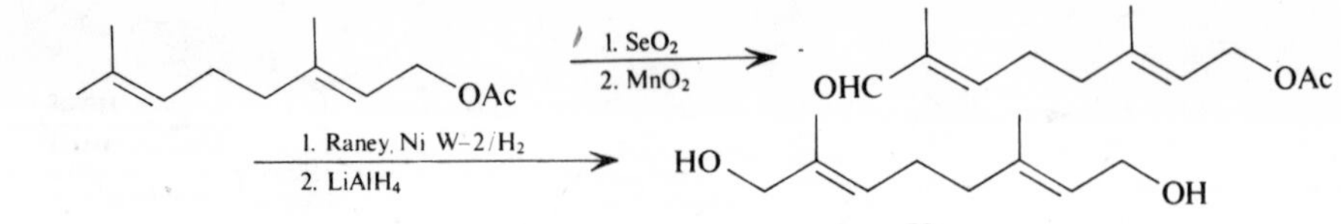

OAc

1. SeO₂
2. MnO₂

OHC ... OAc

1. Raney, Ni W–2/H₂
2. LiAlH₄

HO ... OH

Scheme 116 **52**

CH(OMe)₂ + MeCHO

(PhCO)₂O₂
80 °C, 40 h
70 %

(MeO)₂CH ... O

(EtO)₂PCH₂CO₂Me
NaH/DMF

(MeO)₂CH ...CO₂Me

1N H₂SO₄
76 %

OHC ...CO₂Me

73 %, E + 27 % Z

1. ⟍MgBr
—60~ —30 °C
2. Fractional distill'n.
39 %

...CO₂Me
OH

4 eq. MeC(OMe)₃

NO₂
O₂N— —OH, toluene
100 °C, 17h, 73 %

MeO₂C ...CO₂Me

Ba(OH)₂
aq. MeOH

Li(MeOCH₂CH₂O)₂AlH₂
C₆H₆

HO₂C ...CO₂H
53 (m.p. 101—102 °C)

HO ... OH
51

MnO₂

HO ...CHO

Ag₂O

HO ...CO₂H
50

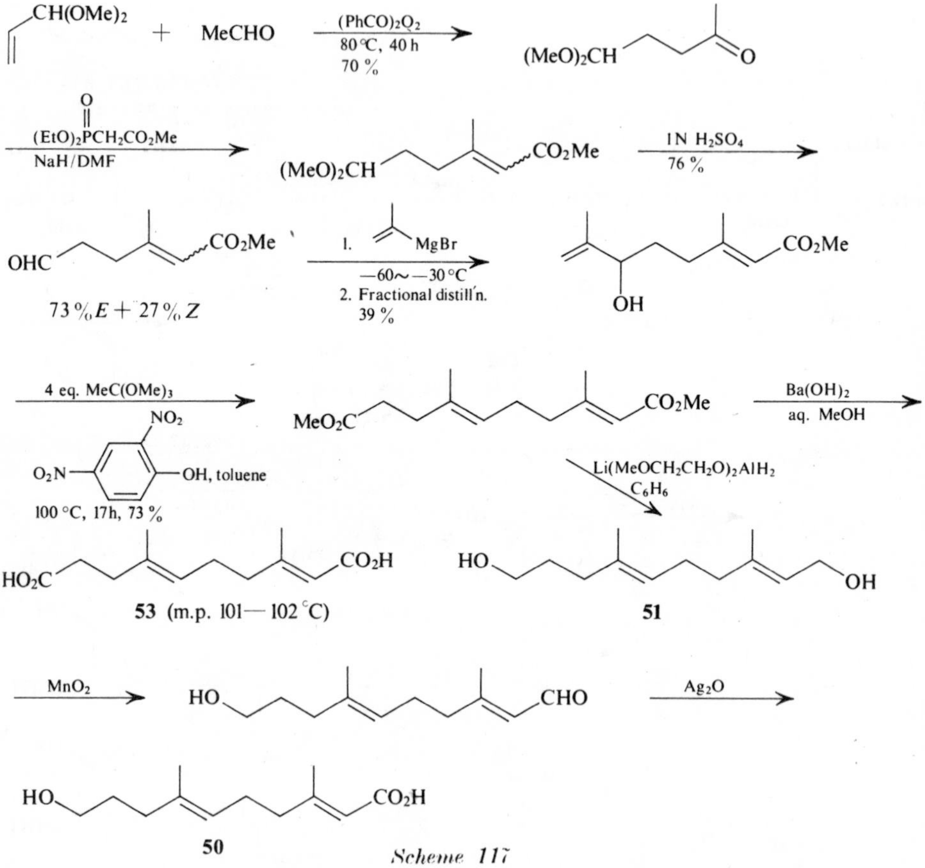

Scheme 117

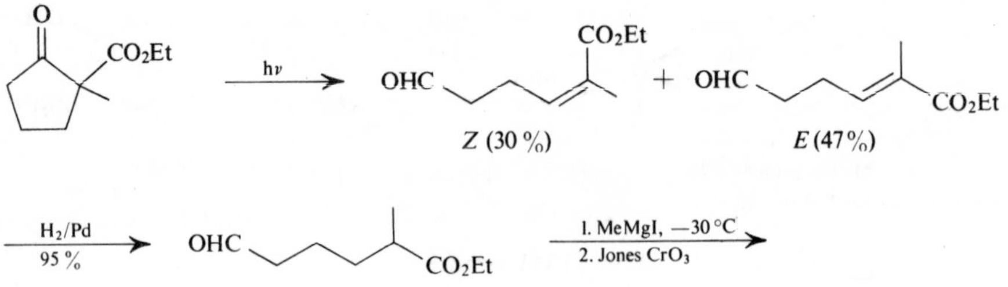

O
⬠CO₂Et

hν

OHC ...CO₂Et
Z (30 %)

+ OHC ...CO₂Et
E (47 %)

H₂/Pd
95 %

OHC ...CO₂Et

1. MeMgI, —30 °C
2. Jones CrO₃

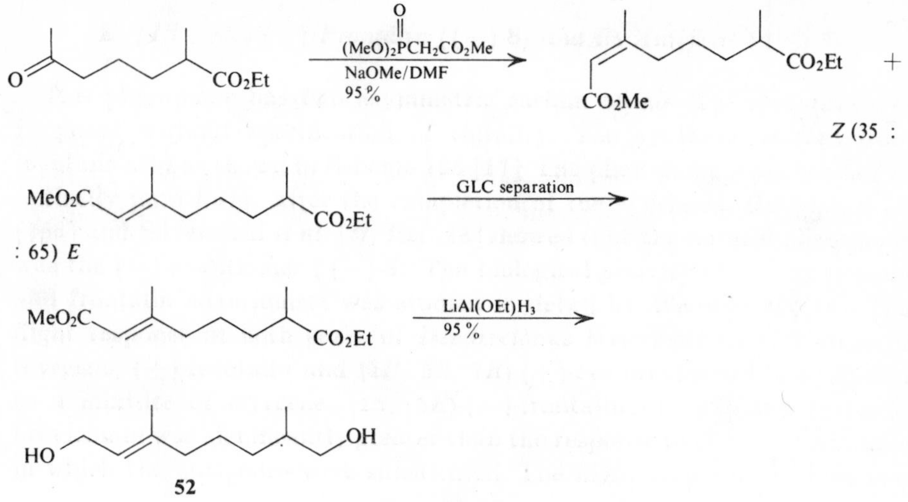

Z (35 :

: 65) E

Scheme 118 (cont'd)

E. (2E : 6E)-3,7-Dimethyl-2,6-decadiene-1,10-dioic Acid (53)

Extraction of hairpencils of about 6500 male monarch butterflies *(Danaus plexippus)* gave 11.8 mg of a solid identified as **53** [154]. A synthesis was accomplished starting from farnesol (Scheme 119) [154].

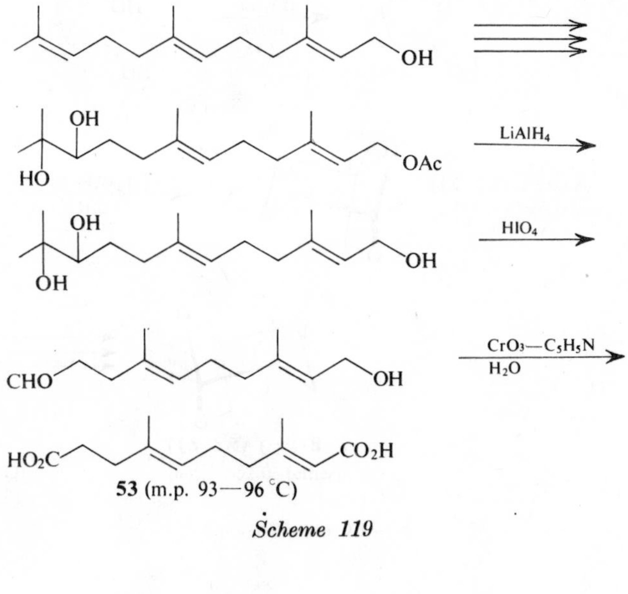

53 (m.p. 93—96 °C)

Scheme 119

F. Neocembrene A (54)

Birch *et al.* isolated this macrocyclic diterpene hydrocarbon as a termite trail pheromone of *Nasutitermes exitosus*, *N. Walkeri* and *N. graveolus* [155]. The stereochemistry was elucidated by Sukh Dev [156]. Two syntheses were achieved utilizing different modes of polyene cyclization (Schemes 120 [157] and 121 [158]).

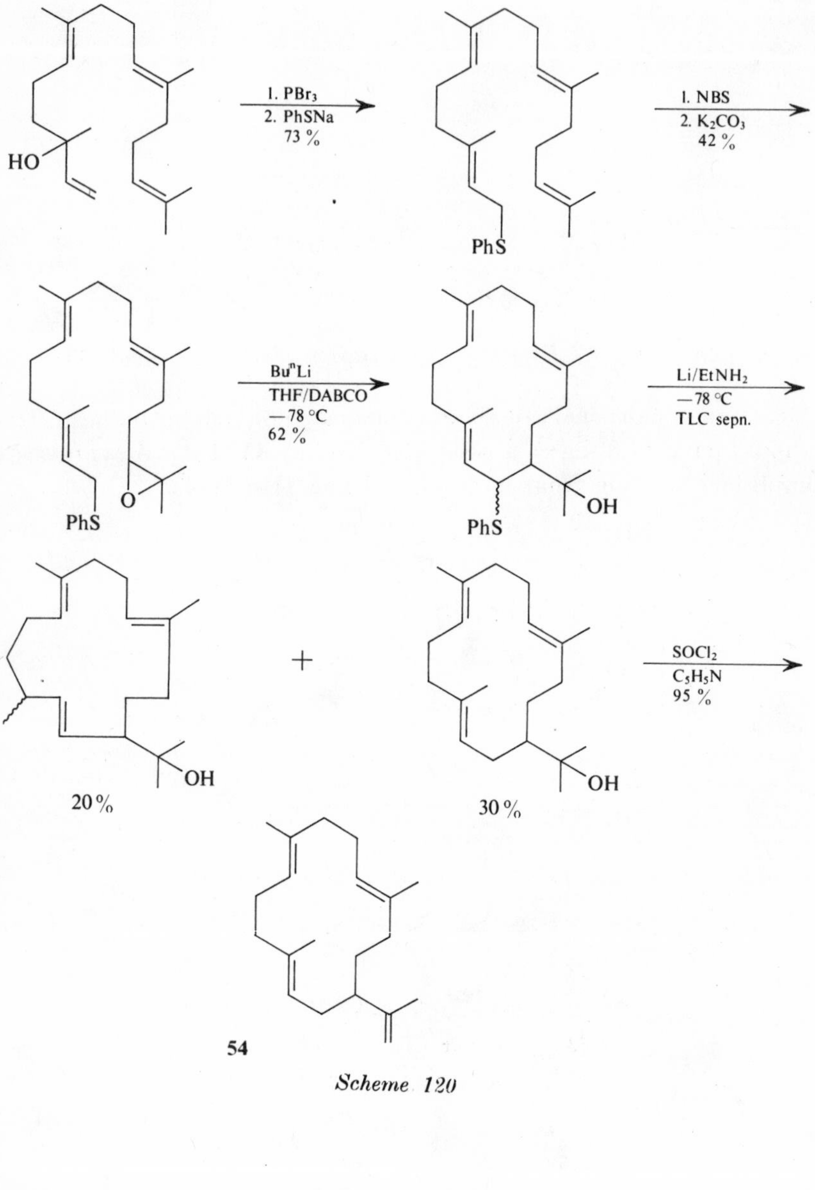

54

Scheme 120

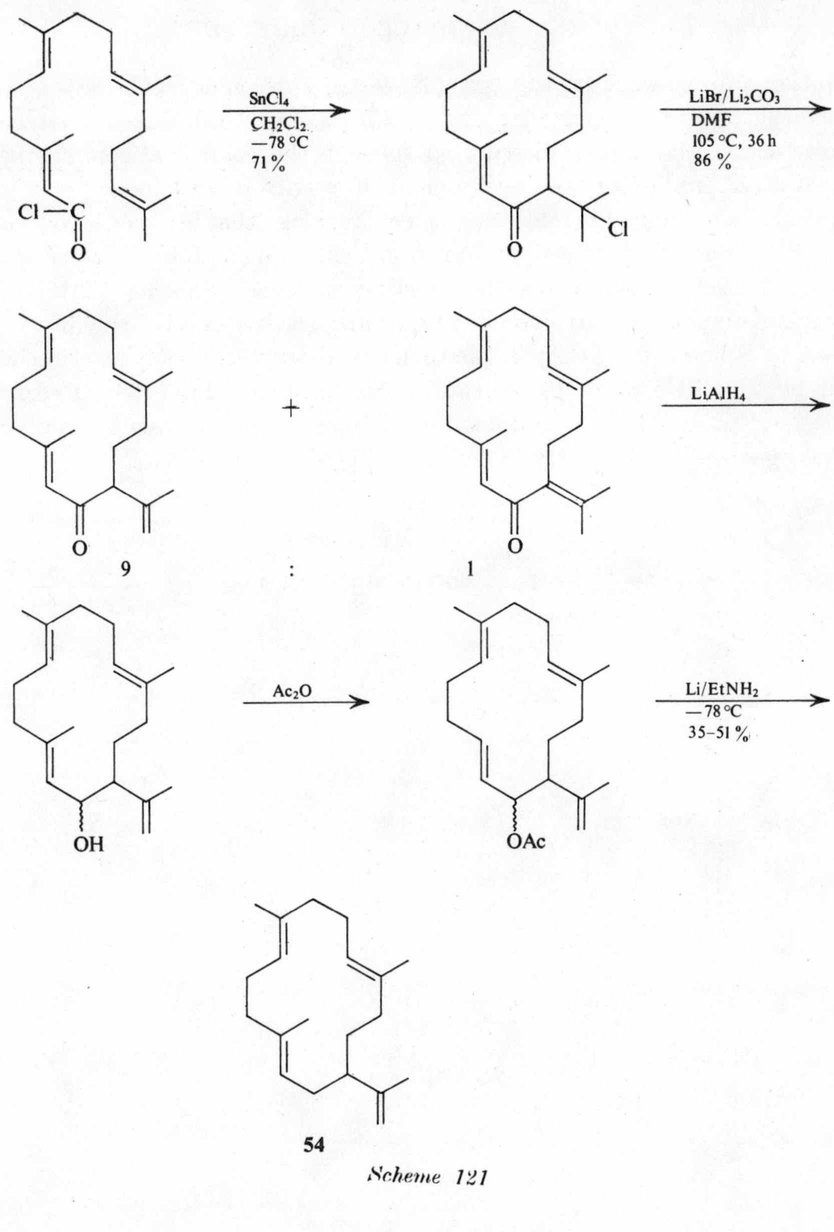

Scheme 121

11. QUEEN SUBSTANCE OF HONEYBEE

Butler and co-workers isolated *(E)*-9-oxo-2-decenoic acid (**55**) as the "queen substance" of honeybee *Apis mellifera* [159, 160]. Queen honeybees secrete a material which, distributed through the colony, affects the bees in two ways, inhibiting the development of ovaries in workers and influencing their behaviour by inhibiting queen rearing (that is, queen-cell construction). Butler's synthesis is shown is Scheme 122 [160]. Barbier *et al.* employed cycloheptanone as the starting material (Scheme 123) [161]. Bestmann's synthesis involves a unique application of ylid chemistry as shown in Scheme 124 [162]. A photochemical fragmentation reaction was used by Doolittle *et al.* to synthesize **55** (Scheme 125) [163]. Recently Trost devised an efficient modification of the Butler synthesis by applying novel organosulfur chemistry (Scheme 126) [164].

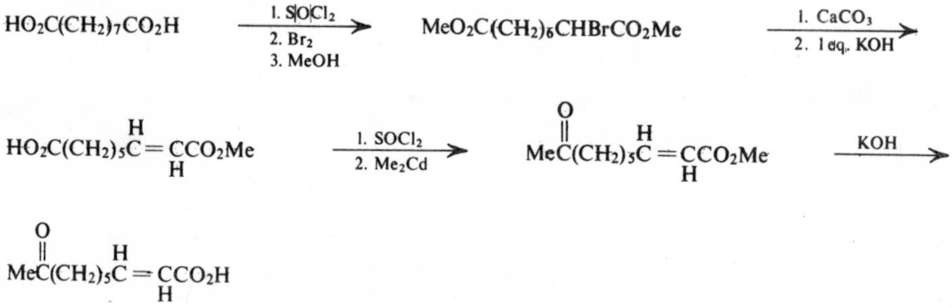

$HO_2C(CH_2)_7CO_2H$ $\xrightarrow[\substack{2.\ Br_2 \\ 3.\ MeOH}]{1.\ SOCl_2}$ $MeO_2C(CH_2)_6CHBrCO_2Me$ $\xrightarrow[\substack{2.\ 1\ eq.\ KOH}]{1.\ CaCO_3}$

$$HO_2C(CH_2)_5C\overset{H}{\underset{H}{=}}CCO_2Me \xrightarrow[\substack{2.\ Me_2Cd}]{1.\ SOCl_2} Me\overset{O}{\overset{\|}{C}}(CH_2)_5C\overset{H}{\underset{H}{=}}CCO_2Me \xrightarrow{KOH}$$

$$Me\overset{O}{\overset{\|}{C}}(CH_2)_5C\overset{H}{\underset{H}{=}}CCO_2H$$

55

Scheme 122

$\xrightarrow[\substack{2.\ Zn}]{1.\ O_3/AcOH,\ 0°C}$ $Me\overset{O}{\overset{\|}{C}}(CH_2)_5CHO$ $\xrightarrow[\substack{C_5H_5N \\ heat \\ 20\%\ overall\ yield}]{CH_2(CO_2H)_2}$ $Me\overset{O}{\overset{\|}{C}}(CH_2)_5C\overset{H}{\underset{H}{=}}CCO_2H$

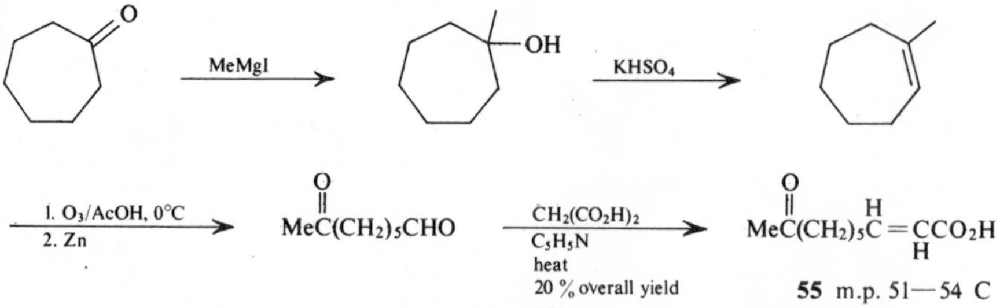

55 m.p. 51—54 C

Scheme 123

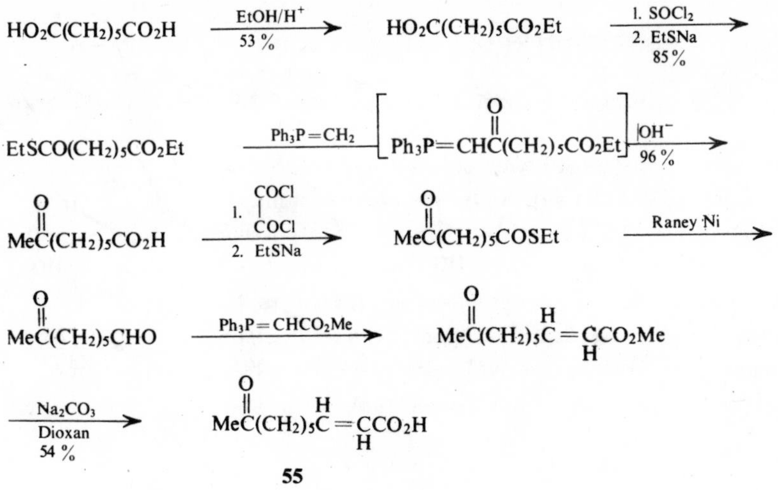

$$HO_2C(CH_2)_5CO_2H \xrightarrow[53\%]{EtOH/H^+} HO_2C(CH_2)_5CO_2Et \xrightarrow[2.\ EtSNa]{1.\ SOCl_2} \quad 85\%$$

$$EtSCO(CH_2)_5CO_2Et \xrightarrow{Ph_3P=CH_2} \left[Ph_3P=CHC(CH_2)_5CO_2Et \right] \xrightarrow[96\%]{|OH^-}$$

$$\underset{MeC(CH_2)_5CO_2H}{\overset{O}{\|}} \xrightarrow[\substack{1.\ \begin{subarray}{l} COCl \\ | \\ COCl \end{subarray} \\ 2.\ EtSNa}]{} \underset{MeC(CH_2)_5COSEt}{\overset{O}{\|}} \xrightarrow{Raney\ Ni}$$

$$\underset{MeC(CH_2)_5CHO}{\overset{O}{\|}} \xrightarrow{Ph_3P=CHCO_2Me} \underset{MeC(CH_2)_5C=CCO_2Me}{\overset{O\qquad\quad H}{\underset{H}{\|}}}$$

$$\xrightarrow[\substack{Dioxan \\ 54\%}]{Na_2CO_3} \underset{MeC(CH_2)_5C=CCO_2H}{\overset{O\qquad\quad H}{\underset{H}{\|}}}$$

55

Scheme 124

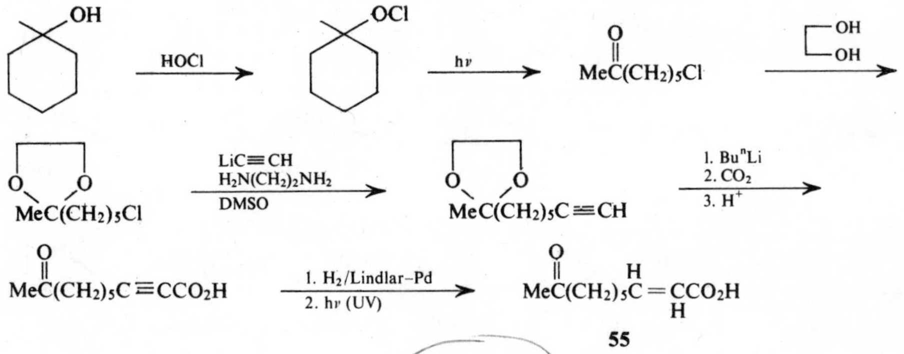

Scheme 125

$$HO_2C(CH_2)_7CO_2Me \xrightarrow[\substack{2.\ Me_2CuLi \\ Ether,\ -78\ ^\circ C \\ 81\%}]{1.\ SOCl_2} \underset{MeC(CH_2)_7CO_2Me}{\overset{O}{\|}} \xrightarrow[C_6H_6,\ TsOH]{\begin{array}{l} -OH \\ -OH \end{array}}$$

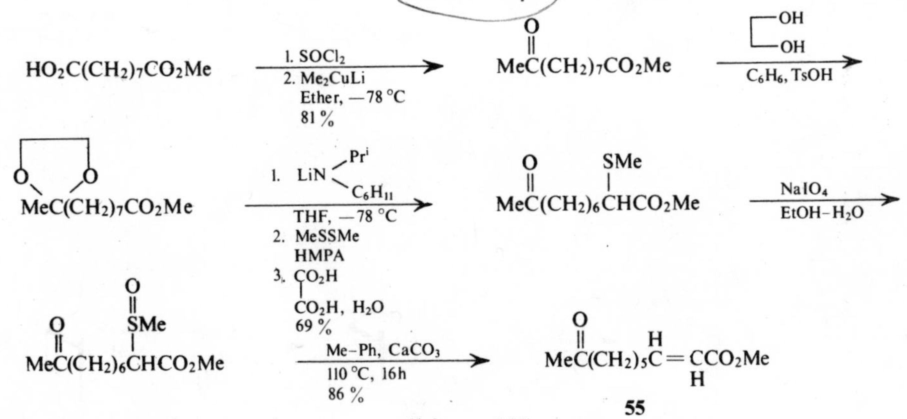

Scheme 126

12. NITROGEN HETEROCYCLES AS PHEROMONES

A. 2,3-Dihydro-3-methyl-1H-pyrrolizin-1-one (56)

This heterocyclic ketone (56) was isolated by the Meinwalds as one of the two major components of the hairpencil secretion of a male Trinidad butterfly *Lycorea ceres ceres* [165]. Later this was also isolated from the queen butterfly, *Danaus gilippus berenice* [150] and from the African monarch, *Danaus chrysippus* [151]. The synthesis is shown in Scheme 127 [165]. In the case of *D. gilippus berenice*, electro-physiological and behavioural studies indicate that this heterocyclic ketone 56 serves as a pheromone. The role of other compounds such as 50–53 remains unknown.

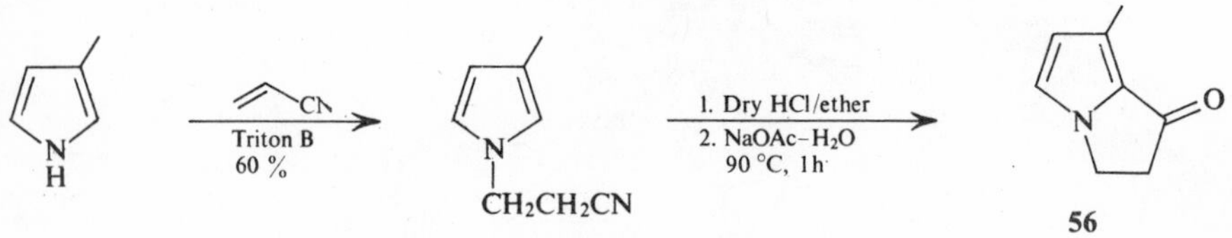

Scheme 127

B. Methyl 4-Methylpyrrole-2-carboxylate (57)

This is the volatile trail pheromone from the leaf-cutting ant, *Atta cephalotes* [166]. A synthesis by Sonnet is shown in Scheme 128 [167].

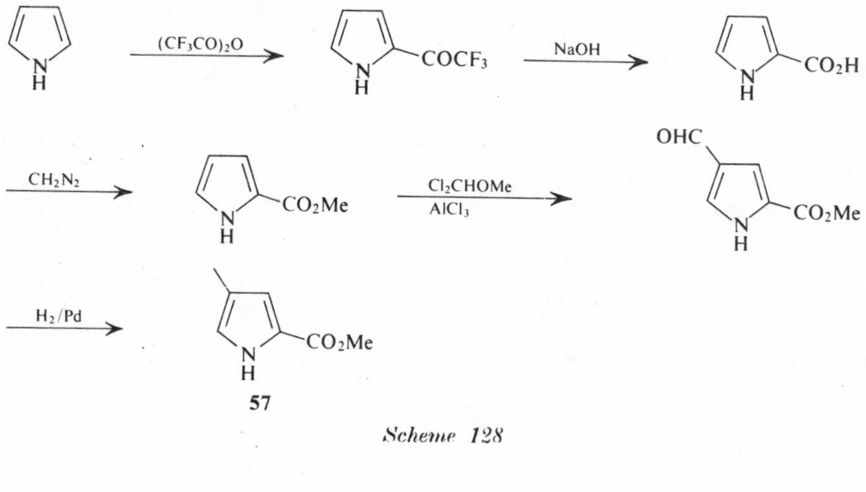

Scheme 128

C. 5-Methyl-3-butyloctahydroindolizine (58)

This is a trail pheromone of the Pharaoh ant, *Monomorium pharaonis* [168]. The synthesis of several stereoisomers of **58** was reported by Oliver and Sonnet (Scheme 129) [169].

80 : 20

7 R. D. C.

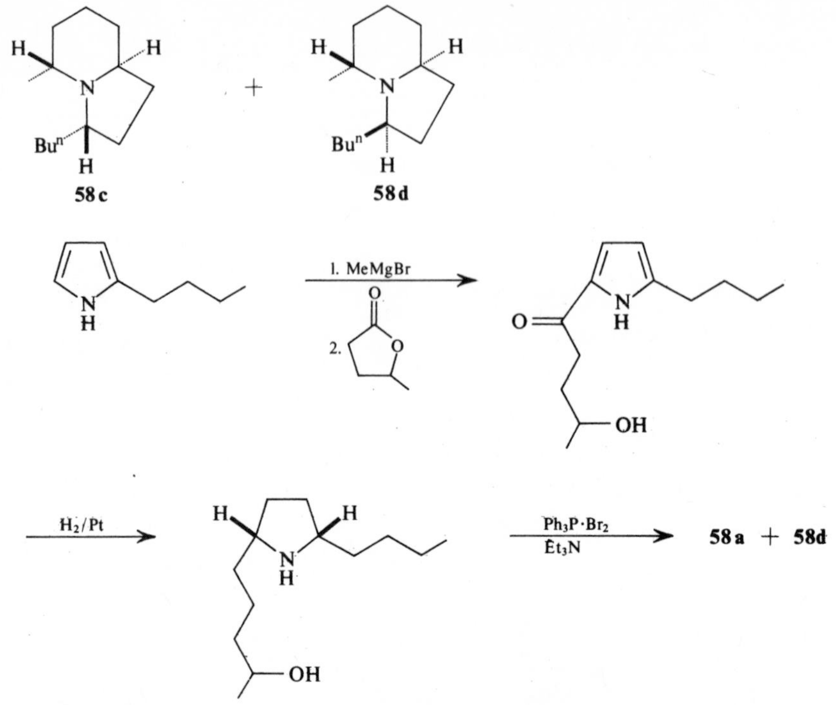

Scheme 129 (cont'd)

13. OPTICALLY ACTIVE PHEROMONES

Pheromone chemistry had never been discussed in three dimensions until 1973. Many pheromones are optically inactive aliphatic compounds. The geometrical isomerism was the chief concern of those who were working in the pheromone field.

However, there are also chiral pheromones. Their absolute stereochemistries ought to be established. Difficulties are often encountered in assigning the absolute stereochemistry of a natural pheromone, because it is obtainable in only minute amounts. A synthesis starting from a compound of known absolute configuration is the best way to settle this problem. In 1973 Mori first demonstrated the utility of this approach by synthesizing the antipodes of the dermestid beetle pheromones (**23** and **24**) [170, 171]. Since then a number of pheromones have been synthesized in optically active forms as detailed below. Now pheromone chemistry has been brought into the world of three dimensions.

There was another reason which stimulated the synthesis of optically active pheromones. It was related to the theory of olfaction. Wright's vibration theory of olfaction predicted the unimportance of optical isomerism in pheromone perception [172]. From the generalization that no instances were known in which one of a pair of optical isomers had an odour and the other did not, Wright inferred that the primary process of olfaction must be a physical rather than a chemical interaction [173]. The slight differences reported in the odours of some optical isomers, he thought, might have resulted from different levels of purity. According to Wright's theory, the vibrational frequencies of an odorous molecule in the fair infrared region $(500-50 \text{ cm}^{-1})$ determine the quality of an odour whereas such factors as volatility, adsorbability and water-lipid solubility determine the strength of the odour [174]. On the other hand, Amoore emphasized the importance of molecular shape in determining the quality of odour [175]. His stereochemical theory is an example of the lock-and-key concept so well known in enzyme and drug theory. An odorous molecule must possess a stereostructure complementary to the sites of the receptors. In fact, a highly significant correlation existed between molecular shape and ant alarm pheromone activity [176]. In Amoore's theory, two enantiomers should be different in their odours, for they are not superimposable.

In 1971 the odour differences between extremely purified (R)-$(-)$-carvone and its (S)-$(+)$-isomer were reported simultaneously by two groups [177, 178]. The (R)-$(-)$-isomer had the odour of spearmint, whereas the antipode was of caraway odour. Anyway, both enantiomers were odorous. More clear-cut results were obviously preferable to settle the dispute between Wright and Amoore. If we study chiral insect pheromones, the relationship between stereostructure and olfaction would be clarified more quantitatively than by employing human noses.

In 1974 three groups reported their works along these lines. Silverstein investigated the alarm pheromone of *Atta texana* [179, 180]. Marumo worked on disparlure, the gypsy moth pheromone [181, 182]. Mori studied *exo*-brevicomin, the western pine beetle pheromone [1, 16, 18]. In these three cases, only one enantiomer of the pheromone was biologically active. This was in full accord with Amoorer's stereochemical theory.

It is now evident that the syntheses of chiral pheromones are worthwhile achievements both chemically and biologically.

7*

A. (S : Z)-(+)-14-Methyl-8-hexadecen-1-ol ((+)-23)
and Methyl (S : Z)-(+)-14-methyl-8-hexadecenoate ((+)-24)

These dermestid beetle pheromones were levorotatory [52]. Their absolute configurations, however, were unknown. Mori synthesized S-pheromones starting from commercially available (S)-(+)-2-methylbutanol [170, 171]. The synthesized S-pheromones were dextrorotatory. Therefore the natural pheromones are shown to possess R-configurations (Scheme 130) [170].

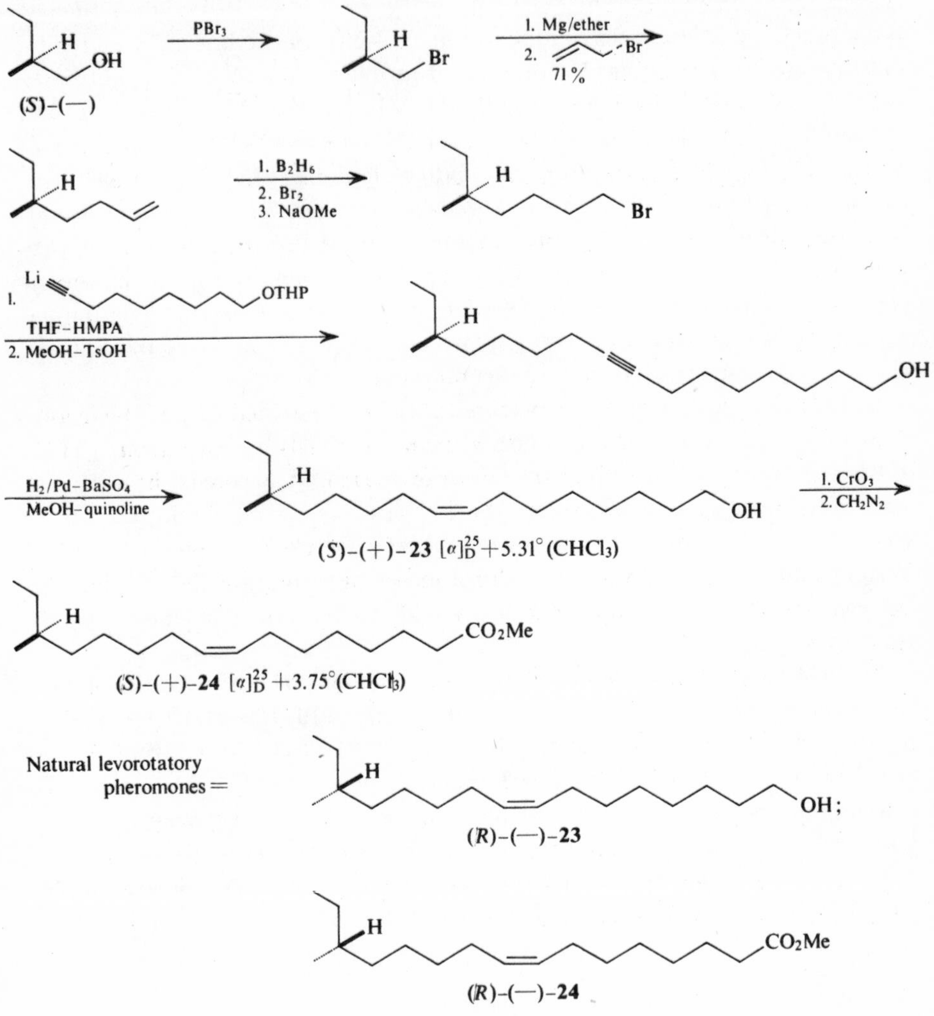

Scheme 130

B. (S)-(+)-4-Methyl-3-heptanone ((+)-59)
and its Antipode ((−)-59)

This compound was identified as the principal alarm pheromone of the leaf-cutting ant, *Atta texana*, without specification of chirality [183]. The synthesis of the *(S)*-ketone utilized the resolved *(S)*-(+)-methylallylacetic acid as the key intermediate (Scheme 131) [179, 180]. The *(R)*-ketone was prepared from *(R)*-(−)-2-methylpentanoic acid (Scheme 131). The *(S)*-(+) enantiomer ((+)-59) was about 400 times more active than the *(R)*-(−)-enantiomer ((−)-59) on workers of *Atta texana*. The (−)-isomer showed no inhibition of the activity of the (+)-enantiomer. The natural pheromones isolated from *Atta texana* and *Atta cephalotes* were both dextrorotatory. Hence the natural pheromone is *(S)*-(+)-4-methyl-3-heptanone. A synthesis of the *(R)*-(−)-isomer from *(R)*-(+)-citronellic acid will be described in Scheme 145 [184].

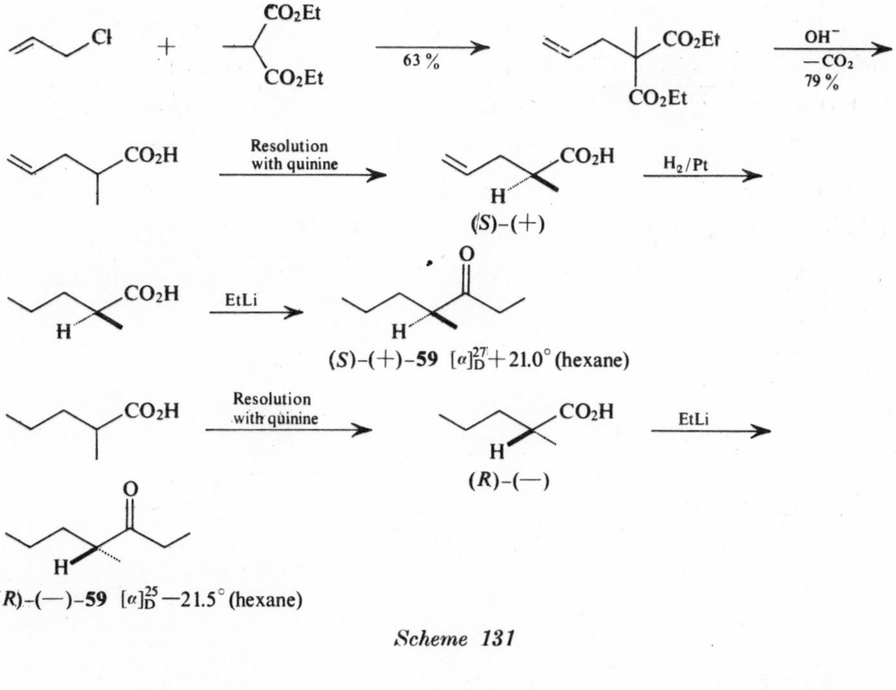

Scheme 131

C. (1R : 5S : 7R)-(+)-exo-Brevicomin ((+)-**6**) and its Antipode ((−)-**6**)

This pheromone possesses three asymmetric carbon atoms and therefore is a highly asymmetric bicyclic compound. However, its 0.05% hexane solution was reported to show no optical rotation between 350 and 250 nm [14]. This observation hampered further study on the absolute stereochemistry of the pheromone until 1974, when both enantiomers were synthesized. The synthesis started from D-(−)- and L-(+)-tartaric acids. The route to (1R : 5S : 7R)-(+)-exo-brevicomin ((+)-**6**) from D-(−)-tartaric acid is shown in Scheme 132 [16]. The (+)-isomer was active on *Dendroctonus*

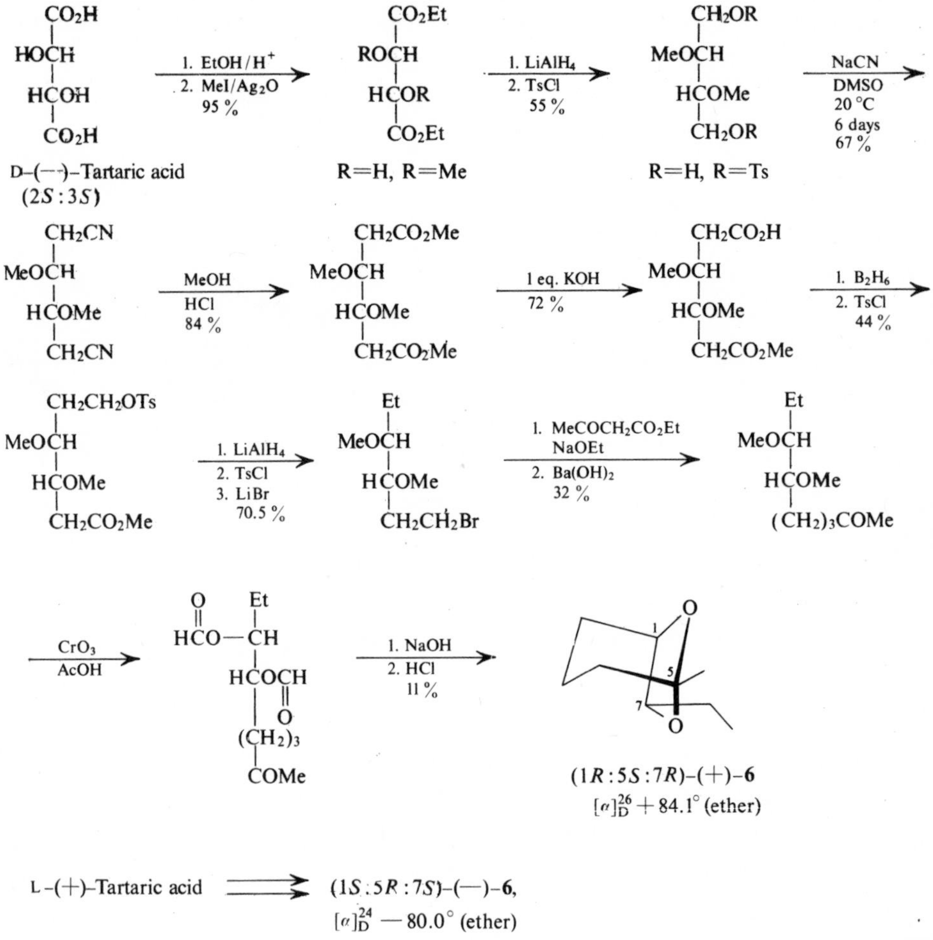

Scheme 132

brevicomis, whereas the antipode was inactive [18]. Two notable features of the synthesis are discrimination of the two carboxyl groups and demethylation by chromic acid oxidation. (The demethylation was unsuccessful with boron trichloride.) After the completion of the synthesis, Silverstein *et al.* reinvestigated the natural pheromone and found the (+)-isomer in cold trap condensates from aerated ponderosa pine logs infested with western pine beetles [*cf.* Ref. 18].

D. *(7R : 8S)-(+)-Disparlure ((+)-15) and its Antipode ((−)-15)*

This gypsy moth pheromone was isolated in so small amounts that its optical rotation could not be determined. The first synthesis by Marumo *et al.* started from L-(+)-glutamic acid as shown in Scheme 133 [181].

L–(+)-Glutamic acid
(*S*)

(4*S* : 5*S*)–**A**, m.p. 66.0 °C   (4*S* : 5*R*)–**A**, m.p. 63.5 °C
(Separated by TLC and repeated recrystallization)

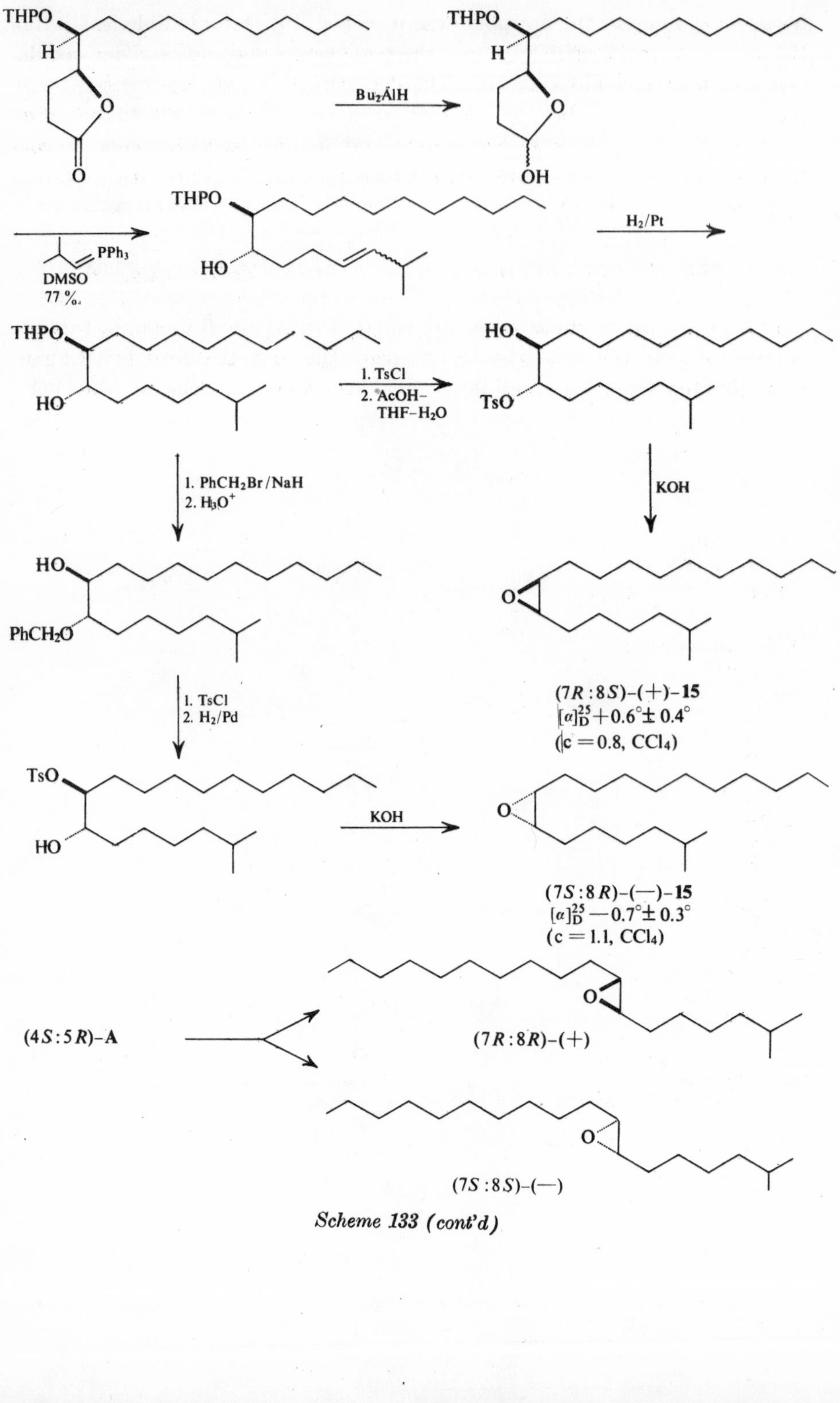

Bu₂AlH

THPO · · ·
H

THPO ·
H
OH

PPh₃
DMSO
77 %.

THPO
HO

H₂/Pt

THPO
HO

1. TsCl
2. AcOH–
   THF–H₂O

HO
TsO

1. PhCH₂Br/NaH
2. H₃O⁺

KOH

HO
PhCH₂O

O

(7R : 8S)-(+)-15
$[\alpha]_D^{25} + 0.6° \pm 0.4°$
(c = 0.8, CCl₄)

1. TsCl
2. H₂/Pd

TsO
HO

KOH

O

(7S : 8R)-(—)-15
$[\alpha]_D^{25} — 0.7° \pm 0.3°$
(c = 1.1, CCl₄)

(4S : 5R)-A

O
(7R : 8R)-(+)

O
(7S : 8S)-(—)

Scheme 133 (cont'd)

The synthesis, however, was not stereoselective and required tedious separation of the diastereomers at the hydroxylactone (A) stage. The optical purity of the hydroxylactone was checked by NMR method. The hydroxylactone (A) was shown to contain 5.8% of its enantiomer. Two enantiomers of the *trans*-analogues were also prepared by this synthesis. EAG and behavioural responses of the gypsy moth to these enantiomers revealed that *cis*-(+)-disparlure was the most effective. The racemic disparlure came second, while *cis*-(−)-disparlure inhibited the activity of the *cis*-(+)-isomer. *trans*-Disparlures were not significantly different from the control [182].

The second synthesis by Mori *et al.* was stereoselective and started from L(+)-tartaric acid as shown in the Scheme 134 [185]. An intermediate in the brevicomin synthesis (see Scheme 132) was utilized in this case, too. In this synthesis the tosyloxy alcohols, the immediate precursors to disparlure enantiomers, were obtained as crystalline compounds. Disparlure enantiomers were, therefore, obtained in optically pure forms. Field tests by J. P. Vité confirmed the inhibitory action of (−)-disparlure.

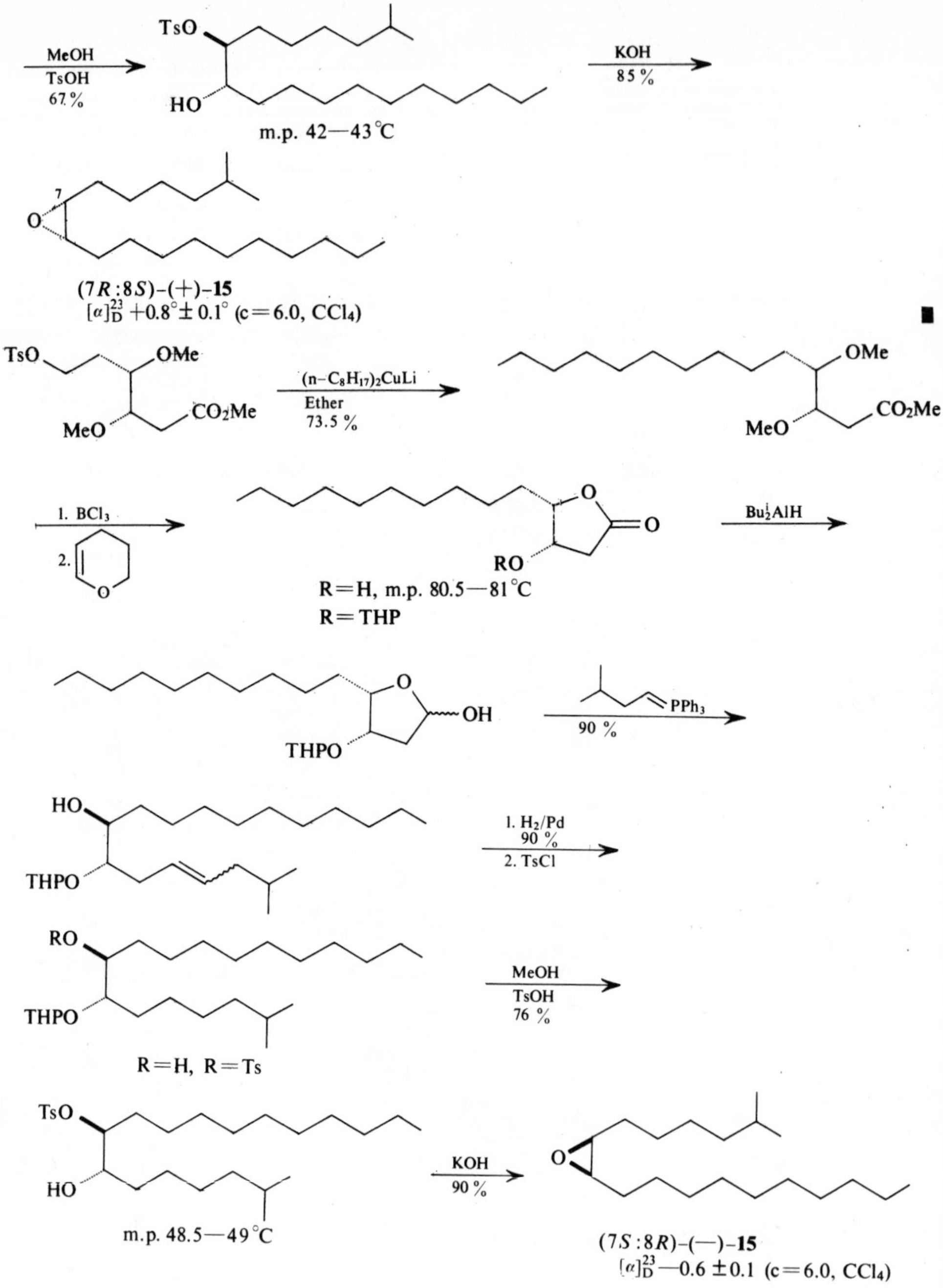

(7R:8S)-(+)-**15**
$[\alpha]_D^{23}$ +0.8°± 0.1° (c = 6.0, CCl₄)

(7S:8R)-(—)-**15**
$[\alpha]_D^{23}$ —0.6 ± 0.1 (c = 6.0, CCl₄)

Scheme 134 (cont'd)

E. (1S : 5R)-(—)-Frontalin ((—)-8) and its Antipode ((+)-8)

This pheromone has two asymmetric carbon atoms. The structure was proposed without specification of chirality. The synthesis started from levulinic acid as shown in Scheme 135 [17]. The pheromone was obtained in optically pure form. After the completion of the synthesis, Renwick et al. [186] and Silverstein et al. [cf. Ref. 18] showed that the natural pheromone was the (—)-enantiomer ((—)-8). The biological activity of exo-brevicomin and frontalin enantiomers was studied in detail by Wood et al. [18]. The flight response of both sexes of Dendroctonus brevicomis to a mixture of myrcene, (±)-frontalin and (1R, 5S, 7R)-(+)-exo-brevicomin ((+)-6) and to a mixture of myrcene, (1S, 5R)-(—)-frontalin ((—)-8) and (±)-exo-brevicomin was significantly greater than the response to the same mixtures in which the antipodes were substituted. The flight response to these two

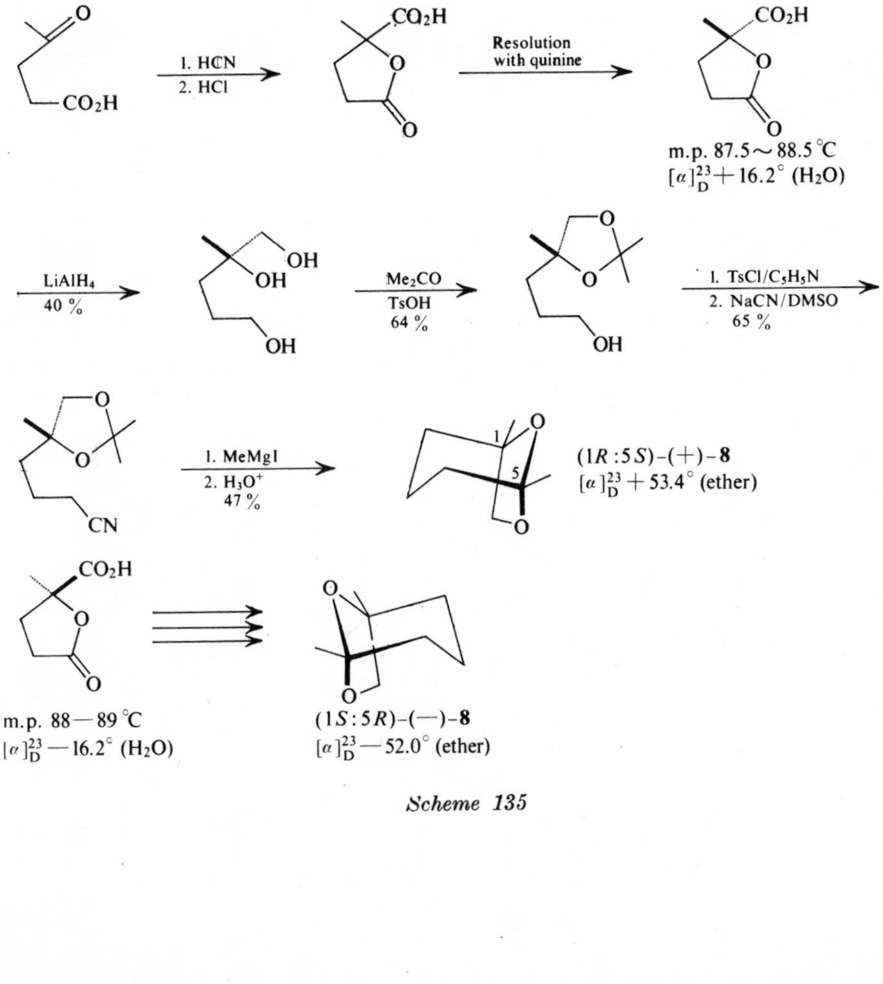

Scheme 135

mixtures was also greater than the response to the ternary mixture of myrcene
(±)-frontalin and (±)-*exo*-brevicomin. When evaporated with ponderosa
pine terpentine, (−)-frontalin was active in the field, whereas its antipode
was not.

F. *(1S : 2R : 4S : 5R)-(−)-α-Multistriatin ((−)-42)*

The natural pheromone is levorotatory [187]. Since the relative stereochemistry of α-multistriatin had been deduced as **42**, it was enough to
determine the absolute configuration of only one carbon atom in order to
establish the absolute stereochemistry. This was accomplished by starting
the synthesis from *(R)*-(+)-glyceraldehyde as shown in Scheme 136 [188].
The final separation was carried out by preparative GLC. The synthesized
α-multistriatin was levorotatory. Therefore the natural pheromone possesses
1*S* : 2*R* : 4*S* : 5*R*-stereochemistry.

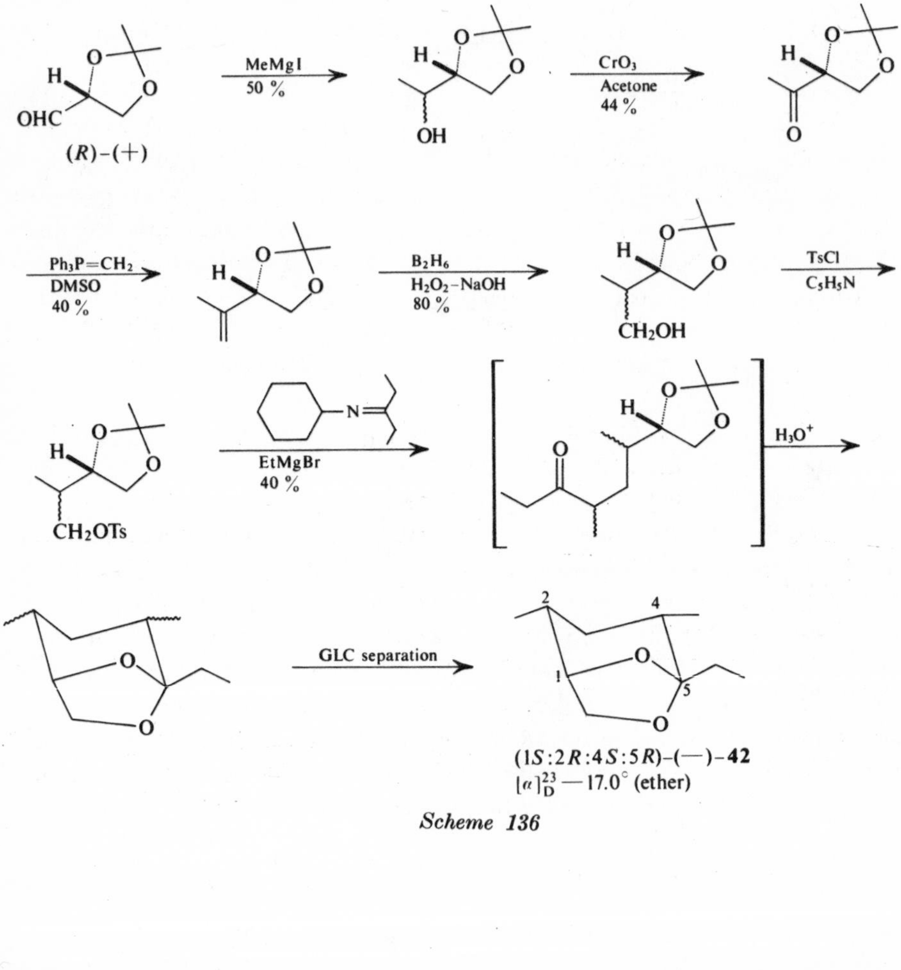

$(1S:2R:4S:5R)-(—)-$**42**
$[\alpha]_D^{23}$ — 17.0° (ether)

Scheme 136

G. (S)-(−)-Ipsenol ((−)-**43**) and its Antipode ((+)-**43**)

Natural ipsenol, isolated by Silverstein *et al.* from the frass of *Ips paracon-fusus* was levorotatory : $[\alpha]_D^{25}-17.5° \pm 0.7°$ (EtOH) [122]. The synthesis started from leucine involving a chiral epoxide and a chiral α-methylene-γ-lactone as intermediates (Scheme 137) [189, 190]. *(S)*-(+)-Leucine yielded (−)-ipsenol. The natural pheromone was therefore of *S*-configuration. Similarly *(R)*-(−)-leucine gave the (+)-antipode. The biological activity of the enantiomers was studied by Vité *et al.* [191]. The five-spined engraver beetle *Ips grandicollis* aggregated only in response to the *(S)*-(−)-isomer. The antipode proved nearly inactive. The biological activity of the racemate was inferior to the *(S)*-(−)-isomer when released in comparable quantity, but there was no indication of definite response inhibition by the *(R)*-(+)-isomer.

H. (R)-(−)-Ipsdienol ((−)-**44**)

Natural ipsdienol was dextrorotatory : $[\alpha]_D^{20} + 10° \pm 0.9°$ (MeOH) [122]. The synthesis of [R]-ipsdienol started from *(R)*-(+)-glyceraldehyde acetonide as shown in Scheme 138 [192] *via* a chiral epoxide. The synthesized *(R)*-ipsdienol was levorotatory. The natural pheromone was therefore of *S*-configuration. In this case the synthetic pheromone was not optically pure (ca. 50% optical purity) and unsuitable for biological study. The carbohydrate starting material such as glyceraldehyde is of limited utility, because of inaccessibility to the antipodal series. Hence it may be difficult to obtain (+)-multistriatin or (+)-ipsdienol from carbohydrates.

I. (1R : 4S : 5R) -(+)-2-Pinen-4-ol ((+)-trans-Verbenol, (+)-**60**) and its Antipode ((−)-**60**)

trans-Verbenol (**60**) was shown to be present in the hindguts of the bark beetles, *Dendroctonus brevicomis* and *D. frontalis* [193] and later isolated from the hindguts of female *Dendroctonus ponderosae* as a population aggregation pheromone [194]. However, it is not clear whether the pheromone is dextrorotatory or levorotatory. The pure enantiomers of *trans*-verbenol were synthesized from α-pinene (Scheme 139) [195]. Fairly optically pure *trans*-verbenol was converted to the 3β-acetoxyetienate (**A**) which was repeatedly recrystallized to effect purification. Removal of the steroid portion by reductive cleavage yielded optically pure *trans*-verbenol (**60**).

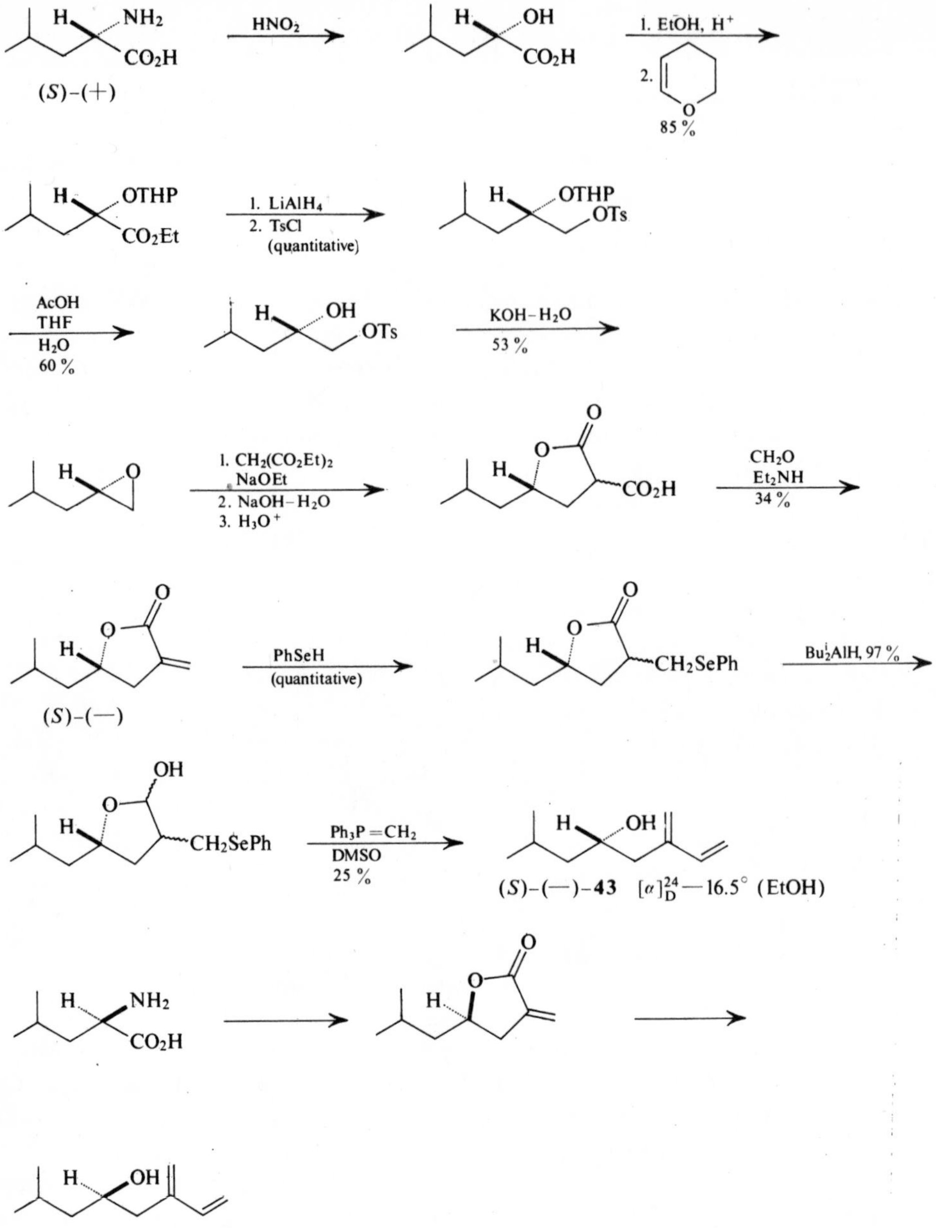

$(S)-(+)$

$(S)-(-)$

$(S)-(-)-43$ $[\alpha]_D^{24} - 16.5°$ (EtOH)

$(R)-(+)-43$ $[\alpha]_D^{24} + 17.3°$ (EtOH)

Scheme 137

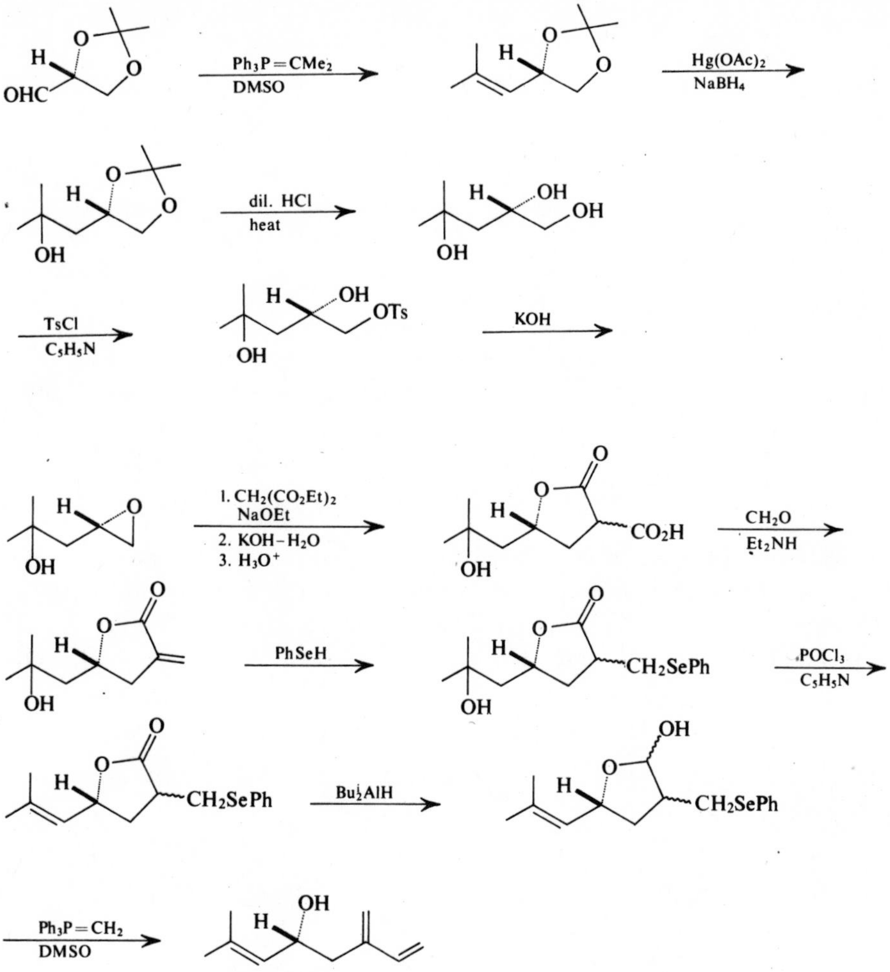

(R)-(—)-**44**
$[\alpha]_D^{20} - 5.0°$ (MeOH)

Scheme 138

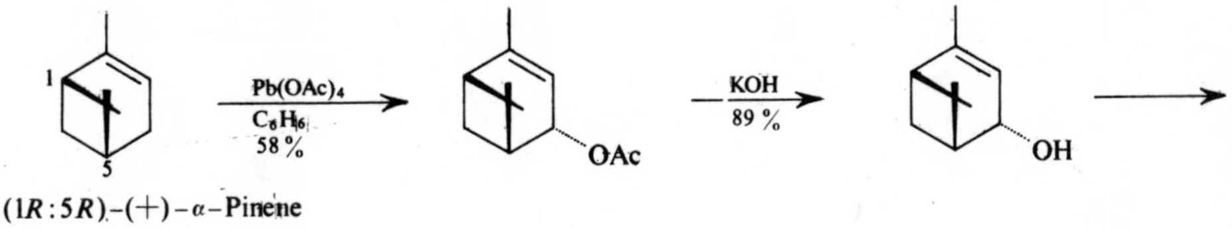

(1*R* : 5*R*)-(+)-α-Pinene

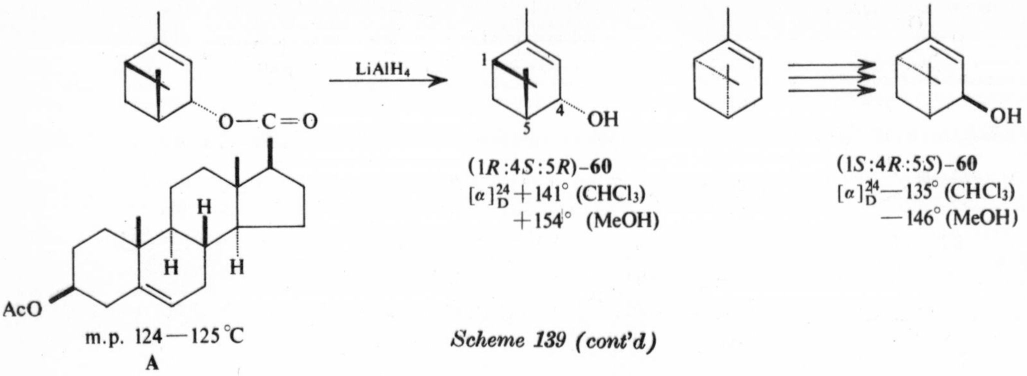
LiAlH₄
O—C=O
OH
OH
AcO
(1R:4S:5R)-60
[α]$^{24}_{D}$ +141° (CHCl₃)
+154° (MeOH)
(1S:4R:5S)-60
[α]$^{24}_{D}$ −135° (CHCl₃)
−146° (MeOH)
m.p. 124—125 °C
A

Scheme 139 (cont'd)

*J. (1S : 4S : 5S)-2-Pinen-4-ol ((S)-cis-Verbenol, (S)-**61**) and its Antipode ((R)-**61**)*

cis-Verbenol (**61**) was first isolated from the male frass of a bark beetle, *Ips paraconfusus*, as a component of the aggregation pheromone [122]. Later it was found among other bark beetles such as *Ips latidens* [196] and *Ips calligraphus* [197]. (1*R* : 4*S* : 5*R*)-2-Pinen-4-ol (*trans*-verbenol, **60**)

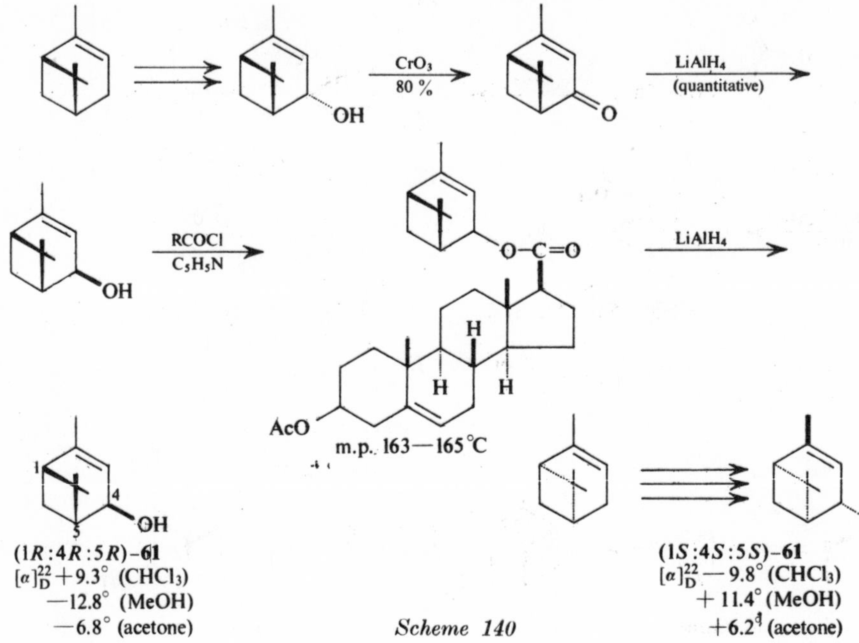
CrO₃
80 %
LiAlH₄
(quantitative)
OH
O
RCOCl
C₅H₅N
O—C=O
LiAlH₄
AcO
m.p. 163—165 °C
OH
OH
(1R:4R:5R)-61
[α]$^{22}_{D}$ +9.3° (CHCl₃)
−12.8° (MeOH)
−6.8° (acetone)
(1S:4S:5S)-61
[α]$^{22}_{D}$ −9.8° (CHCl₃)
+11.4° (MeOH)
+6.2° (acetone)

Scheme 140

was converted to (1R : 4R : 5R)-2-pinen-4-ol (*cis*-verbenol, **61**) as shown in Scheme 140 [198]. In this case, too, the crystalline 3β-acetoxyetienate of *cis*-verbenol was repeatedly recrystallized. The optically pure (1R : 4R : 5R)-2-pinen-4-ol was dextrorotatory in chloroform, but levorotatory in methanol or in acetone. Since the natural pheromone is known to be dextrorotatory in methanol or in acetone, it is (1S : 4S : 5S)-2-pinen-4-ol or *(S)-cis*-verbenol. The biological activity of both enantiomers of *cis*-verbenol was tested on *Ips typographus* and on *Ips calligraphus*. Only *(S)-cis*-verbenol proved to be active [199]. Deploying the isomers at equal rate, *(R)-cis*-verbenol does not interfere with the response of *Ips calligraphus* to *(S)-cis*-verbenol. However, released at a tenfold higher concentration, *(R)-cis*-verbenol strongly inhibits response to the *(S)*-isomer [199].

K. (1R : 2S)-(+)-Grandisol ((+)-45)

Natural grandisol is known to be dextrorotatory, [α]$_D$ + 50° ± 10° [131]. A synthesis of (1R : 2S)-grandisol (**45**) from (1S : 5S)-(−)-β-pinene was accomplished by Hobbs and Magnus as shown in Scheme 141 [200, 201]. The synthesized grandisol was dextrorotatory : [α]$_D^{21.5}$ + 14.7° (hexane). The natural grandisol is therefore 1R : 2S. The key feature of the synthesis was the selective functionalization of the *gem*-dimethyl groups and the photochemical ring cleavage reaction. The final product was purified as a crystalline *p*-nitrobenzoate.

8 R. D. C.

OAc

OH

$\xrightarrow[\substack{C_5H_5N \\ 59\%}]{POCl_3}$

OAc

$\xrightarrow[\substack{CH_2Cl_2 \\ 48\%}]{CrO_3 \cdot C_5H_5N}$

OAc

O

$\xrightarrow[90\%]{H_2/Pd}$

OAc

O

H

$\xrightarrow[\substack{MeOH \\ NaHCO_3 \\ 60\%}]{h\nu}$

OHC

OAc

H

$\xrightarrow[\substack{CH_2Cl_2 \\ 75\%}]{(Ph_3P)_3RhCl}$

OAc

H

$\xrightarrow{LiAlH_4}$

OH

4 1
3 2
H

1R:2S

45

$O-\overset{O}{\underset{}{C}}$ — NO₂ (p-nitrobenzoate, $-O\overset{\Vert}{C}-$)

H

m.p. 73—74 °C

$[\alpha]_D^{21.5} +14.7°$ (hexane)

Scheme 141 (cont'd)

L. (S)-(+)-Sulcatol, 6-Methyl -5-hepten-2-ol (9), and its Antipode (10)

This is a population aggregation pheromone produced by males of *Gnathotrichus sulcatus*, an economically important ambrosia beetle in the Pacific coast of North America [19]. By detailed NMR analysis using the MTPA-ester method, the natural pheromone was shown to be a 65 : 35 mixture of the (S)-(+)- and (R)-(−)-enantiomers. The racemate was obtained by the sodium borohydride reduction of 6-methyl-5-hepten-2-one [19]. Mori synthesized both enantiomers in optically pure state starting from glutamic acid (Scheme 142) [20]. In laboratory and field bioassays, *G. sulcatus* responded to sulcatol only when both enantiomers were present. Response was greater to racemic sulcatol than to a mixture (65 : 35) of the *(S)-(+)*- and *(R)-(−)*-enantiomers, the naturally occurring isomeric ratio. This fact implicates the presence of enantiomer-specific active sites on the receptor proteins in the same or different cells [21].

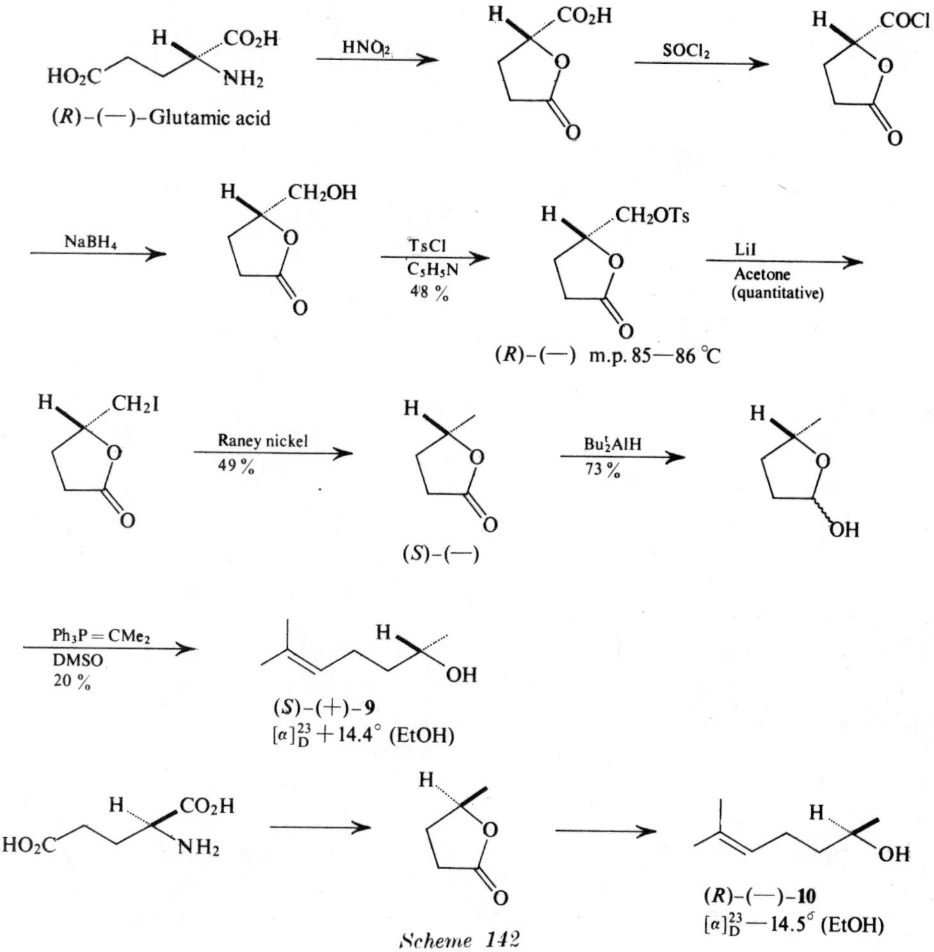

$(R)-(−)$–Glutamic acid

$(R)-(−)$ m.p. 85—86 °C

$(S)-(−)$

$(S)-(+)-$**9**
$[\alpha]_D^{23} + 14.4°$ (EtOH)

$(R)-(−)-$**10**
$[\alpha]_D^{23} - 14.5°$ (EtOH)

Scheme 142

*M. (S)-(+)-Manicone ((+)-**38**) and its Antipode ((−)-**38**)*

Manicone (**38**) is one of the alarm pheromones of ants. The structure was proposed without specification of chirality [97]. *(S)-(+)*-Manicone ((+)-**38**) and its antipode were synthesized by Banno and Mukaiyama employing the titanium tetrachloride-promoted reaction of 3-trimethylsilyloxy-2-pentene with *(S)*-(+) or *(R)*-(−)-2-methylbutanol. The *S*-isomer was 97% optically pure, while the *R*-isomer was of 60% optical purity (Scheme 143) [202].

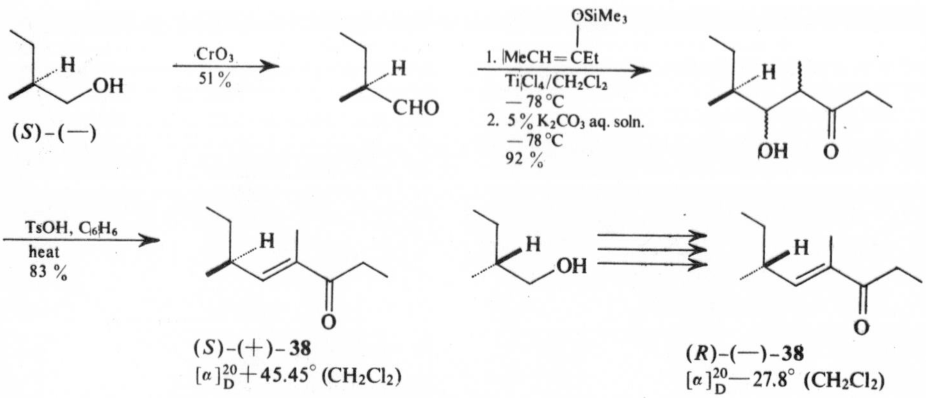

Scheme 143

N. (3R : 4R) threo-(+)-4-Methylheptan-3-ol ((+)-**62**)

( )-4-Methylheptan-3-ol (( )-**62**) and α-multistriatin (**42**) are beetle-produced pheromones responsible for the aggregation of the smaller European elm bark beetles, *Scolytus multistriatus* [119]. The relative and absolute stereochemistry of ( )-**62** was clarified by synthetic means. Firstly, racemic *threo*-(**62**) and *erythro*-4-methylheptan-3-ol (**63**) were prepared from nerol and geraniol, respectively, as shown in Scheme 144 [184]. The natural pheromone was identical with the *threo*-isomer on the basis of IR, NMR and GLC. Secondly, (3R : 4R)-*threo*-4-methylheptan-3-ol (**62**) was synthesized from *(R)*-(+)-citronellic acid as shown in Scheme 145. The synthesized alcohol was dextrorotatory. The natural and levorotatory pheromone therefore possesses (3S : 4S)-absolute stereochemistry, antipodal to (+)-**62**. The optical purity of the synthetic product was checked by its conversion to the optically pure antipode [(R)-( )-**59**] of the alarm pheromone of *Atta texana* [(S)-(+)-**59**].

Scheme 144

Scheme 145

14. PHEROMONES AS TARGETS IN ORGANIC SYNTHESIS

We have now analyzed the various syntheses of about sixty insect pheromones. The challenges posed by structural chemists are fully answered by
synthetic chemists culminating in stereospecific and chiral syntheses.
Nature's diversity to be revealed by pheromone chemists will continuously
provide new targets for ingenious syntheses and stimulate new ideas among
synthetic chemists.

REFERENCES

1. MORI, K., 9th IUPAC International Symposium on Chemistry of Natural Products, Ottawa, 1974, Abstracts 32G.
2. KARLSON, P., SCHNEICLER, D., Naturwissenschaften, 60, 113 (1973).
3. MACCONNELL, J. G., SILVERSTEIN, R. M., Angew. Chem. intern. Ed., 12, 644 (1973).
4. EVANS, D. A., GREEN, C. L., Chem. Soc. Rev., 3, 74 (1974).
5. EITER, K., Pure. Appl. Chem., 41, 201 (1975).
6. BUTENANDT, A., HECKER, E., Angew. Chem., 73, 349 (1961).
7. BUTENANDT, A., HECKER, E., HOPP, M., KOCH, W., Liebigs Ann. Chem., 658,
39 (1962).
8. TRUSCHEIT, E., EITER, K., Liebigs Ann. Chem., 658, 65 (1962).
9. ROELOFS, W. L., ARN, H., Nature, 219, 513 (1968).
10. ROELOFS, W. L., COMEAU, A., J. Insect Physiol., 17, 435 (1971).
11. KLUN, J. A., CHAPMAN, O. L., MATTES, K. C., BEROZA, M., SONNET, P. E., Science,
181, 661 (1973).
12. BEROZA, M., MUSCHIK, G. M., GENTRY, C. R., Nature, 244, 149 (1973).
13. HUMMEL, H. E., GASTON, L. K., SHOREY, H. H., KAAE, R. S., BYRNE, K. J.,
SILVERSTEIN, R. M., Science, 181, 873 (1973).
14. SILVERSTEIN, R. M., BROWNLEE, R. G., BELLAS, T. E., WOOD, D. L., BROWNE,
L. E., Science, 159, 889 (1968).
15. VITÉ, J. P., RENWICK, J. A. A., Naturwissenschaften, 58, 418 (1971).
16. MORI, K.. Tetrahedron, 30, 4223 (1974).
17. MORI, K. Tetrahedron, 31, 1381 (1975).
18. WOOD, D. L., BROWNE, L. E., EWING, B., LINDAHL, K., BEDARD, W. D., TILDEN,
P. E., MORI, K., PITMAN, G. B., HUGHES, P. R., Science, 192, 896 (1976).
19. BYRNE, K. J., SWIGAR, A. A., SILVERSTEIN, R. M., BORDEN, J. H., STOKKINK,
E., J. Insect Physiol., 20, 1895 (1974).
20. MORI, K., Tetrahedron, 31, 3011 (1975).
21. BORDEN J. H., CHONG, L., MCLEAN, J. A., SLESSOR, K. N., MORI, K., Science,
192, 894 (1976).
22. SCHNEIDER, D., Scientific American, 28 (July, 1974).
23. BUTENANDT, A., TAM, N. D., Z. Physiol. Chem., 308, 277 (1957).
24. PATTENDEN, G., STADDON, B. W., Ann. Entomol. Soc. Amer., 63, 900 (1970).
25. BERGER, R. S., CANERDAY, T. D., J. Econ. Entomol., 61, 452 (1968).
26. HENDERSON, H. E., WARREN, F. L., J. South. Afr. Chem. Inst., 23, 9 (1970).
27. WEATHERSTON, J., ROELOFS, W. L., COMEAU, A., SANDERS, C. J., Can. Entomol.,
103, 1741 (1971).
28. KONDO, K., NEGISHI, A., TUNEMOTO, D., Angew. Chem. intern. Ed., 13, 407 (1974).
29. CARLSON, D. A., MAYER, M. S., SILHACEK, D. L., JAMES, J. D., BEROZA, M., BIERL,
B. A., Science, 174, 76 (1971).
30. BESTMANN, H. J., VOSTROWSKY, O., PLATZ, H., Chem. Zeitung, 98, 161 (1974).
31. EITER, K., Naturwissenschaften, 59, 468 (1972).

32. CARGILL, R. L., ROSENBLUM, M. G., *J. Org. Chem.*, 37, 3971 (1972).
33. HO, TSE-LOK, WONG, C. M., *Canad. J. Chem.*, 52, 1923 (1974).
34. GRIBBLE, G. W., SANSTEAD, J. K., *J. C. S. Chem. Commun.*, *1973*, 735.
35. BIERL, B. A., BEROZA, M., COLLIER, C. W., *Science*, 170, 88 (1970).
36. BESTMANN, H. J., VOSTROWSKY, O., *Tetrahedron Letters*, *1974*, 207.
37. EITER, K., *Angew. Chem. intern. Ed.*, 11, 60 (1972).
38. SHAMSHURIN, A. A., REKHTER, M. A., VLAD, L. A., *Khim. Prir. Soedin.*, 9, 545 (1973).
39. CHAN, T. H., CHANG, E., *J. Org. Chem.*, 39, 3264 (1974).
40. CARDÉ, R. T., ROELOFS, W. L., DOANE, C. C., *Nature*, 241, 474 (1974).
41. BERGER, R. S., *Ann. Entomol. Soc. Amer.*, 59, 767 (1966).
42. ROELOFS, W. L., COMEAU, A., SELLE, R., *Nature*, 224, 723 (1969).
43. MORI, K., UCHIDA, M., MATSUI, M., *Tetrahedron*, 33, (1977).
44. SEKUL, A. A., SPARKS, A. N., *J. Econ. Entomol.*, 60, 1270 (1967).
45. TAMAKI, Y., NOGUCHI, H., YUSHIMA, T., *Appl. Entomol. Zool.*, 6, 139 (1971).
46. WARTHEN, D., *J. Med. Chem.*, 11, 371 (1968).
47. JACOBSON, M., HARDING, C., *J. Econ. Entomol.*, 61, 394 (1968).
48. BESTMANN, H. J., RANGE, P., KUNSTMANN, R., *Chem. Ber.*, 104, 65 (1971).
49. NESBITT, B. F., BEEVOR, P. S., HALL, D. R., LESTER, R., DYCK, V. A., *J. Insect Physiol.*, 21, 1883 (1975).
50. NESBITT, B. F., BEEVOR, P. S., HALL, D. R., LESTER, R., DYCK, V. A., *Insect Biochem.*, 6, 105 (1976).
51. FUKUI, H., MATSUMURA, F., Ma, M. C., BURKHOLDER, W. E., *Tetrahedron Letters*, *1974*, 3563.
52. RODIN, J. O., SILVERSTEIN, R. M., BURKHOLDER, W. E., GORMAN, J. E., *Science*, 165, 904 (1969).
53. DE GRAW, J. I., RODIN, J. O., *J. Org. Chem.*, 36, 2902 (1971).
54. RONMESTANT, M. L., PLACE, P., GORE, J., *Tetrahedron Letters*, *1976*, 677.
55. BUTENANDT, A., BECKMANN, R., HECKER, E., *Z. physiol. Chem.*, 324, 71 (1961).
56. BUTENANDT, A., BECKMANN, R., STAMM, D., *Z. physiol. Chem.*, 324, 81 (1961).
57. NEGISHI, E., LEW, G., YOSHIDA, T., *J. C. S. Chem. Commun.*, *1973*, 874.
58. NORMANT, J. F., AMMERCON, A., VILLIERAS, J., *Tetrahedron Letters*, *1975*, 1465.
59. ROELOFS, W. L., COMEAU, A., HILL, A., MILICEVIC, G., *Science*, 174, 297 (1971).
60. McDONOUGH, L. M., GEORGE, D. A., BUTT, B. A., RUTH, J. M., HILL, K. R., *Science*, 177, 177 (1972).
61. DESCOINS, C., HENRICK, C. A., *Tetrahedron Letters*, *1972*, 2999.
62. MORI, K., *Tetrahedron*, 30, 3807 (1974).
63. HENRICK, C. A., SIDDALL, J. B., *U. S. Pat. 3*, 818, 049 *Chem. Abstr.*, 81, 63136 (1974)
64. NESBITT, B. F., BEEVOR, P. S., COLE, R. A., LESTER, R., POPPI, R. G., *J. Insect Physiol.*, 21, 1091 (1975).
65. NESBITT, B. F., BEEVOR, P. S., COLE, R. A., LESTER, R., POPPI, R. G., *Tetrahedron Letters*, *1973*, 4669.
66. ROELOFS, W. L., KOCHANSKY, J., CARDE, R., ARN, H., RAUSCHER, S., *Mitt. Schweiz. Entomol. Ges.*, 46, 71 (1973).
67. NICHOLAS, K. M., PETTIT, R., *Tetrahedron Letters*, *1971*, 3475.
68. DESCOINS, C., SAMAIN, D., *Tetrahedron Letters*, *1976*, 745.
69. DESCOINS, C., IUPAC 9th International Symposium on Chemistry of Natural Products, Ottawa, 1974, *Abstracts* 22E.
70. LABOVITZ, J. N., HENRICK, C. A., CORBIN, V. L., *Tetrahedron Letters*, *1975*, 4209.
71. TAMAKI, Y., NOGUCHI, H., YUSHIMA, T., *Appl. Entomol. Zool.*, 8, 200 (1973).
72. NESBITT, B. F., BEEVOR, P. S., COLE, R. A., LESTER, R., POPPI, R. G., *Nature, New Biology*, 244, 208 (1973).
73. TAMAKI, Y., YUSHIMA, T., *J. Insect Physiol.*, 20, 1005 (1974).
74. GOTO, G, SHIMA, T., SHIMA, T., MASUYA, H., MASUOKA, Y., HIRAGA, K., *Chemistry Letters*, *1975*, 103.
75. HALL, D. R., BEEVOR, P. S., LESTER, R., POPPI, R. G., NESBITT, B. F., *Chem. and Ind.*, *1975*, 216.

76. SILVERSTEIN, R. M., RODIN, J. O., BURKHOLDER, W. E., GORMAN, J. E., *Science*, *157*, 85 (1967).

77. BIERL, B. A., BEROZA, M., STATEN, R. T., SONNET, P. E., ADLER, V. E., *J. Econ. Entomol.*, *67*, 211 (1974).

78. SONNET, P. E., *J. Org. Chem.*, *39*, 3793 (1974).

79. MORI, K., TOMINAGA, M., MATSUI, M., *Tetrahedron*, *31*, 1846 (1975).

80. BESTMANN, H. J., KOSCHATSKY, K. H., STRANSKY, W., VOSTROWSKY, O., *Tetrahedron Letters*, *1976*, 353.

81. ANDERSON, R. J., HENRICK, C. A., *J. Am. Chem. Soc.*, *97*, 4327 (1975).

82. JACOBSON, M., REDFERN, R. E., JONES, W. A., ALDRIDGE, M. H., *Science*, *170*, 542 (1970).

83. KUWAHARA, Y., HARA, H., ISHII, S., FUKAMI, H., *Science*, *171*, 801 (1971).

84. BRADY, W. E., TUMLINSON, III, J. H., BROWNLEE, R. G., SILVERSTEIN, R. M., *Science*, *171*, 802 (1972).

85. SU, H. C. F., MAHANY, P. G., BRADY, U. E., *J. Econ. Entomol.*, *66*, 845 (1973).

86. BESTMANN, H. J., VOSTROWSKY, O., PLENCHETTE, A., *Tetrahedron Letters*, *1974*, 779.

87. KOCHANSKY, J., TETTE, J., TASCHENBERG, E. F., CARDÉ, R. T., KAISSLING, K. E., ROELOFS, W. L., *J. Insect Physiol.*, *21*, 1977 (1975).

88. TUMLINSON, J. H., YONCE, C. E., DOOLITTLE, R. E., HEATH, R. R., GENTRY, C. R., MITCHELL, E. R., *Science*, *185*, 614 (1974).

89. TAI, A., MATSUMURA, F., COPPEL, H. C., *J. Org. Chem.*, *34*, 2180 (1969).

90. HORLER, D. F., *J. Chem. Soc. (C)*, *1970*, 859.

91. LANDOR, P. D., LANDOR, S. R., MUKASA, S., *J. C. S. Chem. Commun.*, 1971, 1638.

92. DESCOINS, C., HENRICK, C. A., SIDDALL, J. B., *Tetrahedron Letters*, *1972*, 3777.

93. BAUDOUY, R., GORE, J., *Synthesis*, *1974*, 573.

94. MICHELOT, D., LINSTRUMELLE, G., *Tetrahedron Letters*, *1976*, 275.

95. MORI, K., HASHIMOTO, H., TAKENAKA, Y., TAKIGAWA, T., *Synthesis*, *1975*, 720.

96. RÖLLER, H., BIEMANN, K., BJERKE, J. S., NORGARD, D. W., McSHAN, W. H., *Acta Entomol. Bohemoslav.*, *65*, 208 (1968).

97. FALES, H. M., BLUM, M. S., CREWE, R. M., BRAND, J. M., *J. Insect Physiol.*, *18*, 1077 (1972).

98. KATZENELLENBOGEN, J. A., UTAWANIT, T., *J. Am. Chem. Soc.*, *96*, 6153 (1974).

99. NISHIDA, R., FUKAMI, H., ISHII, S., *Appl. Entomol. Zool.*, *10*, 10 (1975).

100. NISHIDA, R., SATO, T., KUWAHARA, Y., FUKAMI, H., ISHII, S., *Agr. Biol. Chem.*, *40*, 1407 (1976).

101. SATO, T., NISHIDA, R., KUWAHARA, Y., FUKAMI, H., ISHII, S., *Agr. Biol. Chem.*, *40*, 391 (1976).

102. SCHWARZ, M., OLIVER, J. E., SONNET, P. E., *J. Org. Chem.*, *40*, 2410 (1975).

103. BURGSTAHLER, A. W., WEIGEL, L. O., BELL, W. J., RUST, M. K., *J. Org. Chem.*, *40*, 3456 (1975).

104. ROSENBLUM, L. D., ANDERSON, R. J., HENRICK, C. A., *Tetrahedron Letters*, *1976*, 419.

105. SMITH, R. G., DATERMAN, G. E., DAVES, JR., G. D., *Science*, *188*, 63 (1975).

106. SMITH R. G., DAVES, JR., G. D., DATERMAN, G. E., *J. Org. Chem.*, *40*, 1593 (1975).

107. MORI, K., UCHIDA, M., MATSUI, M., *Tetrahedron*, *33*, 289 (1977).

108. BELLAS, T. E., BROWNLEE, R. G., SILVERSTEIN, R. M., *Tetrahedron*, *25*, 5149 (1969).

109. WASSERMAN, H. H., BARBER, E. H., *J. Am. Chem. Soc.*, *91*, 3674 (1969).

110. MUNDY, B. P., OTZENBERGER, R. D., DeBERNARDIS, A. R., *J. Org. Chem.*, *36*, 2390 (1971).

111. KNOLLE, J., SCHÄFER, H. J., *Angew. Chem. intern. Ed.*, *14*, 758 (1975).

112. KOCIENSKI, P. J., OSTROW, R. W., *J. Org. Chem.*, *41*, 398 (1976).

113. LOOK, M., *J. Chem. Ecol.*, *2*, 83 (1976).

114. BYROM, N. T., CRIGG, R., KONGKATHIP, B. *J. C. S. Chem. Commun.*, *1976*, 216.

115. MORI, K., *Agr. Biol. Chem.*, In the press.

116. KINZER, G. W., FENTIMAN, JR., A. F., PAGE, T. F., FOLTZ, R. L., VITE, J. P. *Nature*, *221*, 477 (1969).

117. D'SILVA, T. D. J., PECK, D. W., *J. Org. Chem.*, *37*, 1828 (1972).
118. MORI, K., KOBAYASHI, S., MATSUI, M., *Agr. Biol. Chem.*, *39*, 1889 (1975).
119. PEARCE, G. T., GORE, W. E., SILVERSTEIN, R. M., PEACOCK, J. W., AUTHBERT, R. A., LANIER, G. N., SIMEONE, J. B., *J. Chem. Ecol.*, *1*, 115 (1975).
120. GORE, W. E., PEARCE, G. T., SILVERSTEIN, R. M., *J. Org. Chem.*, *40*, 1705 (1975).
121. GORE. W. E.. ARMITAGE, I. M.. *J. Org. Chem.*, *41*, 1926 (1976).
122. SILVERSTEIN, R. M., RODIN, J. O., WOOD, D. L., *Science*, *154*, 509 (1966).
123. REECE, C. A., RODIN, J. O., BROWNLEE, R. G., DUNCAN, W. G., SILVERSTEIN, R. M., *Tetrahedron*, *24*, 4249 (1968).
124. VIG, O. P., ANAND, R. C., KAD, G. L., SEHGAL, J. M., *J. Indian Chem. Soc.*, *47*, 999 (1970).
125. KATZENELLENBOGEN, J. A. ,LENOX, R. S., *J. Org. Chem.*, *38*, 326 (1973).
126. WILSON, S. R., PHILLIPS, L. R., *Tetrahedron Letters*, *1975*, 3047.
127. RILEY, R. G., SILVERSTEIN, R. M., KATZENZLLENBOGEN, J. A., LENOX, R. S., *J. Org. Chem.*, *39*, 1957 (1974).
128. MORI, K., *Agr. Biol. Chem.*, *38*, 2045 (1974).
129. GARBERS, C. F., SCOTT, F., *Tetrahedron Letters*, *1976*, 1625.
130. TUMLINSON, J. H., HARDEE, D. D., GUELDNER, R. C., THOMPSON, A. C., HEDIN, P. A., MINYARD, J. P., *Science*, 166, 1010 (1969).
131. TUMLINSON, J. H., GUELDNER, R. C., HARDEE, D. D., THOMPSON, A. C., HEDIN, P. A., MINYARD, J. P., *J. Org. Chem.*, *36*, 2616 (1971).
132. ZURFLÜH, R., DUNHAM L. L., SPAIN, V. L., SIDDALL, J. B., *J. Am. Chem. Soc.*, *92*, 425 (1970).
133. GUELDNER, R. C., THOMPSON, A. C., HEDIN, P. A., *J. Org. Chem.*, *37*, 1854 (1972).
134. KOSUGI, H., SEKIGUCHI, S., SEKITA, R., UDA, H., *Bull. Chem. Soc. Japan*, *49*, 520 (1976).
135. CARGILL, R. L., WRIGHT, B. W., *J. Org. Chem.*, *40*, 120 (1975).
136. BILLUPS, W. E., CROSS, J. H., SMITH, C. V., *J. Am. Chem. Soc.*, *95*, 3438 (1973).
137. AYER, W. A., BROWNE, L. M., *Canad. J. Chem.*, *52*, 1352 (1974).
138. STORK, G., COHEN, J. F., *J. Am. Chem. Soc.*, *96*, 5270 (1974).
139. BABLER, J. H., *Tetrahedron Letters*, *1975*, 2045.
140. TROST, B. M., KEELEY, D. E., *J. Org. Chem.*, *40*, 2013 (1975).
141. BABLER, J. H., MORTELL, T. R., *Tetrahedron Letters*, *1972*, 669.
142. PELLETIER, S. W., MODY, N. V., *J. Org. Chem.*, *41*, 109 (1976).
143. BEDOUKIAN, R. H., WOLINSKY, J., *J. Org. Chem.*, *40*, 2154 (1975).
144. COOKE, JR., M. P., *Tetrahedron Letters*, *1973*, 1281, 1983.
145. BOWLUS, S. B., KATZENELLENBOGEN, J. A., *Tetrahedron Letters*, *1973*, 1277.
146. BOWLUS, S. B., KATZENELLENBOGEN, J. A., *J. Org. Chem.*, *38*, 2733 (1973).
147. MORIZUR, J. P., MUZARD, G., BASSELIER, J.-J., KOSSANYI, J., *Bull. Soc. chim. France*, *1975*, 257.
148. OUANNES, C., LANGLOIS, Y., *Tetrahedron Letters*, *1975*, 3461.
149. MEINWALD, J., CHALMERS, A. M., PLISKE, T. E., EISNER, T., *Tetrahedron Letters* *1968*, 4893.
150. MEINWALD, J., MEINWALD, Y. C., MAZZOCCHI, R. H., *Science*, *164*, 1174 (1969).
151. MEINWALD, J., THOMPSON, W. R., EISNER, T., OWEN, D. F., *Tetrahedron Letters*, *1971*, 3485.
152. MILES, D. H., LOEW, P., JOHNSON, W. S., KLUGE, A. F., MAINWALD, J., *Tetrahedron Letters*, *1972*, 3019.
153. MORIZUR, J. P., BIDAN, G, KOSSANYI, J., *Tetrahedron Letters*, *1975*, 4167.
154. MEINWALD, J., CHALMERS, A. M., PLISKE, T. E., EISNER, T., *J. C. S. Chem. Commun.*, *1969*, 86.
155. BIRCH, A. J., BROWN, W. V., VORRIE, J. E. T., MOORE, B. P., *J. Chem. Soc. (Perkin L)*, *1972*, 2653.
156. PATIL, V. D., NAYAK, U. R., DEV, SUKH, *Tetrahedron*, *29*, 341 (1973).
157. KODAMA, M., MATSUKI, Y., ITO, S., *Tetrahedron Letters*, *1975*, 3065.
158. KITAHARA, Y., KATO, T., KOBAYASHI, T., MOORE, B. P., *Chemistry Letters*, *1976*, 219.
159. BUTLER, C. G., CALLOW, R. K.. JOHNSON, N. C., *Nature*, *184*, 1871 (1959).

160. Butler, C. G., Callow, R. K., Johnson, N. C., *Proc. Roy. Soc. (B)*, *155*, 417 (1961).
161. Barbier, M., Lederer, E., Nomura, T., *Compt. Rend.*, *251*, 1133 (1960).
162. Bestmann, H. J., Kunstmann, R., Schulz, H., *Liebigs Ann. Chem.*, *699*, 33 (1966).
163. Doolittle, R. E., Blum, M. S., Boch, R., *Ann. Entomol. Soc. Amer.*, *63*, 1180 (1970).
164. Trost, B. M., Salzmann, T. N., *J. Org. Chem.*, *40*, 148 (1975).
165. Meinwald, J., Meinwald, Y. C., *J. Am. Chem. Soc.*, *88*, 1305 (1966).
166. Riley, R. G., Silverstein, R. M., Carroll, B., Carroll, R., *J. Insect Physiol.*, *20*, 651 (1974).
167. Sonnet, P. E., *J. Med. Chem.*, *15*, 97 (1972).
168. Ritter, F. J., Rotgams, I. E. M., Talman, E., Verwiel, P. E. J., Stein, F., *Experientia*, *29*, 530 (1973).
169. Oliver, J. E., Sonnet, P. E., *J. Org. Chem.*, *39*, 2662 (1974).
170. Mori, K., *Tetrahedron Letters*, *1973*, 3869.
171. Mori, K., *Tetrahedron*, *30*, 3817 (1974).
172. Roderick, W. R., *J. Chem. Education*, *43*, 510 (1966).
173. Wright, R. H., *Nature*, *198*, 782 (1963).
174. Wright, R. H., "The Science of Smell", George Allen and Unwin Ltd., London, (1964).
175. Amore, J. E., "Molecular Basis of Odor", Charles C. Thomas Publisher, Springfield (1970).
176. Amoore, J. E., Palmieri, G., Wanke, E., Blum, M. S., *Science*, *165* 1266 (1969).
177. Russell, G. F., Hills, J. I., *Science*, *172*, 1043 (1971).
178. Friedman, L., Miller, J. G., *Science*, *172*, 1044 (1971).
179. Riley, R. G., Silverstein, R. M., Moser, J. C., *Science*, *183*, 760 (1974).
180. Riley, R. G., Silverstein, R. M., *Tetrahedron*, *30*, 1171 (1974).
181. Iwaki, S., Marumo, S., Saito, T., Yamada, M., Katagiri, K., *J. Am. Chem. Soc.*, *96*, 7842 (1974).
182. Yamada, M., Saito, T., Katagiri, K., Iwaki, S., Marumo, S., *J. Insect Physiol.*, *22*, 755 (1976).
183. Moser, J. C., Brownlee, R. G., Silverstein, R. M., *J. Insect Physiol.*, *14*, 529 (1968).
184. Mori, K., *Tetrahedron*, *33*, (1977).
185. Mori, K., Takigawa, T., Matsui, M., *Tetrahedron Letters*, In the press.
186. Renwick, J. A. A., Personal communication to K. M. dated June 16, 1975.
187. Silverstein, R. M., Personal communication to K. M. dated Aug. 12, 1975.
188. Mori, K., *Tetrahedron*, *32*, (1976).
189. Mori, K., *Tetrahedron Letters*, *1975*, 2187.
190. Mori, K., *Tetrahedron*, *32*, 1101 (1976).
191. Vité, J. P., Hedden, R., Mori, K., *Naturwissenschaften*, *63*, 43 (1976).
192. Mori, K., *Tetrahedron Letters*, *1976*, 1609.
193. Renwick, J. A. A., *Contrib. Boyce Thompson Inst.*, *23*, 355 (1967).
194. Pitman, G. B., Vité, J. P., Kinzer, G. W., Fentiman, Jr., A. F., *Nature*, *218*, 168 (1968).
195. Mori, K., *Agr. Biol. Chem.*, *40*, 415 (1976).
196. Wood, D. L., Stark, R. W., Silverstein, R. M., Rodin, J. O., *Nature*, *215*, 206 (1967).
197. Renwick, J. A. A., Vité, J. P., *J. Insect Physiol.*, *18*, 1215 (1972).
198. Mori, K., Mizumachi, N., Matsui, M., *Agr. Biol. Chem.*, *40*, 1611 (1976).
199. Vité, J. P., Personal communication dated July 27, 1976.
200. Hobbs, P. D., Magnus, P. D., *J. C. S. Chem. Commun.*, *1974*, 856.
201. Hobbs, P. D., Magnus, P. D., *J. Am. Chem. Soc.*, *98*, 4595 (1976).
202. Banno, K., Mukaiyama, T., *Chemistry Letters*, *1976*, 279.

IV. SYNTHESIS OF INSECT JUVENILE HORMONES

1. INTRODUCTION

C. M. Williams's pioneering work to find juvenile hormone (abbreviated to JH) activity in ethereal extracts of the abdomina of the adult male giant silk moth, *Hyalophora cecropia*, was the key to the subsequent chemical investigation of juvenile hormones [1]. In 1965, Röller *et al.* isolated the first juvenile hormone from this source [2, 3] and in 1967 proposed its structure except for the stereochemistry of the oxide ring [4]. Its first synthesis soon followed and the plain structure of the juvenile hormone was firmly established as **1** [5]. Soon afterwards a new juvenile hormone was isolated from the same source by Meyer *et al.* [6, 7] and shown to be **2**. The third juvenile hormone was isolated from an organ culture of corpora allata of the tobacco hornworm moth, *Manduca sexta* and identified as **3** [8]. These juvenile hormones are now called JH I (**1**), JH II (**2**) and JH III (**3**), respectively [9]. The absolute stereochemistry of the oxide ring was later determined as shown in the formulas. The earlier stage of juvenile hormone research is reviewed by Röller and Dahm [10].

These structure assignments were followed by large number of syntheses. The non-stereoselective syntheses were devised mainly for large-scale preparations of juvenile hormones to test their possible use as agrochemicals. This aspect will be treated in Section IV. 2. The stereoselective syntheses were of more academic nature at first to develop new olefination reactions, but later modified to be usable as preparative means. This phase will be discussed in Section IV. 3. The necessity for an efficient stereoselective synthesis can be understood by examining the following data on the structure-activity relationship of juvenile hormone stereoisomers (Table II). The natural (2*E* :

Table II

Juvenile Hormone Activity of the Stereoisomers of JH I [10]

2E : 6E : 10Z-isomer			5000	TU/μg*
E	E	E	2000	
E	Z	Z	200	
E	E	E	150	
Z	E	Z	10	
Z	E	E	10	
Z	Z	Z	10	
Z	Z	E	10	
Natural JH I			5000	

* TU *(Tenebrio* unit) is defined as the minimum amount of a JH-active substance which will induce a positive response in 40% of the *Tenebrio molitor* pupae injected.

6E : 10Z)-isomer is the most active one, while the (2Z : 6Z)-isomers are almost inactive on the yellow mealworm, *Tenebrio molitor*. It is therefore important to synthesize only the most active isomer. The syntheses of chiral juvenile hormones were important in establishing the absolute stereochemistry of juvenile hormones and at the same time in estimating the biological activity of both enantiomers. This will be detailed in Section 4.

Natural products with juvenile hormone activity are also present in the plant kingdom. Sláma and Williams reported the existence of "the paper factor" in American papers and balsam firs which inhibited the normal metamorphosis of a bug, *Pyrrhocorris apterus* [11]. Bowers *et al.* isolated this compound and named it juvabione [12]. This was identified as methyl todomatuate (4) [12]. The syntheses of this and related natural products either as racemates or in optically active forms are detailed in Section IV. 5.

Williams's argument on juvenile hormones as the third generation pesticides [13] caused a great deal of investigations concerning the synthesis and biological evaluation of juvenile hormone analogues. This aspect will not be treated here, because there are too many juvenile hormone analogues with varying degrees of practical applicability. However, our own work on juvenile hormone mimics will be reviewed very briefly in Chapter V (Concluding Remarks).

There are many reviews on juvenile hormone chemistry and biology [14–18]. Staal's review on juvenile hormone mimics summarizes the present status of applied researches [18].

2. NON-STEREOSELECTIVE SYNTHESES
OF JUVENILE HORMONES

The existing syntheses are summarized chronologically with specification of the key reactions used. A synthesis published with experimental details is marked by an asterisk.

A. *The First Synthesis of Dahm, Trost and Röller*
— Wadsworth-Emmons reaction —

The first synthesis of the racemic JH I was carried out by employing the Wadsworth-Emmons reaction three times, as shown in Scheme 146 [5]. Separation of the geometrical isomers was carried out after each condensation reaction. This synthesis yielded all of the possible stereoisomers of JH I. The (2E : 6E : 10Z)-isomer was identical with the natural JH I. The products were also used to study the structure-activity relationship.

B. *The Second Synthesis of Dahm, Trost and Röller*
— Julia cleavage and Wadsworth-Emmons reaction —

This synthesis utilized Julia's cyclopropane cleavage reaction at the first stage (Scheme 147) [19]. This provided the (2E : 6E : 10E)-isomer which was not identical with JH I.

C. *The USDA Synthesis*
— Julia cleavage, Wadsworth-Emmons and Wittig reactions —

A group of workers in Agricultural Research Service, Beltsville, published two syntheses as shown in Schemes 148, and 149 [20]. They obtained a stereoisomeric mixture as the final product, which was used for their biological studies.

D. *Synthesis by Mori et al.**
—Carroll and Wadsworth-Emmons reactions —

This synthesis involved the Carroll reaction and the Wadsworth-Emmons reaction in the key olefination steps resulting in a stereoisomeric mixture of JH I (**1**), JH II (**2**) and its position isomer (**5**) as shown in Scheme 150 [21]. The pure (2E : 6E) and (2Z : 6E)-**5** were prepared by securing the pure (6E)-ketone (**A**) which could be obtained by purification as its crystalline semicarbazone (Scheme 151) [22].

Scheme 146

Scheme 147

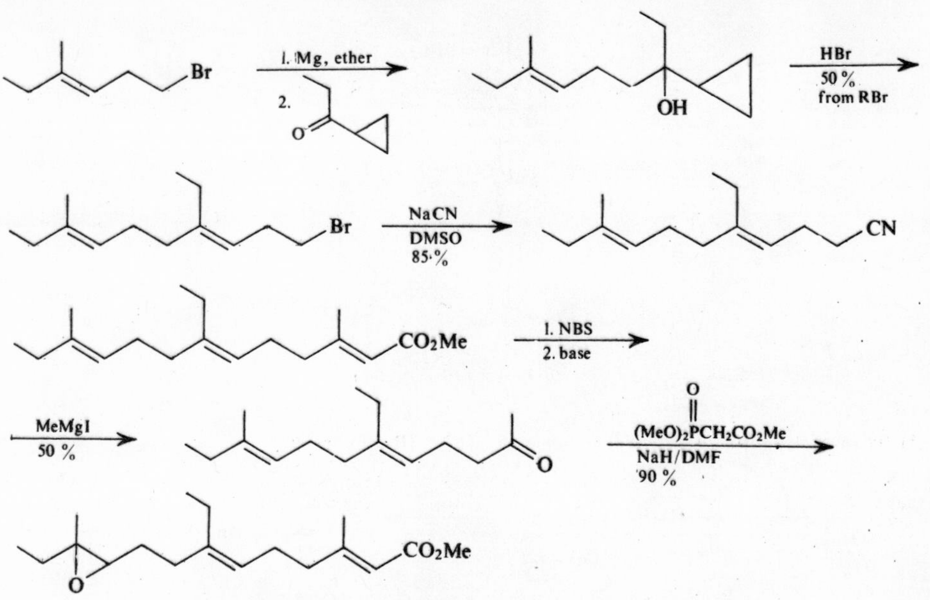

Scheme 148

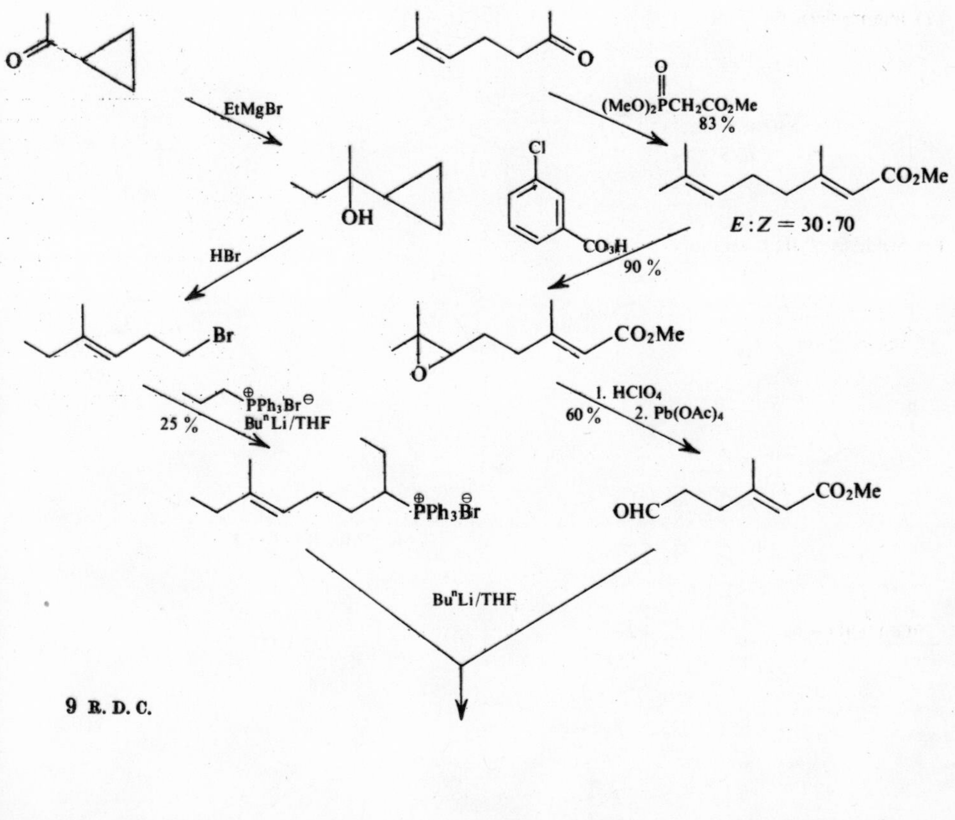

9 R. D. C.

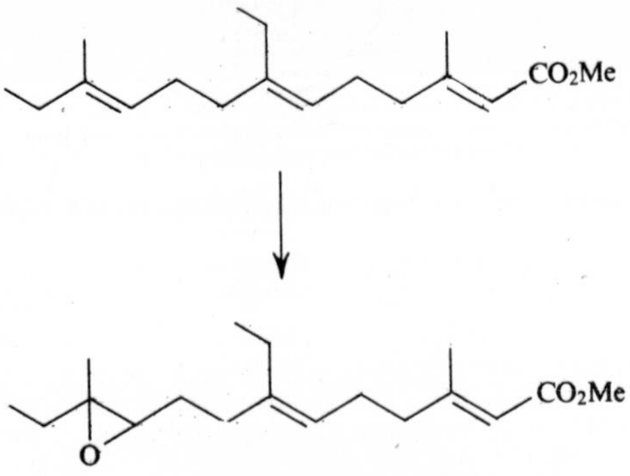

Scheme 149 (cont'd)

(1) Intermediates for JH I and position isomer of JH II   (R=Et or Me)

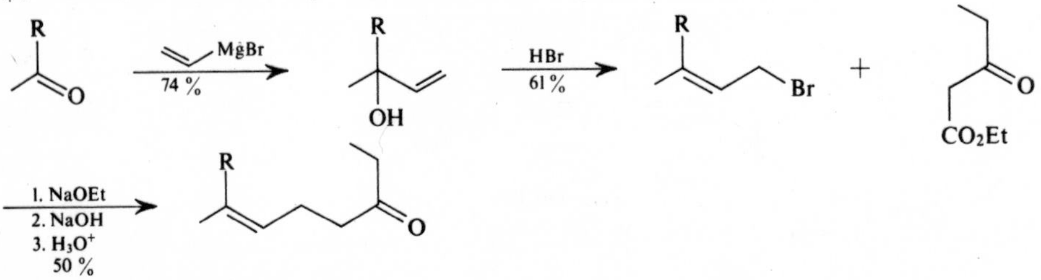

(2) Intermediates for JH II

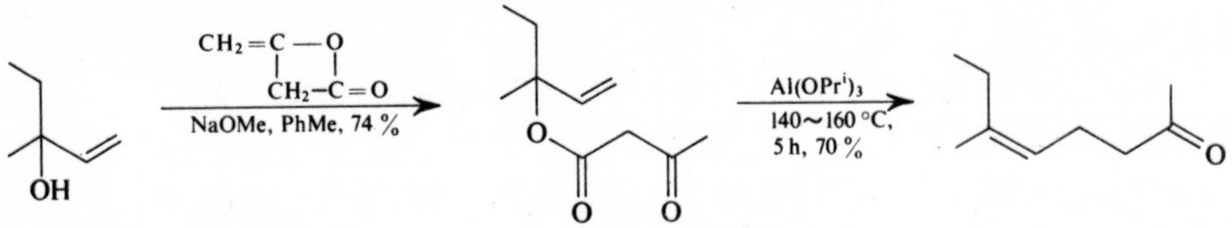

(3) Synthesis of JH I, JH II and 5

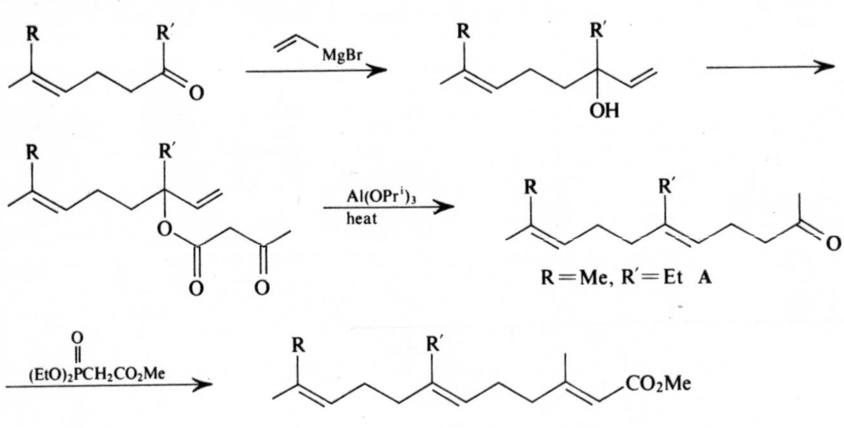

R=Me, R'=Et A

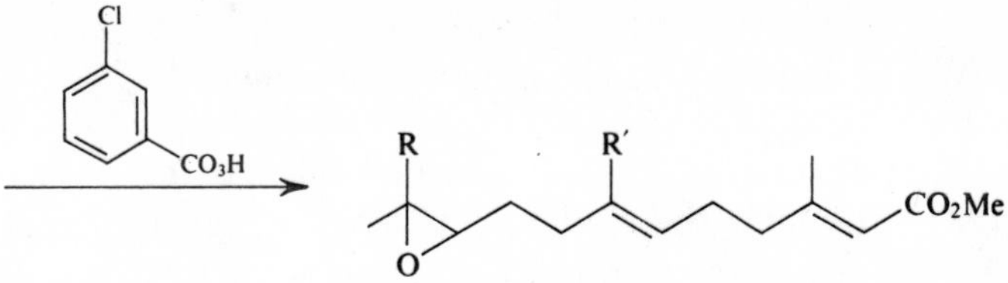

JH I   R = R' = Et (1)
II   R = Et, R' = Me (2)
Isomer 5   R = Me, R' = Et

Scheme 150 (cont'd)

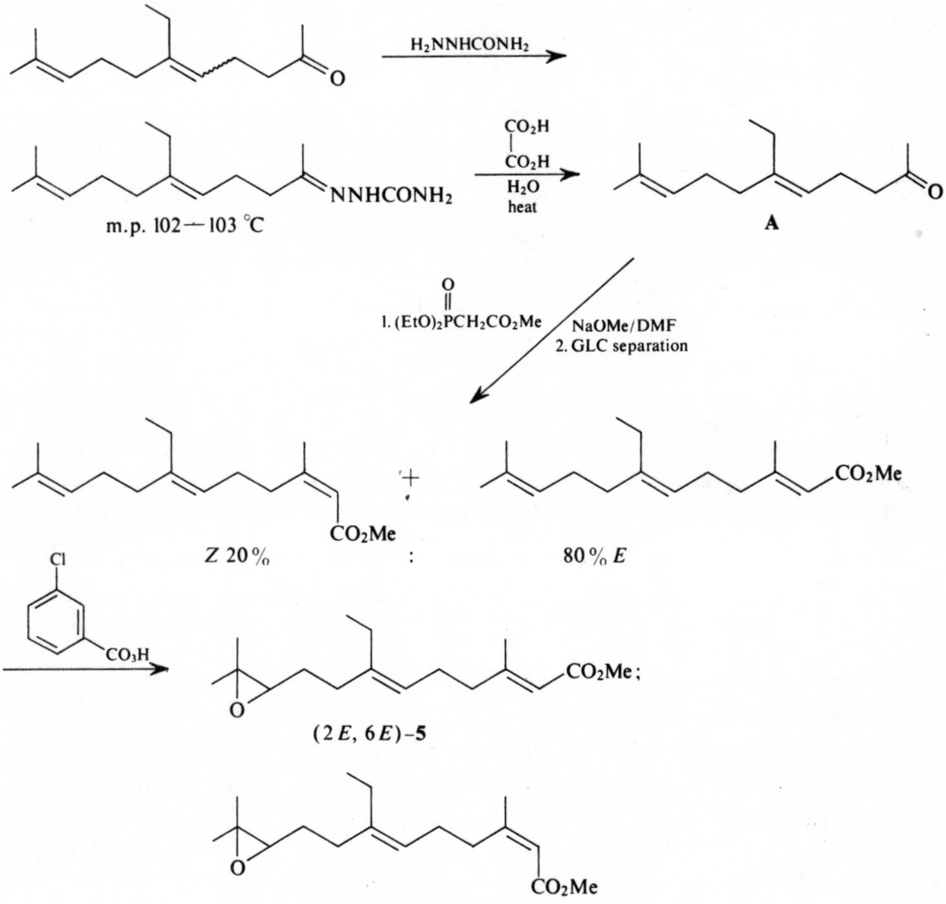

m.p. 102—103 °C

Scheme 151

9*

E. Synthesis by Cavill et al.*
— Wittig and Wadsworth-Emmons reactions —

Cavill in Australia devised an interesting synthesis starting from furan (Scheme 152) [23]. Although the synthesis is lengthy, separation of the isomers was executed whenever a mixture was produced to obtain about 60 mg of pure racemic JH I (1). Another interesting feature of this work was the utilization of not an olefin but a glycol system as the precursor of the terminal oxide ring. This prevented the formation of 6,7-epoxide or diepoxide sometimes resulting in the final epoxidation stage of other syntheses. Separation of the desired 3,4-*threo*-triol (A) from the undesired 3,4-*erythro*-isomer was effected by chromatography over alumina–boric acid (30 : 1) with chloroform–methanol as an eluent.

F. Synthesis by Pommer et al.*
— Carroll, Wittig and Reformatsky reactions —

Pommer *et al.* at BASF, FRG, reported a synthesis of JH I stereoisomeric mixture (Scheme 153) [24]. They also utilized the Carroll reaction twice.

G. Synthesis by Schulz and Sprung
— Wittig reactions —

The Schering workers synthesized ($\pm$)-JH I by utilizing the Wittig reactions in the construction scheme $C_4 + C_6 + C_5 + C_2$ (Scheme 154) [25]. Each isomer was separated by distillation through a spinning band column.

H. Synthesis by Atherton and Pfiffner
— Acetylene chemistry and Wadsworth-Emmons reaction —

The Hoffman-La Roche synthesis used techniques familiar in vitamin A synthesis. All the stereoisomers of JH I were prepared and separated by column chromatography or fractional distillation (Scheme 155) [26, 27]. Very useful NMR and GLC data of every stereoisomer are included in this work [27].

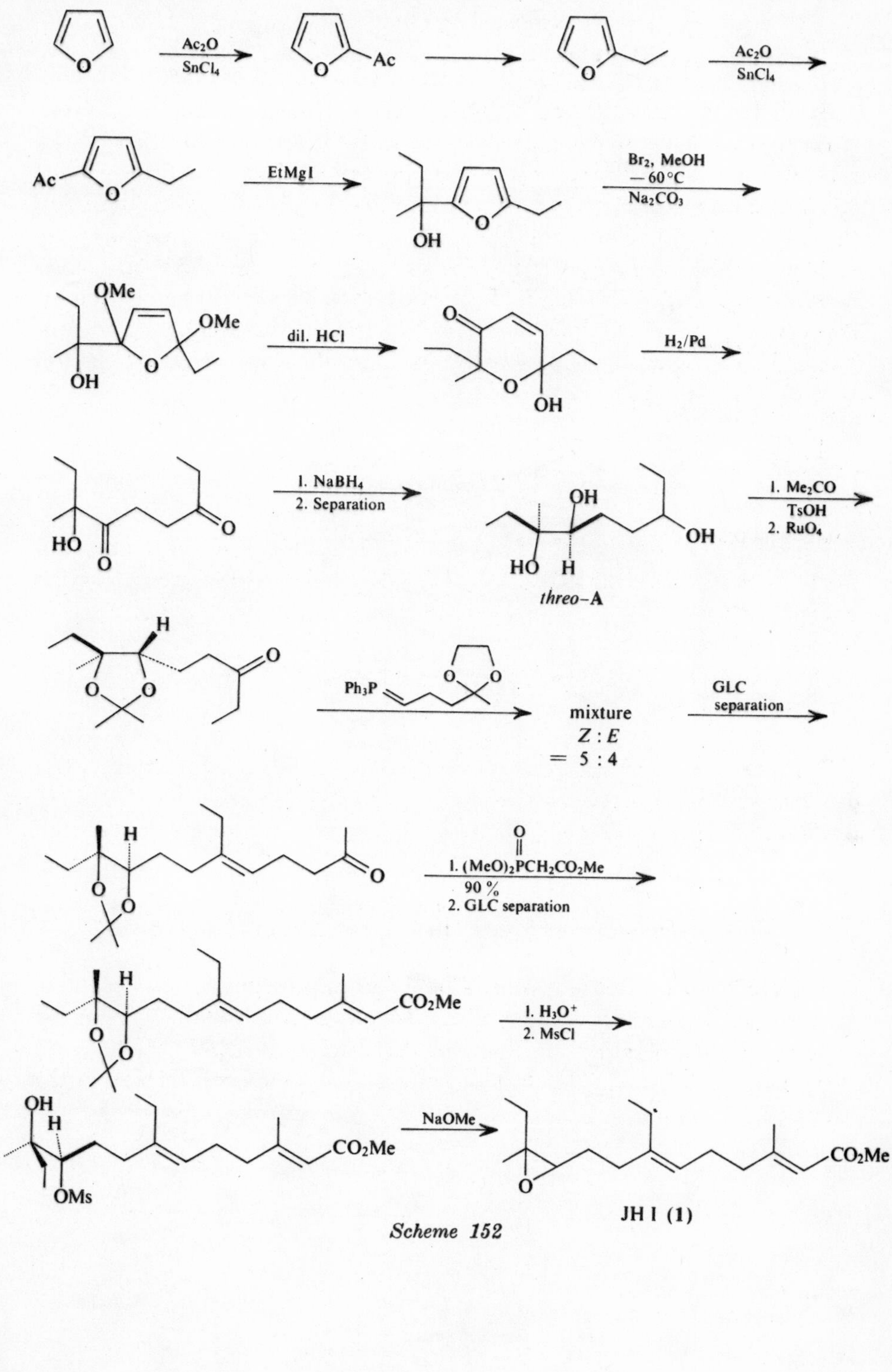

Scheme 152

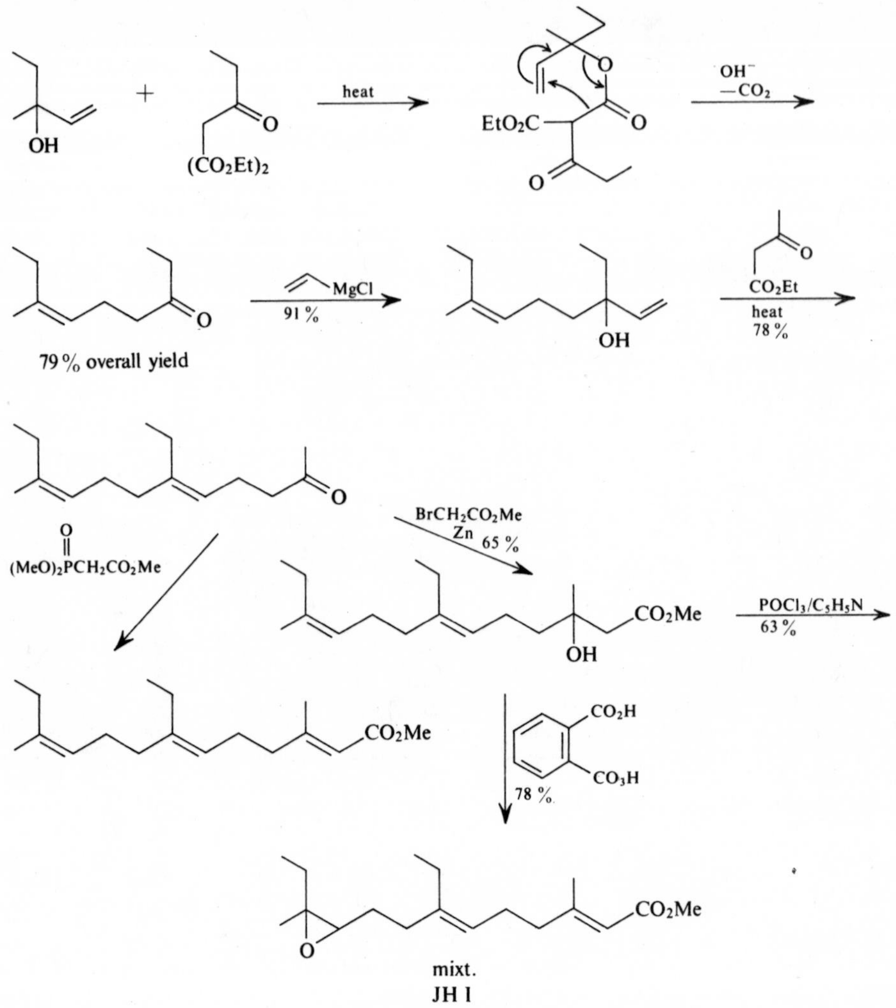

OH
(CO2Et)2
heat
EtO2C
O
OH⁻
−CO2
79 % overall yield
MgCl
91 %
OH
CO2Et
heat
78 %
O
(MeO)2PCH2CO2Me
BrCH2CO2Me
Zn 65 %
CO2Me
POCl3/C5H5N
63 %
CO2H
CO3H
78 %
mixt.
JH I

Scheme 153

Scheme 154

Scheme 155

I. Synthesis by Findlay and MacKay*
— Claisen rearrangement, Wittig and Wadsworth-Emmons reactions —

This New Brunswick synthesis aimed at conciseness, convenience and economy to provide JH materials in suitable quantities for biological study; it was executed as shown in Scheme 156 [28, 29, 30]. Separation of each isomer was carried out by preparative GLC. By this synthesis ($\pm$)-JH I and ($\pm$)-JH II (Scheme 157) were obtained.

J. Synthesis by Anderson et al.*
— Organocopper chemistry —

This synthesis, originating from the Zoecon Corporation, Palo Alto, is an application of organocopper chemistry [see Equation (35), p. 22] as shown in Scheme 158 [31, 56]. Although these reactions made possible the conversion of farnesol into JH I stereoisomers, the desired ($2E : 6E : 10Z$)-trienoic ester could not be obtained.

K. Synthesis by van Tamelen and McCormick
— Organocopper chemistry —

This synthesis is similar to 2-J but differs from it by utilizing an allylic chloride instead of acetate as the substrate for the substitution by the organocopper reagent (Scheme 159) [32]. This synthesis produced the desired ($2E : 6E : 10Z$)-trienoic ester together with other geometrical isomers.

L. Synthesis by Mori et al.*
— Julia cleavage and Wadsworth-Emmons reaction —

This is a general method of synthesis devised for the rapid and efficient preparation of JH I and its analogues with different alkyl groups on the carbon chain to give stereoisomeric mixtures. The synthesis is straightforward and proceeds in good or moderate yield as shown in Scheme 160 [33] for the synthesis of a stereoisomeric mixture of ($\pm$)-JH I. Some practically important JH analogues have been prepared by this method.

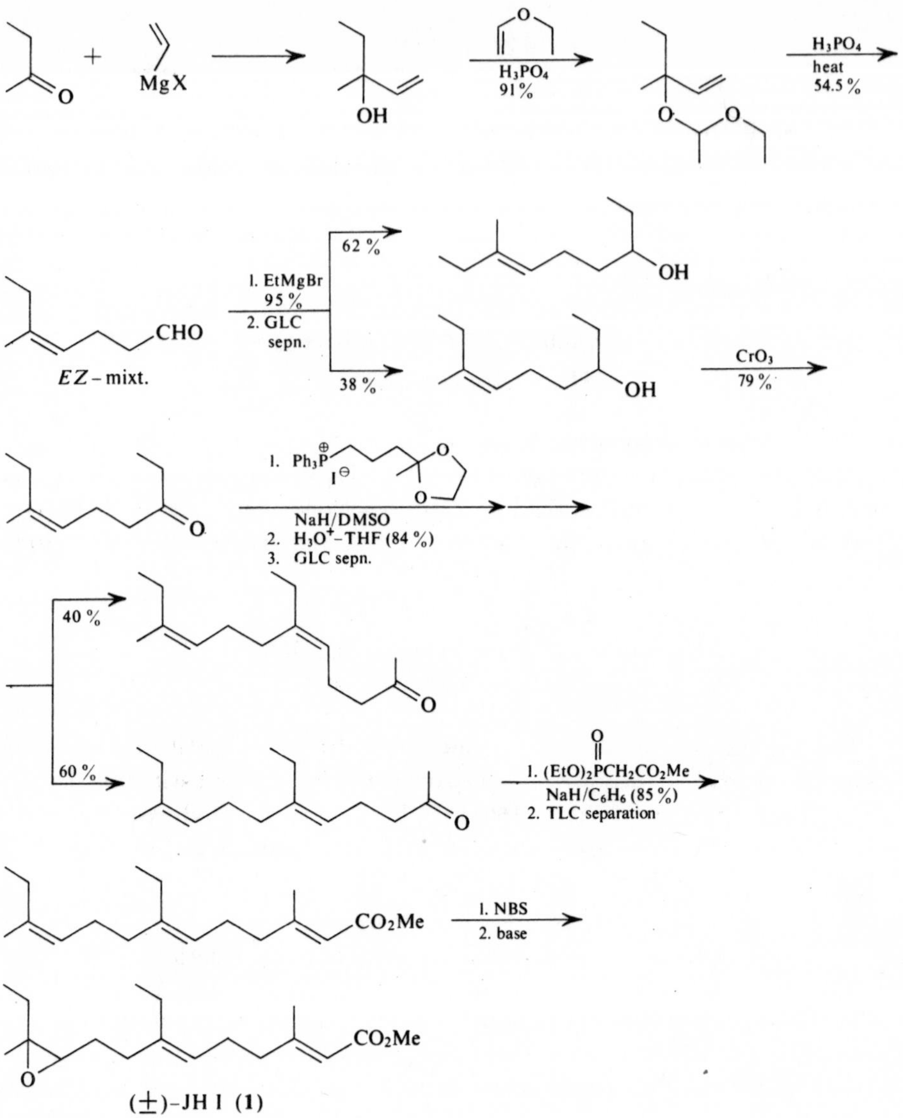

Scheme 156

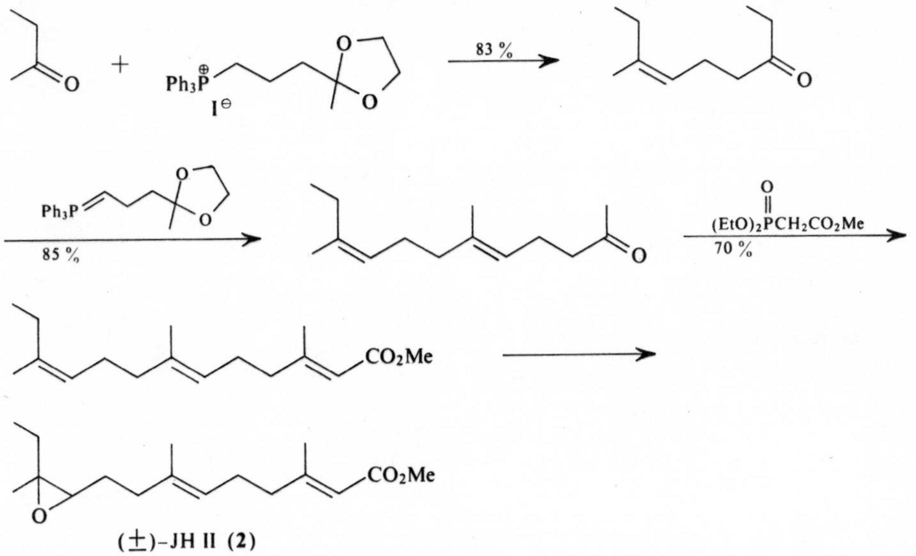

Scheme 157

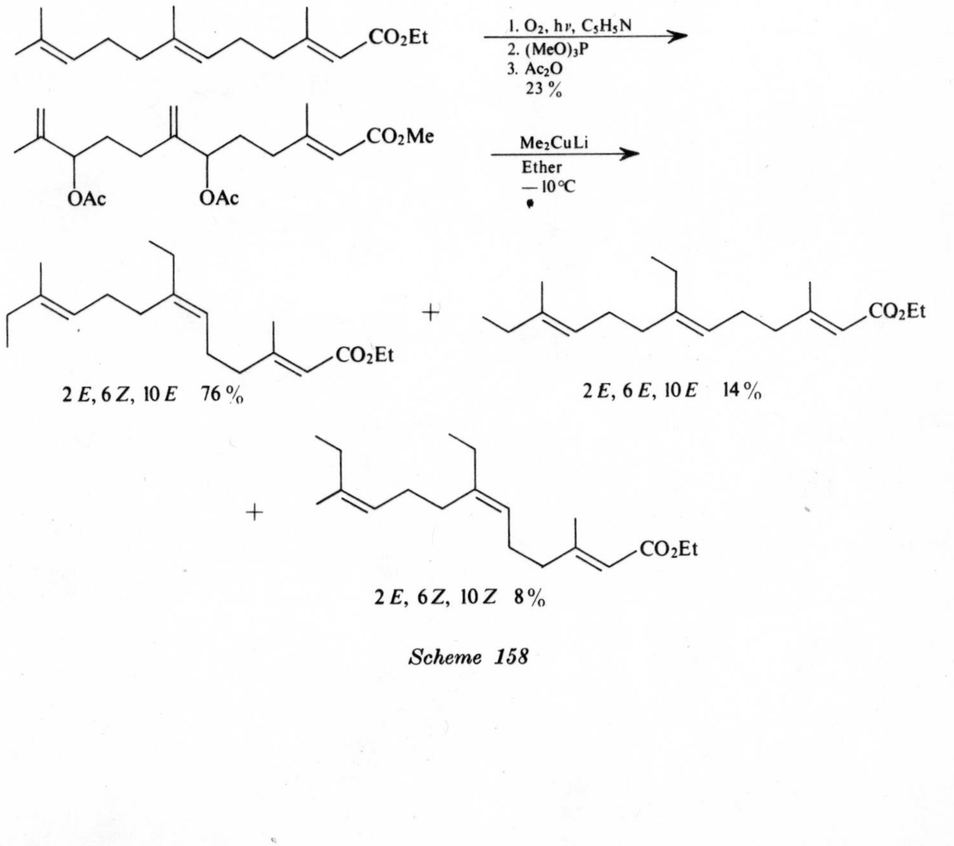

2 E, 6 Z, 10 E   76 %

2 E, 6 E, 10 E   14 %

2 E, 6 Z, 10 Z   8 %

Scheme 158

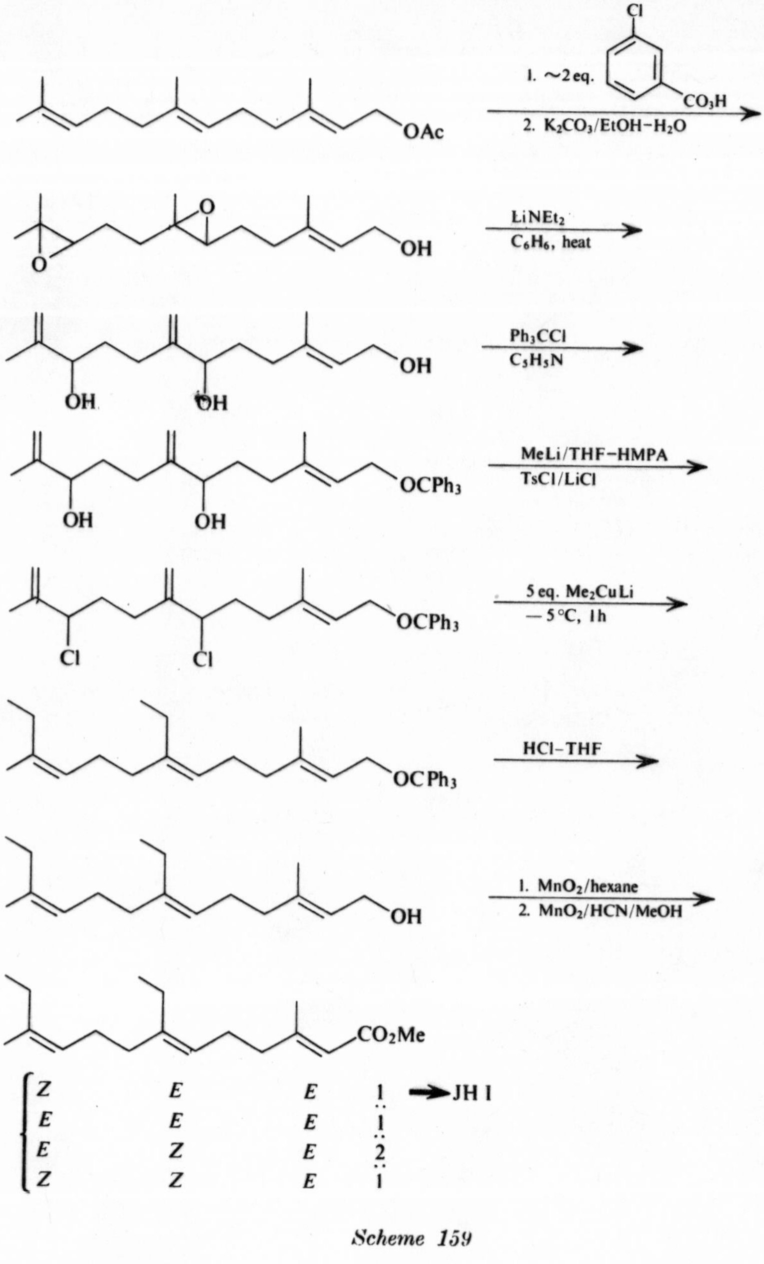

Scheme 159

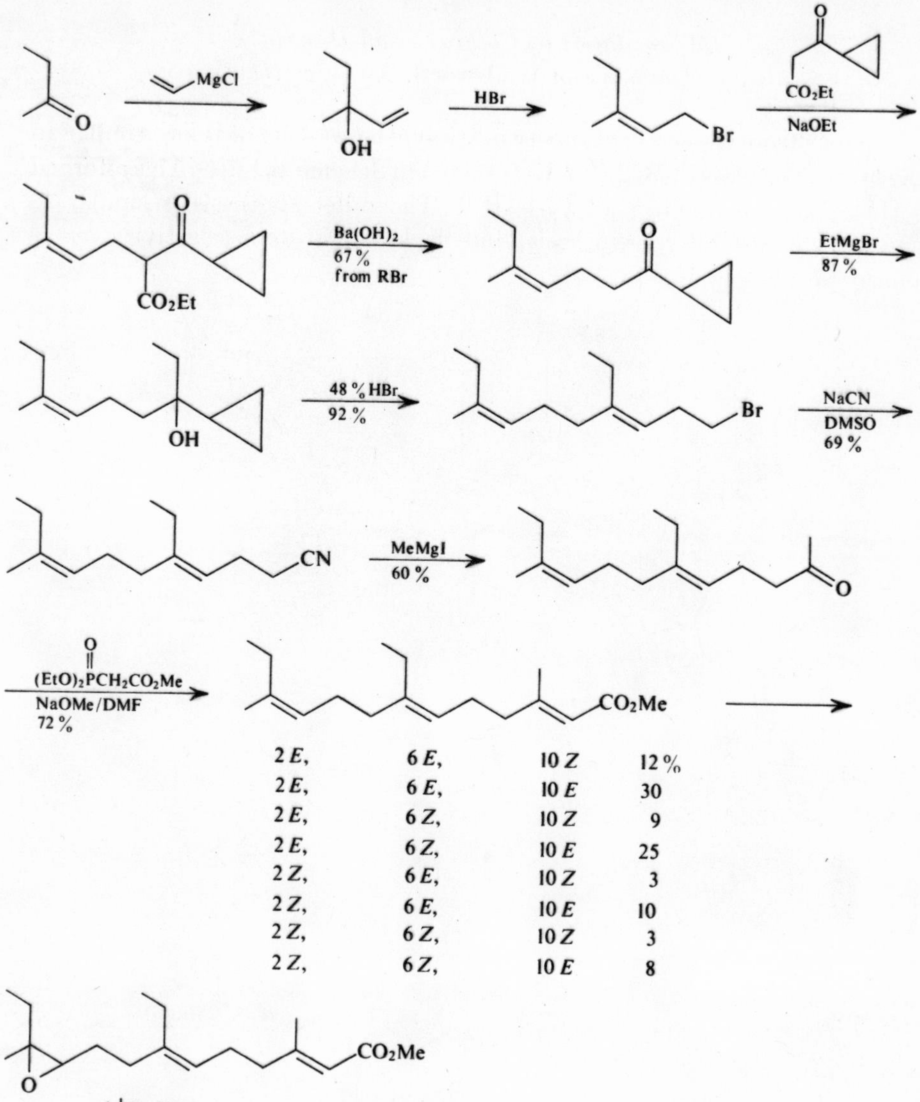

2 E,	6 E,	10 Z	12 %
2 E,	6 E,	10 E	30
2 E,	6 Z,	10 Z	9
2 E,	6 Z,	10 E	25
2 Z,	6 E,	10 Z	3
2 Z,	6 E,	10 E	10
2 Z,	6 Z,	10 Z	3
2 Z,	6 Z,	10 E	8

(±)-JH I
Stereoisomeric mixture

Scheme 160

M. Synthesis by Cochrane and Hanson*
— Julia cleavage and Wadsworth-Emmons reaction

A paper from Sussex contains two JH syntheses. One of them, similar to the other syntheses (2-B, 2-C, 2-E) is shown in Scheme 161 [34]. This afforded a stereoisomeric mixture of (±)-JH I. The other synthesis is similar to Corey's stereoselective synthesis, but lacks high stereoselectivity; it is shown in Scheme 162 [34].

| 2 E, | 6 E, | 10 Z | 9.8% |
| 2 E, | 6 E, | 10 E | 28.9% |

Scheme 161

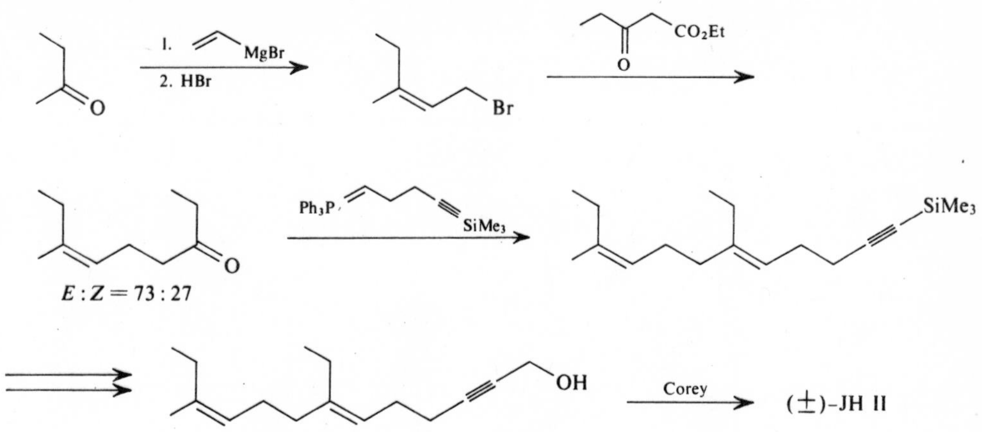

Scheme 162

N. *Synthesis of* (±)-*JH II by Mori et al.**
- Julia cleavage and Wadsworth-Emmons reaction

This is a modification of the earlier Mori synthesis (2-L). The *(Z)*-C_7-alcohol obtained as depicted in Equation (46) was used as the starting material as shown in Scheme 163 [35]. The intermediate ketone was purified as the semicarbazone to give a pure crystalline derivative of the (5E : 9Z)-ketone. The desired (2E : 6E : 10Z)-trienoic ester was obtained by preparative GLC. Racemic JH II prepared by this synthesis served as the starting material for the microbial preparation of the chiral JH II (see Scheme 195, p. 181) [78].

O. *Synthesis by Fráter*
– Claisen and Cope rearrangements

This synthesis utilized both the ester enolate Claisen rearrangement [36, 37] and the Cope rearrangement. The route is shown in Scheme 164 [38]. Unfortunately the reactions are not stereoselective and result in stereo-isomeric mixtures.

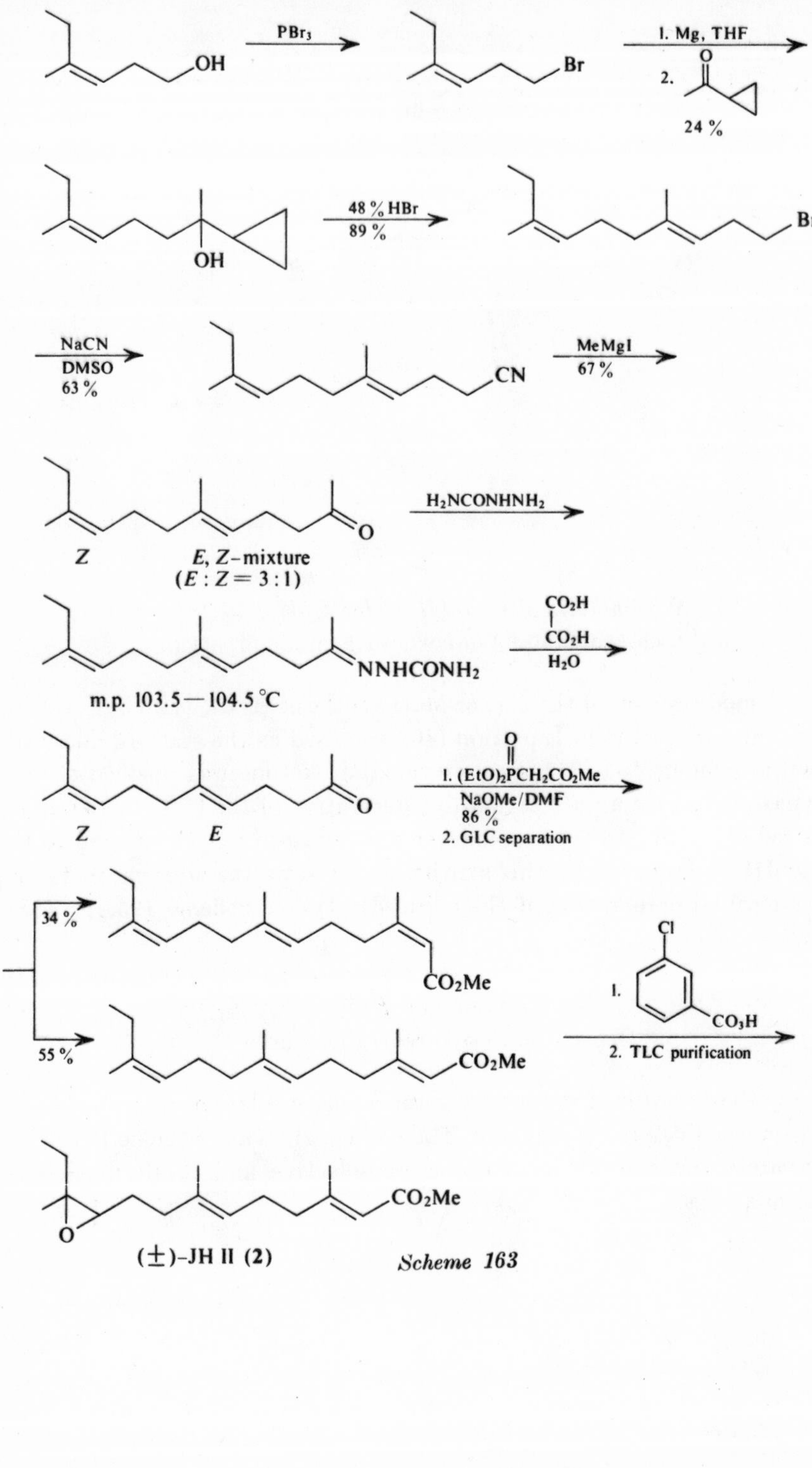
OH
PBr3
Br
1. Mg, THF
2.
O
24 %
OH
48 % HBr
89 %
Br
NaCN
DMSO
63 %
CN
MeMgI
67 %
O
Z
E, Z-mixture
(E : Z = 3 : 1)
H2NCONHNH2
NNHCONH2
m.p. 103.5—104.5 °C
CO2H
CO2H
H2O
O
Z
E
O
1. (EtO)2PCH2CO2Me
NaOMe/DMF
86 %
2. GLC separation
34 %
CO2Me
55 %
CO2Me
Cl
1.
CO3H
2. TLC purification
CO2Me
O
(±)-JH II (2)

Scheme 163

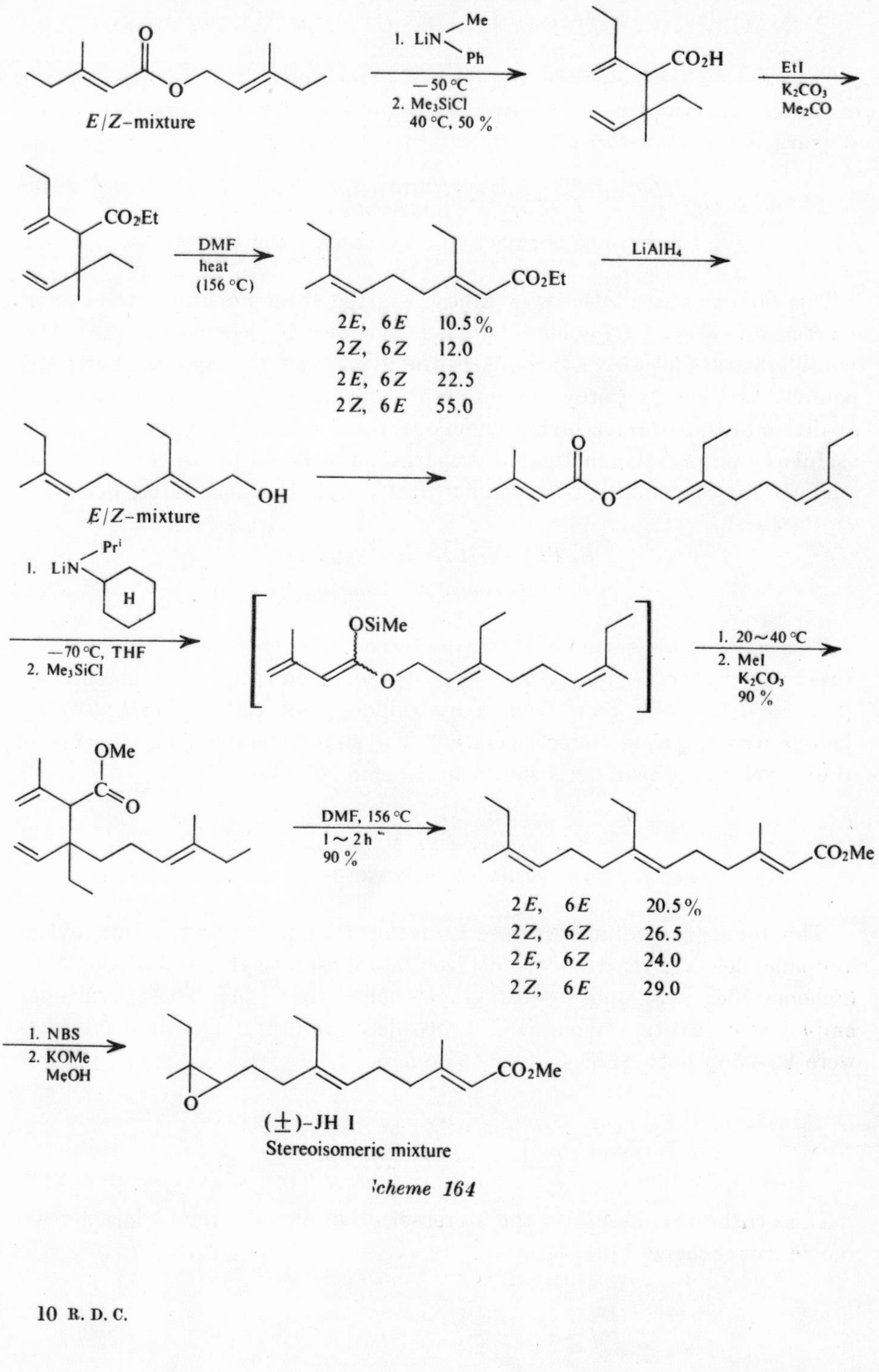

E/Z-mixture

1. LiN(Me)(Ph)
−50 °C
2. Me₃SiCl
40 °C, 50 %

EtI
K₂CO₃
Me₂CO

DMF
heat
(156 °C)

2E,	6E	10.5%
2Z,	6Z	12.0
2E,	6Z	22.5
2Z,	6E	55.0

LiAlH₄

E/Z-mixture

1. LiN(Pr^i)(H)
−70 °C, THF
2. Me₃SiCl

1. 20~40 °C
2. MeI
K₂CO₃
90 %

DMF, 156 °C
1 ~ 2 h
90 %

2E,	6E	20.5%
2Z,	6Z	26.5
2E,	6Z	24.0
2Z,	6E	29.0

1. NBS
2. KOMe
MeOH

(±)-JH I
Stereoisomeric mixture

Scheme 164

10 R. D. C.

3. STEREOSELECTIVE SYNTHESES OF JUVENILE HORMONES

The existing syntheses are summarized chronologically with specification of the key reactions used. A synthesis published with experimental details is marked by an asterisk.

A. Corey's First Synthesis
— Acetylene chemistry and organocopper reagent —

This famous stereoselective synthesis started from p-methoxytoluene as a precursor of the (10Z)-olefinic linkage as shown in Scheme 165 [39]. The notable feature of this synthesis is the utilization of organocopper compounds. A review by Corey himself on his syntheses of juvenile hormones is available [40]. Although highly ingenious, the synthesis is too lengthy to be useful as a preparative method of preparing juvenile hormones for biological studies. The lengthiness is a common feature of the earlier stereoselective syntheses.

B. The First Zoecon Synthesis
— Fragmentation reaction —

This synthesis is quite unique in the respect that the stereochemistry of a fused ring system is transcripted into the olefin geometry by fragmentation (Scheme 166) [41]. Thus from a hydrindenedione the key (5E : 9Z)-C_{15}-ketone was prepared stereoselectively. The stereoselective ring cleavage of the bicyclic intermediate is shown in Scheme 167.

C. Johnson's First Synthesis
— Julia cleavage —

The Johnson modification [see Equation (47), p. 25] of the Julia cyclopropane cleavage reaction was utilized in Johnson's syntheses of ($\pm$)-JH I (Scheme 168) [42] and ($\pm$)-JH II (Scheme 169) [43]. These syntheses employed no exotic reagent and proceeded smoothly. The final products were 92–95% pure (2E : 6E : 10Z)-isomers.

D. Johnson's Second Synthesis
— Claisen rearrangement —

This synthesis is based on the stereoselective olefinic ketal Claisen rearrangement (Scheme 170) [44].

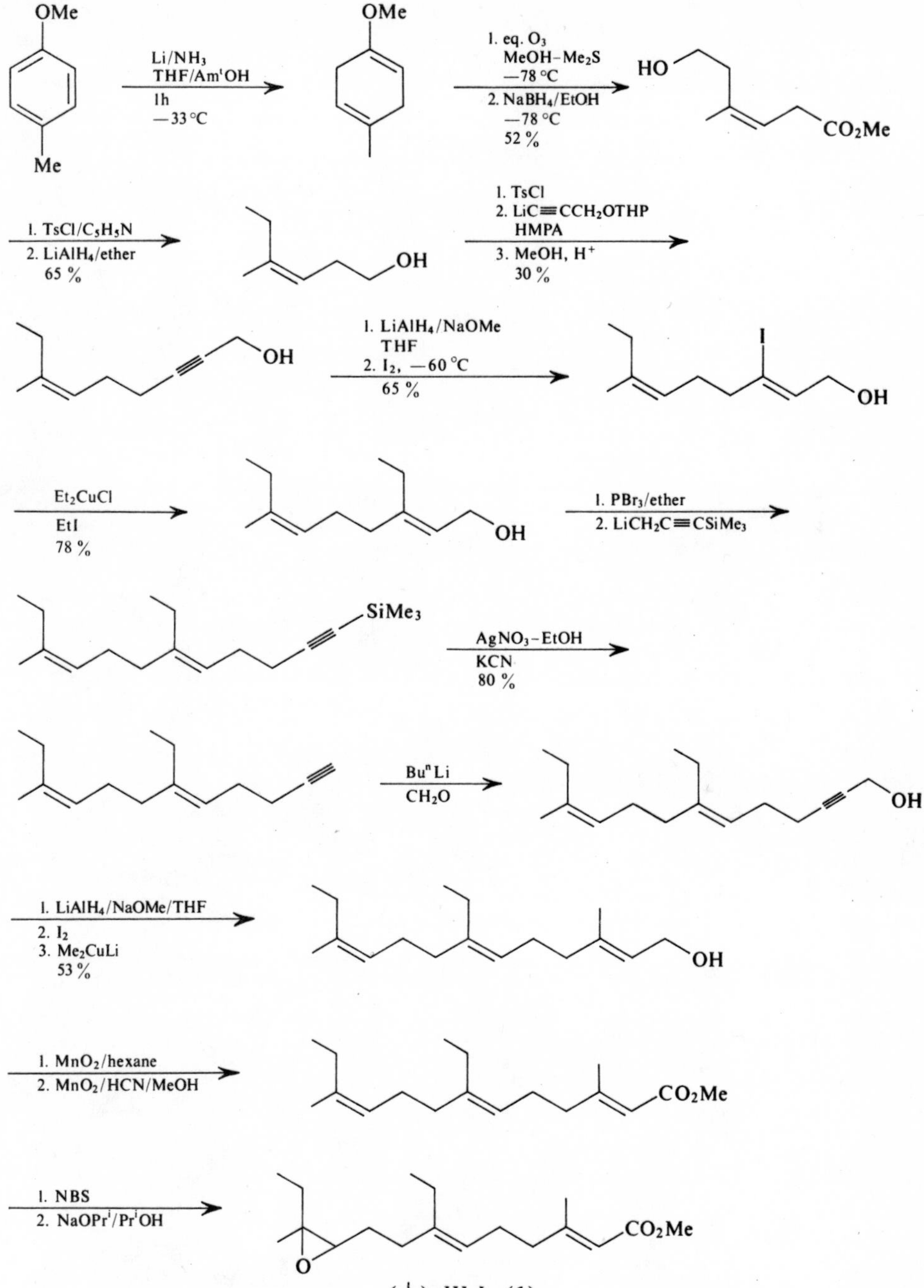

(±)-JH I   (1)

Scheme 165

Scheme 166

Scheme 167

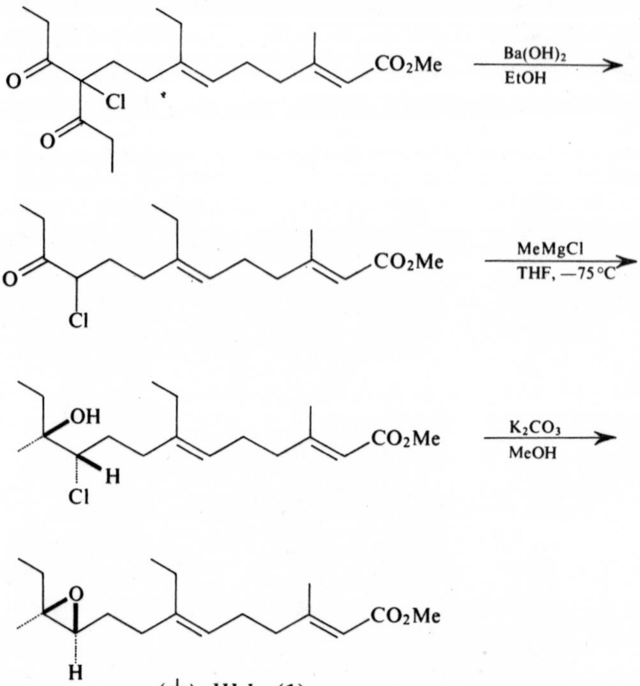

(±)-JH I (1)

Scheme 168 (cont'd)

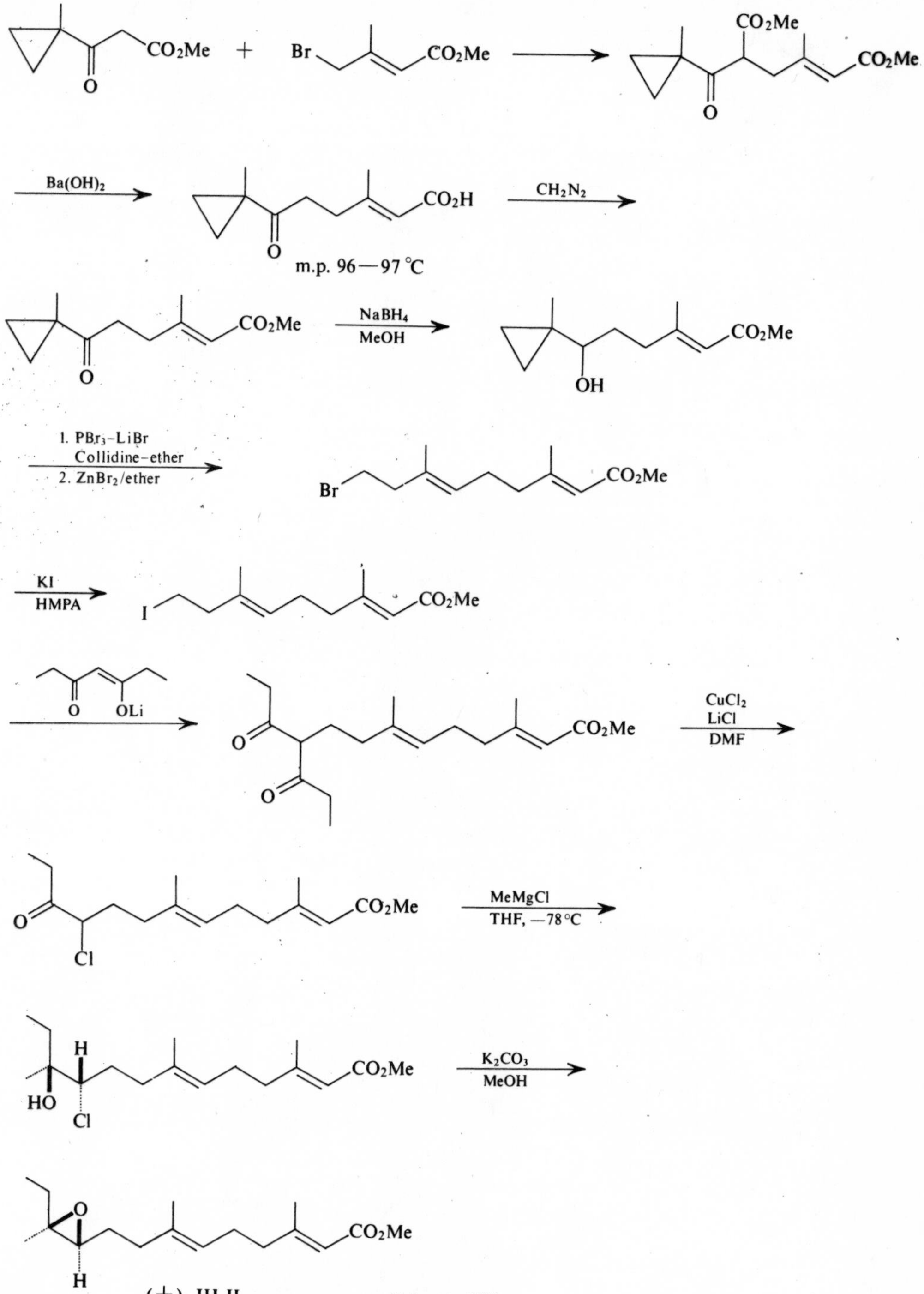

(±)-JH II   Scheme 169

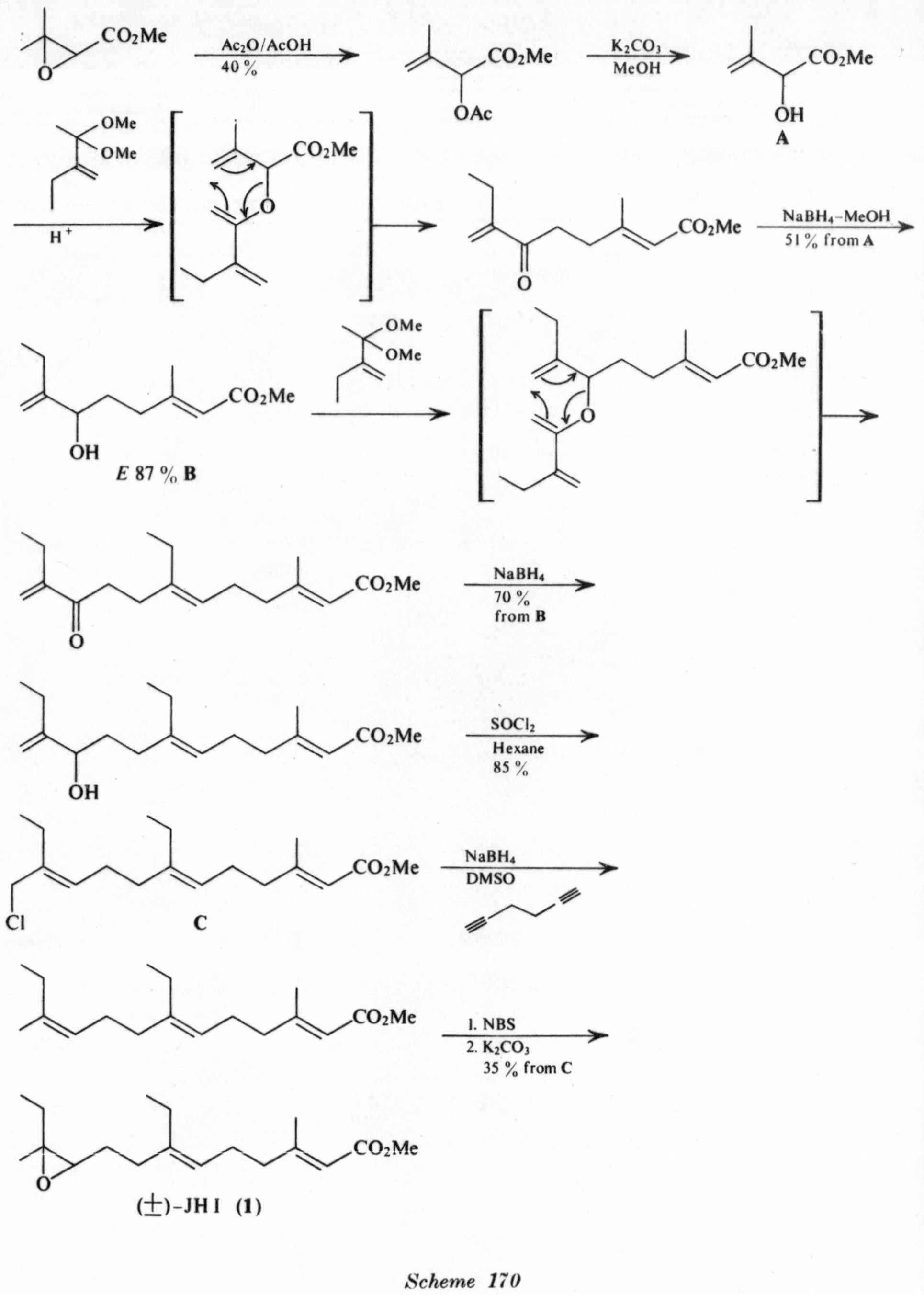

Scheme 170

E. The Second Zoecon Synthesis*
— Chloroketal Claisen rearrangement —

A modification of 3-D was reported by the Zoecon-Stanford group employing a chloroketal instead of the olefinic ketal in Johnson's synthesis (Scheme 171) [45, 46]. This modified route does not involve the conventional trienoic ester precursor.

F. Corey's Second Synthesis
— Modified Wittig reaction —

Corey and Yamamoto developed a highly stereoselective and concise synthesis of ($\pm$)-JH I, JH II, JH III and the position isomer 5 of JH II. This depended crucially on the utilization of β-oxido phosphonium ylides [see Equations (51) and (52), p. 27] [47, 48]. The Z-C_8-alcohol [see Equations (43) and (53) p. 24, 27] was used as the starting material for the synthesis of ($\pm$)-JH I and II [49] by the routes outlined in Scheme 172. The synthesis of ($\pm$)-JH III and 5 is shown in Scheme 173 [50].

G. van Tamelen's Synthesis
— Biellmann coupling —

Racemic JH I was synthesized by coupling the C_6- and C_{11}- synthons utilizing Biellmann's procedure for squalene synthesis [see Equation (56) p. 28]. The route is shown in Scheme 174 [51, 52]. The same coupling was used independently by Mori et al. [58] and by Grieco [60] to synthesize ($\pm$)-JH II.

H. Mori's First Synthesis*
— Julia cleavage —

This synthesis is based on the stereoselective ring cleavage of alkyl ethynyl cyclopropyl, carbinol [see Equation (46) p. 25] and is a modification of the non-stereoselective synthesis by Mori et al. (2-L). The route is shown in Scheme 175 [53, 54].

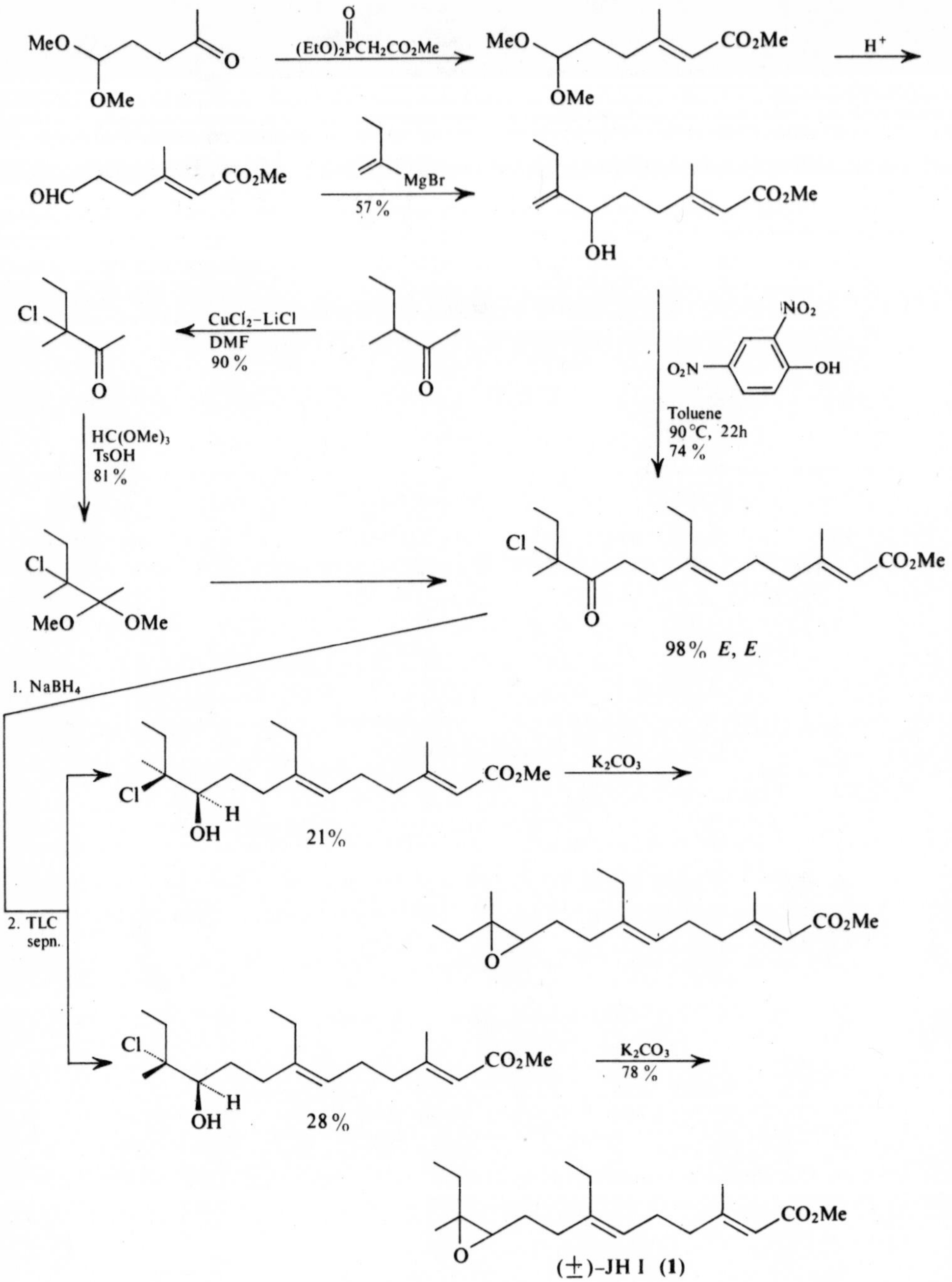

98% E, E

(±)-JH I (1)

Scheme 171

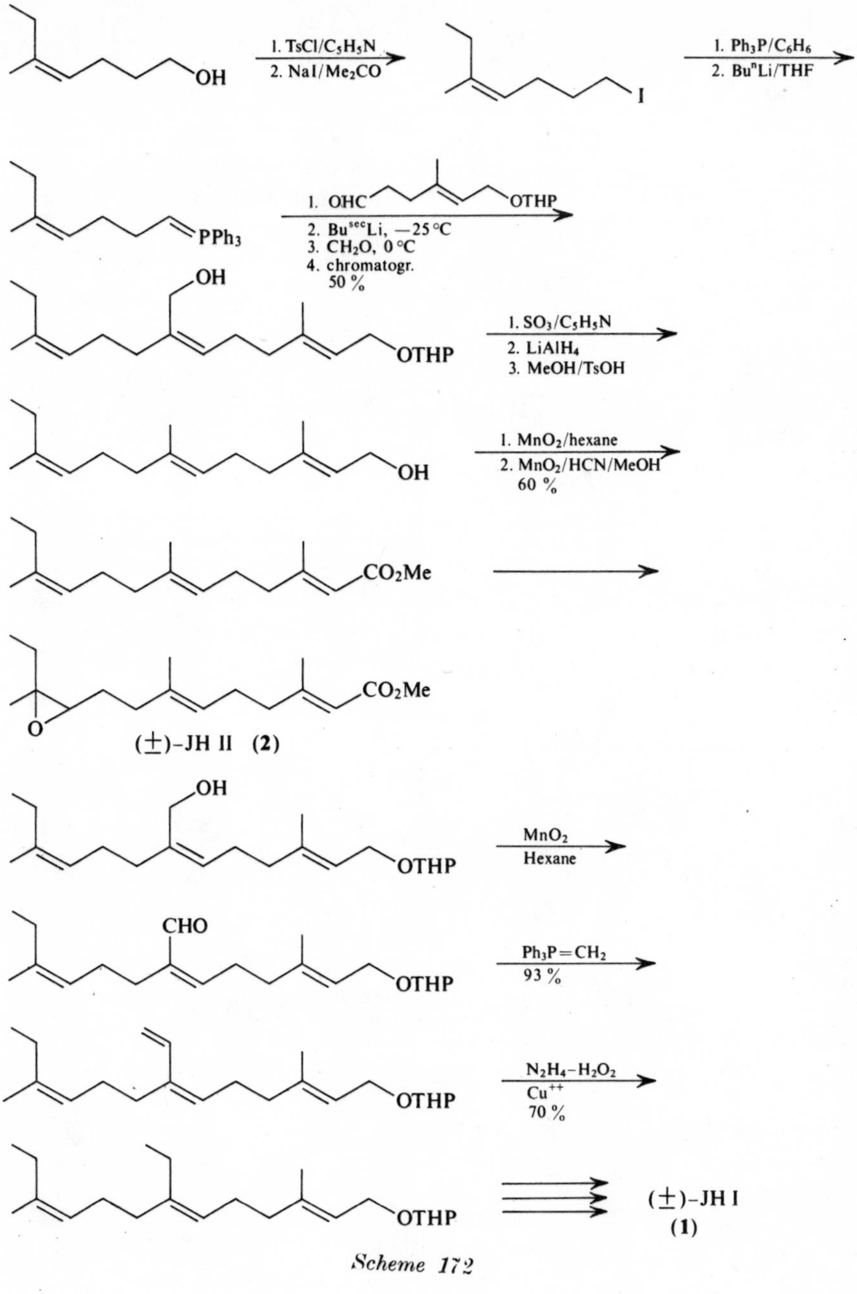

1. TsCl/C$_5$H$_5$N
2. NaI/Me$_2$CO

1. Ph$_3$P/C$_6$H$_6$
2. Bu^{n}Li/THF

PPh$_3$

1. OHC⁀⁀OTHP
2. Bu^{sec}Li, −25 °C
3. CH$_2$O, 0 °C
4. chromatogr.
50 %

OH

OTHP

1. SO$_3$/C$_5$H$_5$N
2. LiAlH$_4$
3. MeOH/TsOH

OH

1. MnO$_2$/hexane
2. MnO$_2$/HCN/MeOH
60 %

CO$_2$Me

CO$_2$Me

O

(±)-JH II (2)

OH

OTHP

MnO$_2$
Hexane

CHO

OTHP

Ph$_3$P=CH$_2$
93 %

OTHP

N$_2$H$_4$–H$_2$O$_2$
Cu^{++}
70 %

OTHP

(±)-JH I
(1)

Scheme 172

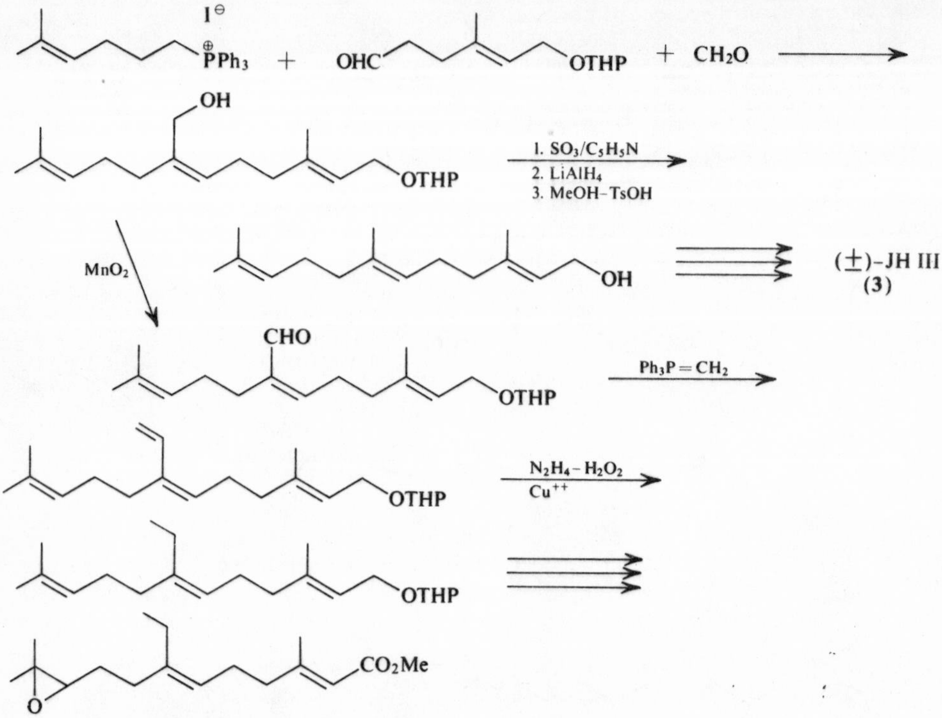

I⊖
⊕PPh3
OHC
OTHP
+ CH2O
OH
OTHP
1. SO3/C5H5N
2. LiAlH4
3. MeOH–TsOH
MnO2
OH
(±)-JH III
(3)
CHO
OTHP
Ph3P=CH2
OTHP
N2H4–H2O2
Cu++
OTHP
CO2Me
O

Position isomer (**5**) of (±)-JH II

Scheme 173

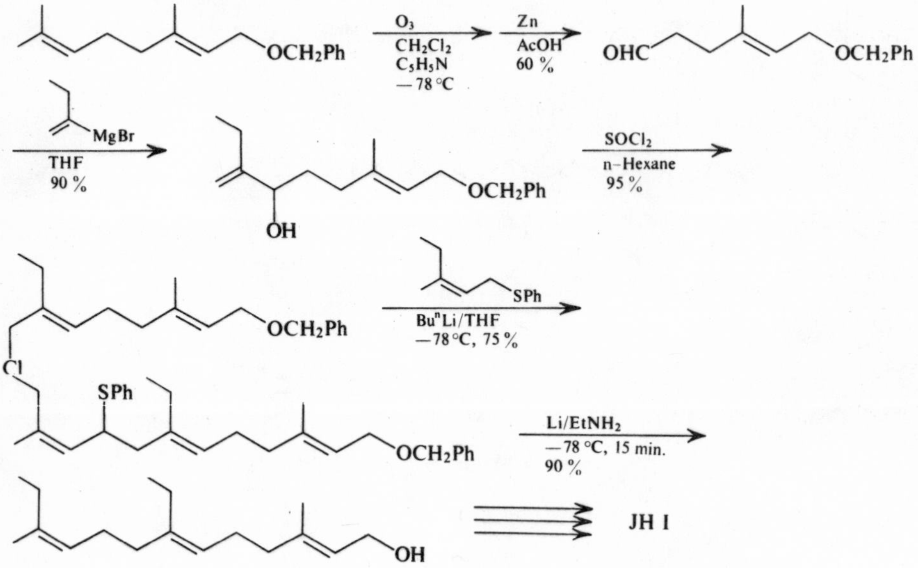

OCH2Ph
O3
CH2Cl2
C5H5N
−78 °C
Zn
AcOH
60 %
OHC
OCH2Ph
MgBr
THF
90 %
OCH2Ph
OH
SOCl2
n-Hexane
95 %
SPh
OCH2Ph
BunLi/THF
−78 °C, 75 %
Cl
SPh
OCH2Ph
Li/EtNH2
−78 °C, 15 min.
90 %
JH I
OH

Scheme 174

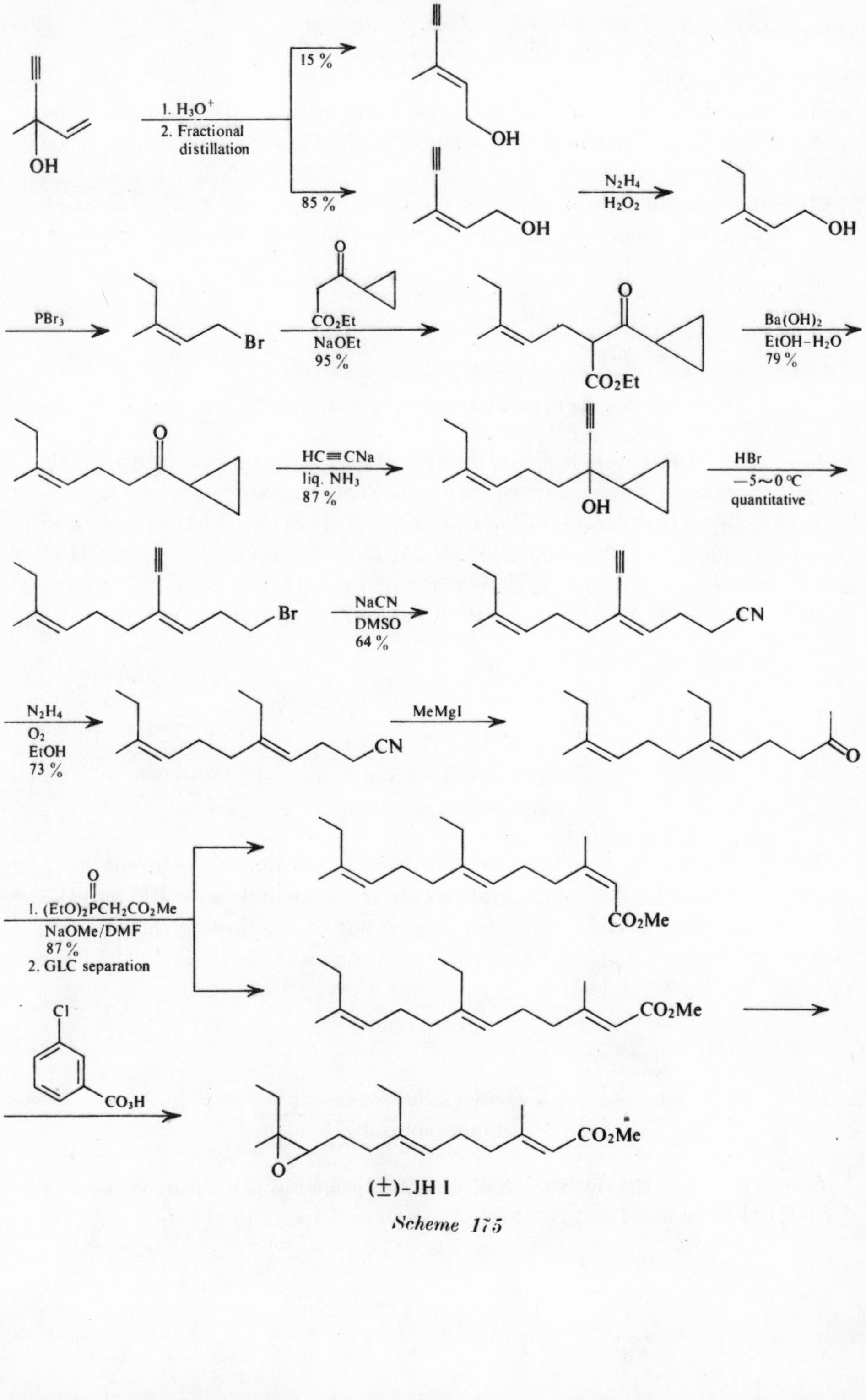

Scheme 175

I. The Third Zoecon Synthesis*
Ortho ester Claisen rearrangement

This is a conversion of methyl epoxygeranate into ($\pm$)-JH I avoiding the intermediacy of the conventional trienoic ester whose epoxidation can be troublesome when one works on a large scale. In this synthesis the oxide ring is generated *via* the chloroketone as shown in Scheme 176 [55]. The intermediate aldo ester has been prepared by two different routes.

J. The Fourth Zoecon Synthesis*
Wittig and organocopper chemistry

Since methyl farnesoate is readily available, its conversion into racemic juvenile hormones is highly attractive. The Zoecon group reported the conversion of ($\pm$)-JH III to ($\pm$)-JH II (Scheme 177) [56]. ($\pm$)-JH III was also transformed into the 10E-isomer of ($\pm$)-JH II (Scheme 178) [56]. ($\pm$)-JH II was then converted into a 1 : 1 mixture of ($\pm$)-JH I and its (6Z)-isomer (Scheme 179) [56]. A good preparative method of methyl farnesoate is also included in this paper.

K. Mori's Second Synthesis*
Biellmann coupling

This synthesis, like van Tamelen's, utilized the Biellmann coupling. ($\pm$)-JH II was synthesized from geranyl acetate as shown in Scheme 180 [57, 58]. A synthesis of ($\pm$)-JH III was also carried out by employing the coupling reaction (Scheme 181) [59]. ($\pm$)-JH III was converted to ($\pm$)-JH II by the conventional method [59].

L. Grieco's Synthesis
Biellmann coupling

Grieco reported the derivation of useful intermediates for the synthesis of ($\pm$)-JH II from nerol and geraniol as shown in Scheme 182 [60].

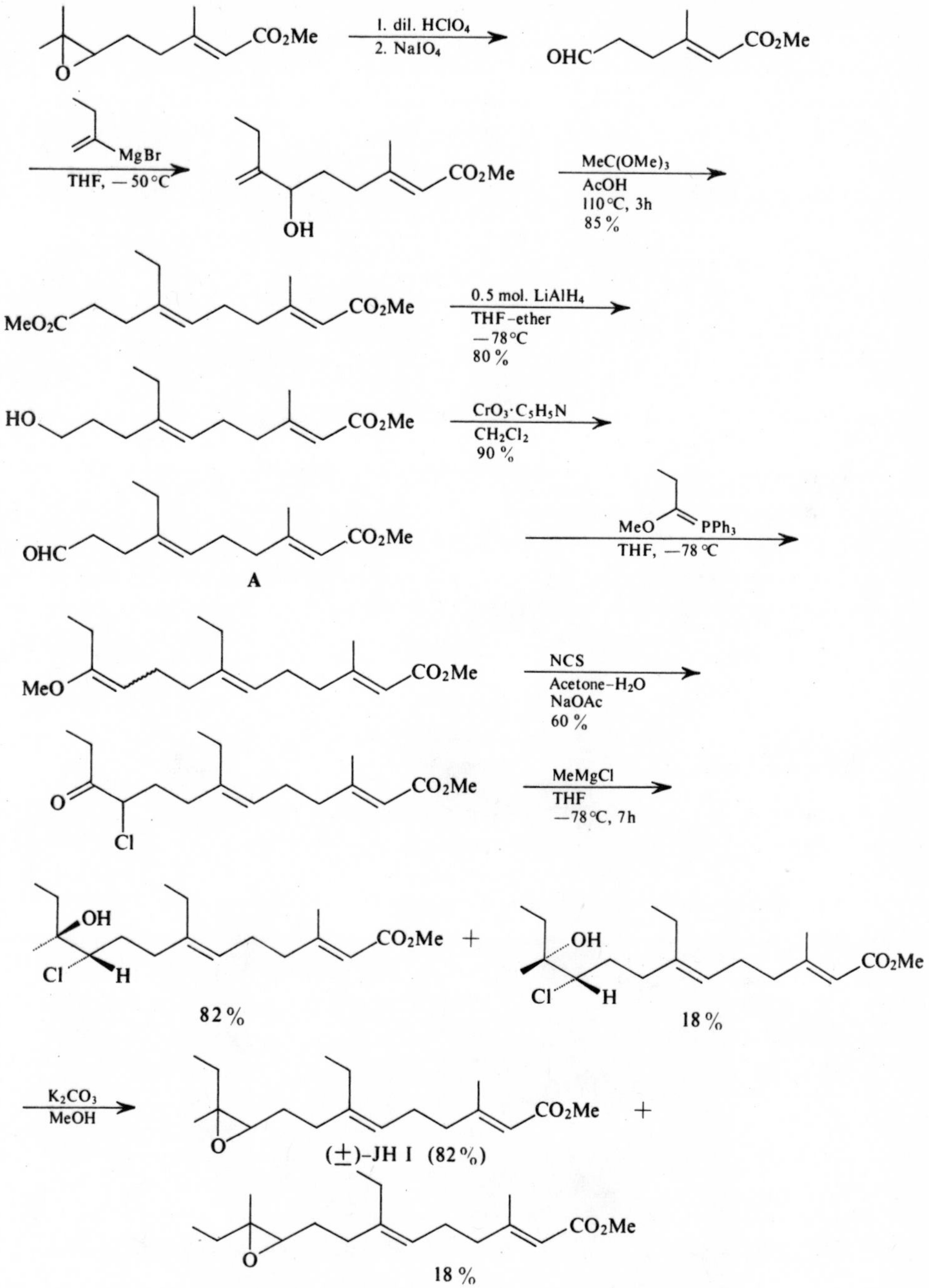

Reaction conditions and intermediates:

1. dil. $HClO_4$
2. $NaIO_4$

$MgBr$, THF, $-50\,°C$

$MeC(OMe)_3$, AcOH, $110\,°C$, 3h, 85%

0.5 mol. $LiAlH_4$, THF–ether, $-78\,°C$, 80%

$CrO_3 \cdot C_5H_5N$, CH_2Cl_2, 90%

A

MeO PPh_3, THF, $-78\,°C$

NCS, Acetone–H_2O, NaOAc, 60%

MeMgCl, THF, $-78\,°C$, 7h

82%   18%

K_2CO_3, MeOH

$(\pm)$-JH I (82%)

18%

Scheme 176 (cont'd)

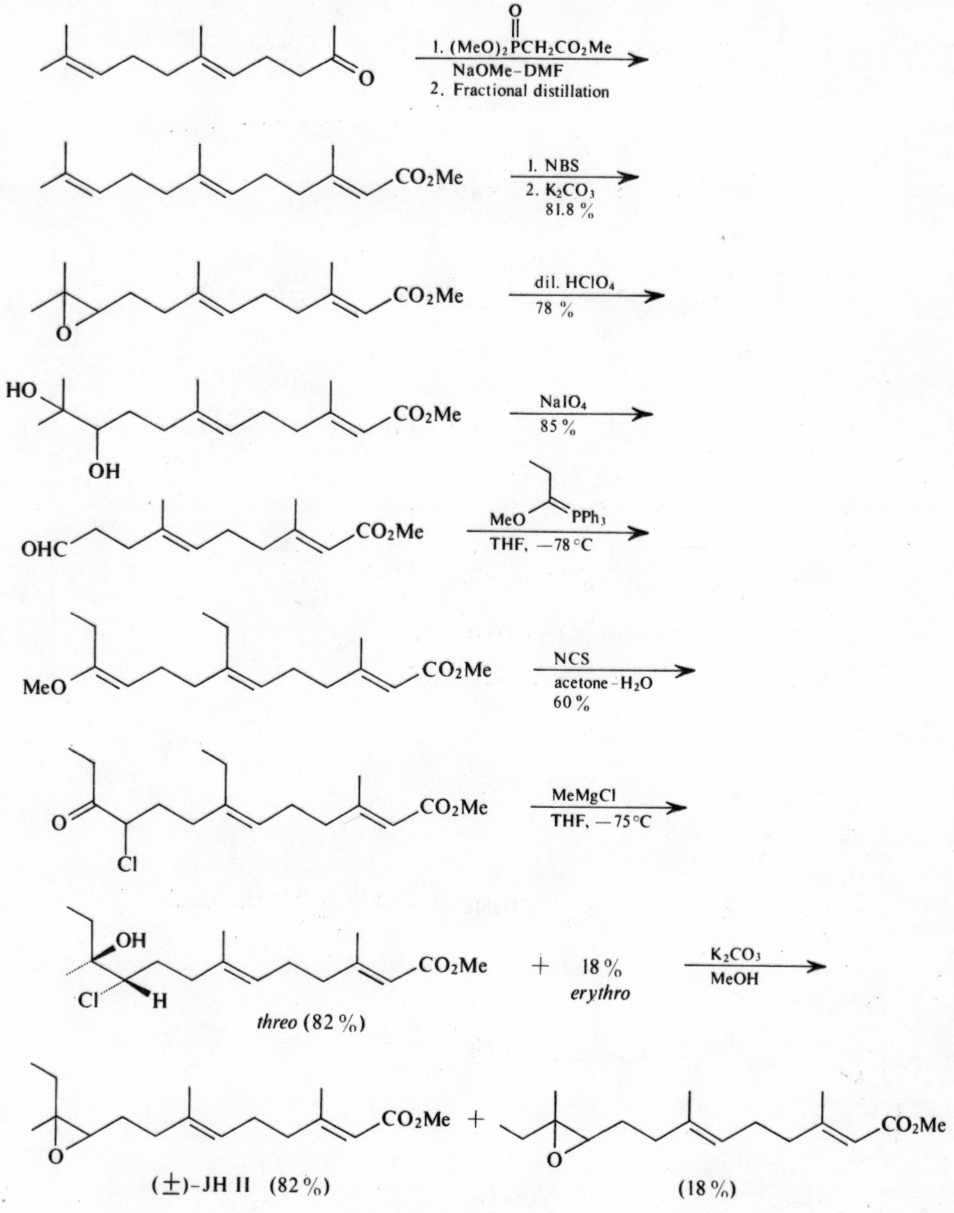

Scheme 177

11 R. D. C.

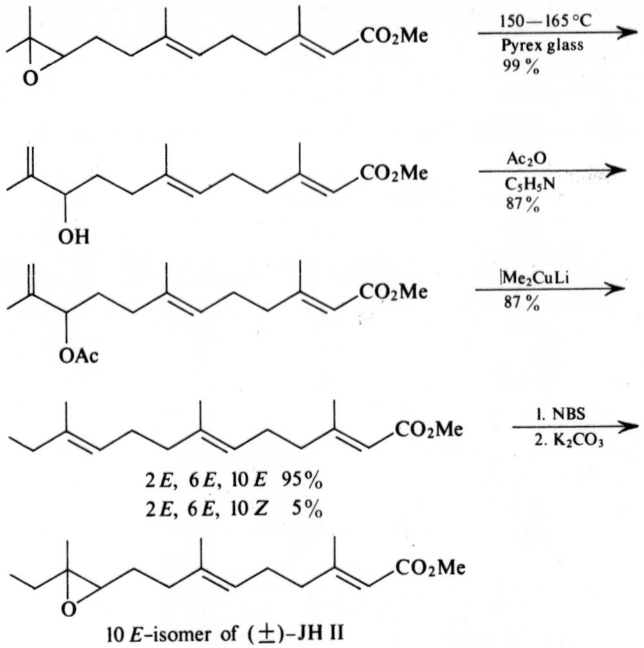

2 E, 6 E, 10 E 95%
2 E, 6 E, 10 Z   5%

10 E-isomer of (±)-JH II

Scheme 178

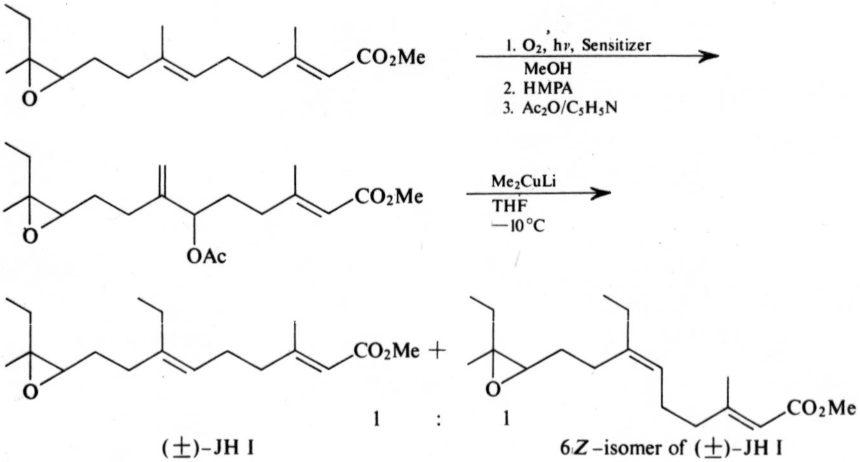

(±)-JH I   1   :   1   6 Z-isomer of (±)-JH I

Scheme 179

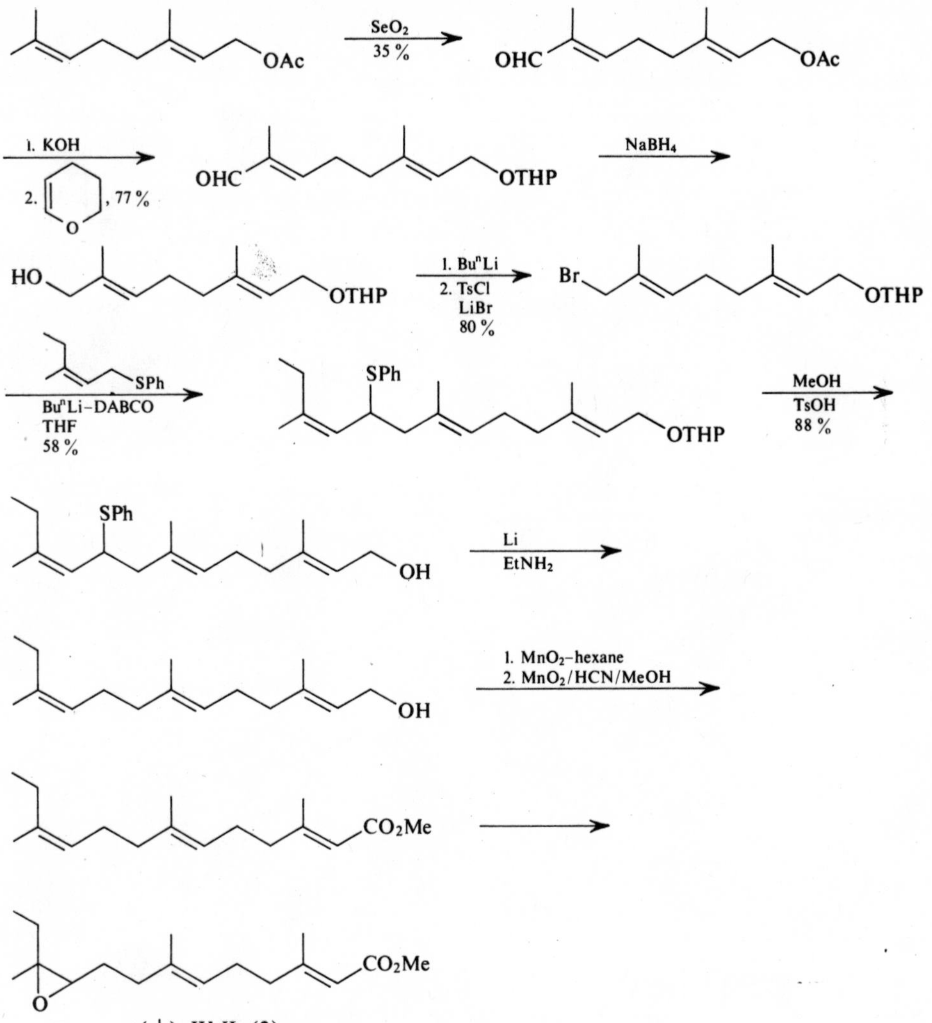

(±)-JH II (2)

Scheme 180

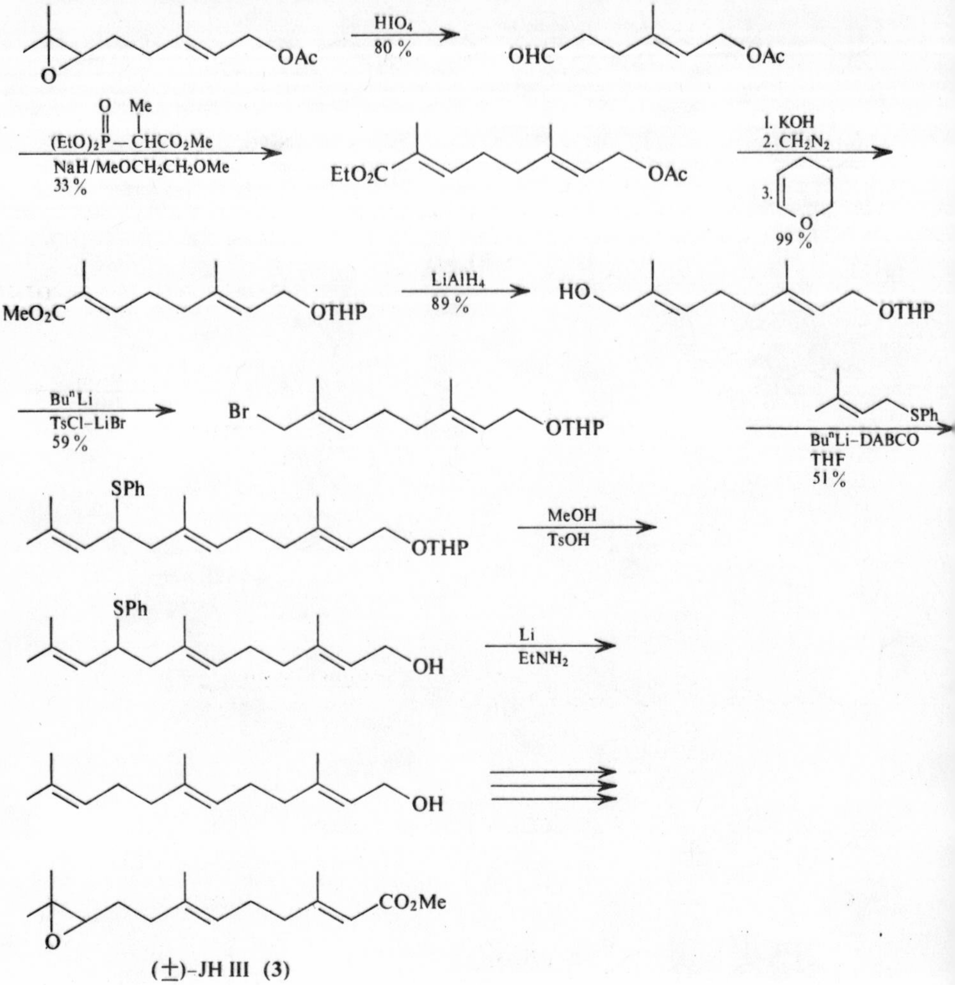

$(\pm)$-JH III (3)

Scheme 181

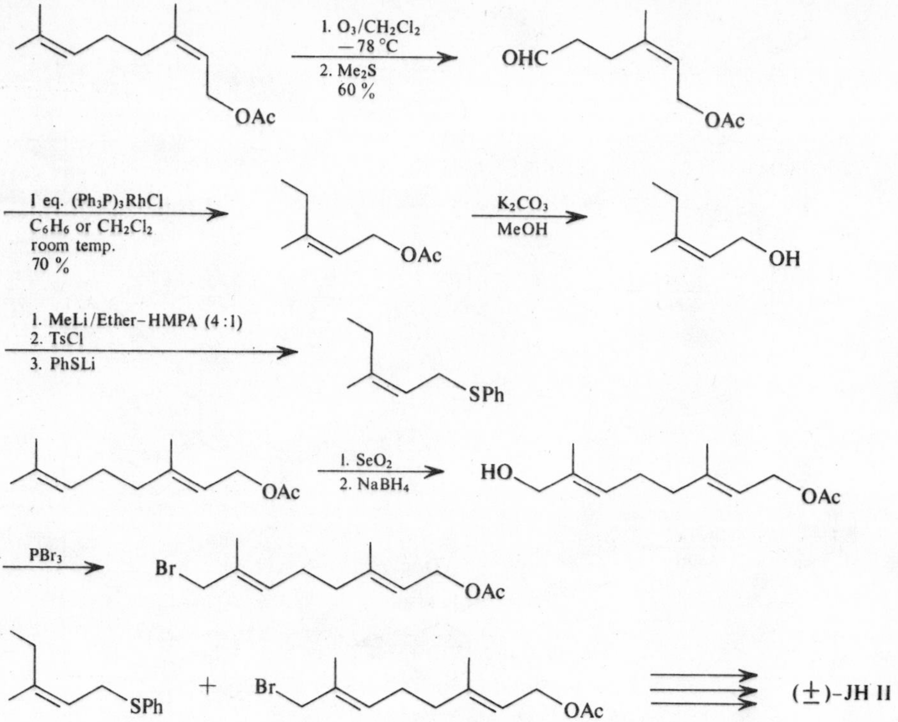

Scheme 182

M. Kondo's Synthesis
— Organosulfur chemistry —

Kondo *et al.* reported an interesting synthesis of (±)-JH I based on the condensation of dihydrothiopyrans. The sulfur atoms could easily be removed by reductive desulfurization. This synthesis yielded (±)-JH I (Scheme 183) and the key C_{15}-ketone (Scheme 184) [61]. Two quite similar syntheses followed shortly afterwards [62, 63].

N. The Roussel-Ucla; Synthesis by Toromanoff et al.
— Organosulfur chemistry —

This route is shown in Scheme 185 [62]. The bis-sulfoxide was used which was easier to alkylate than Kondo's bis-thiopyran.

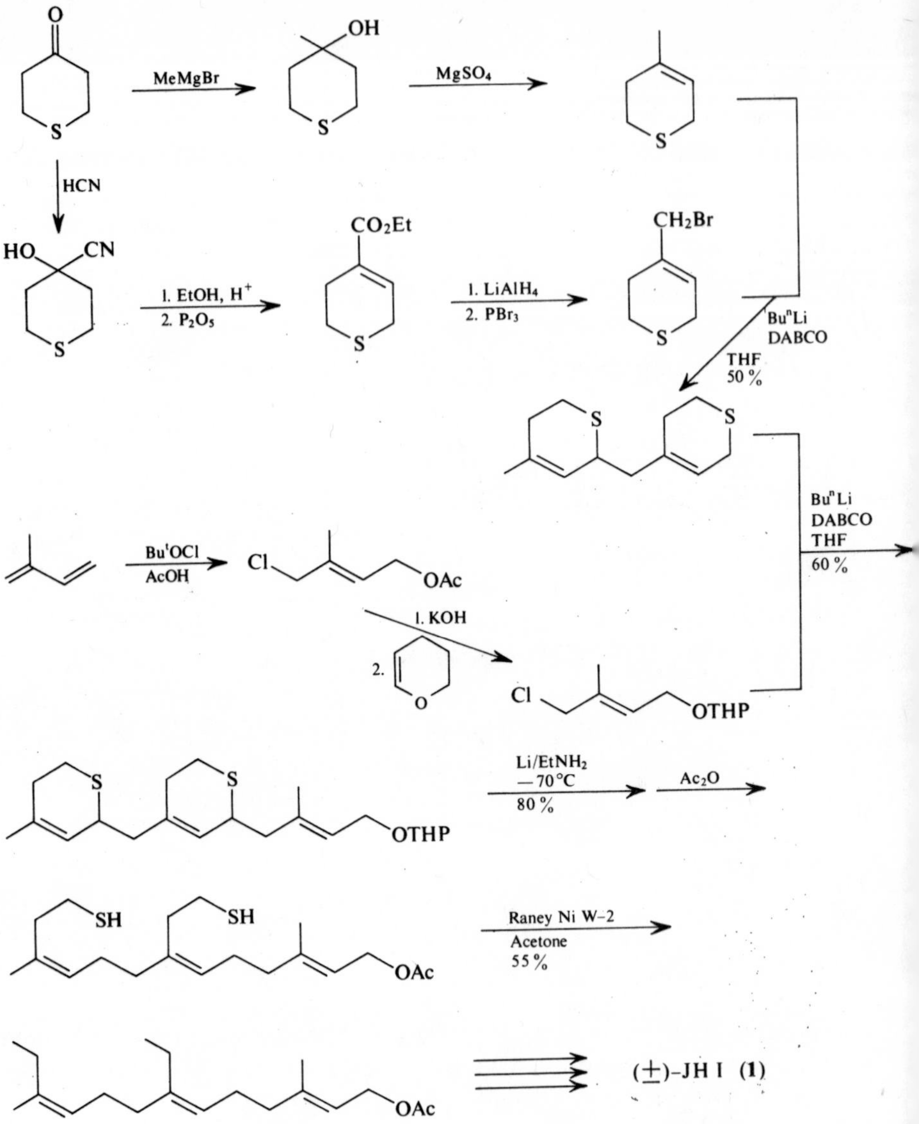

Scheme 183

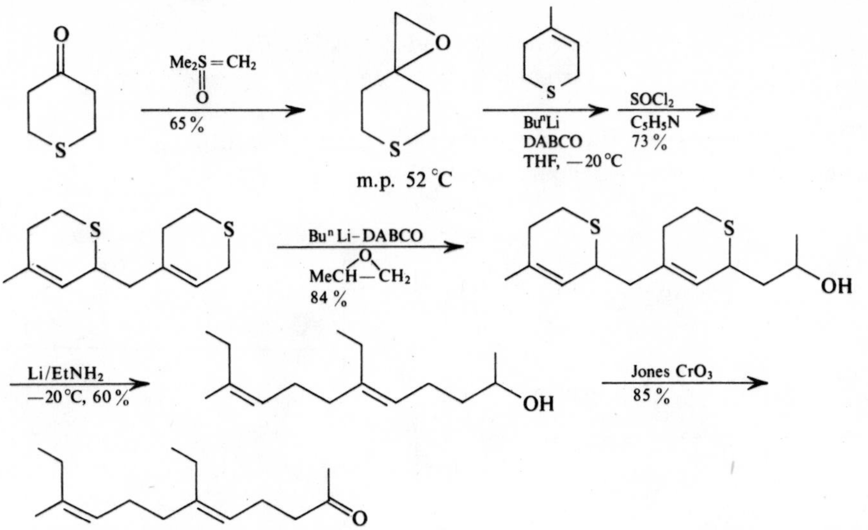

Scheme 184

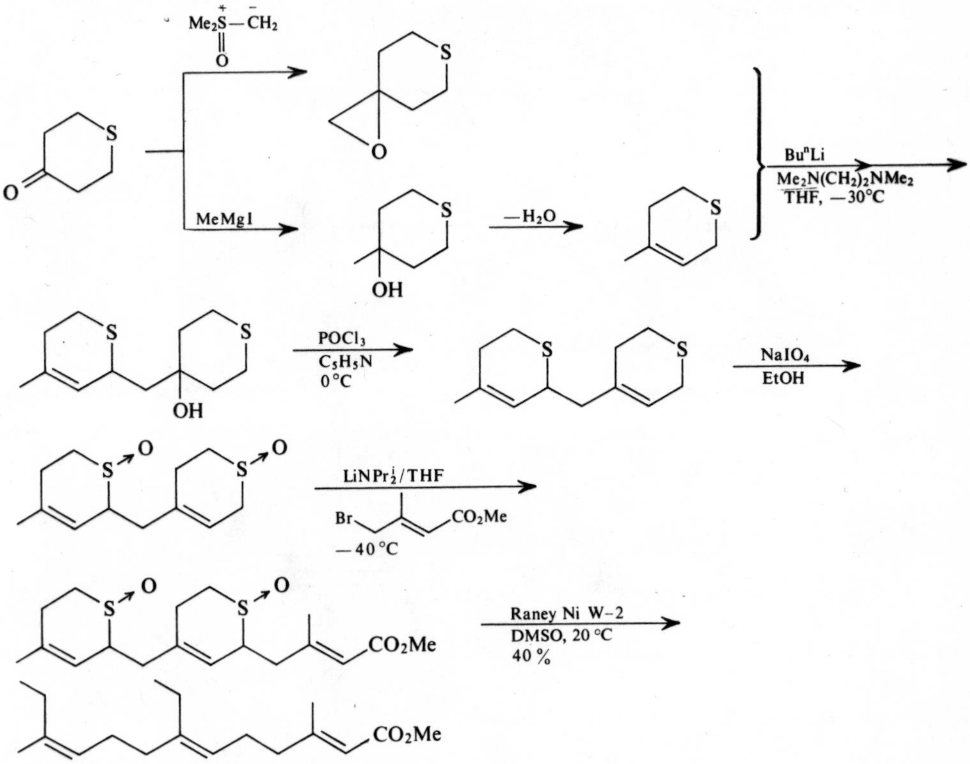

Scheme 185

O. Synthesis by Stotter and Hornish
— Organosulfur chemistry —

This synthesis from the University of Texas at Austin is quite similar to Kondo's and shown in Scheme 186 [63].

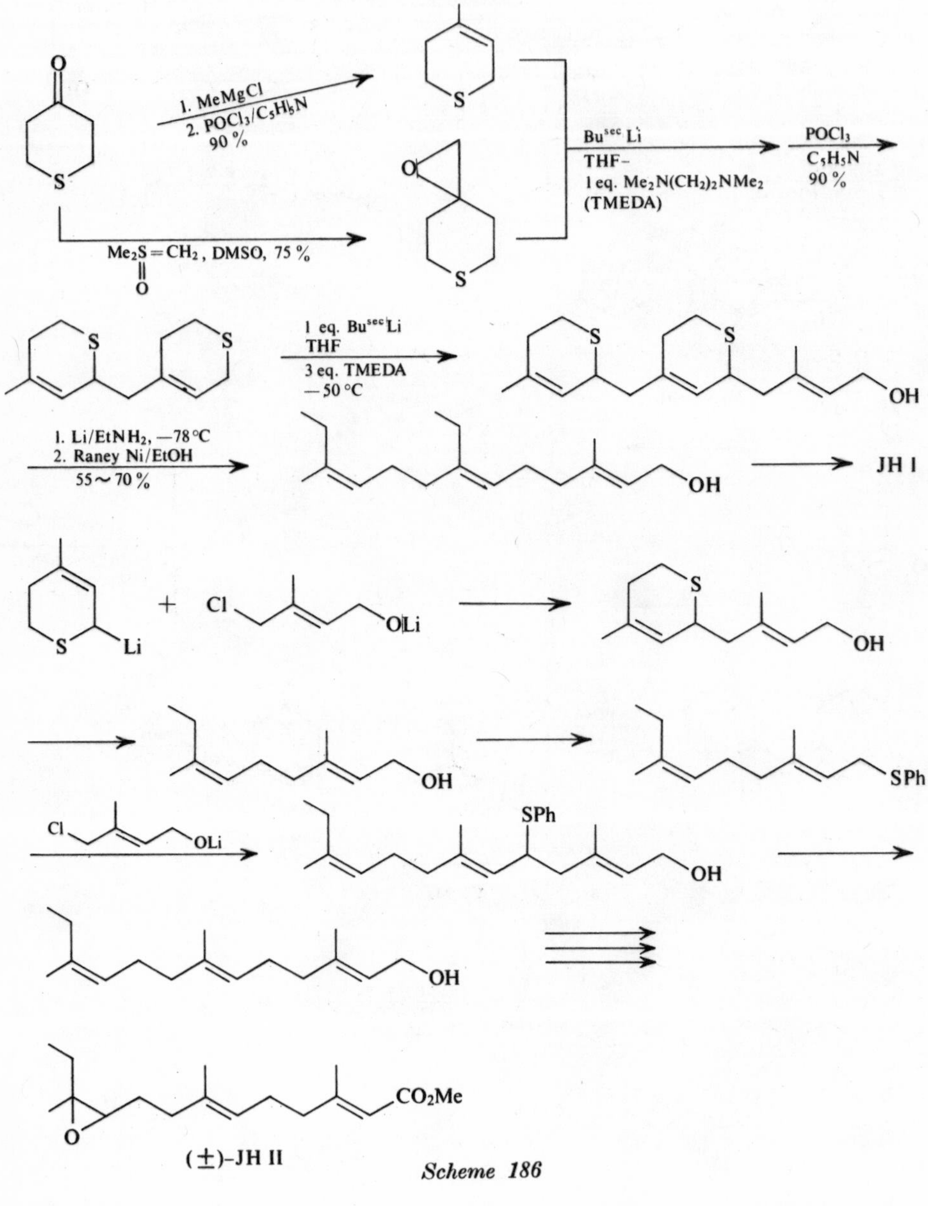

Scheme 186

P. Mukaiyama's Synthesis
— Organosulfur chemistry and organocopper reagent —

Organocopper reagents substitute a β-thiophenyl group in α, β-unsaturated esters as shown in Equations (30) and (31). This was utilized by Mukaiyama et al. for the synthesis of juvenile hormones [64, 65]. Scheme 187 outlines the synthesis leading to ($\pm$)-JH I [64].

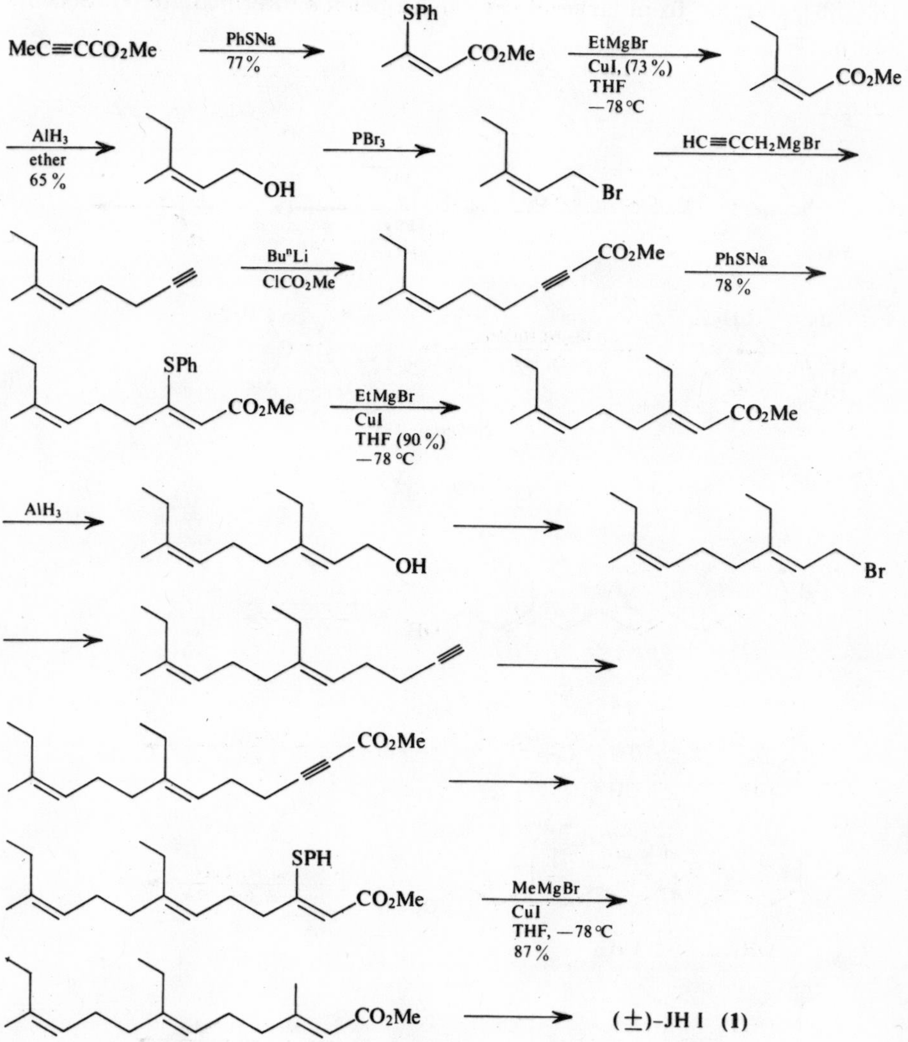

$MeC\equiv CCO_2Me$ $\xrightarrow[77\%]{PhSNa}$ [SPh / CO$_2$Me structure] $\xrightarrow[\substack{CuI, (73\%) \\ THF \\ -78°C}]{EtMgBr}$ [CO$_2$Me structure]

$\xrightarrow[\substack{ether \\ 65\%}]{AlH_3}$ [OH structure] $\xrightarrow{PBr_3}$ [Br structure] $\xrightarrow{HC\equiv CCH_2MgBr}$

[alkyne structure] $\xrightarrow[ClCO_2Me]{Bu^nLi}$ [CO$_2$Me structure] $\xrightarrow[78\%]{PhSNa}$

[SPh / CO$_2$Me structure] $\xrightarrow[\substack{CuI \\ THF (90\%) \\ -78°C}]{EtMgBr}$ [CO$_2$Me structure]

$\xrightarrow{AlH_3}$ [OH structure] $\longrightarrow$ [Br structure]

$\longrightarrow$ [alkyne structure] $\longrightarrow$

[CO$_2$Me structure] $\longrightarrow$

[SPH / CO$_2$Me structure] $\xrightarrow[\substack{CuI \\ THF, -78°C \\ 87\%}]{MeMgBr}$

[CO$_2$Me structure] $\longrightarrow$ ($\pm$)-JH I (1)

Scheme 187

Q. The Yamamoto-Sharpless Synthesis
— Organocopper chemistry —

Yamamoto, Sharpless *et al.* developed an interesting olefin synthesis starting from an allylic alcohol as shown in Scheme 188 [66]. The vanadium-catalyzed epoxidation yielded only *erythro*-epoxy alcohol and thence a *Z*-olefin. This reaction was used in a synthesis of ($\pm$)-JH I as shown in Scheme 189 [66], starting from farnesol *via* van Tamelen's intermediate (*cf.* Scheme 159 p. 140).

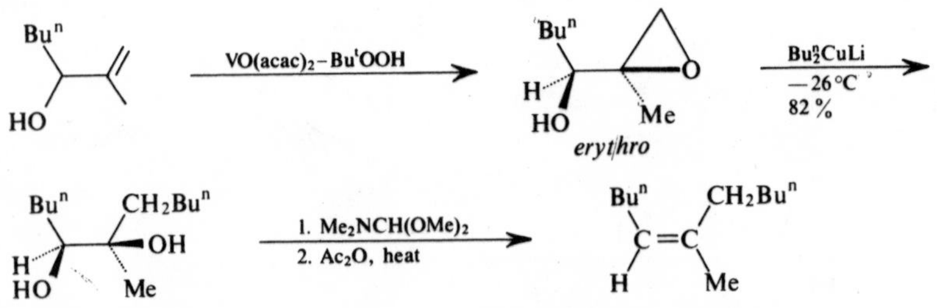

Scheme 188

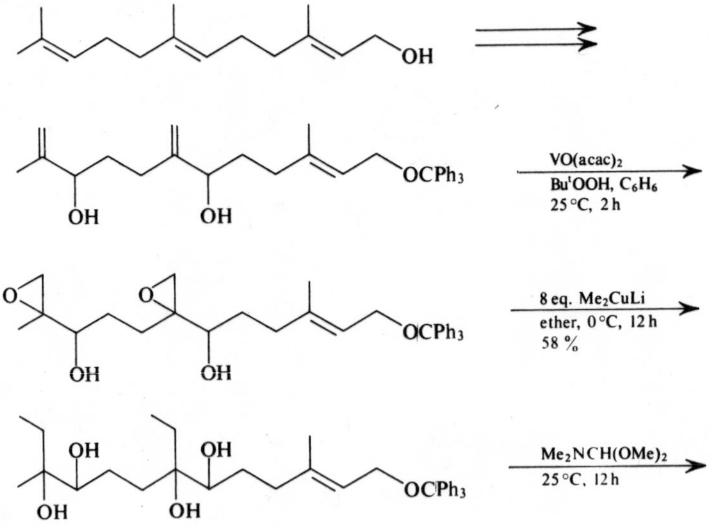

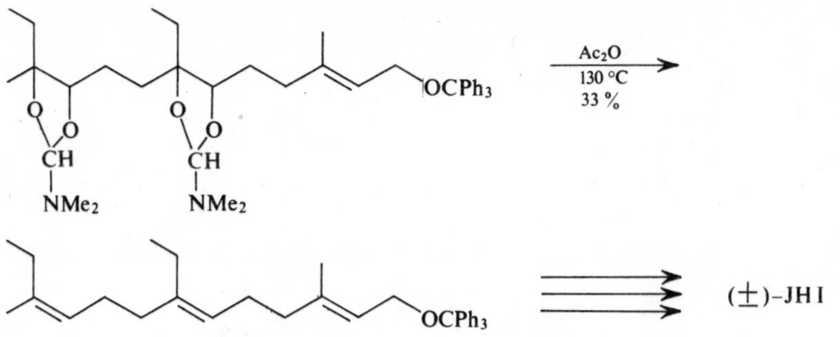

Scheme 189 (cont'd)

4. SYNTHESES OF OPTICALLY ACTIVE JUVENILE HORMONES

As the biological activities of the synthetic juvenile hormones were found to be almost equal to those of the natural hormones, the question arose whether the latter were racemic or optically active. In 1970 isolation of the natural hormones was achieved by Meyer et al. from Hyalophora cecropia on a scale that permitted measurement of the optical rotation of the pure juvenile hormone preparation [67]. Since the difference between JH I and II involves a carbon atom which is relatively distant from the chiral centre C-10, it seemed unnecessary to separate the preparation into its two components. The measurement was performed with 1.3720 mg of a pure preparation that consisted of 90.2 mole % of JH I and 9.8 mol % of JH II and a plain positive ORD curve was observed. The rotation at 589 nm was estimated by extrapolation and found to be $[\alpha]_D^{\cong} + 7°$. Since there is no reason to presume different configurations for the two juvenile hormones, the determined values are considered representative for the ORD of both JH I and II. Theoretical considerations were attempted to tentatively assign (10R : 11S)-stereochemistry to JH I and II [67]. Later Meyer applied Horeau's method to the threo-α-glycol derived from the juvenile hormones and concluded that the juvenile hormone possesses (10R : 11S)-stereochemistry [68] (Scheme 190).

The above observation prompted the efforts of chemists to synthesize optically active juvenile hormones. The first objective was of course to establish firmly the stereochemistry of the natural juvenile hormones. The second one was to learn something about the biological activity of the antipodes of the natural products.

The syntheses detailed below are based on (i) the resolution of starting materials; (ii) microbial resolution or chiral reactions, and (iii) utilization

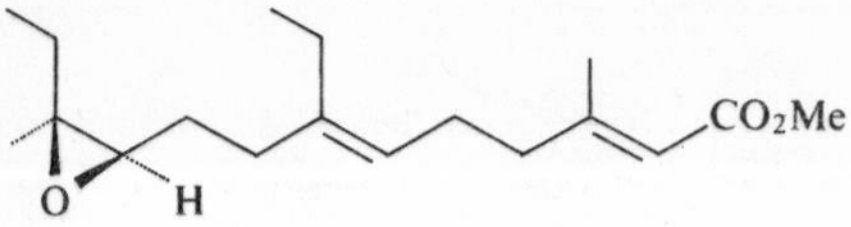

(10R : 11S)-(+)-JH I (1)

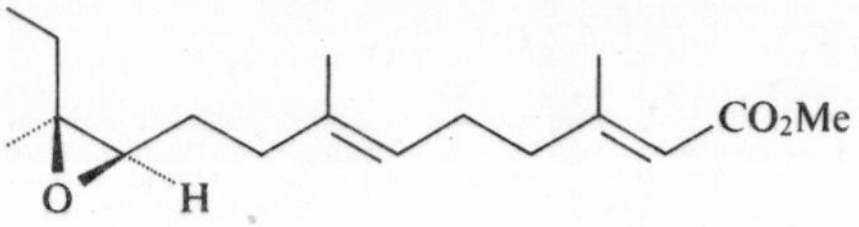

(10R : 11S)-(+)-JH II (2)

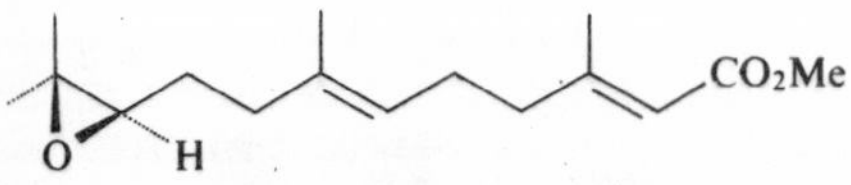

(10R)-(+)-JH III (3)

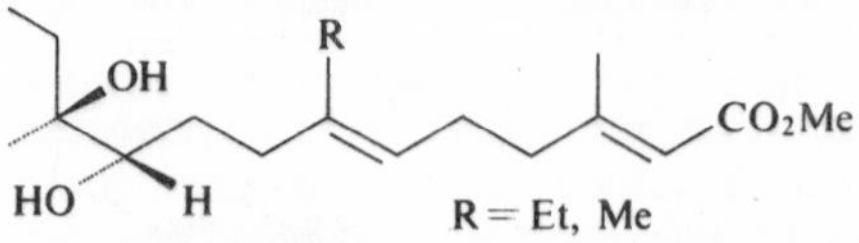

R = Et, Me

JH-*threo*-α-glycol

Scheme 190

of chiral starting materials. These are three representative methods of chiral syntheses.

These studies established the (10R : 11S)-stereochemistry of the juvenile hormones in 1971. It is still very difficult to synthesize optically pure juvenile hormones, and there exist some uncertainties concerning the biological activities of the antipodal juvenile hormones. The synthesis of 100% optically pure enantiomers of the juvenile hormones is still a challenge to synthetic chemists.

A. Synthesis by Loew and Johnson

This work was carried out according to the previous stereoselective synthesis, utilizing chloroketal Claisen rearrangement (3-E, Scheme 171, p. 154); however, optically active starting materials were employed. The synthesis is shown in Scheme 191 [69]. The first phase was the preparation of both enantiomers of α-chloro-α-methylbutyric acid (A) which was converted to the required chloroketals (B). Subsequent operations leading to (+)- and (−)-JH I were same as those outlined in Scheme 171. Since the absolute configuration of A was unknown, it was impossible to assign the absolute configuration of JH I by this synthesis alone. The stereochemical assignment was accomplished by Nakanishi et al. by applying their new CD method, using tris(dipivaloylmethanato) praseodymium. The synthetic (+)-JH I was shown to possess (10R : 11S)-configuration [70, 71]. In Scheme 191 the absolute configurations of the intermediates are depicted according to this conclusion. The bioassay of these synthetic JH enantiomers showed that (+)-JH I, $[\alpha]_D^{26}$ + 12.2°, was approximately nine times more active than the (−)-isomer on the wax moth, *Galleria mellonella*. On *Tenebrio molitor*, the (+)-isomer was 6–8 times more active than the enantiomer. However, the synthetic levorotatory and unnatural JH I was not optically pure, and might have contained up to 19% of the (+)-isomer, which could account for most, or even all, of the observed biological activity. Hence further work must be done before quantitative conclusions can be reached regarding the biological activity of (−)-JH.

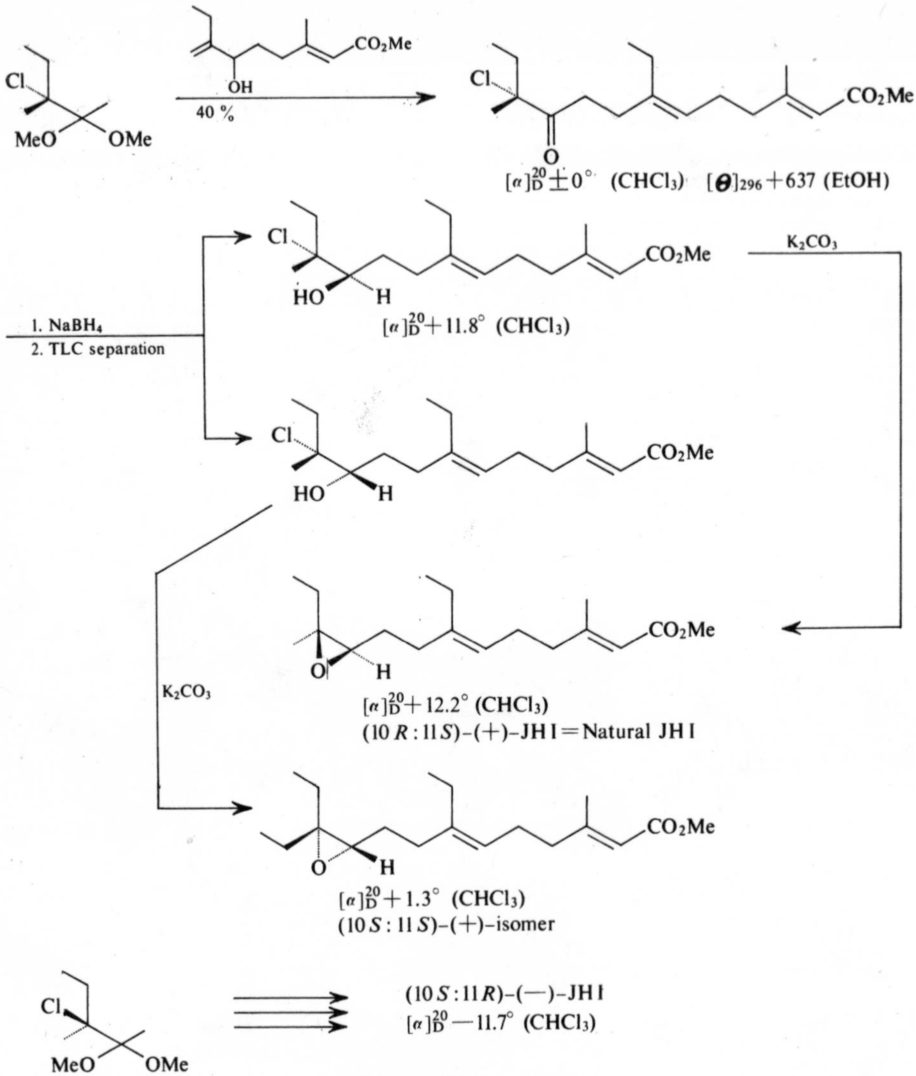

Cl
MeO
OMe
CO2Me
OH
40 %
Cl
CO2Me
O
[α]20D ±0° (CHCl3) [θ]296 +637 (EtOH)
Cl
HO
H
CO2Me
K2CO3
[α]20D +11.8° (CHCl3)
1. NaBH4
2. TLC separation
Cl
HO
H
CO2Me
O
H
CO2Me
K2CO3
[α]20D +12.2° (CHCl3)
(10R:11S)-(+)-JH I = Natural JH I
O
H
CO2Me
[α]20D +1.3° (CHCl3)
(10S:11S)-(+)-isomer
Cl
MeO
OMe
(10S:11R)-(−)-JH I
[α]20D −11.7° (CHCl3)

Scheme 191 (cont'd)

B. Synthesis by Faulkner and Petersen

Faulkner and Petersen accomplished the synthesis of both enantiomeric forms of JH I from starting materials of known absolute configuration thus establishing the stereochemistry of natural JH I. This synthesis, published simultaneously with that of Loew and Johnson, was thoughtfully designed

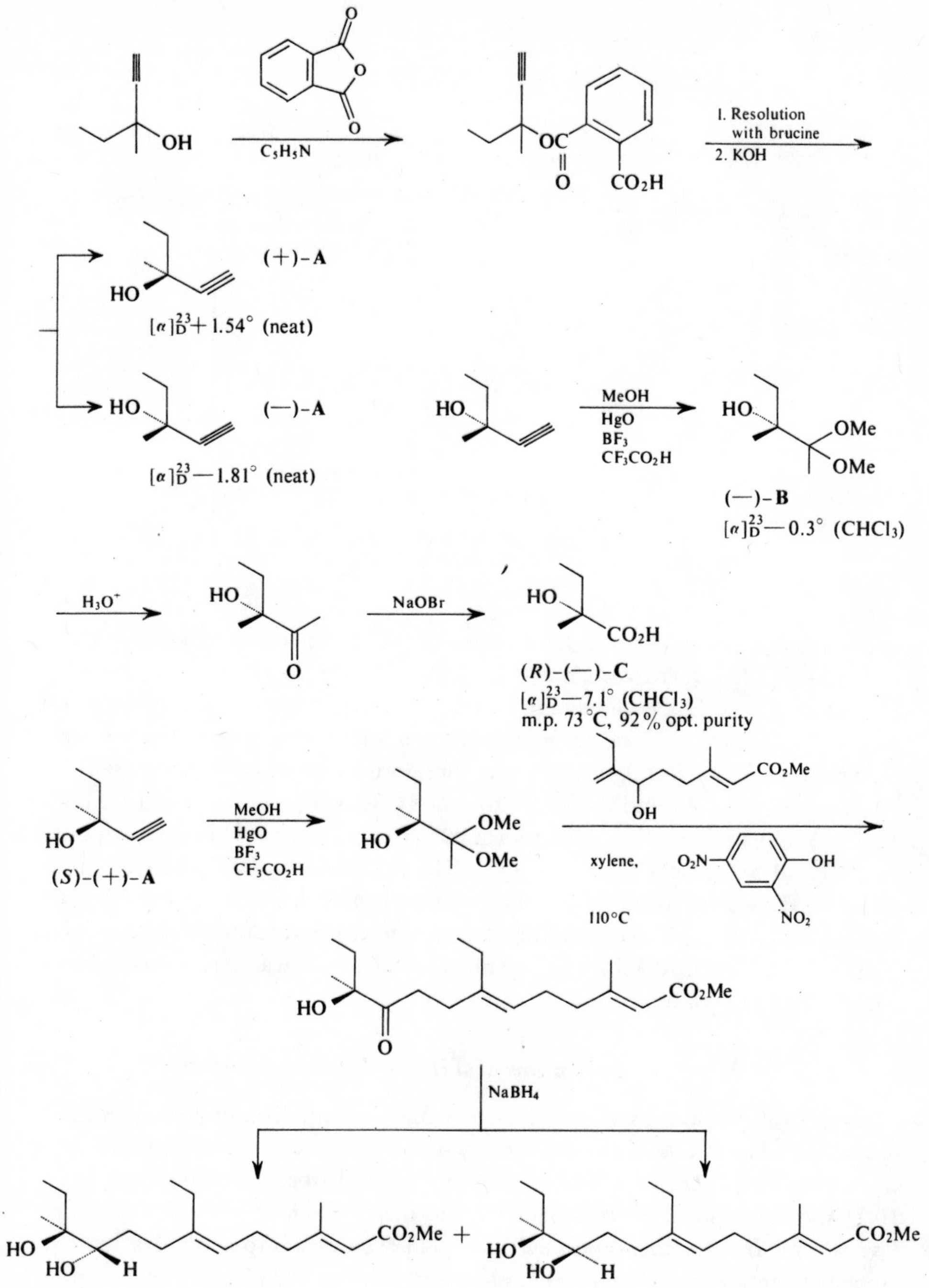

OH
C5H5N
OC
O
CO2H
1. Resolution with brucine
2. KOH
(+)-A
HO
[α]23D +1.54° (neat)
HO
(−)-A
[α]23D −1.81° (neat)
HO
MeOH
HgO
BF3
CF3CO2H
HO
OMe
OMe
(−)-B
[α]23D −0.3° (CHCl3)
H3O+
HO
O
NaOBr
HO
CO2H
(R)-(−)-C
[α]23D −7.1° (CHCl3)
m.p. 73 °C, 92% opt. purity
HO
(S)-(+)-A
MeOH
HgO
BF3
CF3CO2H
HO
OMe
OMe
CO2Me
OH
xylene, 110 °C
O2N
OH
NO2
HO
O
CO2Me
NaBH4
HO
HO
H
CO2Me +
HO
HO
H
CO2Me

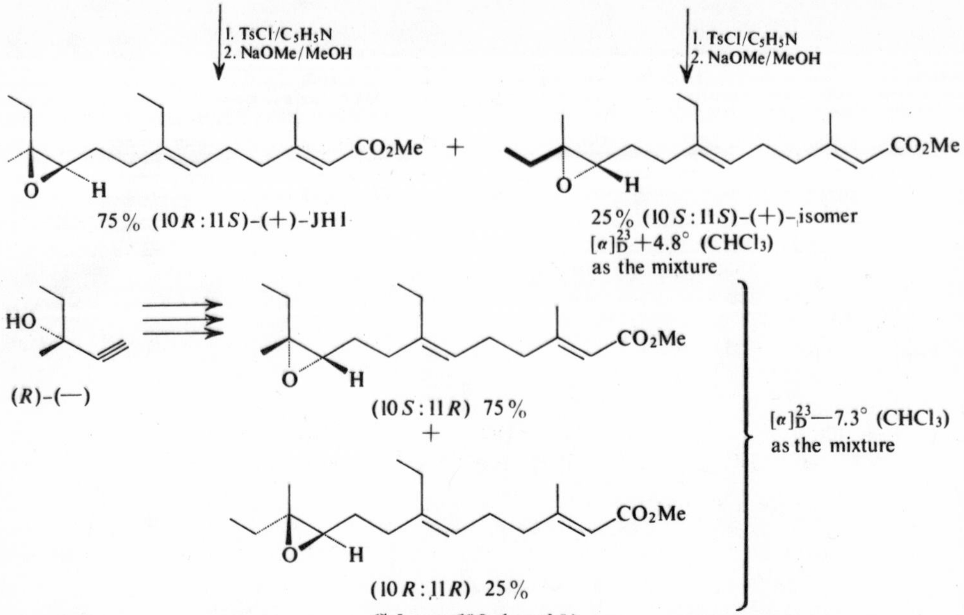

Scheme 192 (cont'd)

and employed hydroxyketal enantiomers (**B**) of known absolute configuration in the ketal Claisen rearrangement as shown in Scheme 192 [72, 73]. 3-Methyl-1-pentyn-3-ol (**A**) was resolved into two enantiomers. The (−)-enantiomer ((−)-**A**) was converted to the known (R)-(−)-α-hydroxy-α-methylbutyric acid (**C**). R-Configuration was therefore assigned to the (−)-acetylenic alcohol ((−)-**A**) and (−)-2,2-dimethoxy-3-methylpentan-3-ol ((−)-**B**). The (−)-hydroxyketal ((−)-**B**) was of 92% optical purity while its antipode, (+)-B, had an optical purity of 85%. The synthesis of JH I starting from (S)-(+)-**B** resulted in its (10R : 11S)-isomer which was contaminated with 25% of the (10S : 11S)-isomer. This sample was dextrorotatory : $[\alpha]_D^{23} + 4.8°$ (CHCl$_3$). Since natural JH I was also dextrorotatory, it was concluded to have the (10R : 11S)-configuration.

C. Microbial Derivation of JH III by Marumo et at.

Since 1971 Marumo et al. studied the fungal metabolism of (±)-epoxyfarnesol, (±)-JH III and related compounds to obtain chiral metabolites. Optically fairly pure (+)- and (−)-epoxyfarnesol were prepared from (−)-10,11-dihydroxyfarnesol obtained by the metabolism of (±)-10,11-epoxyfarnesol by *Helminthosporium sativum* [74]. The absolute configurations of these products were determined as shown in Scheme 193 [74, 75] by convert-

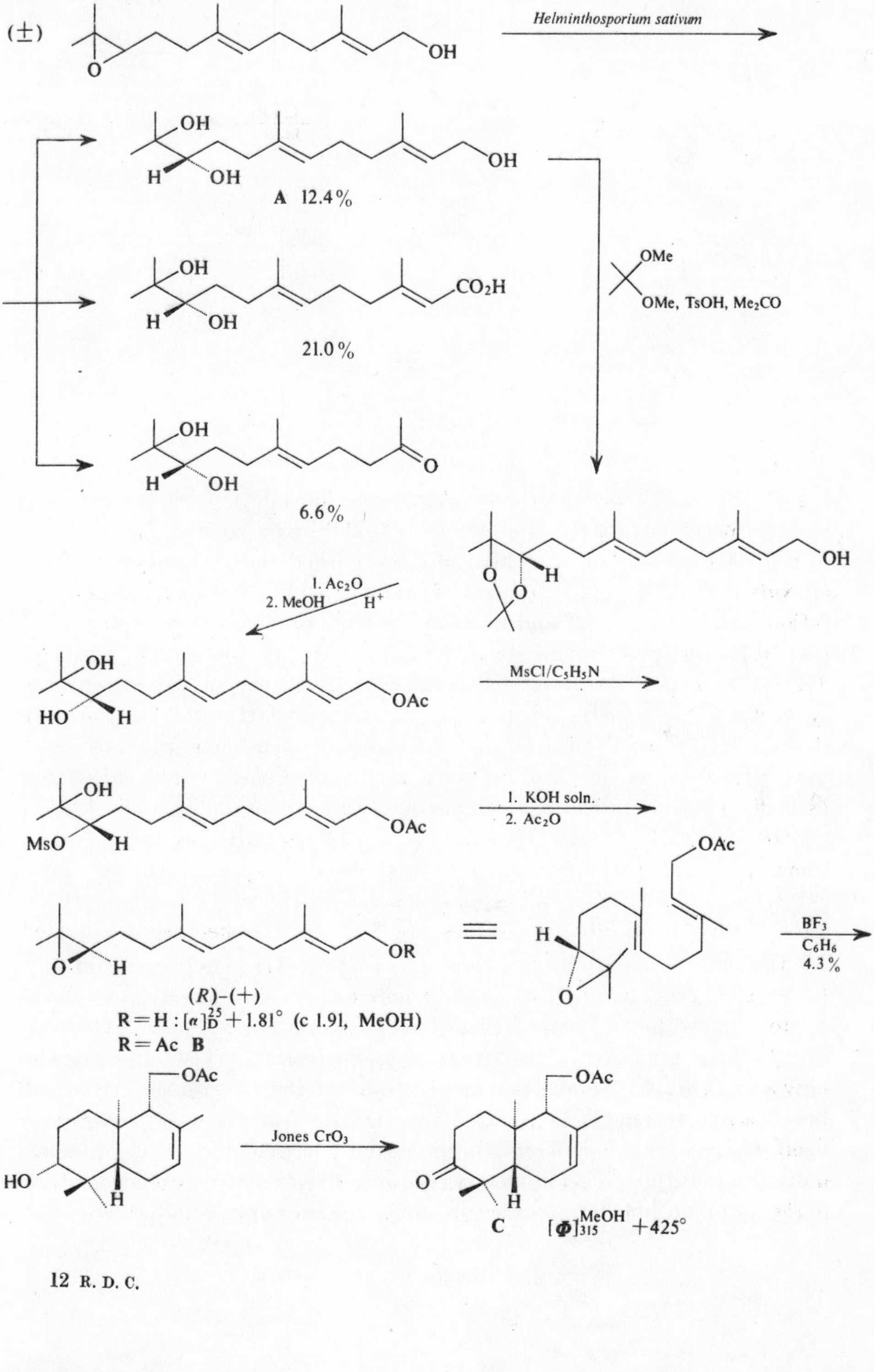
(±)
OH
Helminthosporium sativum
OH
H
OH
OH
A 12.4%
OH
CO2H
H
OH
21.0%
OMe
OMe, TsOH, Me2CO
OH
H
OH
O
6.6%
OH
O
H
O
1. Ac2O
2. MeOH H+
OH
OAc
HO
H
MsCl/C5H5N
OH
OAc
MsO
H
1. KOH soln.
2. Ac2O
OAc
OR
O
H
H
O
BF3
C6H6
4.3%
(R)-(+)
R=H : [α]25D +1.81° (c 1.91, MeOH)
R=Ac B
OAc
HO
H
Jones CrO3
OAc
O
H
C [Φ]MeOH315 +425°

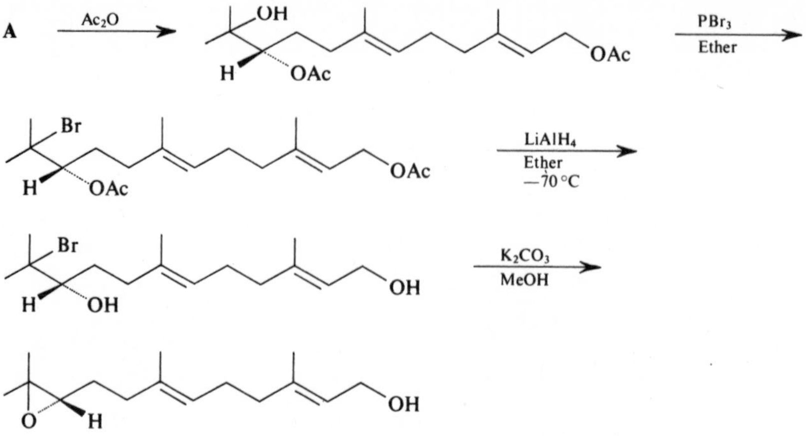

(S)-(—)

$[\alpha]_D^{25} - 1.83°$ (c 1.70, MeOH)

Scheme 193 (cont'd)

ing (—)-10,11-dihydroxyfarnesol (**A**) into a bicyclic ketone (**C**) *via* (+)-epoxyfarnesol acetate (**B**). The ketone (**C**) exhibited a positive Cotton effect in its ORD curve. This unequivocally established the β-orientation of the epoxide ring in (+)-epoxyfarnesol (**B**) as depicted in the formula (R-configuration). *(R)*-(+)-JH III and its antipode were prepared from methyl *(S)*-(—)-10,11-dihydroxyfarnesoate of fungal origin, but the optical purity of JH III thus obtained was unsatisfactory. In an earlier experiment the synthetic *(R)*-(+)-JH III had $[\alpha]_D$ + 3.7° (MeOH) and its antipode showed $[\alpha]_D$ − 3.2° (MeOH) [76]. In a recent experiment purer samples were prepared by metabolism with a fungus *Colletotrichum nicotianae* (Scheme 194) [77]. The optical purities were about 90%, $[\alpha]_D$ + 5.75° (MeOH) for *(R)*-(+)-JH III and $[\alpha]_D$ − 5.44° (MeOH) for the *(S)*-(—)-isomer [77]. This inability of fungi to produce 100% optically pure products led Marumo to attempt a chemical resolution *via* the 3β-acetoxyetienyl ester of ethyl 10,11-dihydroxyfarnesoate. The diastereomers were separated by TLC and yielded optically pure *(R)*-(+)-JH III ethyl ester and *(S)*-(—)-JH III ethyl ester. Their juvenile hormone activity was assayed on the allatectomized fourth instar larvae of the silkworm *Bombyx mori*. The natural (+)-form exhibited a strong activity, whereas its (—)-enantiomer had only a weak activity, about one-fiftieth (1/50) of the (+)-isomer. This small but distinct activity was thought to originate from the (—)-enantiomer itself. The remarkable difference in the activity between the two enantiomers indicated that there must be a strict relationship between the stereochemistry of the hormone and the chiral nature of the receptor of insects.

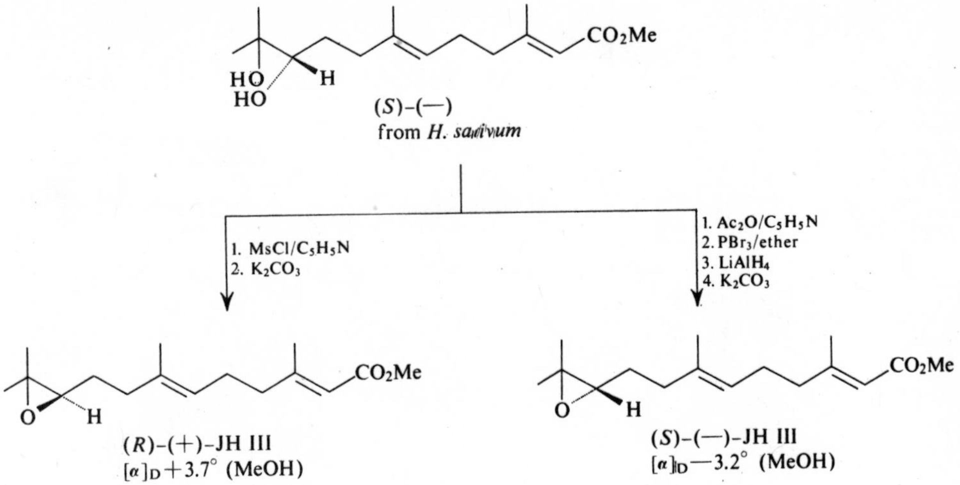
CO2Me
HO
HO
H
(S)-(−)
from H. sativum
1. MsCl/C5H5N
2. K2CO3
1. Ac2O/C5H5N
2. PBr3/ether
3. LiAlH4
4. K2CO3
CO2Me
O
H
(R)-(+)-JH III
[α]D+3.7° (MeOH)
CO2Me
O
H
(S)-(−)-JH III
[α]D−3.2° (MeOH)

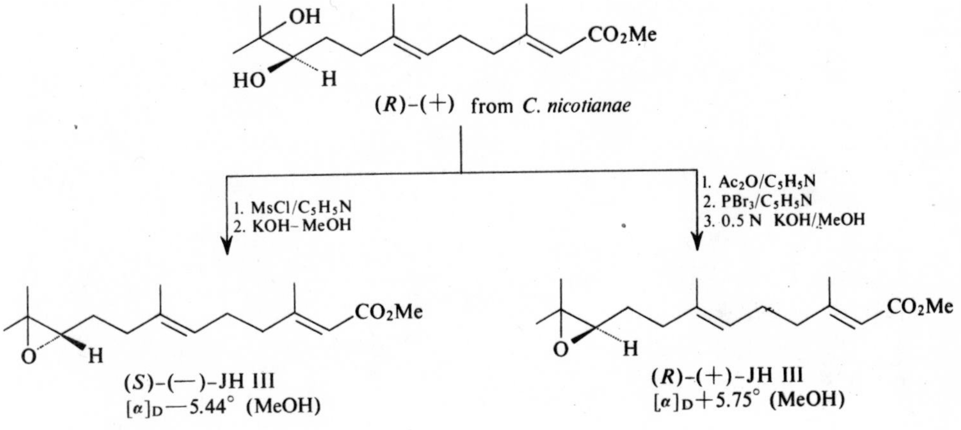
OH
CO2Me
HO
H
(R)-(+) from C. nicotianae
1. MsCl/C5H5N
2. KOH–MeOH
1. Ac2O/C5H5N
2. PBr3/C5H5N
3. 0.5 N KOH/MeOH
CO2Me
O
H
(S)-(−)-JH III
[α]D−5.44° (MeOH)
CO2Me
O
H
(R)-(+)-JH III
[α]D+5.75° (MeOH)

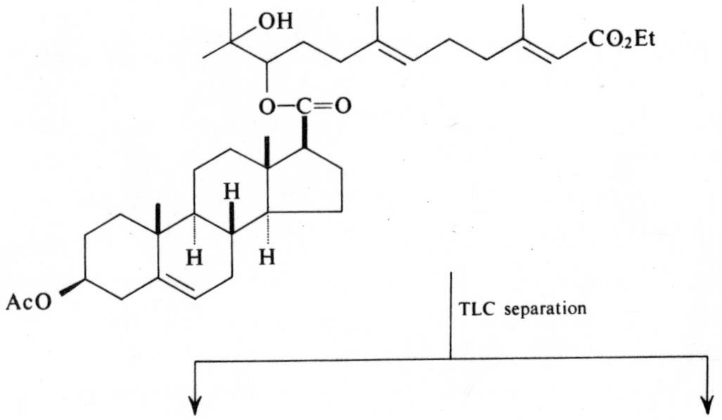
OH
CO2Et
O−C=O
H
H
H
AcO
TLC separation

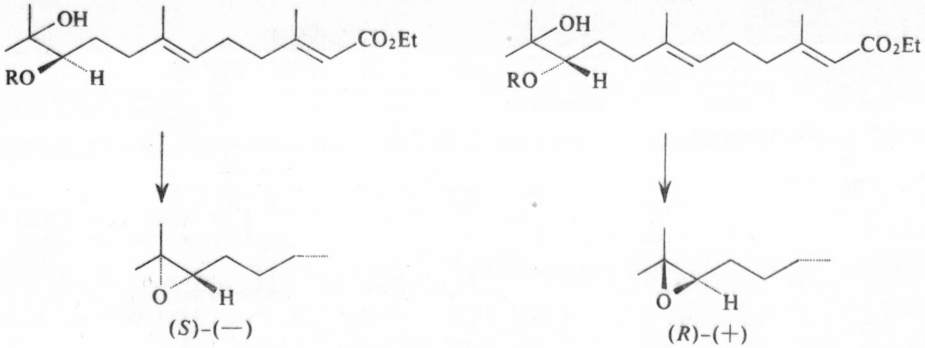

$(S)-(-)$ $(R)-(+)$

Scheme 194 (cont'd)

D. Microbial Derivation of JH II by Marumo et al.

Starting from $(\pm)$-JH II prepared by Mori *et al.* (2-N), Imai and Marumo obtained $(+)$-JH II and its antipode. $(\pm)$-JH II was reduced with lithium aluminium hydride to $(\pm)$-10,11-epoxyhomofarnesol. This was shaken with the precultured mycelia of *Helminthosporium sativum* to give seven metabolites as shown in Scheme 195 [78]. The acids were purified as methyl esters. One of them was identified as $(10S : 11R)-(-)$-JH II, $[\alpha]_D - 12.8°$, and the (10S)-dihydroxy ester was converted to $(10R : 11S)-(+)$-JH II, $[\alpha]_D + 11.7°$. These values, when compared with that of Johnson's $(+)$-JH I $(+12.2°)$, indicated the high optical purities of these metabolites, although no direct proof of this was provided.

E. Synthesis of (R)-(+)-10,11-Epoxyfarnesol by Yamada et al.

$(S)-(+)$-Glutamic acid was converted to $(R)-(+)$-10,11-epoxyfarnesol as shown in Scheme 196 [79, 80]. The synthesis was somewhat lengthy but afforded the final product with an $[\alpha]_D$ value as high as $+ 6.7°$ $(cf. + 1.81°$ for the fungal metabolite [74]). An obvious extension of this work to the synthesis of JH III has not yet been reported.

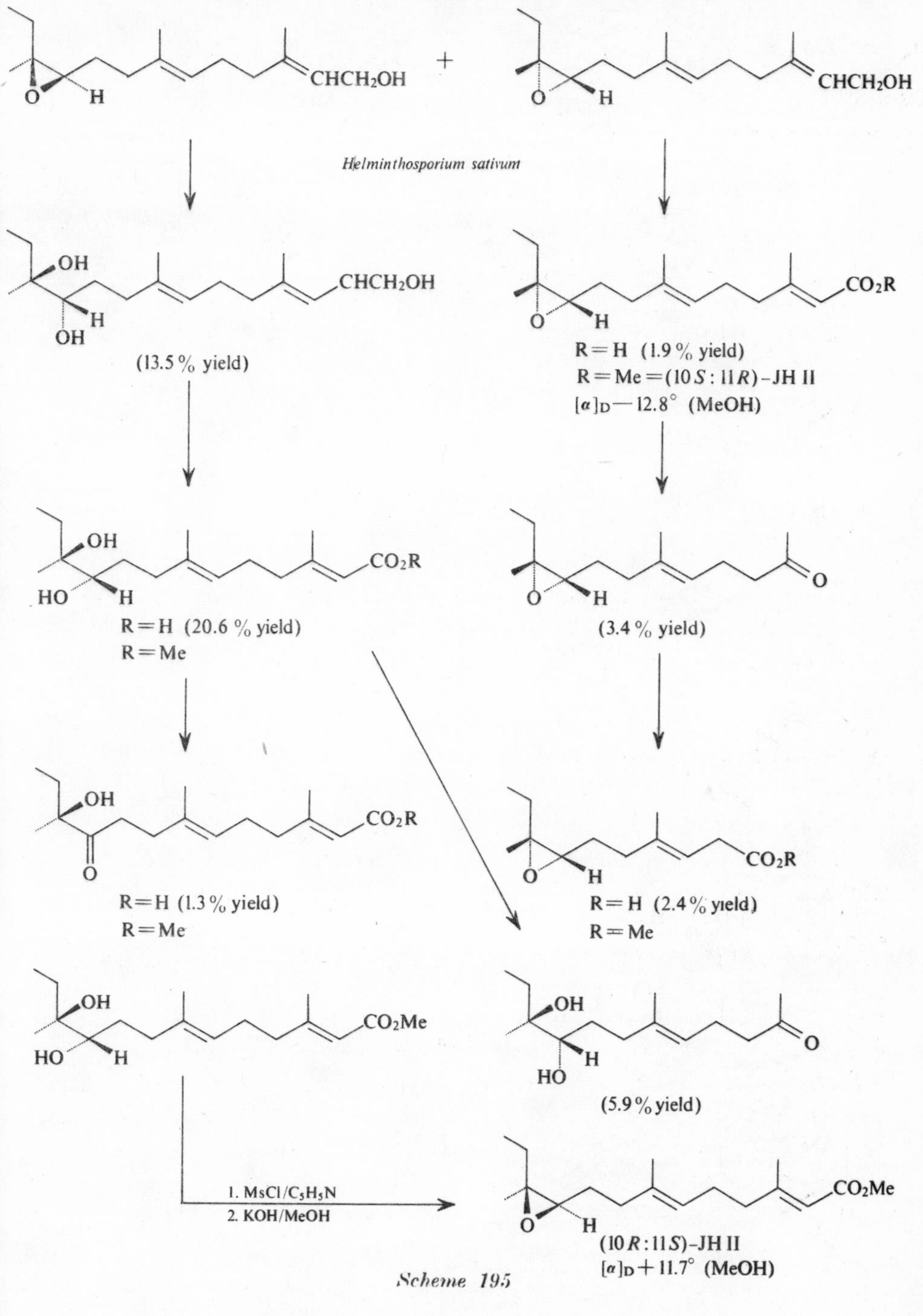

Helminthosporium sativum

(13.5 % yield)

R=H (1.9 % yield)
R=Me =(10 S : 11 R)–JH II
[α]ᴅ— 12.8° (MeOH)

R=H (20.6 % yield)
R=Me

(3.4 % yield)

R=H (1.3 % yield)
R=Me

R=H (2.4 % yield)
R=Me

(5.9 % yield)

1. MsCl/C₅H₅N
2. KOH/MeOH

(10 R : 11 S)–JH II
[α]ᴅ+ 11.7° (MeOH)

Scheme 195

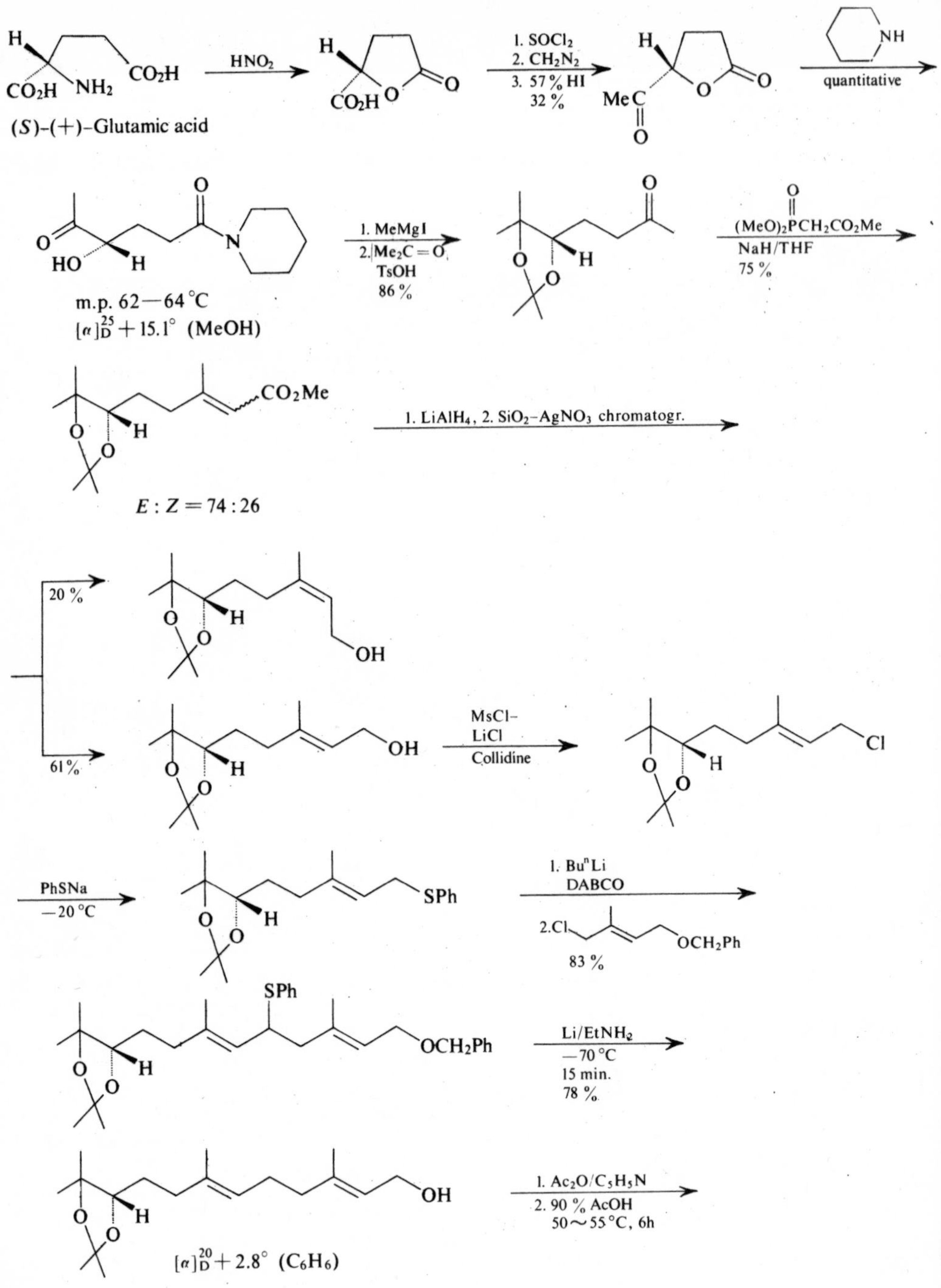

HNO2
1. SOCl2
2. CH2N2
3. 57 % HI
32 %
quantitative
(S)-(+)-Glutamic acid
m.p. 62—64 °C
[α]D25 +15.1° (MeOH)
1. MeMgI
2. Me2C=O, TsOH
86 %
(MeO)2PCH2CO2Me
NaH/THF
75 %
CO2Me
E : Z = 74 : 26
1. LiAlH4, 2. SiO2–AgNO3 chromatogr.
20 %
61 %
OH
MsCl–LiCl
Collidine
Cl
PhSNa
−20 °C
SPh
1. BunLi
DABCO
OCH2Ph
83 %
Li/EtNH2
−70 °C
15 min.
78 %
[α]D20 +2.8° (C6H6)
1. Ac2O/C5H5N
2. 90 % AcOH
50∼55 °C, 6h

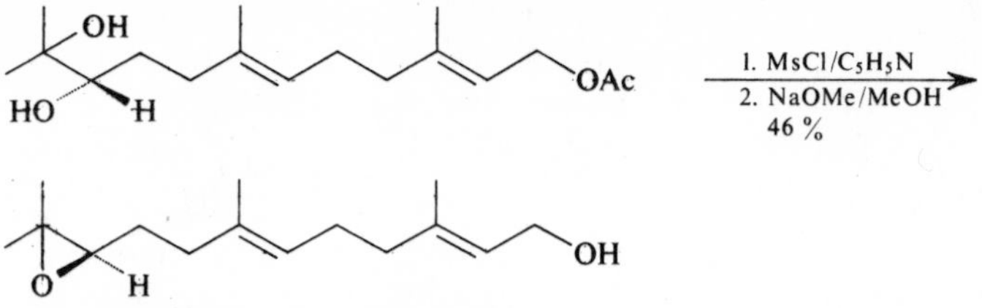

$(R)-(+)-10, 11-$Epoxyfarnesol

$[\alpha]_D^{25} +6.7°$ (c 1.24, MeOH)

Scheme 196 (cont'd)

5. SYNTHESES OF JUVABIONE AND DEHYDROJUVABIONE

Before discussing the individual syntheses, it seems necessary to summarize the present conclusion on the stereochemistry of natural $(+)$-juvabione, because there is considerable confusion in the literature data in this respect.

$(+)$-Juvabione (**4**), first isolated by Bowers *et al.* [12], was identified as the methyl ester of a known sesquiterpene, $(+)$-todomatuic acid (**6**). This bisabolene-type acid was discovered by Tutihasi in 1940 [81]. Momose proposed its correct plain structure in 1941 [82]. Nakazaki and Isoe [83] assigned the $(4R:1'R)$-absolute stereochemistry, as represented by **6**, based upon comparisons of the molecular rotations ($[M]_D$) of the acid and its derivatives

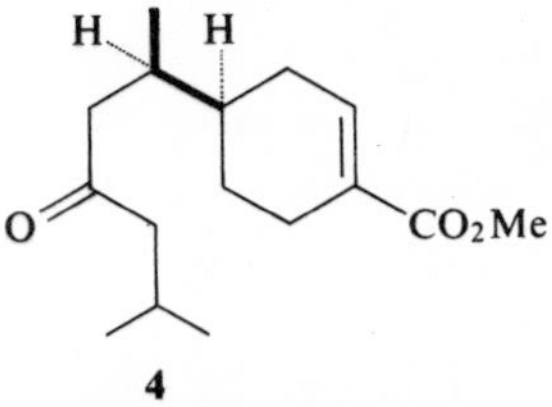

4
$(+)$-Juvabione

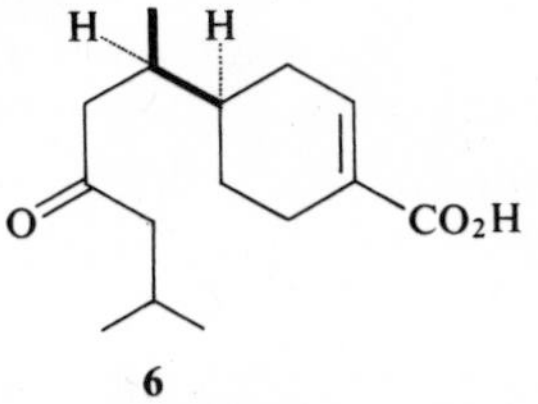

6
$(+)$-Todomatuic acid

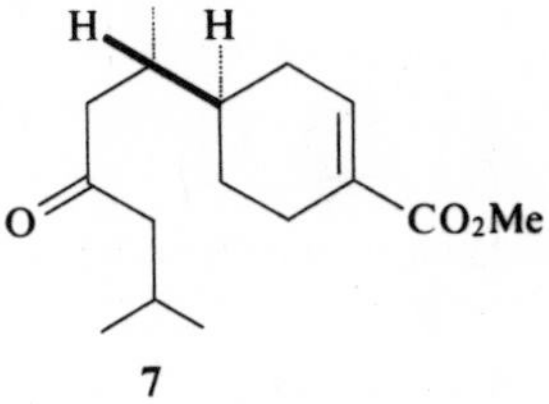

7

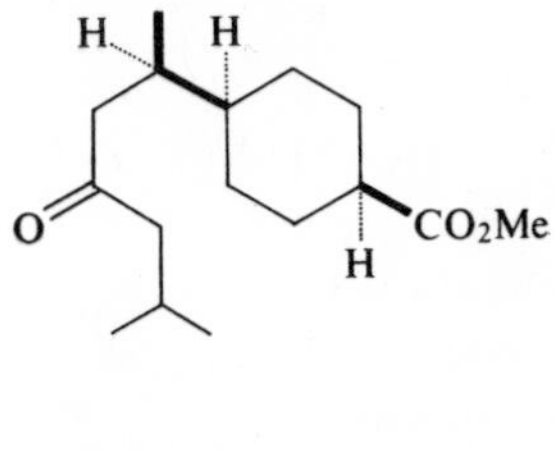

8
$(R)-cis$-Dihydrojuvabione

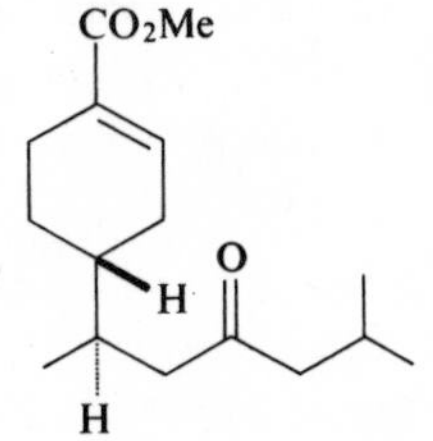

4'
$(4R:1'R)-(+)$-Juvabione

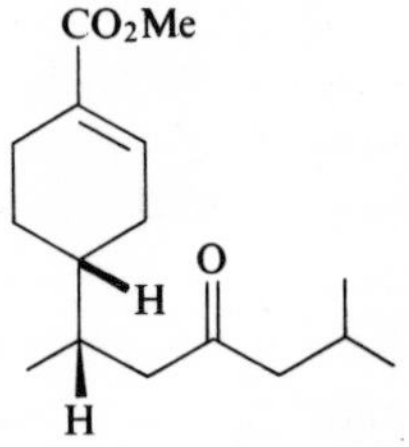

7'
$(4R:1'S)-(+)$-Epijuvabione

with those of other sesquiterpenes of known absolute stereochemistry. However, this assignment was questioned and revised as $4R : 1'S$ by Pawson and co-workers [84–86] in connection with their synthetic studies coupled with an X-ray analysis of a synthetic intermediate (vide infra, 5-E). The revision was widely accepted and (+)-juvabione was depicted as **7** in many publications including some 1976 papers [102, 107]. Recently this conclusion was challenged by two independent groups surveying sesquiterpenes with juvenile hormone activity in Canadian Douglas fir (Pseudotsuga menziesii). Sakai and Hirose isolated methyl (+)-todomatuate, $[\alpha]_D^{24} + 67.7°$ (CHCl$_3$), and identified it with an authentic sample of Isoe by direct comparison of UV, IR, NMR, MS, ORD and CD [87]. Surprisingly, the ORD and CD curves of Sakai's methyl (+)-todomatuate were different from those of "natural (+)-juvabione" reported by Pawson et al. [86]. Instead, they coincided with those of "(+)-epijuvabione" with ($4R : 1'R$)-stereochemistry [86]. Therefore methyl (+)-todomatuate isolated from the Douglas fir as well as Isoe's authentic todomatuic acid and Bowers's (+)-juvabione have the same ($4R : 1'R$)-absolute stereochemistry. Rogers et al. [88, 89] also isolated (+)-todomatuic acid from Douglas fir as the methyl ester, $[\alpha]_D^{24} + 65.9°$ (CHCl$_3$), whose CD curve was identical with that reported by Pawson et al. for "(+)-epijavabione" [86]. It therefore became clear that the authentic sample of "natural (+)-juvabione" used for the identification by Pawson et al. was not methyl (+)-todomatuate. Černý supplied the authentic "natural (+)-juvabione" which was isolated from Czechoslovakian balsam fir, Abies balsamea [90, 91]. It yielded, upon hydrolysis, an acid melting at 64–65°C [86, 90, 91], while the melting point of (+)-todomatuic acid was reported to be 57–59°C [12, 81–83]. The compound isolated by Černý et al. [90, 91] and identified as the ($4R : 1'S$)-isomer by Pawson et al. [86] was erroneously named and assumed to be "(+)-juvabione." Evidently it is ($4R : 1'S$)-(+)-epijuvabione. Thus there must exist in nature at least two epimers of juvabione, the ($4R : 1'R$)-form being found in North America [12, 87, 88] and the ($4R : 1'S$)-form found in Europe [90, 91]. This case study of juvabione stereochemistry is particularly instructive for natural product chemists. They should never neglect a direct comparison of their compound with an authentic sample not only on the basis of conventional spectral and chromatographic methods, but also by chiroptical methods to ensure stereochemical identity. If the Czech group had directly compared their "(+)-juvabione" with Bowers's original (+)-juvabione, the confusion might not have taken place. Rogers and Manville isolated another compound from the Douglas fir, cis-dihydrotodomatuic acid, which showed juvenile hormone activity as the methyl ester (8). This new compound also possessed (1′R)-stereochemistry [88, 89].

In conclusion, (+)-juvabione is the isomer with (4R : 1′R)-stereochemistry (4), while the (4R : 1′S)-isomer is (+)-epijuvabione (7). All the synthetic works described hereafter were reinterpreted in the light of this conclusion and formulas in the original papers were revised when necessary.

A. Mori's Synthesis of (±)-Juvabione and (±)-Epijuvabione

The first synthesis of racemic juvabione was achieved in 1967 (Scheme 197) [92, 93]. It was non-stereoselective and generated a diastereomeric mixture of (±)-todomatuic acid (A) and (±)-epitodomatuic acid (B). Their methyl esters (i.e., (±)-juvabione 4 and (±)-epijuvabione 7) were inseparable by GLC and showed identical spectral (IR, NMR, UV) properties. However, they could be separated as their semicarbazones. An acid obtained from the crystalline semicarbazone was also crystalline. In the original paper [93] this was thought to be (±)-todomatuic acid and widely accepted as such. But it actually was (±)-epitodomatuic acid (B) considering both the revision of stereochemistry and the stereoselective syntheses by Birch et al. [99] and Ficini et al. [105]. The oily semicarbazone yielded oily (±)-todomatuic acid (A). Bioassay on Pyrrhocoris apterus indicated that both (±)-juvabione and (±)-epijuvabione were biologically active [93]. The full paper records detailed IR and NMR data of these racemic compounds [93].

B. Ayyar's Synthesis of a Mixture of (±)-Juvabione and (±)-Epijuvabione

Soon after the announcement of Mori's synthesis, Ayyar et al. reported a similar but independent synthesis of a stereoisomeric mixture of (±)-juvabione and (±)-epijuvabione (Scheme 198) [94, 95]. However, they did not separate the diastereomeric mixture of todomatuic acids but purified it as S-benzylthiuronium salt to obtain only one acid of m.p. 65–66°C which was undoubtedly the same compound as Mori's crystalline acid. Thus their "(±)-juvabione " obtained by methylation of non-crystalline "todomatuic acids" was a mixture of (±)-juvabione and (±)-epijuvabione which was inseparable by various chromatographic means.

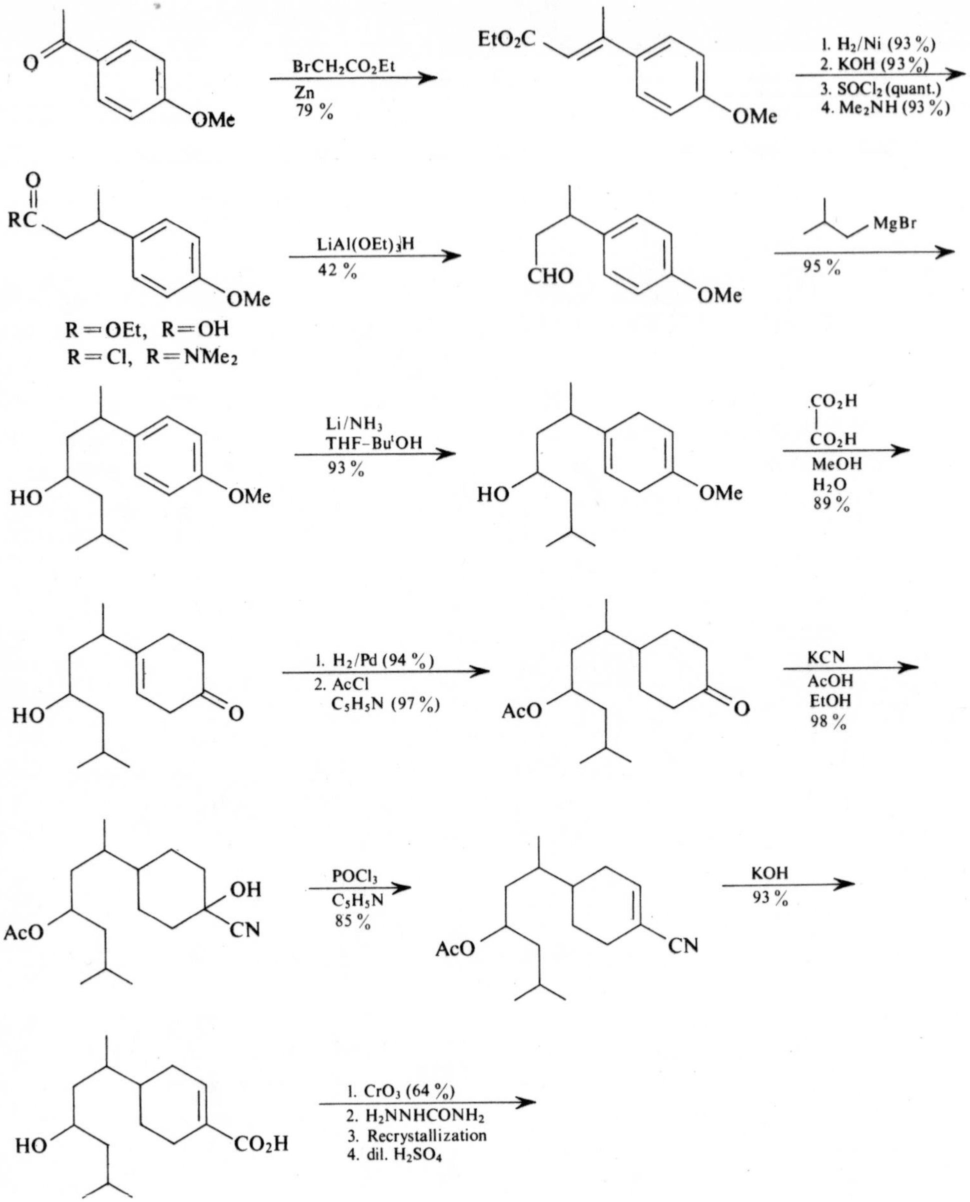

Reaction scheme with reagents labeled:

BrCH₂CO₂Et, Zn, 79 %

1. H₂/Ni (93 %)
2. KOH (93 %)
3. SOCl₂ (quant.)
4. Me₂NH (93 %)

R=OEt, R=OH
R=Cl, R=NMe₂

LiAl(OEt)₃H
42 %

MgBr
95 %

Li/NH₃
THF–BuᵗOH
93 %

CO₂H
CO₂H
MeOH
H₂O
89 %

1. H₂/Pd (94 %)
2. AcCl
C₅H₅N (97 %)

KCN
AcOH
EtOH
98 %

POCl₃
C₅H₅N
85 %

KOH
93 %

1. CrO₃ (64 %)
2. H₂NNHCONH₂
3. Recrystallization
4. dil. H₂SO₄

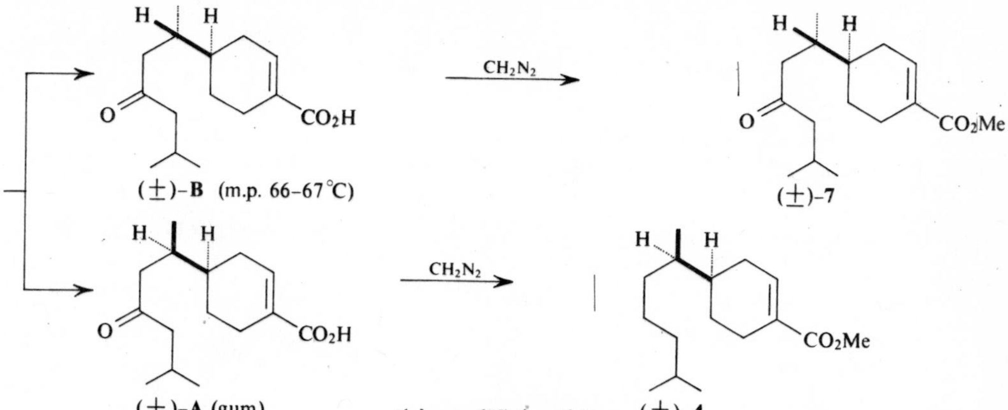

$(\pm)$-**B** (m.p. 66–67°C)

$(\pm)$-**7**

$(\pm)$-**A** (gum)

Scheme 197 (cont'd)

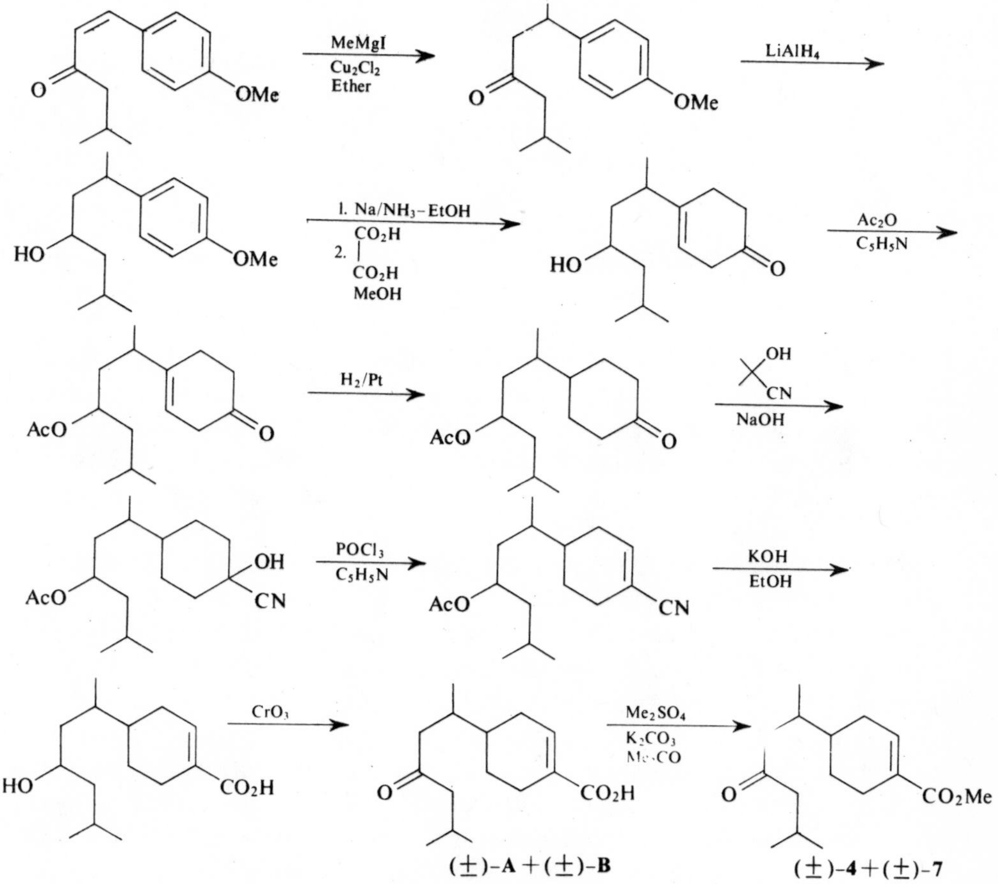

$(\pm)$-**4**

$(\pm)$-**A** + $(\pm)$-**B**

$(\pm)$-**4** + $(\pm)$-**7**

Scheme 198

C. Synthesis of a Mixture of (±)-Dehydrojuvabione and (±)-Epidehydrojuvabione by Mori et al.

(+)-Dehydrojuvabione was isolated by Černý et al. as a congener of their "(+)-juvabione" [90, 91]. Although no careful chiroptical study has been made on (+)-dehydrojuvabione and its derivatives, it probably belongs to the same stereochemical series as that of Černý's "(+)-juvabione" on biogenetical grounds. Therefore, (+)-dehydrojuvabione probably possesses (4R : 1'S)-stereochemistry as depicted in **9**. This should be proved in the future. Mori et al. synthesized a stereoisomeric mixture of (±)-dehydro-juvabione (**9**) and (±)-epidehydrojuvabione (**10**) starting from an inter-mediate used in the synthesis of (±)-juvabione as outlined in Scheme 199 [96, 97]. The synthesis was straightforward and yielded a stereoisomeric mixture of dehydrotodomatuic acids, one of which crystallized. The stereo-chemistry of this crystalline racemate could not be decided but tentatively assigned as depicted (**C**) in analogy with (±)-epitodomatuic acid. The final product was indistinguishable from the natural (+)-dehydrojuvabione on the basis of IR, NMR and GLC and showed juvenile hormone activity of the same order [97].

D. Birch's Synthesis of a Mixture of (±)-Juvabione and (±)-Epijuvabione and Synthesis of (±)-Epijuvabione

Birch and co-workers developed a synthesis of a mixture of (±)-juvabione and (±)-epijuvabione [98, 99]. This synthesis could be modified to yield only (±)-epijuvabione by separating an intermediate. Firstly, their synthe-sis leading to a diastereomeric mixture is outlined in Scheme 200 [99]. The relative stereochemistry at the two asymmetric centres was generated by a Dields–Alder reaction between 1-methoxy-1,3-cyclohexadiene and (E)-6-methyl-2-hepten-4-one. The reaction, however, was not stereoselective and yielded two adducts in equal amounts. The mixture underwent an acid-catalyzed α, β-fragmentation to give the required bisabolane-type carbon skeleton. The remaining conventional operations gave a mixture of (±)-juvabione and (±)-epijuvabione in 55% yield from the starting 6-methyl-2-hepten-4-one. This is an efficient synthesis indeed.

Fortunately the Diels–Alder adducts were separable into two pure iso-mers by fractional distillation and one of them, with the higher boiling point, served as the starting material for the synthesis of (±)-epijuvabione (**7**) as shown in Scheme 201 [98, 99]. After the separation step, the synthesis was stereoselective, although non-regioselective at the dehydration stage

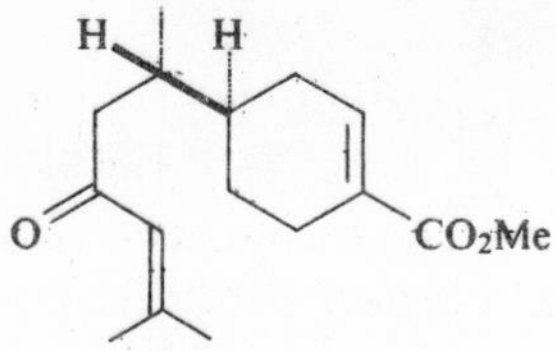

9

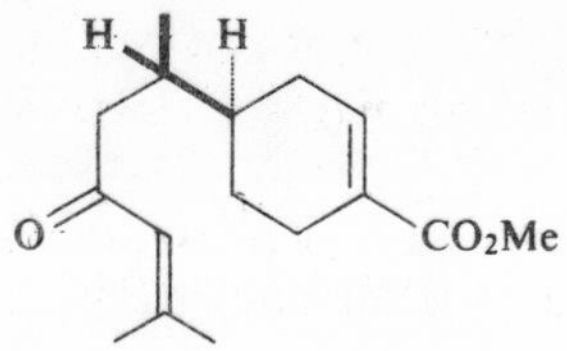

10

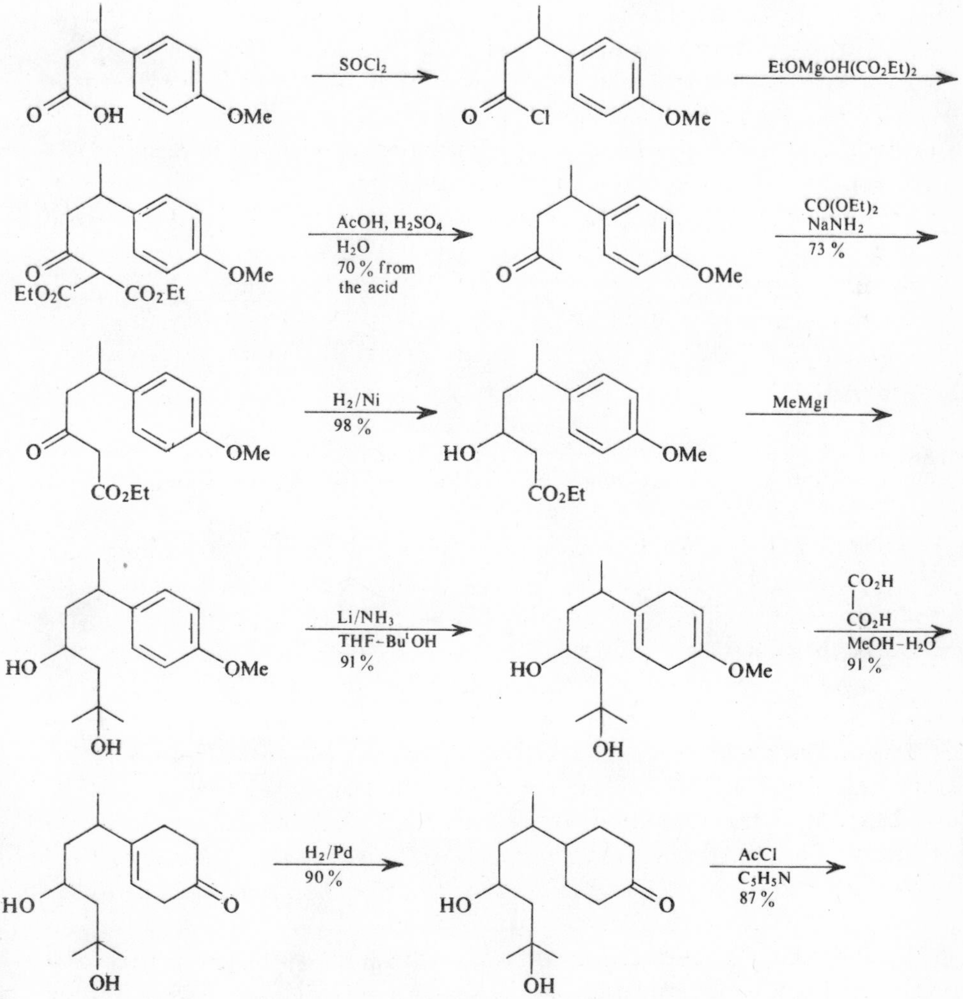

SOCl₂

EtOMgOH(CO₂Et)₂

AcOH, H₂SO₄
H₂O
70 % from
the acid

CO(OEt)₂
NaNH₂
73 %

H₂/Ni
98 %

MeMgI

Li/NH₃
THF–BuᵗOH
91 %

CO₂H
CO₂H
MeOH–H₂O
91 %

H₂/Pd
90 %

AcCl
C₅H₅N
87 %

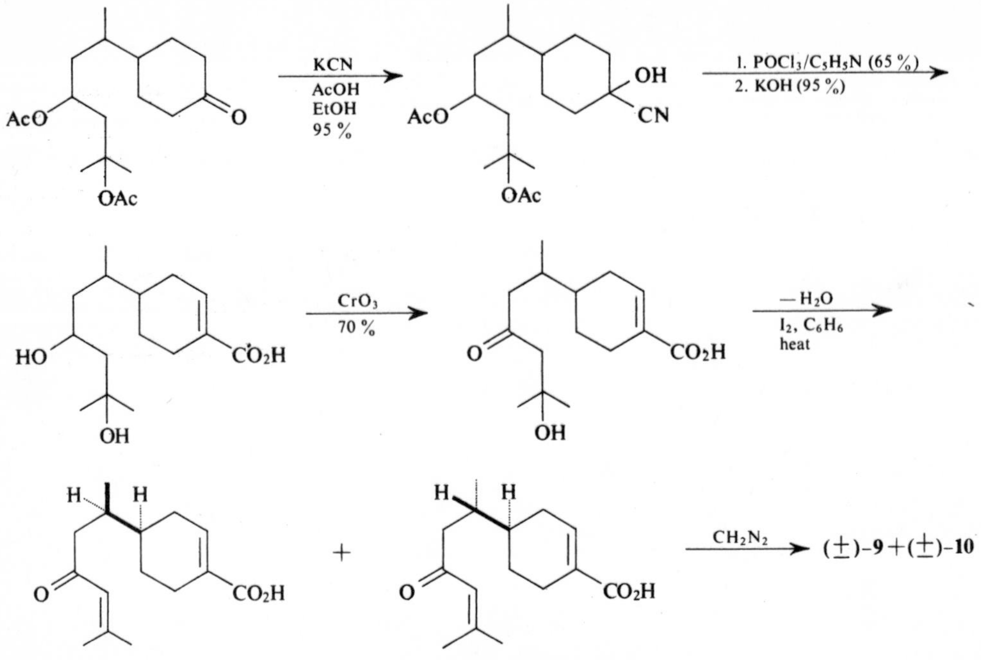

$(\pm)$-C m.p. 66–67 °C

Scheme 199 (cont'd)

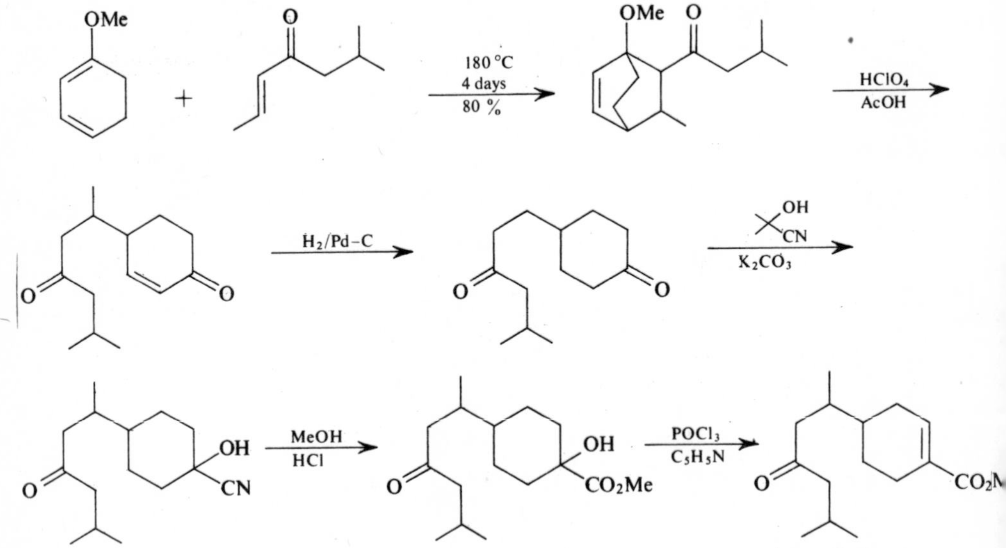

$(\pm)$-4+$(\pm)$-7

Scheme 200

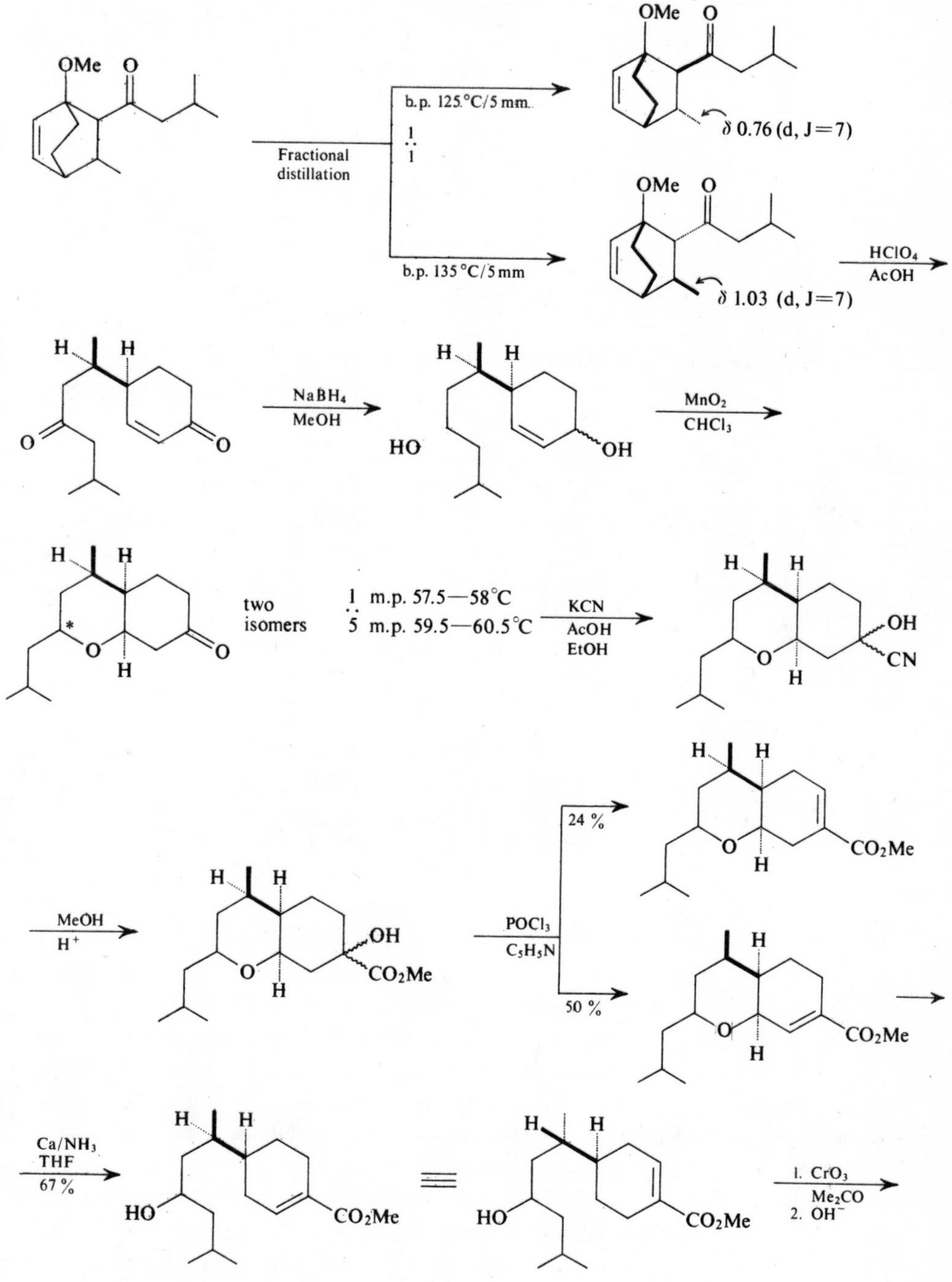
OMe
O
Fractional distillation
b.p. 125 °C/5 mm
1 : 1
b.p. 135 °C/5 mm
δ 0.76 (d, J=7)
δ 1.03 (d, J=7)
HClO4 AcOH
NaBH4 MeOH
HO
OH
MnO2 CHCl3
two isomers
1 m.p. 57.5—58 °C
5 m.p. 59.5—60.5 °C
KCN AcOH EtOH
CN
MeOH H+
CO2Me
POCl3 C5H5N
24 %
50 %
Ca/NH3 THF 67 %
1. CrO3 Me2CO
2. OH−

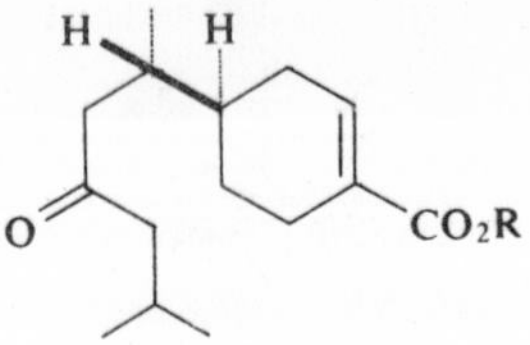

(±)-7   R=Me
(±)-Epitodomatuic acid
m.p. 66-67 °C
R=H

Scheme 201 (cont'd)

of the hydroxy ester. The relative stereochemistry of the Diels–Alder adduct was assigned by NMR. The lower-boiling adduct showed a high-field methyl signal at $\delta = 0.76$ ppm (d, $J = 7$ Hz). This can only be assigned to an *endo*-methyl group, which falls within the shielding cone of the olefinic bond. In contrast, the higher boiling adduct displays a resonance at $\delta = 1.03$ ppm (d, $J = 7$ Hz) corresponding to a non-shielded methyl group with *exo*-configuration. This assignment determined the stereochemistry of the final product to be that of (±)-epijuvabione (**7**), as depicted. Actually, the hydrolysis of their final product gave (±)-epitodomatuic acid with m.p. 66–67°C. A synthesis starting from the lower-boiling adduct should lead to (±)-juvabione (**4**).

E. Syntheses of Natural (+)-Juvabione, its Enantiomer (-)-Juvabione, and their Diastereomers (+)- and (—)-Epijuvabione by the Hoffmann-LaRoche Group

Pawson *et al.* synthesized all of the four possible stereoisomers of juvabione in optically pure state [85, 86]. They published ORD and CD spectra of their synthetic juvabione isomers and these data were especially important in the subsequent stereochemical studies on (+)-juvabione and related natural products. As stated previously, the nomenclature used in this paper should be revised considering recent works of Sakai and Hirose [87]. Thus "(+)-juvabione" in this paper is actually (+)-epijuvabione and "(+)-epijuvabione" is (+)-juvabione. The correct names will be used hereafter.

Pawson employed *(R)*-(+)-limonene and its antipode as the starting materials of known absolute configuration (Scheme 202). Hydroboration of *(R)*-(+)-limonene gave a diastereomeric mixture of (+)-(4R)-*p*-1-menthen--9-ols, whose 3,5-dinitrobenzoates were fractionally crystallized to effect

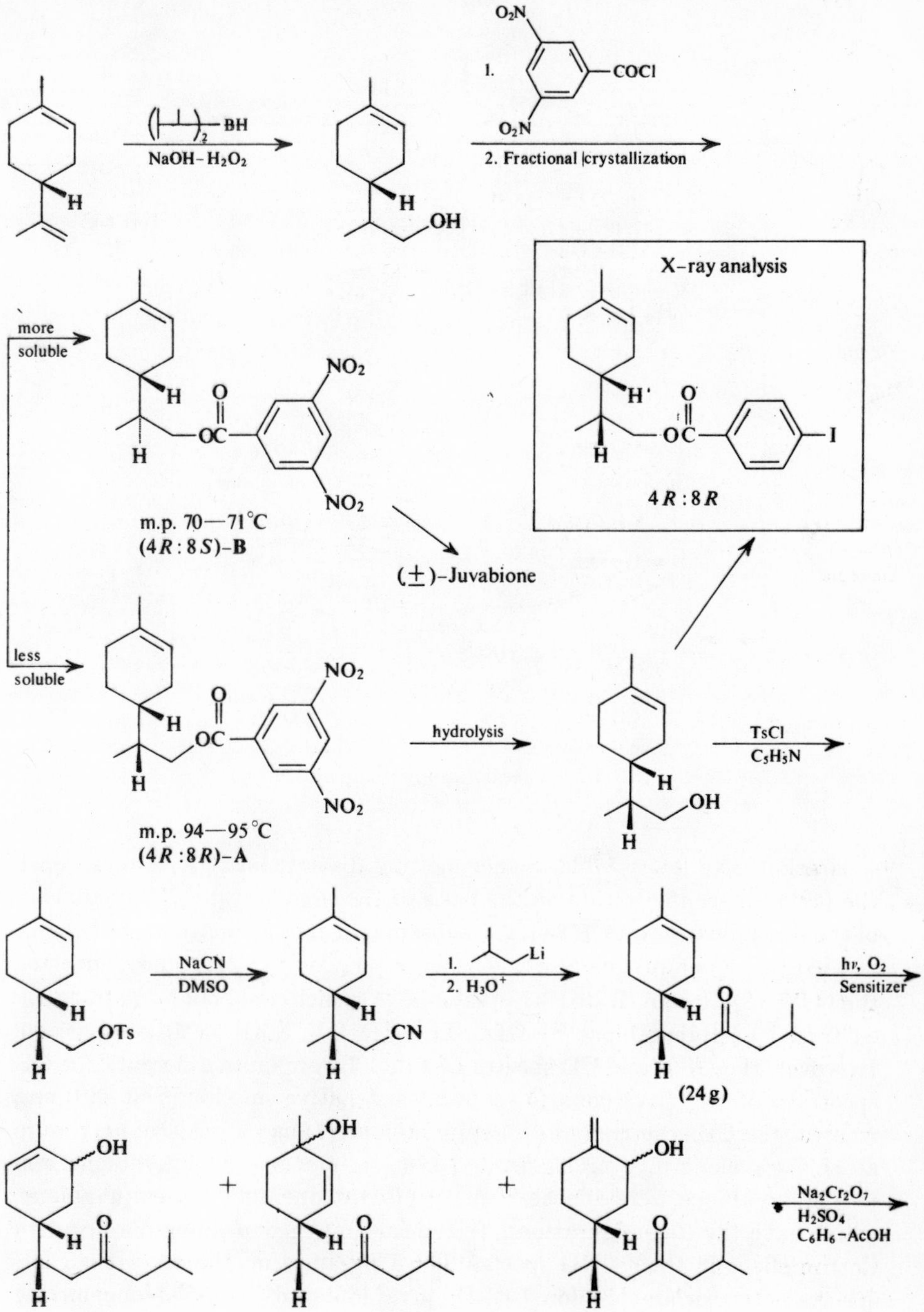
BH
NaOH–H2O2
H
OH
1.
O2N
COCl
O2N
2. Fractional crystallization
more soluble
less soluble
NO2
NO2
O
OC
H
m.p. 70—71°C
(4R : 8S)–B
(±)–Juvabione
X–ray analysis
OC
I
4R : 8R
m.p. 94—95°C
(4R : 8R)–A
hydrolysis
TsCl
C5H5N
OTs
NaCN
DMSO
CN
Li
2. H3O+
(24 g)
hν, O2
Sensitizer
Na2Cr2O7
H2SO4
C6H6–AcOH

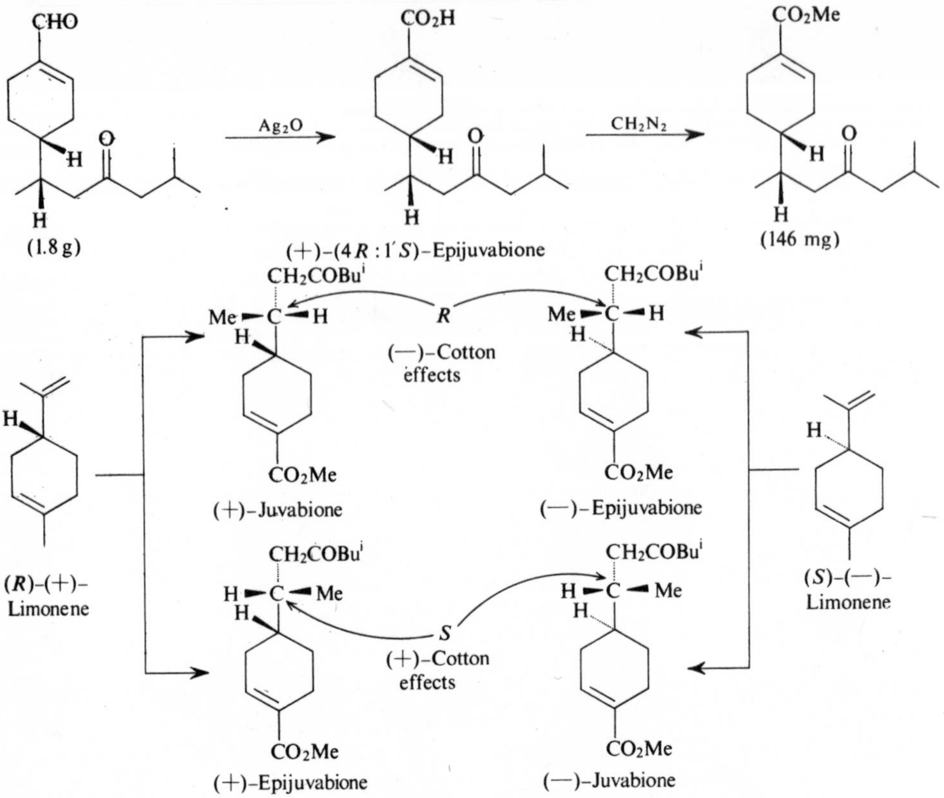

Scheme 202 (cont'd)

separation. The less soluble, higher-melting diastereomer (**A**) was assigned the (4*R* : 8*R*)-configuration on the basis of the single-crystal X-ray analysis of the *p*-iodobenzoate (**A'**) [84]. The subsequent steps as shown in the Scheme 202 led to (+)-epijuvabione (**7**). The same sequence of reactions converted the (4*R* : 8*S*)-alcohol (**B**) to (+)-juvabione (**4**) which could not be distinguished from (+)-epijuvabione by GLC, TLC, IR, UV, NMR or MS comparison. However, the ORD and CD spectra of **4** and **7** were quite different. The CD spectrum of (+)-juvabione (**4**) showed a negative maximum at 291 nm, whereas the CD spectrum of (+)-epijuvabione (**7**) had a positive maximum at this wavelength. Starting from *(S)*-(−)-limonene, (−)-juvabione and (−)-epijuvabione were synthesized. (+)-Juvabione and (−)-epijuvabione, which have the *R*-configuration β to the carbonyl group, showed a negative Cotton effect in their ORD spectra and a negative maximum in their CD spectra in the carbonyl region. (+)-Epijuvabione and (−)-juvabione, having the *S*-configuration β to the carbonyl group, had positive ORD Cotton effects and positive CD maxima. Thus, in these cases, the sign of the carbonyl

Cotton effect is determined solely by the configuration at the β-carbon atom. The Hoffman–La Roche synthesis is the only existing synthesis of optically pure juvabiones and has made possible to distinguish between (+)-juvabione and (+)-epijuvabione, by finding out their differences in chiroptical measurements.

It should be noted that these four stereoisomers did not reveal any large differences in the activity as shown below [100] (Table III). (+)-Juvabione seems to be most active.

Table III

Biological Activity of Stereoisomers of Juvabione

Compound	Test animals	
	Pyrrhocoris apterus	*Dysdercus cingulatus*
(4*R* : 1′*R*)-(+)-Juvabione	1*	0.08
(4*S* : 1′*S*)-(−)-Juvabione	8	1
(4*R* : 1′*S*)-(+)-Epijuvabione	3	0.5
(4*S* : 1′*R*)-(−)-Epijuvabione	3	0.6
(±)-Juvabione	1	0.4

* The values of juvenile hormone activity are expressed in units of μg of the compound per insect which causes, by topical application in acetone, formation of larval-adult intermediates. The nomenclature of the compounds is revised.

F. Synthesis of a Mixture of (−)*-Juvabione and* (−)*-Epijuvabione*
by Farges and Veschambre

To avoid difficulty encountered by Pawson *et al.* in oxidizing the allylic methyl group originating from limonene (see Scheme 201), Farges and Veschambre employed *(S)*-(−)-perillyl alcohol as the starting material (which has an allylic hydroxymethyl group) as outlined in Scheme 203 [101]. (Pawson *et al.* attempted to use perillaldehyde, but its optical purity was unsatisfactory for the preparation of optically pure juvabione [86]). The hydroxyl group of perillyl alcohol was protected as the p-methylbenzyl ether which could be cleaved under mild conditions. Steps shown in the Scheme led to a mixture of (−)-juvabione and (−)-epijuvabione of unknown optical purity.

13*

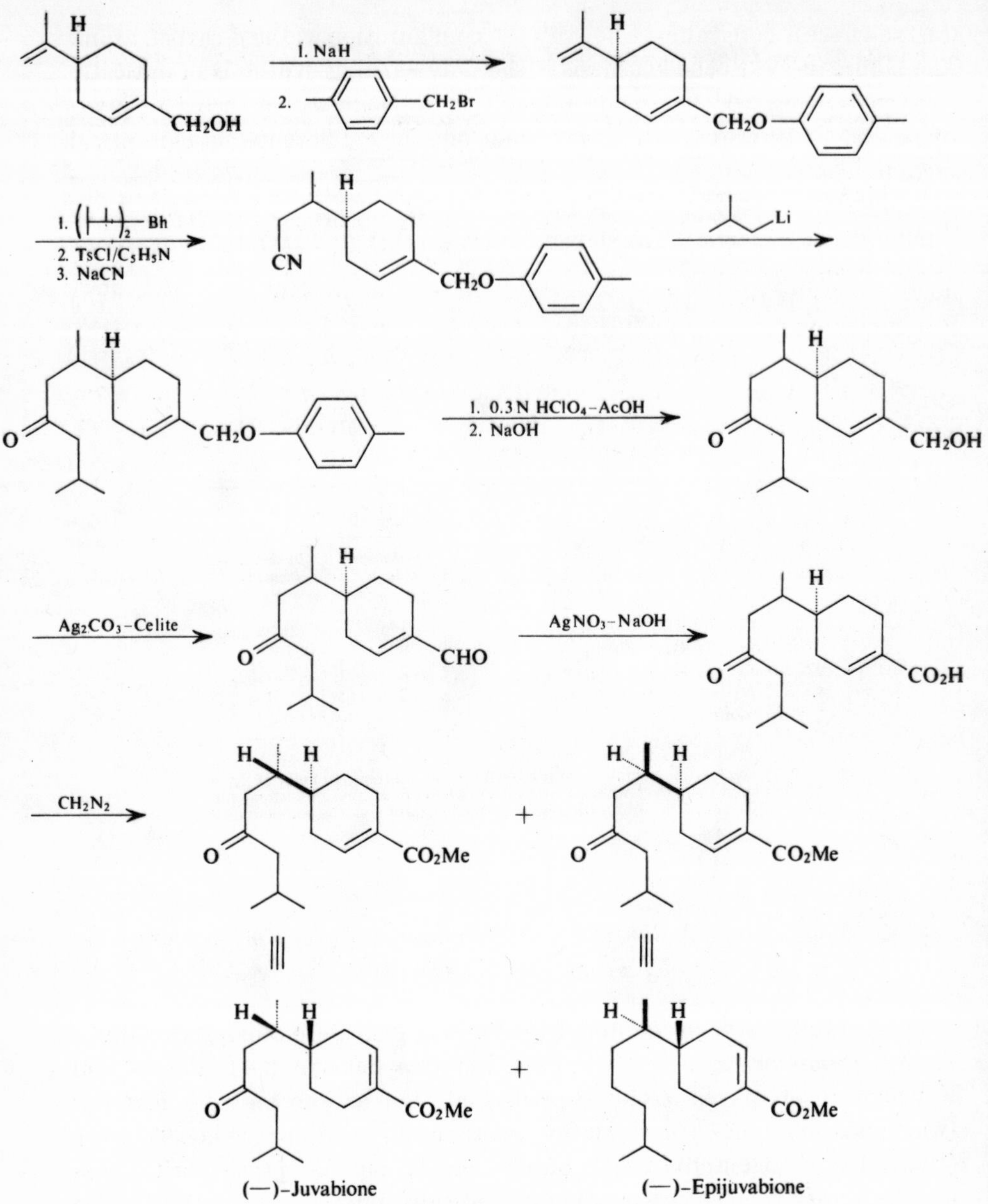

(—)-Juvabione   +   (—)-Epijuvabione

Scheme 203

G. Stereoselective Synthesis of (±)-Epijuvabione by Ficini et al.

In the course of her extensive investigation on ynamines [102], Ficini discovered a stereoselective fragmentation reaction of amino-bicyclo[4.2.0] octenones such as **A** or **B** to give stereochemically pure keto-acids such as **C** or **D**. The steric course of the reaction differs according to the reaction conditions and it was possible to control the stereochemistry of the keto-acids by using different conditions as shown in Scheme 204 [103, 104]. Starting from the keto-acid **C**, Ficini et al. completed the first stereoselective synthesis of (±)-epijuvabione [105]. At that time, the acid **C** was thought to have the correct stereochemistry leading to (±)-juvabione. However, in view of the present knowledge of the juvabione stereochemistry, the acid

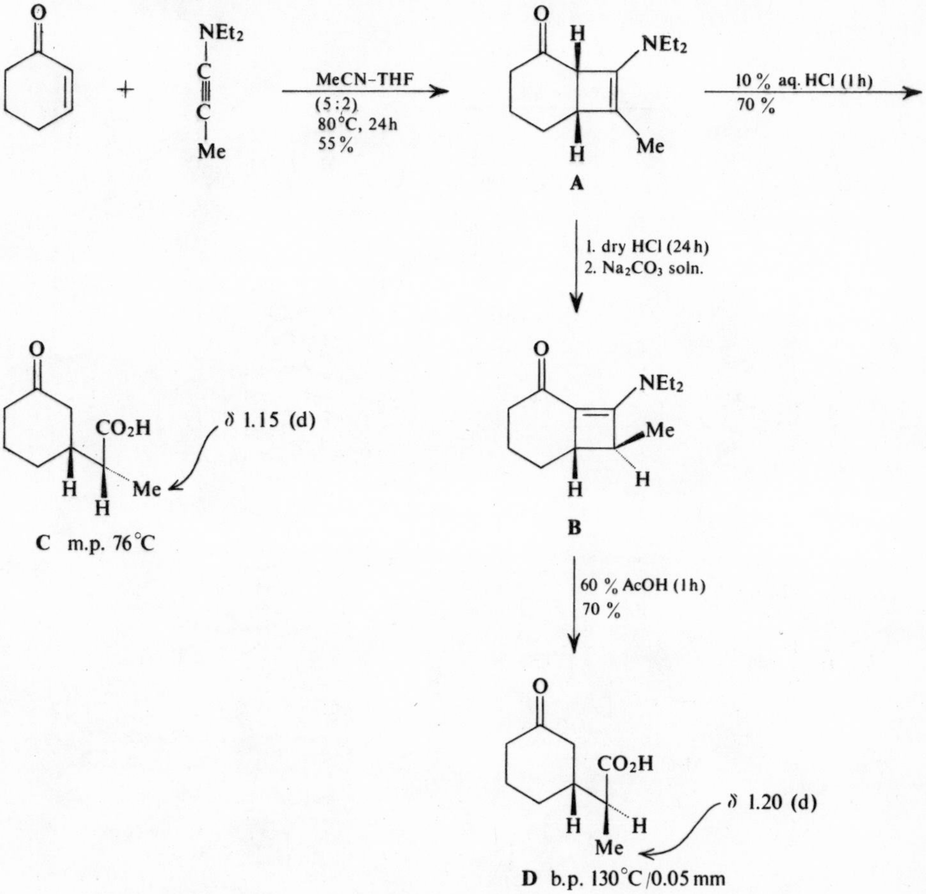

Scheme 204

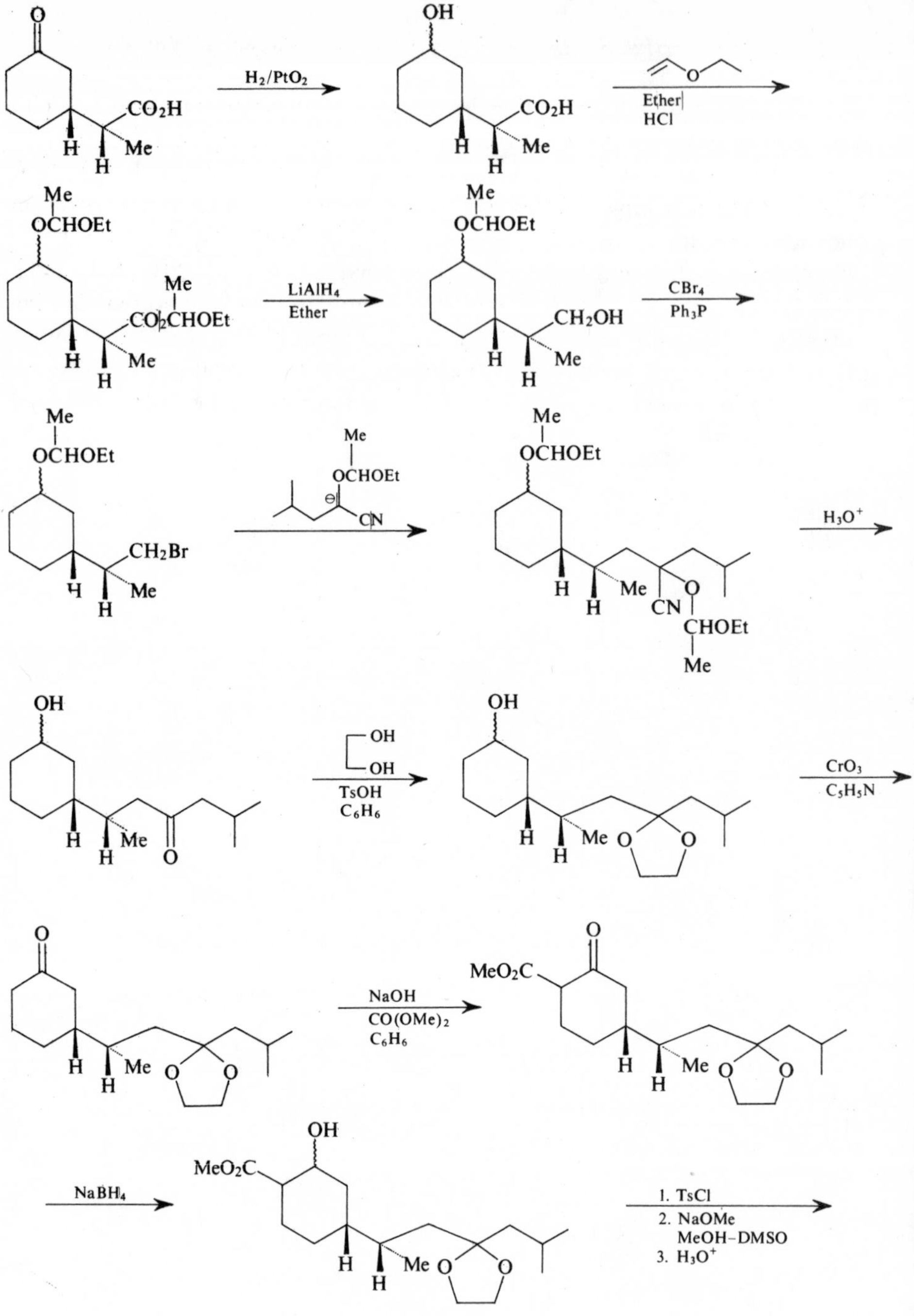
O
CO2H
H
Me
H2/PtO2
OH
Ether
HCl
OCHOEt
CO2CHOEt
LiAlH4
Ether
CH2OH
CBr4
Ph3P
CH2Br
CN
H3O+
TsOH
C6H6
CrO3
C5H5N
NaOH
CO(OMe)2
MeO2C
NaBH4
1. TsCl
2. NaOMe
MeOH–DMSO
3. H3O+

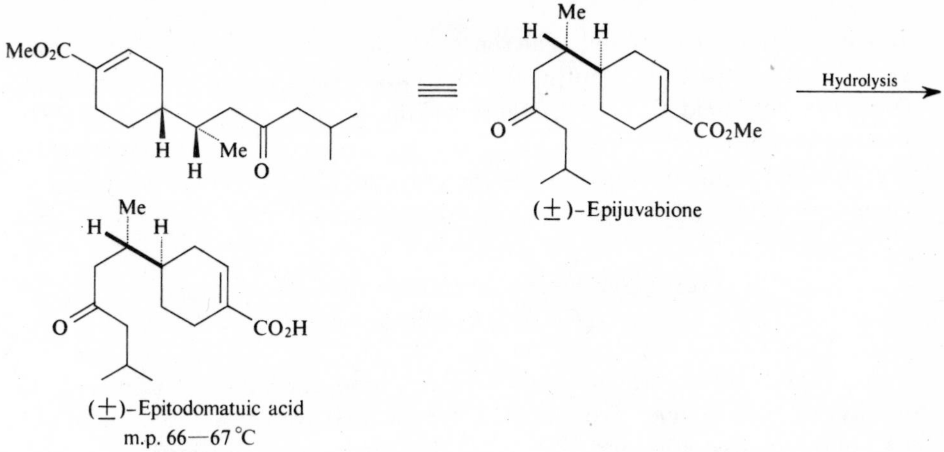

MeO2C
H
Me
H
O
Me
H
H
O
CO2Me
Hydrolysis
(±)-Epijuvabione
Me
H
H
O
CO2H
(±)-Epitodomatuic acid
m.p. 66—67 °C

Scheme 205 (cont'd)

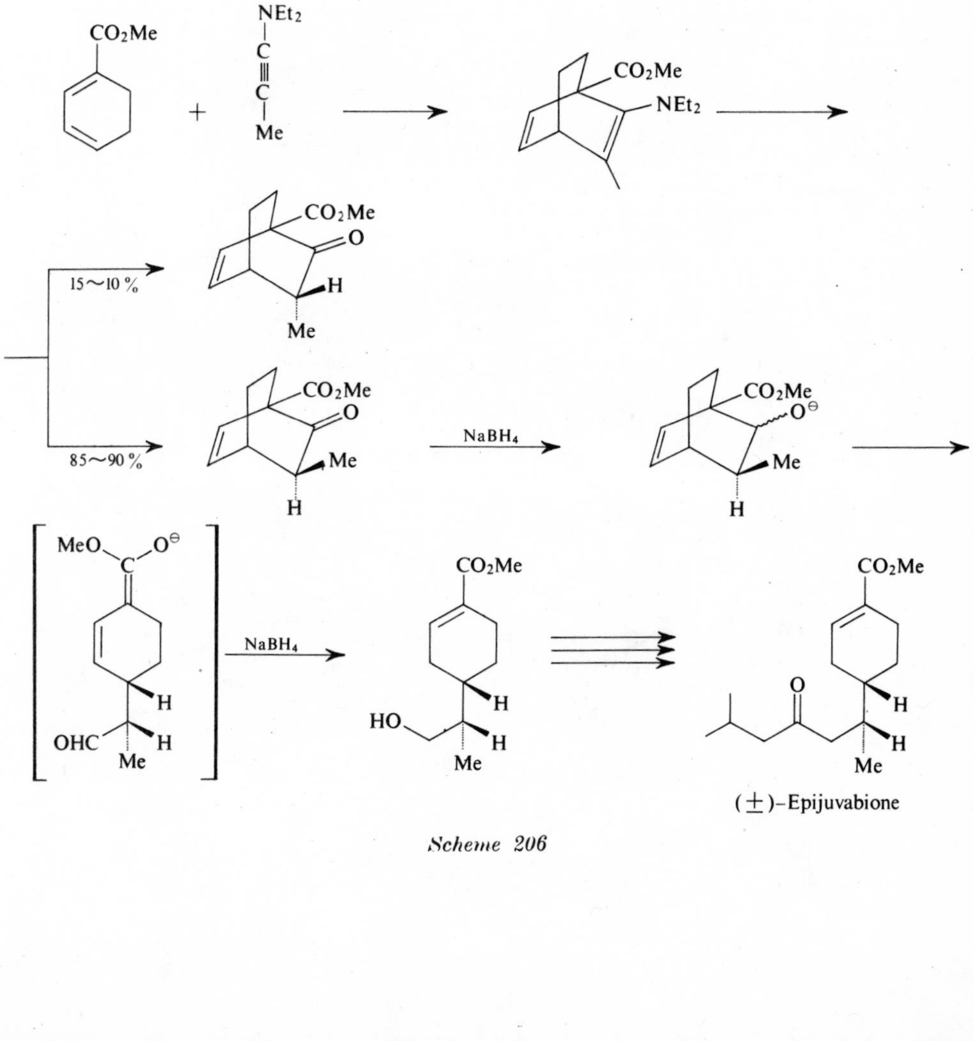

CO2Me
NEt2
C
C
Me
CO2Me
NEt2
CO2Me
O
H
Me
15~10 %
CO2Me
O
Me
H
85~90 %
NaBH4
CO2Me
O⊖
Me
H
MeO
O⊖
C
H
OHC
H
Me
NaBH4
CO2Me
H
HO
H
Me
CO2Me
O
H
H
Me
(±)-Epijuvabione

Scheme 206

D will lead to (±)-juvabione. The route is shown in Scheme 205. The synthesis led in 11 steps to (±)-epijuvabione in an overall yield of 13%, starting from the keto-acid **C**, or 6% starting from cyclohexenone. Ficini briefly commented on another stereoselective synthesis of (±)-epijuvabione utilizing an α, β-fragmentation process (Scheme 206) in her review on ynamine chemistry [102].

H. Trost's Synthesis of a Mixture of (+)-Juvabione and (+)-Epijuvabione

In order to illustrate the utility of his new acyl anion equivalent, 2-methyl-thioacetic acid, Trost synthesized a mixture of (+)-juvabione and (+)-epijuvabione starting from (+)-perillaldehyde as outlined in Scheme 207 [106].

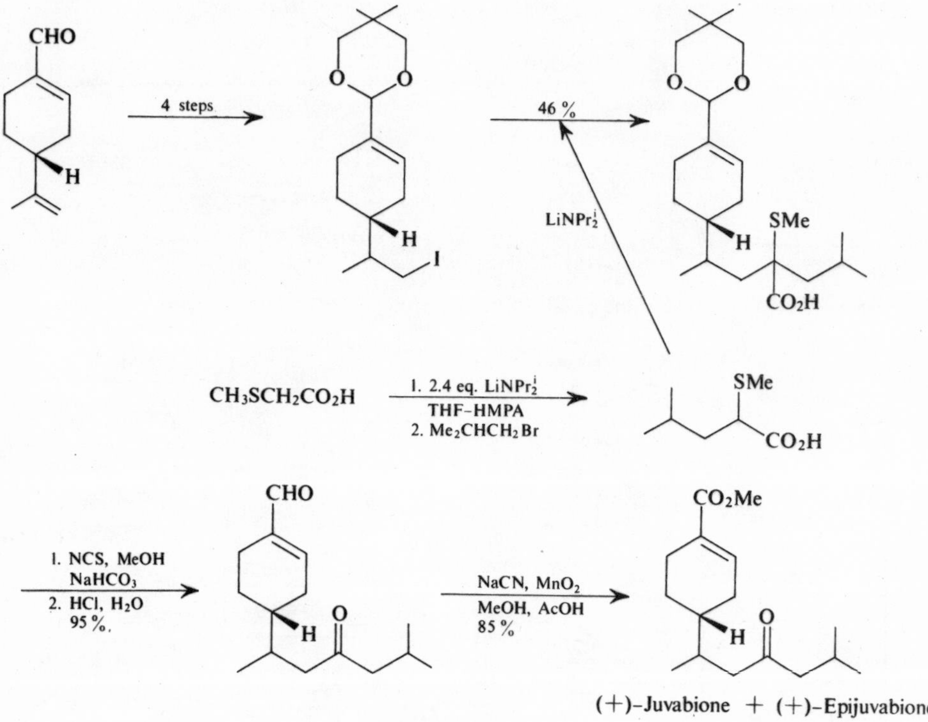

Scheme 207

I. Synthesis of a Mixture of (±)-Juvabione and (±)-Epijuvabione by Negishi et al.

Application of Brown's hydroboration-carbonylation reaction provided the simplest, efficient synthesis of juvabione stereoisomeric mixture [107]. The synthesis started from (±)-perillartine (perillaldehyde oxime) as shown in Scheme 208, and it was completed in as few as 5 steps. The product thus isolated was shown to be a nearly 1 : 1 mixture of juvabione and epijuvabione as judged by the ^{13}C-NMR spectrum. The methyl and methylene carbon atoms adjacent to the acyclic asymmetric carbon atom exhibit closely appearing doublets at 16.42 and 16.52, and 47.79 and 47.91 ppm (relative to tetramethylsilane), respectively. Several other carbon atoms including the two asymmetric methine carbon atoms also exhibit doublets. Attempts to observe the two isomers separately by GLC, HPLC or ^1H-NMR remained unsuccessful. Crystalline (±)-epitodomatuic acid, m.p. 64–65°C, was obtained.

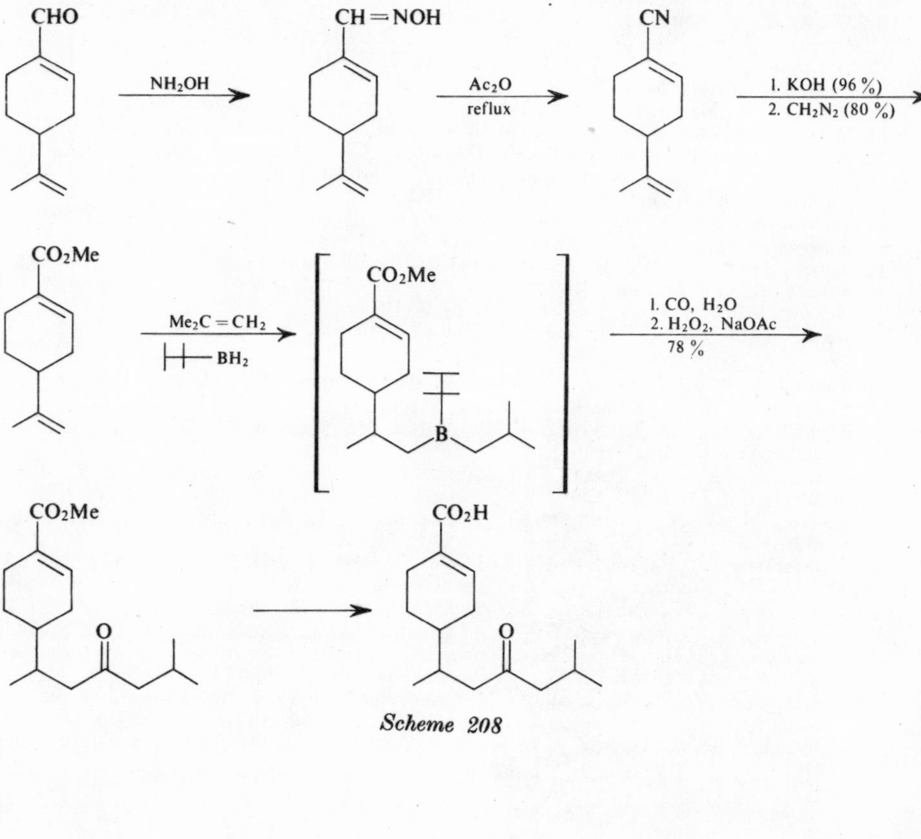

Scheme 208

6. JUVENILE HORMONES AS TARGETS IN ORGANIC SYNTHESIS

A review on juvenile hormone synthesis is almost equivalent to a review on the synthesis of trisubstituted olefins. The study on juvenile hormone synthesis has greatly increased our knowledge of chemistry of olefins and will continue in doing so.

REFERENCES

1. WILLIAMS, C. M., *Nature, 178,* 212 (1956).
2. RÖLLER, H., BJERKE, J. S., *Life Science, 4,* 1617 (1965).
3. RÖLLER, H., BJERKE, J. S., HOLTHAUS, L. M., NORGARD, D. W., McSHAN, W. H., *J. Insect Physiol., 15,* 379 (1969).
4. RÖLLER, H., DAHM, K. H., SWEELEY, C. C., TROST, B. M., *Angew. Chem. intern. Ed., 6,* 179 (1967).
5. DAHM, K. H., TROST, B. M., RÖLLER, H., *J. Am. Chem. Soc., 89,* 5292 (1967).
6. MEYER, A. S., SCHNEIDERMAN, H. A., HANZMANN, E., KO, J. H., *Proc. Nat. Acad. Sci. U. S. A., 60,* 853 (1968).
7. MEYER, A. S., HANZMANN, E., SCHNEIDERMAN, H. A., GILBERT, L. I., BOYETTE, M., *Arch. Biochem. Biophys., 137,* 190 (1970).
8. JUDY, K. J., SCHOOLEY, D. A., DUNHAM, L. L., HALL, M. S., BERGOT, B. J., SIDDALL, J. B., *Proc. Nat. Acad. Sci. U. S. A., 70,* 1509 (1973).
9. SCHOOLEY, D. A., JUDY, K. J., BERGOT, B. J., HALL, M. S., SIDDALL, J. B., *Proc. Nat. Acad. Sci. U. S. A., 70,* 2921 (1973).
10. RÖLLER, H., DAHM, K. H., *Recent Progress in Hormone Research, 24,* 651 (1968).
11. SLÁMA, K., WILLIAMS, C. M., *Proc. Nat. Acad. Sci. U. S. A., 54,* 411 (1965).
12. BOWERS, W. S., THOMPSON, H. M., UEBEL, E. C., *Science, 154,* 1020 (1966).
13. WILLIAMS, C. M., *Scientific American, 217,* 13 (July, 1967).
14. TROST, B. M., *Accounts Chem. Res., 3,* 120 (1970).
15. Papers presented at the Swiss Symposium on Juvenile Hormones, *Mitt. Schweiz. Entomol. Ges., 44,* No. 1–2 (1971).
16. MENN, J. J., BEROZA, M. (Eds), "Insect Juvenile Hormones", Academic Press, New York and London, (1972).
17. SLÁMA, K., *Ann. Rev. Biochem., 40,* 1079 (1971).
18. STAAL, G. B., *Ann. Rev. Entomol., 20,* 417 (1975).
19. DAHM, K. H., RÖLLER, H., TROST, B. M., *Life Sciences, 7,* 129 (1968).
20. BRAUN, B. H., JACOBSON, M., SCHWARZ, M., SONNET, P. E., WAKABAYASHI, N., WATERS, R. M., *J. Econ. Entomol., 61,* 866 (1968).
21. MORI, K., STALLA-BOURDILLON, B., OHKI, M., MATSUI, M., BOWERS, W. S., *Tetrahedron, 25,* 1667 (1969).
22. MORI, K., OHKI, M., STALLA-BOURDILLON, B., MATSUI, M., BOWERS, W. S., *Agr. Biol. Chem., 33,* 1792 (1969).
23. CAVILL, G. W. K., LAING, D. G., WILLIAMS, P. J., *Austral. J. Chem., 22,* 2145 (1969).
24. HOFFMANN, W., PASEDACH, H., POMMER, H., *Liebigs Ann. Chem., 729,* 52 (1969).
25. SCHULZ, H., SPRUNG, I., *Angew. Chem. intern. Ed., 8,* 271 (1969).
26. ATHERTON, F. R., PFIFFNER, A., *Belg. Pat., 725,* 576 (1968).
27. PFIFFNER, A., "Aspects of Terpenoid Chemistry and Biochemistry", (Ed. T. W. Goodwin), Academic Press, New York, 1971, pp. 95–135.
28. FINDLAY, J. A., MACKAY, W. D., *Chem. Commun., 1969,* 733.
29. FINDLAY, J. A., MACKAY, W. D., *J. Chem. Soc. (C), 1970,* 2631.
30. FINDLAY, J. A., *Mitt. Schweiz. Entomol. Ges., 44,* 65 (1971).
31. ANDERSON, R. J., HENRICK, C. A., SIDDALL, J. B., *J. Am. Chem. Soc., 92,* 735 (1970).

32. VAN TAMELEN, E. E., MCCORMICK, J. P., *J. Am. Chem. Soc.*, *92*, 737 (1970).
33. MORI, K., MITSUI, T., FUKAMI, J., OHTAKI, T., *Agr. Biol. Chem.*, *35*, 1116 (1971).
34. COCHRANE, J. S., HANSON, J. R., *J. Chem. Soc. (Perkin I.)*, *1972*, 361.
35. MORI, K., SATO, A., MATSUI, M., *Agr. Biol. Chem.*, *36*, 1931 (1972).
36. IRELAND, R. E., MUELLER, R. H., *J. Am. Chem. Soc.*, *94*, 5897 (1972).
37. IRELAND, R. E., MÜLLER, R. H., WILLARD, A. K., *J. Org. Chem.*, *41*, 986 (1976) and references cited therein.
38. FRATER, G., *Helv. Chim. Acta*, *58*, 442 (1975).
39. COREY, E. J., KATZENELLENBOGEN, J. A., GILMAN, N. W., ROMAN, S. A., ERICKSON, B. W., *J. Am. Chem. Soc.*, *90*, 5618 (1968).
40. COREY, E. J., *Mitt. Schweiz. Entomol. Ges.*, *44*, 87 (1971).
41. ZURFLÜH, R., WALL, E. N., SIDDALL, J. B., EDWARDS, J. A., *J. Am. Chem. Soc.*, *90*, 6224 (1968).
42. JOHNSON, W. S., LI, T-t., FAULKNER, D. J., CAMPBELL, S. F., *J. Am. Chem. Soc.*, *90*, 6225 (1968).
43. JOHNSON, W. S., CAMPBELL, S. F., KRISHNAKUMARAN, A., MEYER, A. S., *Proc. Nat. Acad. Sci. U. S. A.*, *62*, 1005 (1969).
44. JOHNSON, W. S., BROCKSOM, T. J., LOEW, P., RICH, D. H., WERTHEMANN, L., ARNOLD, R. A., LI, T-t., FAULKNER, D. J., *J. Am. Chem. Soc.*, *92*, 4463 (1970).
45. LOEW, P., SIDDALL, J. B., SPAIN, V. L., WERTHEREMANN, L., *Proc. Nat. Acad. Sci. U. S. A.*, *67*, 1462 (1970).
46. LOEW, P., SIDDALL, J. B., SPAIN, V. L., WERTHEREMANN, L., *Proc. Nat. Acad. Sci. U. S. A.*, *67*, 1824 (1970).
47. COREY, E. J., YAMAMOTO, H., *J. Am. Chem. Soc.*, *92*, 226, 3523 (1970).
48. COREY, E. J., SHULMAN, J. I., YAMAMOTO, H., *Tetrahedron Letters*, *1970*, 447.
49. COREY, E. J., YAMAMOTO, H., *J. Am. Chem. Soc.*, *92*, 6636 (1970).
50. COREY, E. J., YAMAMOTO, H., *J. Am. Chem. Soc.*, *92*, 6637 (1970).
51. VAN TAMELEN, E. E., MCCURRY, P., HUBER, U., *J. Am. Chem. Soc.*, *68*, 1294 (1971).
52. MCCURRY JR., P. M., "Insect Juvenile Hormones", (Eds. J. J. Menn, M. Beroza), Academic Press, New York, 1972, p. p. 237—247.
53. MORI, K., OHKI, M., SATO, A., MATSUI, M., *Tetrahedron*, *28*, 3739 (1972).
54. MORI, K., *Tetrahedron*, *28*, 3747 (1972).
55. HENRICK, C. A., SCHAUB, F., SIDDALL, J. B., *J. Am. Chem. Soc.*, *94*, 5374 (1972).
56. ANDERSON, R. J., HENRICK, C. A., SIDDALL, J. B., ZURFLÜH, R., *J. Am. Chem. Soc.*, *94*, 5379 (1972).
57. MORI, K., OHKI, M., MATSUI, M., *Agr. Biol. Chem.*, *36*, 1085 (1972).
58. MORI, K., OHKI, M., MATSUI, M., *Tetrahedron*, *30*, 715 (1974).
59. OHKI, M., MORI, K., MATSUI, M., *Agr. Biol. Chem.*, *38*, 175 (1974).
60. GRIECO, P. A., *J. C. S. Chem. Commun.*, *1972*, 486.
61. KONDO, K., NEGISHI, A., MATSUI, K., TUNEMOTO, D., MASAMUNE, S., *J. C. S. Chem. Commun.*, *1972*, 1311.
62. DEMOUTE, J.-P., HAINAUT, D., TOROMANOFF, E., *Compt. rend. Acad. Sci., Ser. C*, *277*, 49 (1973).
63. STOTTER, P. L., HORNISH, R. E., *J. Am. Chem. Soc.*, *95*, 4444 (1973).
64. KOBAYASHI, S., MUKAIYAMA, A., *Chemistry Letters*, *1974*, 1425.
65. KOBAYASHI, S., MUKAIYAMA, T., *Chemistry Letters*, *1975*, 535.
66. TANAKA, S., YAMAMOTO, H., NOZAKI, H., SHARPLESS, K. B., MICHAELSON, R. C., CUTTING, J. D., *J. Am. Chem. Soc.*, *96*, 5254 (1974).
67. MEYER, A. S., HANZMANN, E., *Biochem. Biophys. Res. Commun.*, *41*, 891 (1970).
68. MEYER, A. S., HANZMANN, E., MURPHY, R. C., *Proc. Nat. Acad. Sci. U. S. A.*, *68*, 2312 (1971).
69. LOEW, P., JOHNSON, W. S., *J. Am. Chem. Soc.*, *93*, 3765 (1971).
70. NAKANISHI, K., SCHOOLEY, D. A., KOREEDA, M., DILLON, J., *Chem. Commun.*, *1971*, 1235.
71. DILLON, J., NAKANISHI, K., *J. Am. Chem. Soc.*, *97*, 5417 (1975).
72. FAULKNER, D. J., PETERSEN, M. R., *J. Am. Chem.*, *93*, 3766 (1971).
73. FAULKNER, D. J., PETERSEN, M. R., *J. Am. Chem.*, *95*, 553 (1973).
74. SUZUKI, Y., MARUMO, S., *Chem. Commun.*, *1971*, 1199.

75. SUZUKI, Y., MARUMO, S., *Tetrahedron Letters*, *1972*, 1887.
76. SUZUKI, Y., IMAI, K., MARUMO, S., MITSUI, T., *Agr. Biol. Chem.*, *36*, 1849 (1972).
77. IMAI, K., MARUMO, S., OHTAKI, T., *Tetrahedron Letters*, *1976*, 1211.
78. IMAI, K., MARUMO, S., MORI, K., *J. Am. Chem. Soc.*, *96*, 5925 (1974).
79. YAMADA, S., OH-HASHI, N., ACHIWA, K., *Tetrahedron Letters*, *1976*, 2557
80. YAMADA, S., OH-HASHI, N., ACHIWA, K., *Tetrahedron Letters*, *1976*, 2561.
81. TUTIHASI, R., HANAZAWA, T., *J. Chem. Soc. Japan*, *61*, 1045 (1940).
82. MOMOSE, T., *J. Pharm. Soc. Japan*, *61*, 289 (1941).
83. NAKAZAKI, M., ISOE, S., *Bull. Chem. Soc. Japan*, *36*, 1198 (1963).
84. BLOUNT, J. F., PAWSON, B. A., SAUCY, G., *Chem. Commun.*, *1969*, 715, 1016.
85. PAWSON, B. A., CHEUNG, H.-C., GURBAXANI, S., SAUCY, G., *Chem. Commun.*, *1968*, 1057.
86. PAWSON, B. A., CHEUNG, H.-C., GURBAXANI, S., SAUCY, G., *J. Am. Chem. Soc.*, *92*, 336 (1970).
87. SAKAI, T., HIROSE, Y., *Chemistry Letters*, *1973*, 491, 825.
88. ROGERS, I. H., MANVILLE, J. F., *Canad. J. Chem.*, *50*, 2380 (1972).
89. ROGERS, I. H., MANVILLE, J. F., SAHOTA, T., *Canad. J. Chem.*, *52*, 1192 (1974).
90. ČERNÝ, V., DOLEJŠ, L., LÁBLER, L., ŠORM, F., SLÁMA, K., *Tetrahedron Letters*, *1967*, 1053.
91. ČERNÝ, V., DOLEJŠ, L., LÁBLER, L., ŠORM, F., SLÁMA, K., *Coll. Czech. Chem. Commun.*, *32*, 3926 (1967).
92. MORI, K., MATSUI, M., *Tetrahedron Letters*, *1967*, 2515.
93. MORI, K., MATSUI, M., *Tetrahedron*, *24*, 3127 (1968).
94. AYYAR, K. S., RAO, G. S. K., *Tetrahedron Letters*, *1967*, 4677.
95. AYYAR, K. S., RAO, G. S. K., *Canad. J. Chem.*, *46*, 1467 (1968).
96. MORI, K., MATSUI, M., *Tetrahedron Letters*, *1967*, 4853.
97. MORI, K., MATSUI, M., YOSHIMURA, I., SAEKI, K., *Agr. Biol. Chem.*, *34*, 1204 (1970).
98. BIRCH, A. J., MACDONALD, P. L., POWELL, V. H., *Tetrahedron Letters*, *1969*, 351.
99. BIRCH, A. J., MACDONALD, P. L., POWELL, V. H., *J. Chem. Soc. (C)*, *1970*, 1469.
100. ŠORM, F., *Mitt. Schweiz. Entomol. Ges.*, *44*, 7 (1971).
101. FARGES, G., VESCHAMBRE, H., *Bull. Soc. chim. France*, *1973*, 3172.
102. FICINI, J., *Tetrahedron*, *32*, 1449 (1976).
103. FICINI, J., TOUZIN, A. M., *Tetrahedron Letters*, *1972*, 2093.
104. FICINI, J., TOUZIN, A. M., *Tetrahedron Letters*, *1972*, 2097
105. FICINI, J., D'ANGELO, J., NOIRÉ, J., *J. Am. Chem. Soc.*, *96*, 1213 (1974).
106. TROST, B. M., TAMARU, Y., *Tetrahedron Letters*, *1975*, 3797.
107. NEGISHI, E., SABANSKI, M., KATZ, J. J., BROWN, H. C., *Tetrahedron*, *32*, 925 (1976).

V. CONCLUDING REMARKS

We have surveyed various syntheses of insect pheromones and juvenile hormones which undoubtedly manifest the power of modern synthetic chemistry in executing stereoselective or chiral syntheses. The methodology will continue to progress in the future, and less expensive stereoselective syntheses will be made possible. For optically active compounds, more practical and efficient methods of asymmetric syntheses and resolutions will be developed. The stereoselective synthesis of juvabione with correct absolute stereochemistry is a challenging problem in the juvabione field. A particularly interesting problem is the generation of the correct absolute configuration of the asymmetric carbon atom on the free-rotating side chain. Apparently, the interesting molecules in insect chemistry will continue to be the targets of many synthetic efforts.

Finally it seems appropriate to make a short comment on the practical aspects of insect chemistry, although it is not the purpose of this article to review the flood of synthetic works on so-called "JH-mimics" or the use of pheromones as insect monitoring systems. The comment is based largely on the work of Mori *et al*. During 1969–1970 several JH-mimics were synthesized by the route outlined in Scheme 160 of Chapter IV. Their insecticidal activities were tested on rice stem-borer *(Chilo suppressalis)* and mosquito *(Culex pipiens)* [1]. None of them was satisfactory as an insecticide. However, scientists in the Zoecon Corporation, Palo Alto, U.S.A., were successful in killing mosquito larvae by their JH-mimics. Their insect growth regulator ZR-515 (Altosid, **1**) was extraordinarily effective and its ID_{50} value on the last instar larvae of the yellow fever mosquito, *Aedes aegypti*, was 0.00014 ppm, while that of ($\pm$)-JH I was as large as 0.15 ppm [2]. The insecticidal use is the major trend in applications of JH-mimics.

In 1971 Akai and his co-workers found an increased accumulation of silk protein accompanying juvenile hormone-induced prolongation of larval life in the silkworm *Bombyx mori* utilizing Mori's synthetic juvenile hormones [3]. The implication of this discovery is quite clear: JH-mimics can be used to increase the yield of silk. Nihmura *et al.* continued and developed this investigation using Mori's JH-mimics and established a practical method of utilizing JH mimics in silkworm rearing [4]. The significance of this work became even greater when it was found that silkworm fed on artificial diets instead of the traditional and costly mulberry leaves, could produce ordinary or even bigger cocoons when JH-mimics were administered orally [4]. The JH-mimics such as **2**, **3** and **4** (as stereoisomeric mixtures) were particularly active on *Bombyx mori* and 0.3 µg per larva of these compounds effected 20–30% increase in the yield of silk when orally administered [4, 5, 6]. Akai reviewed his work on the influence of the juvenile hormones on the growth and metamorphosis of *Bombyx* larvae [7]. Mori *et al.* concluded their works on the synthesis of JH-mimics by a paper entitled "The effect of molecular chain length on biological activity of juvenile hormone analogs" [8]. It was found that both the size of the terminal

Fig. 1. Workers feeding silkworms with artificial diets containing a juvenile hormone analogue

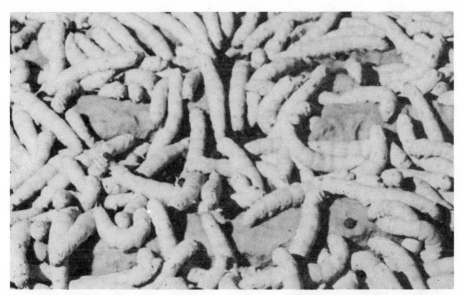

Fig. 2. Silkworms do not eat mulberry leaves, but prefer artificial diets

Fig. 3. Cocoons are harvested

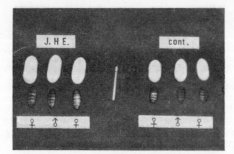

Fig. 4. Bigger cocoons (left) are produced by JH treatments*.
*Figures 1—4 were made available by the courtesy of Dr. M. Nihmura, Chuo-Sanken Co., Sayama City, Saitama, Japan

Fig. 5. The pheromone trap baited with 3,13-octadecadienyl acetate attracted many cherry tree borers shown by Kenji Mori.
(By the courtesy of Otsuka Pharmaceutical Co., Ltd. and Fukushima Prefectural Horticultural Experiment Station, Japan)

alkyl group and the molecular chain length are important for high juvenile hormone activity. The optimal chain length for high activity in *Bombyx mori* was shown to be 17 atoms. Figures 1–4 are photographs showing the practical application of JH-mimics in silkworm rearing in Japan. Noteworthy is the use of a pasty artificial diet instead of mulberry leaves as shown in Figures 1 and 2.

The practical use of insect pheromones is illustrated by Figure 5; the author himself is showing the pheromone traps in a peach orchard baited with a 1 : 1 mixture of $(3Z : 13Z)$- and $(3E : 13Z)$-3,13-octadecadienyl acetates (0.8 mg each). Numerous cherry tree borers (*Synanthedon hector* Butler) are caught on the sticky plates. The number of the trapped moths reflects the population density of this insect in the orchard and gives information useful in pest control.

In conclusion, the syntheses of insect pheromones and juvenile hormones are academically fascinating as well as practically important and are full of future potentialities.

This review covers the literatures published before June 1976.

*

    The author would like to express his gratitude to Professor Cs. Szántay for inviting him to write this article. His thanks are due to Professor M. Matsui, the Dean, Faculty of Agriculture of the University of Tokyo, for encouragement. He thanks his wife Keiko Mori for typing the manuscripts not only of this review, but also almost all of his papers on synthetic chemistry.

REFERENCES

1. MORI, K., *Mitt. Schweiz. Entomol. Ges.*, *44*, 17 (1971).
2. HENRICK, C. A., STAAL, G. B., SIDDALL, J. B., *J. Agr. Food Chem.*, *21*, 354 (1973).
3. AKAI, H., KIGUCHI, K., MORI, K., *Appl. Entomol. Zool.*, *6*, 218 (1971).
4. NIHMURA, M., AOMORI, S., MORI, K., MATSUI, M., *Agr. Biol. Chem.*, *36*, 889 (1972).
5. OZAWA, Y., MORI, K., MATSUI, M., *Agr. Biol. Chem.*, *37*, 2373 (1973).
6. NIHMURA, M., AOMORI, S., OZAWA, Y., MORI, K., MATSUI, M., *Appl. Entomol. Zool.*, *9*, 34 (1974).
7. AKAI, H., KIGUCHI, K., MORI, K., *Bull. Sericult. Expt. Station (Tokyo)*, *25*, 287 (1973) (in Japanese).
8. MORI, K., TAKIGAWA, T., MANABE, Y., TOMINAGA, M., MATSUI, M., KIGUCHI, K., AKAI, H., OHTAKI, T., *Agr. Biol. Chem.*, *39*, 259 (1975).

B. STOIANOVA–IVANOVA

COMPOSITION OF BULGARIAN
ROSE FLOWER CONCRETE
THE STRUCTURE AND BIOGENESIS
OF ITS COMPONENTS

I. INTRODUCTION

Since the remote past people have always been enchanted by the beauty of roses and their fragrance and have always shown great interest in the plant. It is known from ancient Egyptian inscriptions that roses were familiar as early as in the reign of Rameses II in that country. Egyptians extracted products for embalming from roses, thus preserving the bodies of the dead.

In Greek mythology roses were dedicated to Aphrodite and Dionysius; Sappho wrote songs about the rose being a symbol of beauty, love and youth. The Romans also admired roses [1].

Egyptians, Hellenes and Romans used the rose as a universal medicine. Rose preparations were prescribed for treatment of fever conditions, heart and brain ailments, jaundice, toothache, wounds and burns, tuberculosis, etc. [1].

It is believed that Syria is the homeland of *Rosa damascena* Mill. In the past it was cultivated in the environs of Damascus. Probably, *via* Turkey it was brought over to Bulgaria when the Ottomans invaded the Balkan Peninsula. Hadji Kalpha, the Ottoman geographer, is the only one to give information in writing on the introduction of the rose into the Balkan Peninsula in his book "Rumelia and Bosnia". In it mention is made of rose gardens in the environs of Adrianople [2].

It is only for 300 years that roses have been grown as a commercial crop in Bulgaria. Having found shelter in the Valley of Roses, from a primitive form (a hybrid of *Rosa gallica* and *Rosa canina*), it has been cultivated as a variety, known under the name *Rosa Kazanlik* all over the world at present.

The Valley of Roses is protected from the cold winds of the north, and from the warm summer winds which blow from the south drying both land and vegetation. The vast forests which cover the slopes of both mountain massifs (the Balkan Range and the Sredna Gora Mountains) help to retain moisture in the soil and air. Numerous rivulets and streams, rushing down from both massifs into the Toundja and Strema rivers, are brimful of water in May when roses blossom. They also maintain the air moisture in the Valley of Roses. It is mainly under the effect of these factors that considerable changes have taken place in the evolution of *Rosa damascena* Mill., transforming the stamens into petals and thus, from a rose of few petals, it has become a thirty-petal oil-bearing rose. It is in this way that the rose crop, specific to Bulgaria, has been developed. And at present, just as in the past, Bulgaria occupies the foremost place in the production of rose oil among countries making essential oils [3]. The fact that the quality of Bulgarian rose oil, obtained by hydrodistillation, is unsurpassed and highly appraised all over the world is of no lesser significance.

Interest in rose oil is growing also from a therapeutical point of view. The curative properties of Bulgarian rose oil for gallbladder and liver ailments, for spastic conditions of the stomach muscles and for bronchial asthma are well-known.

Thus it is not strange that the Bulgarian oil-bearing rose and the products obtained from it have been of interest since the past up to present times to both foreign and Bulgarian researchers [4, 5]. The first studies by Markownikoff and Reformatski on the composition of stearoptene from the Bulgarian rose oil [6] merit attention. Subsequent studies by Guenther, Garnier, Gieldemeister, Hoffmann and Naves are particularly valuable.

P. Raikov [7] is considered as the pioneer of these studies among Bulgarian researchers. In 1898 a standard method of determining the freezing point of rose oil was suggested by him. A. Zlatarov has also contributed to these studies. Yet, these initial researches in Bulgaria were only accidental ones. It was as late as 1951 that regular studies on the composition of rose oil, obtained from the Bulgarian oil-bearing rose, were launched under the guidance of D. Ivanov [8–17].

In their report to the Third International Essential Oil Congress, N. Nikolov and I. Ognyanov note that in spite of the effort of foreign and Bulgarian researchers to establish the composition of Bulgarian rose oil, it contains still unidentified micro-components and the evaluation of its properties is still determined by the skilful olfaction of experts, dealers in perfumes [3]. These micro-components could be of significance not only for their excellent perfumery properties, but also in respect of the therapeutical properties of rose oil and of preparations made from it.

Concrete and its components (wax and absolute) is another important product of the Bulgarian oil-bearing rose. They just like rose oil, obtained by hydrodistillation, also find large-scale application in cosmetics, perfum-

ery and dermatology, and are commercial products of first rate significance. Literature data relating to them are, however, very scanty, and their
composition is almost unknown.

This paper summarizes the results of our investigations on the composition
of the wax and absolute from concrete of the Bulgarian oil-bearing rose.
Along with this, certain conclusions are drawn concerning the biogenesis of
the straight-chain wax components. The conclusions are based mainly on
the correlations in the quantitative relations of the components, on analogies
in the structures of these components and also on results obtained from the
follow-up of the changes in the composition of the wax during the period
the bud develops into a flower.

II. CONCRETE FROM BULGARIAN OIL-BEARING ROSE.
GENERAL CHARACTERISTICS

The concrete is obtained from rose flowers by extraction with a light organic solvent (usually petroleum ether) [18, 19] and subsequent removal of
the solvent.

It is believed that the preparation of rose flower concrete is a more modern
method for the isolation of aromatic (having a pleasant odour) substances
of the rose than their isolation by steam distillation. The rose concrete
("essence de rose concrète") contains both readily volatile components
(possessing the pleasant smell of the rose flower) and also not readily volatile
components (mainly paraffins) which serve to retain the volatile components
of the flower. The separation of the concrete into "wax" and "absolute"
is done by dissolution in hot alcohol (saturated solution) and cooling of the
solution to 0°C. Under these conditions, the higher molecular and, due to
this, not so readily volatile, components which are not readily soluble in
alcohol, are precipitated. The latter are filtered off and constitute the wax.
Absolute *("essence de rose absolue")* is obtained from the filtrate by eva-
poration of the solvent. It contains more low-molecular components, and
hence the more readily volatile components of the concrete.

Both concrete and absolute are used in perfumery and cosmetics on a
large scale. According to the data quoted by Guenther [18], the amount of
the rose concrete produced exceeds that of the distilled rose oil. The main
centres for the production of concrete are in the Grasse region in France,
and to a lesser extent, in Morocco. However, *Rosa centifolia* is only grown
in both countries. The flowers of this rose proved to be unsuitable for steam
distillation (hydrodistillation), since they yield an insignificant amount of

distilled oil. The Bulgarian oil-bearing roses, *Rosa damascena* Mill. and in part *Rosa alba* L. may be processed either by hydrodistillation or by extraction with a light organic solvent. The preparation of concrete in Bulgaria was introduced by Charles Garnier, who in 1904 built an equipment for the extraction of rose flower, consisting of six rotating extractors. His example was followed by some of the big producers of rose oil in Bulgaria, and there were 32 sets of such equipment in Bulgaria in 1938. The production of concrete in this country reached the 2000 kg mark in the next few years. It was established that one kilogram of concrete was obtained from 400 to 450 kg of rose flower, and about 520 g of absolute was obtainable from one kilogram of concrete [20].

The concrete thus isolated from Bulgarian rose flowers constitutes a light-yellow to dark-brown wax-like mass, having the typical aroma of roses. According to Walbaum and Rosenthal [21], concrete of Bulgarian rose flowers has a freezing point 41–46.5°C, (44.4°C on an average) and an acid number between 31 and 56. In the opinion of Guenther, the data concerning the composition of concrete and absolute are scanty, since they have not been studied carefully, unlike the rose oil obtained by steam distillation. It is noted, however, that phenylethyl alcohol, which is an insignificant component of the rose oil when obtained by hydrodistillation of the flower, is an important component of the products obtained by extraction. Glichitch and Naves [22] subjected Bulgarian concrete from roses to steam distillation under reduced pressure and obtained a volatile oil which contained 63.7% of phenylethyl alcohol, 22.1% of citronellol, and 13.7% of geraniol and nerol. According to Naves [23] insignificant amounts of eugenol, eugenol acetate and traces of a ketone are contained in the rose concrete.

It is obvious from what has been stated so far that the concrete is one of the main products in the processing of rose flower. It is also evident that the composition of the concrete, as well as that of the products obtained from it, wax and absolute, have not been sufficiently studied.

Our studies relate mainly to the composition of the wax, since it is the component of the concrete which has been investigated to a lesser extent. A more profound study of the composition of the wax, including its microcomponents, is certainly indispensable also in view of our desire to contribute to the settlement of the widely discussed problem of the biogenesis of the straight-chain components of plant waxes and, in particular, of normal hydrocarbons with even and odd numbers of carbon atoms. The composition of the absolute, although not studied methodically so far, should logically be close to that of the rose oil, to the composition of which the greatest part of studies has been dedicated. In the case of the absolute the main question is the difference between its composition and the composition of the rose oil obtained by hydrodistillation, as well as the presence of other, not so readily volatile components, lacking in the rose oil. The latter are contained in the concrete, and as a result of certain solubility in alcohol, they may pass in part or entirely into the absolute.

We likewise believe that a detailed investigation of the concrete of rose flower may throw light on the contents of certain micro components of the rose oil, which have not been detected so far, and whose significance has been mentioned in the preface.

III. COMPOSITION OF WAX FROM ROSE FLOWER CONCRETE AND THE STRUCTURES OF ITS COMPONENTS

The first data in the literature on the composition of wax from rose flower are those reported by Prophète [24]. He studied wax from French rose flowers in the region of Grasse. An attempt was made to carry out a complete investigation of the wax: general characteristics, study of the composition of acids, alcohols and hydrocarbons. At the state of technique at that time, however, Prophète was unable to identify the alcohols, the acids and the unsaturated hydrocarbons. His data on the content of saturated hydrocarbons are more complete. He reported that he was able to isolate the normal saturated hydrocarbons C_{30}, C_{27}, C_{26}, C_{23}, C_{22}, C_{21}, C_{20} and C_{16} and he even indicated their percentage. In our opinion [25], however, and also according to Naves and Mazuyer [26], the hydrocarbons isolated by Prophète were only mixtures. As far as unsaturated hydrocarbons are concerned, Prophète noted only the isolation of two bromides, having m.p. 27 °C and 38.5–39 °C.

Simultaneously with our first studies on the wax from concrete of the Bulgarian rose flower, Chibnall, El Mangouri and Piper [27], in 1954, published investigations on the components of long-chain paraffins in the wax of rose flower concrete. The results of studies on the paraffins having a chain longer than 21 carbon atoms are presented in this paper. In the course of these investigations, using fractional vacuum distillation, the authors separated the mixture of higher paraffins contained in the wax of rose flower concrete into a large number of fractions. They carried out a detailed analysis of each of these fractions by determining the melting point, the point of transformation, and by X-ray measurements; they then compared the data obtained with the corresponding values of pure paraffins

and their mixtures. They showed that paraffins with an odd number of
carbon atoms from C_{21} to C_{35} are contained in the wax, but they did not
establish definite data on the presence of paraffins with an even number of
carbon atoms. In their opinion, there are also small amounts of paraffins
with a chain length shorter than C_{21} in the wax, but they have not been
described. Studies on rose wax were carried out simultaneously with ours
also in the Institute of Organic Chemistry and Biochemistry in Czechoslo-
vakia by Šorm and his co-workers [28–31]. The results of these investigations
will be discussed simultaneously with our results in the corresponding
passages.

1. QUANTITATIVE CHANGES IN THE COMPONENTS OF THE WAX DURING THE DEVELOPMENT OF THE BUDS INTO FLOWERS

Unlike other researchers who have investigated the composition of the
wax from rose flower, we have also carried out parallel studies on the wax
from concrete of rose buds and rose flowers, collected by us from the same
bushes, in order to obtain data on the dynamics of component formation.

Rose flowers, big and small buds were simultaneously picked from the
same bushes on a field in the village of Zelenikovo (District of Plovdiv)
early in June, 1963. The crushed flowers and the cut buds were extracted
with petroleum ether free of unsaturated compounds [32]. The amounts of
wax and absolute from all three samples are presented in Table I.

Table I

Wax and Absolute Contents in Rose Bud
and Rose Flower Concrete

Concrete from	Contents per 100 g of concrete		
	wax	absolute	losses
Rose flowers	38.44	53.90	7.66
Big buds	38.97	51.89	9.14
Small buds	38.03	49.30	12.30

The results indicate that wax contents in all three concretes are almost
the same. Differences are smaller than one per cent, and they fall within the
limits of experimental error inherent in the method used for the separation
of the concrete into wax and absolute. The percentage of the absolute isolated
from all three types of concrete seemingly increase from the small buds to the
flowers. If, however, the percentage of the absolute and the losses during its

isolation are added up, as the latter decrease from the small buds to the flowers, equal values are obtained also for the percentage of the absolute. The rise in losses from the flowers towards the small buds may be explained by a higher content of readily volatile compounds in the absolute from the buds.

The results for the changes in the concrete, wax and absolute during the development of the individual bud to flower are presented in Table II, based on data that 100 g of small buds, big buds and rose flower contain on an average 85, 75 and 36 pieces of each, respectively.

Table II

Content of Concrete, Wax and Absolute in 100 Numbers of Small Buds, Big Buds and Flowers

Initial material	Content per 100 flowers or buds					
	concrete (g)		wax (g)		absolute (g)	
Rose flowers	0.9591		0.3688		0.5169	
		0.2097		0.0765		0.1364
Big buds	0.7494		0.2921		0.3805	
		0.1763		0.0741		0.0935
Small buds	0.5731		0.2180		0.2850	

Comparisons show that during the growth of the bud and its transformation into a flower, the amount of concrete and the amounts of wax and absolute, obtained from it, increase. Moreover, the wax content increases to a lesser extent than the amount of the absolute, and this is more markedly so particularly towards the completion of the bud development into flower. The same ratio is preserved when the losses during the isolation of the absolute are taken into account. This course of the changes shows that the components of the wax, the long-chain aliphatic compounds are formed chiefly at the initial stages of bud development, while the components of the absolute (acyclic terpene compounds) are formed mainly in the final stages.

Results of the determinations of certain characteristic numbers of the waxes studied are shown in Table III.

These data show that the content of free acids remains almost unchanged during the growth of the bud into a flower. The largest amount of free and ester-bound acids is present in the wax from rose flowers, and the least in the wax from concrete of small buds. The amount of unsaturated compounds increases in the process of the development of buds into flowers.

Table III

Characteristic Numbers of the Waxes from Rose Buds
and Rose Flowers

Wax from concrete of	Acid number	Saponification number	Ester number	Iodine number
Rose flowers	10.21	44.07	33.86	38.23
Big buds	10.17	43.75	33.58	34.27
Small buds	10.11	40.62	30.51	32.86

The characteristic numbers established for the wax from rose flowers and those determined by us for wax from another harvest [25] are very close to each other. A comparison of the general characteristics of the wax from the concrete of Bulgarian rose flower with those obtained from French rose flower [24] shows that the Bulgarian wax possesses higher saponification, acid, ester and iodine numbers (Table IV).

Table IV

Characteristic Numbers of Wax from Concretes from Bulgarian
and French Rose Flowers

Wax from concrete of	Acid number	Saponification number	Ester number	Iodine number
Bulgarian rose flower (from the environs of the town of Kazanlik), 1938	11.00	48.50	37.50	24.00
Bulgarian rose flower (from Zelenikovo), 1963	10.21	44.07	33.86	38.23
French rose flower (from the region of Grasse)	3.15	29.80	26.65	13.60

Results of the simultaneous investigation of the unsaponifiable and saponifiable substances and of free acids [33] in all three waxes, carried out on ion-exchange resin [34] (Wofatit SBW), are shown in Table V.

Table V

Content of Unsaponifiable and Saponifiable Substances
and Free Acids in Wax from Buds (Small and Big)
and Rose Flower (Percentage of Wax)

Kind of wax	Unsaponifiable	Saponifiable	Free acids	Losses
Rose flowers	67.80	12.80	3.72	15.68
Big buds	68.02	9.56	3.44	18.98
Small buds	71.16	8.36	4.16	16.32

These results show that a considerable part of the waxes is lost during the separation and processing of the samples. However, our experiment to separate a model mixture, containing higher fatty ester and acid on Wofatite SBW, indicated insignificant losses (only about 1%). This gave us grounds to suggest that the losses presented in Table V should be due to products formed during saponification, which were not extracted by the organic solvent. Using the method of Smullin [34], we established with the aid of paper-chromatography that all three samples studied contained considerable amounts of glycerol. According to literature data, up to our investigations no glycerides have been detected in wax from rose flower.

The results of a group chromatographic analysis of the neutral wax from all three samples on aluminum oxide, checked by IR spectra, are presented in Fig. 1.

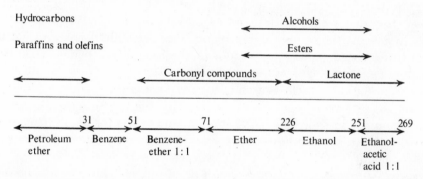

Fig. 1. Group chromatographic analysis of neutral wax on aluminium oxide

Complete separation of the hydrocarbons from the oxygen-containing compounds of the wax samples has been achieved by means of group analysis. A part of the carbonyl compounds has also been isolated in the pure state. It is worthwhile noting that these are the first spectral data on the presence of a carbonyl compound (probably ketone), as well as of a secondary alcohol and lactone in rose flower wax.

The separation into paraffins and olefins has been achieved by means of oxidation with performic acid, hydrolysis of the epoxy compounds obtained, followed by chromatographic separation of the paraffins and glycols. Quantitative data of the group analysis of the three wax samples, as well as those giving the amounts of paraffins and olefins in the hydrocarbon fraction are presented in Table VI.

Table VI

Components of Three Wax Samples, %

Wax from	Petroleum ether		Benzene	Benzene : ether 1 : 1	Ether	Ethanole	Acetic acid : ethanol 1 : 1
	Paraffins	Olefins		Carbonyl compounds	Carbonyl compounds, esters, alcohols		Lactone
Rose flowers	45.51						
	38.60	6.91	0.17	6.43	20.72	1.20	19.05
Big buds	49.46						
	41.07	8.39	0.19	7.78	21.76	0.76	17.78
Small buds	47.52						
	40.20	7.31	0.18	7.66	22.05	1.0	17.98

These data show that the percentage of hydrocarbons is the highest in the wax obtained from big buds, and the lowest in the wax obtained from rose flower. It is seen from Tables V and VI that during the development of the buds to flowers, the amount of unsaponifiables generally decreases (that of the hydrocarbons shows a maximum in the case of big buds), while the amount of saponifiables increases. Taking into account the fact that 45 days are needed for the transformation of a barely noticeable bud into one with a diameter of 5 mm (small buds), 15 days for the transition of the latter into big ones with a diameter of 12–15 mm, and 3 days for the development of the big buds into rose flowers, it is clear that the most significant changes in the amount of unsaponifiables (of hydrocarbons in particular), as well as of saponifiables occur during the transition of the big buds into rose flower. That can clearly be seen in Fig. 2.

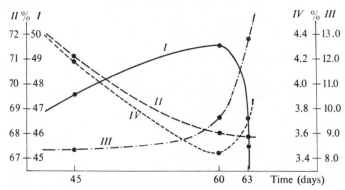

Fig. 2. Change of the amounts of hydrocarbons, unsaponifiables, saponifiables and free acids during the development of the buds into flowers. *I* — Hydrocarbons, *II* — unsaponifiables, *III* — saponifiables, *IV* — free acids

The results obtained from these investigations, namely, that the percentage of unsaponifiables is the highest in the case of small buds, and the amount of the hydrocarbons abruptly drops during the transition from big buds into flowers, make possible the assumption that even though unexpected, the hydrocarbons are not the final products in the metabolism of the wax components. Actually, as early as 1934, Chibnall and Piper assumed in one of their papers [35] that the ketones are final products in the metabolism of the waxes, and not intermediate ones. In 1970 Kolattukudy, using labelled atoms, confirmed reliably this inference from our results.

2. COMPOSITION AND STRUCTURE
OF THE LONG-CHAIN ALIPHATIC HYDROCARBONS

In 1926 Prophète [24] isolated saturated hydrocarbons from rose wax and demonstrated that they contained also unsaturated ones. However, data had been published on the content of hydrocarbons in stereoptene* from rose oil before him [6, 11–13, 37–42].

In the course of our initial studies on the composition of hydrocarbons in the wax from rose concrete [25], the conventional methods were used. It was with their aid that we were able to isolate and establish, in broad outlines, the qualitative and quantitative compositions of the hydrocarbons in the mixture and especially of those present in larger amounts. Later on, using the possibilities of separation and identification offered by thin-layer and gas-liquid chromatographies, we studied again the composition of the hydrocarbons from the wax of rose concrete in greater detail. Thus, we were able not only to determine the complete qualitative and quantitative compositions of the paraffinic and olefinic hydrocarbons, but also to detect another type of hydrocarbon, alkadienes with conjugated double bonds, which had not been established as components of plant waxes before our investigations.

---

* Stereoptene is a product from rose oil obtained by hydrodistillation. It precipitates when the rose oil is dissolved in 70% alcohol and the solution is cooled in ice.

A. Composition and Structure
of the Long-Chain Paraffinic Hydrocarbons

Our first investigations of paraffinic hydrocarbons, using conventional methods, dealt with the wax obtained by large-scale preparation of absolute from concrete [25]. The hydrocarbons were isolated from the unsaponifiables by column chromatography. They constitute 34.5% of the wax, and 56% of the unsaponifiables. The presence of the following paraffinic hydrocarbons was established: C_{31}, C_{30}, C_{29}, C_{28}, C_{27}, C_{25}, C_{23}, C_{22}, C_{20} and C_{19}. However, we were unable to give a reliable estimation of the amounts in which they were represented in the hydrocarbon mixture.

Later on, we carried out a comparative study of the saturated hydrocarbons in buds and flower, using modern methods of the investigation of natural products [43]. In this case the concrete from small buds, big buds and flower was obtained by us, the buds and flower being collected from the same bushes; for the 1963 harvest in the village of Zelenikovo, District of Plovdiv, and for the 1968 harvest in the town of Karlovo [32, 33]. The separation of saturated from unsaturated hydrocarbons was achieved by means of column chromatography of the hydrocarbon mixture on silica gel, impregnated with silver nitrate, by the method employed by Rousseva-Atanasova and Ianak [44]. It was found that the total amount of paraffins in the wax from buds amounted to 39.12%, and that of olefins to 7.46%; in the wax from flower these values were 37.59% and 7.23%, respectively. The results agreed well with those obtained by us in the separation of paraffins and olefins by means of transforming the latter into epoxy compounds [33]; in that case we found 40.21% paraffins and 7.31% olefins in the wax of buds, and 38.60 and 6.90%, respectively, in the wax of flower. These results showed that during the development of the buds into flowers the paraffin : olefin ratio remained practically unchanged.

Results obtained by treatment of the mixture with urea indicated that in both waxes studied the content of strongly branched hydrocarbons was insignificant, about 0.1%. Subsequent processing on molecular sieve of the hydrocarbons obtained from urea adducts from the waxes both from buds and flower, indicated a content of slightly branched hydrocarbons below 1%. The fact is noteworthy that in our experiments with molecular sieve, we were unable to desorb the hydrocarbons from the sieve even after prolonged extraction. Only about 50% of the hydrocarbons retained on the sieve could be desorbed. As there is no guarantee that the degree of desorption is equal for all the individual homologues in the hydrocarbon mixture,

Table VII

Percentage Composition of Normal Paraffins
in the Wax from Rose Buds and Rose Flower Concrete

Number of C-atoms	Wax of buds	Wax of flowers	Number of C-atoms	Wax of buds	Wax of flowers
17	0.4	0.6	25	8.7	6.8
18	0.2	traces	26	0.8	0.7
19	13.9	18.4	27	21.6	18.9
20	1.7	2.2	28	1.2	1.1
21	12.2	17.3	29	12.8	11.3
22	0.9	0.8	30	traces	traces
23	12.3	12.6	31	12.3	8.8
24	1.0	0.6	32	—	—
			33	traces	

we performed a gas-chromatographic study of the saturated hydrocarbons from both waxes immediately after their treatment with urea.

The individual compositions of the hydrocarbons are presented in Table VII.

It is seen that there is no significant difference in the individual compositions of the hydrocarbons in the two waxes. Paraffins with odd-numbered carbon atoms are prevalent, C_{27} being predominant, followed by C_{19}. Of the even-numbered hydrocarbons the amounts of C_{20} and C_{28} are the highest.

Table VIII

Normal Paraffins in the Wax from Flowers
of Two Harvests Prior to Treatment with Urea, %

Number of C-atoms	Harvest 1963	Harvest 1968
19	16.8	14.5
20	2.2	2.3
21	15.8	14.8
22	0.9	1.1
23	9.6	12.2
24	1.1	1.8
25	7.0	7.5
26	2.3	1.4
27	19.2	21.1
28	—	1.5
29	15.2	12.6
30	—	—
31	6.6	9.1

In order to see to what extent the ratios of the individual members remain constant, we carried out gas-liquid chromatography of the paraffins from rose flower of two different harvests, and moreover, from roses picked in two different localities in the Valley of Roses. The results are presented in Table VIII. They show a good repetition and confirm that C_{27} is the predominant hydrocarbon in the wax from rose flower.

As already mentioned, studies on the composition of paraffins from the wax of rose flower (*Rosa damascena* Mill.) were carried out also in the Institute of Organic Chemistry and Biochemistry of the Czechoslovak Academy of Sciences by Wollrab et al. [28, 45, 30]. A comparison of their results on the individual composition of *n*-paraffins with our data shows that Wollrab et al. found the amount of hydrocarbon C_{31} to be the highest, whereas in our case it is C_{27}. It was because of this difference that we performed studies on the paraffinic hydrocarbons from two different harvests, prior to and after treatment with urea, and got a good repetition of the results. The most probable reason for the difference, as well as for others to be mentioned further on, in our opinion, is that we used wax obtained by us personally from rose flower, while Wollrab et al. dealt with wax whose origin was not certain, as it was obtained from a factory in the GDR.

They also found insignificant amounts of paraffins with branched chain. They showed by gas-liquid chromatography that probably two types of branched-chain paraffins were present belonging to two homologous series: 2-methyl and 3-methylparaffins for one, and dimethylparaffins containing either one methyl group each at both ends of the chain, or both methyl groups at one end of the chain, for the other series.

B. Composition and Structure of the Long-Chain Olefinic Hydrocarbons

Olefins in the wax of the oil-bearing rose, just like the paraffins, have been studied by us in two stages. Initially, we used conventional methods [46]. Later on, the results obtained mainly for the individual composition of unsaturated hydrocarbons were revised using modern methods for the isolation and identification of hydrocarbons in natural products [43].

The separation of unsaturated and saturated hydrocarbons was effected by column chromatography on silica gel impregnated with silver nitrate and checked by thin-layer chromatography on silica gel, also impregnated with silver nitrate. The data of thin-layer chromatography indicated the presence of two types of olefins: *cis* and *trans* [47], the *cis* compounds being present in a larger amount. Moreover, thin-layer chromatography revealed that the unsaturated hydrocarbon fraction of the wax also contained another type of unsaturated hydrocarbons with a lower R_f value than that of the olefins, indicating the presence of more unsaturated hydrocarbons than olefins. The separation of the olefinic hydrocarbons from these more un-saturated ones was accomplished by preparative thin-layer chromatography. The presence of *cis-* and *trans*-olefins was also confirmed by IR spectra (maximum at 730 cm^{-1} and at 960 cm^{-1}). Likewise, it was shown by the IR spectra that the double bond was mainly due to $-CH=$ groups (maximum at 3010–3030 cm^{-1}).

Since it was difficult to establish the individual composition of the olefinic hydrocarbons by direct gas chromatography owing to the lack of standards, they were hydrogenated in the presence of Adams catalyst in glacial acetic acid. The paraffins obtained were gas-chromatographed at a programmed temperature from 100 to 275°C. The data on the gas-liquid chromatography of the hydrogenated olefins from bud and flower waxes are presented in Table IX.

Table IX

Paraffins Determined by Gas-liquid Chromatography in the Hydrogenated Olefin Fractions from Rose Bud and Rose Flower Waxes, %

Number of C-atoms	Wax of buds	Wax of flowers	Number of C-atoms	Wax of buds	Wax of flowers
19	3.3	3.0	26	2.3	1.9
20	0.4	0.3	27	21.5	24.5
21	3.4	3.2	28	3.7	3.7
22	0.7	0.4	29	33.5	34.8
23	8.8	6.0	30	0.8	0.8
24	1.4	1.3	31	7.6	8.5
25	11.2	9.6	32	—	—
			33	1.4	2.1

It follows from the results obtained that there is no significant difference in the individual content of olefins in the two waxes. The olefins, just like the paraffins, are present in the homologous series C_{19}–C_{33}. Odd-numbered members are prevalent, C_{29} and C_{27} being the dominant ones.

Our results for the presence of olefinic hydrocarbons in wax from rose flower compared with those of Wollrab et al. [45] agree well in showing the predominance of C_{29} and C_{27} olefins, as well as that of the *cis* compounds. Moreover, by means of ozonization Wollrab [30] obtained data on the content of *cis*-alkenes with 5 and 7 carbon atoms.

C. Composition and Structure of the Long-Chain Diene
Hydrocarbons

As mentioned above, during the separation of the hydrocarbon mixture from the wax of rose flower into saturated and unsaturated hydrocarbons, it was observed that, in addition to *cis-* and *trans-*olefins, also other compounds with lower R_f-values were contained in the unsaturated hydrocarbon fraction. The latter were isolated by preparative thin-layer chromatography [48]. After removal of the solvent in a stream of nitrogen gas, 11.2 mg (0.2% of the wax) of these hydrocarbons was isolated. Using thin-layer chromatography on silica gel–gypsum and petroleum ether as the mobile phase, they showed a spot in the front, an indication that they were actually hydrocarbons. Their IR spectrum had a maximum at 1640 cm^{-1}, 970 cm^{-1}, 3020 cm^{-1}, and a slight splitting of the peak at 1380 cm^{-1}. The UV spectrum in pentane had a maximum at 221 nm (ε 19.500). These data pointed to the presence of a system of conjugated double bonds. The lack of a broad absorption band in the IR spectrum at 1580–1650 cm^{-1} was an indication for the absence of a polyene chain, while the absence of absorption at 990 cm^{-1} and 910 cm^{-1} showed the lack of a terminal methylene group Therefore, the isolated unsaturated hydrocarbons must be dienes, having a system of conjugated double bonds, but not at the end of the chain.

Since the results of investigations of wax from rose flower by us and other researchers, as well as of other plant waxes have shown that paraffinic and olefinic hydrocarbons are usually present as homologous series, we expected that the diene hydrocarbons, isolated by us for the first time, would also represent a homologous series. This assumption was confirmed by hydrogenation of the isolated fraction of the diene hydrocarbons and gas-liquid chromatography of the hydrogenation products. The latter was carried out with programming from 100 to 300°C. The results are given in Table X. These results show that the isolated product is a mixture of conjugated alkadienes in which members with odd and even numbers of carbon atoms in the C_{11}–C_{33} range are present. Moreover, the odd-numbered members are present in a higher amount than the even-numbered ones in the C_{17}–C_{33} range. The C_{19}, C_{29}, C_{27}, C_{21} and C_{25} hydrocarbons (arranged in a descending order of their amount) are prevalent. The paraffins identified in the C_{11}–C_{18} range originate possibly from the diene hydrocarbons with branched chains, since after hydrogenation the hydrocarbon mixture was purified from the unsaturated hydrocarbons before gas-liquid chromatography. The IR spectrum, showing the splitting of the peak at 1380 cm^{-1}, is in agreement with this assumption.

Table X

Hydrocarbons Determined by Gas-liquid Chromatography in
the Hydrogenated Alkadiene Fraction

Number of C-atoms	%	Number of C-atoms	%	Number of C-atoms	%
X_1	0.4	X_{10}	0.3	C_{21}	6.9
C_{11}	1.2	X_{11}	0.7	C_{22}	0.7
X_2	0.2	X_{12}	1.3	C_{23}	4.7
X_3	1.2	C_{15}	3.1	C_{24}	1.0
C_{12}	3.2	X_{13}	traces	C_{25}	6.0
X_4	1.1	X_{14}	0.9	C_{26}	1.3
X_5	0.8	C_{16}	4.6	C_{27}	8.2
X_6	0.3	X_{15}	0.8	C_{28}	2.3
C_{13}	4.5	C_{17}	3.1	C_{29}	9.3
X_7	0.5	X_{16}	traces	C_{30}	1.1
X_8	1.3	C_{18}	1.1	C_{31}	2.8
X_9	1.5	C_{19}	14.2	X_{17}	traces
C_{14}	4.5	C_{20}	2.9	C_{33}	0.8

To corroborate the fact that the conjugated alkadienes are contained in rose flower and are not formed by dehydration of the corresponding α, β-glycols under the catalytic action of the aluminium oxide, we carried out an experiment with a model mixture. To this end we converted olefins from the wax into α, β-glycols by oxidation with performic acid and subsequent hydrolysis. The glycols were chromatographed on a column of aluminium oxide under the same conditions. The course of the chromatography was followed by thin-layer chromatography. No formation of dienes was established.

No alkadienes have been reliably identified in natural waxes so far. Certain experimental facts observed in studying waxes have been interpreted by their authors as an indication of the presence of alkadienes, however, no reference to conjugated double bonds [30] has been made. Thus, the results obtained by us, show for the first time the presence of conjugated alkadienes as components of plant waxes.

The simultaneous presence of straight-chain saturated, olefinic and diene hydrocarbons in the wax of rose flower and the fact that in all three homologous series the hydrocarbons having an odd number of carbon atoms are prevalent with a particularly good correlation of the amounts of the dominant paraffins and olefins, make it possible to assume a biogenetic relationship among them.

The distribution curves of all three types of hydrocarbons in the wax from rose flower are presented in Fig. 3.

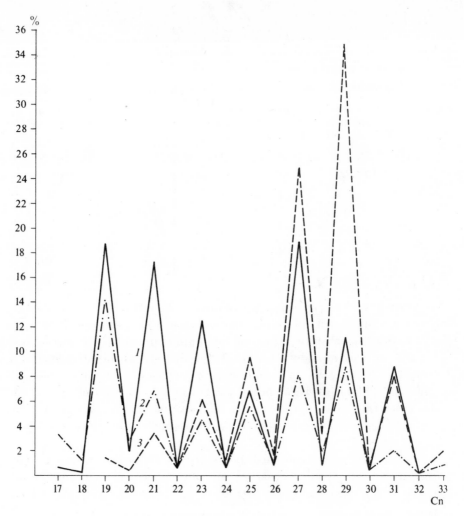

Fig. 3. Distribution curves of paraffins (*1*), alkaldienes (*2*) and olefins (*3*) in wax from rose flower

In addition, as it may be seen, the amounts of olefins with both even and odd numbers of carbon atoms in the C_{17}–C_{29} range continuously increase. C_{29}, C_{27} and C_{25} of the odd-numbered olefins, and C_{28}, C_{26} and C_{24} of the even-numbered ones are prevalent. These results give us grounds to assume a biogenetic relationship between them where the length of the chain is changed by one carbon atom.

3. COMPOSITION AND STRUCTURE
OF THE LONG-CHAIN FATTY ACIDS

The study of the acids in rose flower, like that of the hydrocarbons, was made by us in several stages during the 1962–1970 period.

Prophète [24] had studied the fatty acids in the wax from French rose flower before us. He proceeded, however, with the classical methods of separation and was unable to identify the acids. He showed only that 62.3% of saturated acids and 37.4% of unsaturated ones were contained in the water-insoluble acid fraction. Simultaneously with us, Wollrab [30] carried out investigations on the composition of fatty acids in the wax from *Rosa damascena* Mill. of a non-specified origin.

The results presented in Table V showed that the wax from Bulgarian rose flower contained 67.80% of unsaponifiable, 12.80% of saponifiable and 3.72% of free acids. Our first study of the acids [49], both free and ester-bound, was made by means of paper chromatography using the method of Kaufman. In this way we obtained qualitative indications for the presence of the saturated fatty acids C_8, C_{10}, C_{12}, C_{16}, C_{18} and C_{20}.

Later on, utilizing the possibilities offered by gas-liquid chromatography, we revised our first investigations. Simultaneous studies on the acids occurring in rose buds and rose flower were carried out, too [50, 51]. These

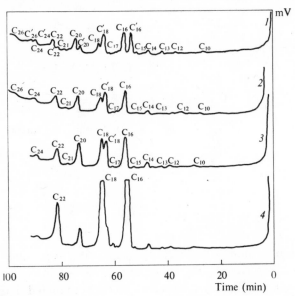

Fig. 4. Chromatogram of methyl esters of ester-bound fatty acids in wax from small buds (*1*), big buds (*2*), rose flowers (*3*) and standards (*4*)

investigations were done with wax from concrete, prepared by us [32]. The
ester-bound acids from all three waxes (from small buds, big buds and rose
flower) were isolated using the procedure described above [49]. They were
transformed into methyl esters by treatment with diazomethane. The esters
were subjected to gas-liquid chromatography on a non-polar immobile
phase under programming of the temperature [50]. Methyl esters of the
stearic, palmitic and behenic acids, methylated under identical conditions,
were used as standards. The chromatograms of the methyl esters of acids
from small buds, big buds and rose flower are given in Fig. 4.

The data giving the composition of ester-bound acids are presented in
Table XI.

Table XI

Ester-bound Acids in the Wax from
Small Buds, Big Buds and Rose Flower, %

Number of C-atoms	Wax from small buds	Wax from big buds	Wax from rose flower
C_{10}	0.55	0.6	0.7
C_{12}	0.4	0.8	1.0
C_{13}	1.4	traces	0.5
C_{14}	3.0	3.1	3.7
C_{15}	1.3	traces	0.5
C'_{16}*	10.7	—	—
C_{16}	17.1	20.7	21.4
C_{17}	traces	traces	0.2
C'_{18}	18.0	22.3	20.7
C_{18}	10.3	17.9	22.0
C_{19}	—	—	traces
C'_{20}	4.5	—	—
C_{20}	11.1	15.3	15.5
C_{21}	traces	0.8	1.3
C'_{22}	2.3	—	—
C_{22}	9.1	13.3	10.3
C'_{24}	3.3	—	—
C_{24}	3.1	5.2	2.2
C'_{26}	traces	—	—
C_{26}	traces	traces	—

* Unsaturated acids with the corresponding number of carbon atoms are designated with C'.

These results show that n-fatty acids with even and odd number of
carbon atoms in the C_{10}–C_{26} range are contained in the waxes from small
and big buds and from rose flower. The odd-numbered acids are present in
insignificant amounts. C_{16} and C_{18} are prevalent among the even-numbered
acids. Yet, while in both kinds of buds the amount of stearic acid is lower

Table XII

Gas-liquid Chromatography of Methyl Esters
of the Free Acids in Rose Bud
and Rose Flower Waxes of the Same Origin

Number of C-atoms	Rose buds		Rose flower	
	Calculated for		Calculated for	
	free acids, %	wax, %	free acids, %	wax, %
1	2	3	4	5
C_8:	1.6	0.067	0.1	0.004
X^*_1	0.3	0.013	traces	traces
X_2	1.6	0.067	0.6	0.022
C_9:	4.0	0.166	3.3	0.123
X_3	1.3	0.054	1.3	0.048
X_4	1.4	0.058	0.6	0.022
X_5	1.6	0.067	1.8	0.067
C_{10}:	3.5	0.146	4.3	0.160
X_6	1.8	0.075	0.1	0.004
X_7	0.5	0.021	0.9	0.034
X_8	0.8	0.033	1.8	0.067
C_{11}:	2.6	0.108	4.4	0.164
X_9	0.2	0.008	0.1	0.004
X_{10}	0.8	0.033	1.3	0.048
C_{12}	1.4	0.058	2.7	0.100
X_{11}	—	—	0.6	0.022
C_{13}:	0.8	0.033	1.3	0.048
C_{13}	0.4	0.017	0.6	0.022
C_{14}:	0.7	0.029	1.1	0.041
C_{14}	0.6	0.025	0.9	0.034
C_{15}:	0.5	0.021	0.9	0.034
C_{15}	0.2	0.008	traces	traces
X_{12}	0.3	0.013	0.3	0.011
C_{16}	21.7	0.903	23.5	0.874
C_{17}:	1.1	0.046	0.7	0.026
C_{17}	0.6	0.025	0.6	0.022
C_{18}:	35.3	1.469	26.3	0.978
C_{18}	7.7	0.320	0.8	0.365
X_{13}	1.3	0.054	—	—
C_{19}	0.7	0.029	0.7	0.026
C_{20}:	0.8	0.033	0.9	0.034
C_{20}	1.1	0.046	2.4	0.089
C_{21}:	0.4	0.017	0.4	0.015
C_{21}	0.2	0.008	0.6	0.022
C_{22}:	0.5	0.021	—	—
C_{22}	0.6	0.025	2.4	0.089
C_{23}	0.2	0.008	0.3	0.011
C_{24}	0.2	0.008	1.1	0.041
C_{25}	0.1	0.004	traces	traces
C_{26}	0.1	0.004	0.3	0.011

* Peaks of unidentified acids, presumably those having an iso structure, are marked by X and the corresponding index.

than that of palmitic acid, in the case of rose flower this relation is reversed. Several unsaturated acids (marked by C' in Table XI) are present chiefly in the wax from small buds, where their total amount is 38.7%. Only C_{18} is represented in a considerable amount in the wax from big buds and rose flower. The changes in the ratios of the unsaturated acids C_{16} and C_{18} to their corresponding saturated analogues in the samples of all three waxes is likewise of interest. The amount of C'_{16} is smaller than that of C_{16}, while the amount of C'_{18} is greater than that of C_{18} in the wax from small buds. Of the unsaturated acids, only C'_{18} remains in the samples of big buds and rose flower, its content still being higher than that of C_{18} in the rose flower sample. These results give grounds to assume that a transformation from unsaturated into saturated acids occurs during the development of the bud into flower, and the latter are esterified at the same time.

The free acids of the waxes from small buds and from rose flower (collected from the same bushes) have been isolated by means of ion-exchange resin. Thin-layer chromatography of the methyl esters on silica gel and silica gel/silver nitrate, as well as the IR spectra, indicate the presence of saturated and unsaturated acids. The results of gas-liquid chromatography of their methyl esters on a non-polar phase (SE-30) at programmed temperature are presented in Table XII. Gas-liquid chromatography of the samples on a polar phase (PEGS), as well as chromatography of a sample of the methyl esters of the free acids from rose wax prior to and after hydrogenation (Fig. 5) indicated that the acid, marked as $C_{18:}$ in the Table, was actually a mixture of three unsaturated C_{18} acids: oleic, linoleic and linolenic (Table XIII).

Table XIII

Contents of Oleic, Linoleic and Linolenic Acids in $C_{18:}$* Unsaturated Acid

Number of C-atoms	Rose buds		Rose flowers	
	Calculated for		Calculated for	
	$C_{18:}$, %	wax, %	$C_{18:}$, %	wax, %
$C_{18:1}$	3.6	0.053	6.3	0.062
$C_{18:2}$	63.2	0.928	46.2	0.456
$C_{18:3}$	33.2	0.488	47.1	0.461

* $C_{18:}$ is the sum of C_{18}-unsaturated acids

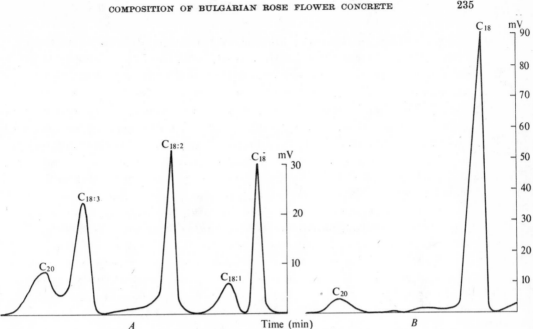

Fig. 5. Gas-liquid chromatography of unhydrogenated (*A*) and hydrogenated (*B*) sample from rose flower wax

The results obtained from a comparative study of the free acids in the waxes from rose buds and rose flower show that the free acids in these waxes do not differ in their qualitative compositions. Both saturated and unsaturated acids are present in homologous series in the C_8–C_{26} range with even and odd numbers of carbon atoms. The total amount of unsaturated acids in the wax from rose buds is 51.8% in relation to the acid mixture and 2.18% in relation to the wax, while that of the saturated ones is 35.4% and 1.49%, respectively. The total amount of unsaturated acids in the wax from rose flower is 43.7% calculated for the acid mixture and 1.63% in relation to the wax, while that of the saturated ones is 45.9% and 1.71%, respectively. Hence, a transformation of unsaturated free acids into saturated ones occurs during the development of the bud into a flower. The $C_{18:}$ unsaturated acids are prevalent in both waxes. Their amount is higher in wax from buds, 35.3% in relation to the acid mixture, and 1.47% in relation to wax, while in the wax from rose flower, it is 26.3% of the acid mixture or 0.98% calculated for the wax. Of the saturated acids, the highest is the amount of palmitic acid in both waxes. Its amount remains almost permanent in both waxes.

A comparison of the results obtained for the free acids in waxes from buds and from flower (Table XII) with those of the ester-bound acids in the same waxes (Table XI) shows that the same acids are present as free and as ester-bound ones. There are differences, however, in a quantitative respect. Thus, the content of free unsaturated acids in the wax from rose buds in relation to the acid mixture is 51.8%, and that of the ester-bound unsaturated ones 38.7%. The content of free unsaturated acids in the wax from rose flower is 43.7%, while that of ester-bound unsaturated acids is 20.7%. It follows from this comparison that during the development of buds into flowers, the unsaturated acids remain mainly in the free state. On the other hand, it is further seen that the saturated acids C_{18}, C_{20}, C_{22} and C_{24} undergo a transformation chiefly into esters during the development of the buds into flowers. For instance, stearic acid in the free state in waxes from rose buds and rose flowers, is 7.7% and 9.8%, respectively, whereas it occurs esterified in the same waxes in 10.3% and 22%, respectively. The C_{20} saturated acid as a free acid in rose buds and rose flower represents 1.1 and 2.4%, respectively, and in ester form 11.1% and 15.5%.

It should be noted that the acids in rose flower wax (free and ester-bound ones) have also been studied by Wollrab [52]. There is a very significant difference, however, in the results obtained by him and those established by us. The most important difference consists in the fact that he did not find unsaturated acids in the wax studied by him. In our opinion, the main reason for this must lie in the initial material. We worked with a wax from Bulgarian rose flower concrete, which we personally isolated from the plant material picked by us while Wollrab studied a wax supplied to him by a factory in the GDR. In his paper, quoted above, he writes in a footnote: "I am indebted to Dr. E. Adler, Chemische Fabrik Miltitz, GDR, for a gift of the sample analyzed here". Another reason could be found in the fact that he used a different procedure for the isolation of the acids, whereby the unsaturated acids were probably polymerized to resin-like products, as mentioned in his paper.

Before the advent of up-to-date chromatographic methods for the identification of fatty acids, it was claimed that only acids with an even number of carbon atoms were present in natural products. It was gas-liquid chromatography which made it possible to establish reliably that natural products, including plant waxes, actually contain homologous series of normal saturated acids with even and odd numbers of carbon atoms, those with even number being dominant. As an exception, the presence of C_{15} fatty acid has been established as a dominant one in *Brassica oleracea* so far.

4. COMPOSITION AND STRUCTURE
OF THE LONG-CHAIN FATTY ALCOHOLS

In most plant waxes the alcohols, both free and bound as esters, are normal saturated primary alcohols in the C_{20}–C_{36} range and possess mainly an even number of carbon atoms. It is also known that in addition to the primary alcohols, also straight-chain higher secondary alcohols are found in plant waxes, in the free state exclusively, but chiefly with an odd number of carbon atoms. The latter are either symmetric or asymmetric. There are also data on primary alcohols with branched chain, mainly iso and anteiso compounds [53].

Studies on the composition of alcohols in rose flower wax likewise were carried out by Prophète for the first time [24]. Using classic methods, he believed he had established the presence of a pseudoceryl alcohol and he gave only the molecular formula of two others.

Our first investigations [54] on the composition of higher alcohols in rose flower wax were done with a wax supplied by the Bulgarska Roza Enterprise. It was the same wax with which also the first studies on the hydrocarbon composition were carried out. The investigation dealt with the total alcohols of the wax (both free and ester-bound). Firstly, the free acids were removed, and the neutral wax was saponified. The alcohols, contained in the unsaponifiables, were isolated by column chromatography on aluminium oxide. The higher fatty alcohols were obtained in the form of a solid, colourless mass, fatty to touch, m.p. 62–68 °C. An attempt was made at identifying these alcohols by paper chromatography of their xanthogenates, yet preliminary comparative experiments indicated that this method was suitable for lower alcohols only. The results, presented in Table XIV, were obtained by oxidation of the alcohols according to Bashkirev et al. [55] and

Table XIV

Paper Chromatography of the Acids Obtained
by Oxidation of the Alcohols in Rose Flower Wax

Standards	R_f	Substance studied	R_f
$C_{17}H_{35}COOH$	0.73	1st spot	0.72
$C_{19}H_{39}COOH$	0.65	2nd spot	0.66
$C_{21}H_{43}COOH$	0.58	3rd spot	0.59
$C_{23}H_{47}COOH$	0.52	4th spot	0.53
$C_{25}H_{51}COOH$	0.45	5th spot	0.45
$C_{27}H_{55}COOH$	0.39	6th spot	0.39

identification of the acids with the aid of paper chromatography by the method of Kaufmann and Das [56].

These first results for alcohols in rose flower wax called for a revision, since they were only of a qualitative character. Later on we developed further our initial investigations, carrying out a simultaneous comparative study of the long-chain alcohols in the buds and flower [57], as this was done in the cases of the hydrocarbons and acids in the same waxes.

Moreover, we already possessed indications based on IR spectral data that free alcohols, both primary and secondary, were contained in rose flower wax [33]. The detection of secondary alcohols in plant waxes was of interest also from the point of view of their biogenesis.

The total primary and secondary alcohols from rose buds and rose flower were isolated by column chromatography on aluminium oxide of the unsaponifiables of the respective wax and subsequent elution with solvents of increasing polarity. The secondary alcohols were eluted with benzene/ether 97 : 3 and in thin-layer chromatography on silica gel/gypsum they gave a spot with an R_f value higher than that of the standard primary alcohol. The IR spectra showed maxima at 1100 cm^{-1} and 3640 cm^{-1}. The primary alcohols were eluted very loosely by a gradient elution with benzene/ether, chiefly at higher ether contents. They were isolated in the pure state by means of preparative thin-layer chromatography on silica gel/gypsum with chloroform as a solvent. The purified product had an R_f value similar to that of an octadecan-1-ol standard. The IR spectrum had maxima at 1050 cm^{-1} and 3640 cm^{-1}. Samples of the unsaponifiable wax from rose buds and rose flower were chromatographed in a similar manner after removal of the free acids from the wax, using the ion-exchange resin Wofatit SBW in order to isolate the free primary and secondary alcohols.

As it has been known for a long time that higher primary alcohols are components of the esters in waxes, it was of interest to examine whether the secondary alcohols in the wax from rose buds and rose flower also participated in the composition of esters. For this purpose a pure ester fraction, isolated by column chromatography of the neutral wax from rose buds and rose flower, was saponified. It was shown by means of thin-layer chromatography that the alcohols isolated from the unsaponifiables were only primary. Using thin-layer chromatography on silica gel impregnated with silver nitrate, with chloroform as the solvent, it was shown that the isolated total primary alcohols, free primary alcohols and secondary alcohols were saturated. To determine the individual composition of the isolated alcohol fractions (total, free primary and secondary) from rose buds and rose flower by gas-liquid chromatography, they were each transformed into paraffins. The reduction was effected according to Downing *et al.* [58]: reduction of the iodides with lithium aluminium hydride. The results of the gasliquid chromatography under programmed temperature of the paraffins, obtained by the reduction of the corresponding alcohol fractions, are presented in Table XV. On the basis of these results, the distribution curves of

Table XV

Composition of the Alcohols in Rose Buds and Rose Flower Waxes, %

Number of C-atoms	Total mixture of primary alcohols		Free primary alcohols		Free secondary alcohols	
	Rose bud wax	Rose flower wax	Rose bud wax	Rose flower wax	Rose bud wax	Rose flower wax
C_{14}	—	—	0.4	—	0.1	—
C_{15}	—	0.1	0.1	—	0.1	0.1
C_{16}	—	0.1	0.1	—	0.1	0.4
C_{17}	0.4	0.3	0.1	0.6	0.1	1.0
C_{18}	0.3	1.4	0.4	0.2	0.1	0.8
C_{19}	0.2	1.0	0.5	0.3	0.1	1.2
C_{20}	6.8	21.8	1.7	3.1	0.6	1.2
C_{21}	1.6	2.6	3.1	0.5	1.5	2.2
C_{22}	14.8	11.6	8.9	15.8	3.8	3.9
C_{23}	2.7	2.5	5.9	1.4	5.4	4.0
C_{24}	20.9	26.9	13.9	18.2	6.2	4.9
C_{25}	2.9	2.1	8.5	6.4	6.3	4.6
C_{26}	15.6	12.0	14.4	15.5	5.7	4.9
C_{27}	3.7	1.8	9.4	3.9	7.2	5.2
C_{28}	14.3	8.6	13.9	20.2	5.0	4.7
C_{29}	3.4	1.4	6.0	1.1	2.9	5.2
C_{30}	8.5	1.8	7.5	7.1	1.5	3.4
C_x	0.9	—	—	—	—	—
C_{31}	1.0	3.5	2.7	3.3	52.5	50.0
C_{32}	1.8	1.4	1.9	1.9	0.1	0.3
C_{33}	traces	traces	0.4	—	0.7	1.8
C_{34}	—	—	0.2	—	—	—

the total primary alcohols in waxes from rose buds and rose flower, as well as those of the free primary alcohols in the same waxes have been plotted (Fig. 6).

It is seen from the distribution curves of the total primary alcohols that during the development of the bud into a flower, the amount of the C_{20} alcohol increases considerably, while that of C_{24} increases to a lesser degree. From the fact that their amounts as free alcohols in buds and flowers are much lower than in the total mixture, it follows that they are synthesized intensively during the development, being transformed into esters at the same time.

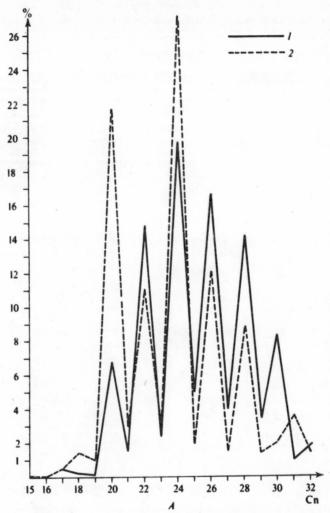

Fig. 6. Distribution curves of free and total primary alcohols in waxes from buds and flowers
A-Total primary alcohols in rose bud wax (*1*). Total primary alcohols in rose flower wax (*2*)

It follows from the distribution curves of the free alcohols that during the development of the buds into flowers, the amount of the even-numbered primary alcohols within the C_{20}–C_{30} range increases, while that of the odd-numbered ones decreases. In the secondary alcohols, found only in the free state, a prevalence of the odd-numbered ones is observed only above C_{27}.

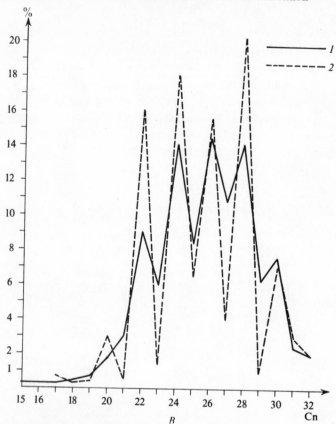

Fig. 6. B–Free primary alcohols in rose bud wax (*1*). Free primary alcohols in rose flower wax (*2*)

The amount of C_{31} is remarkably high. The amount of secondary alcohols in buds in the C_{15}–C_{21} range is smaller than that in the rose flower, while in the C_{25}–C_{28} range it is bigger and increases abruptly both in the buds and in the flower at C_{31}. These data on the secondary alcohols and the fact that they are present only in the free state in rose buds and rose flower, may be interpreted as an indication that they play a considerable part in the biogenetic transformations of the straight-chain components of the wax: they are continuously synthesized and continuously transformed into other components.

Our further studies resulted in the establishment of the presence also of unsaturated secondary alcohols in rose flower wax [59]. In the column chromatography of the unsaponified was, followed by thin-layer chromatography, in the ether fraction we observed, in addition to the spots for the primary and secondary alcohols, still another spot, located in between them. The latter was isolated by preparative thin-layer chromatography. Its IR spectrum had a maximum corresponding to a secondary hydroxyl group (1100 cm^{-1} and 3640 cm^{-1}), as well as a maximum due to a double bond at 1640 cm^{-1}. The ratio of the methyl and methylene groups at 1380 cm^{-1} and 1470 cm^{-1} was typical for compounds with a long straight chain.

The mass spectrum revealed the presence of a homologous series of unsaturated secondary alcohols in the C_{19}–C_{31} range (Table XVI).

Table XVI

Mass Spectral Data of Unsaturated
Alcohols in Rose Flower Wax

Number of C-atoms	M$^+$	M—H$_2$O	M—111
19	0.2	1.1	0.5
20	0.2	1.0	0.5
21	0.3	1.6	2.1
22	0.2	1.0	2.0
23	1.5	5.0	1.5
24	1.0	1.3	1.3
25	0.3	1.0	1.2
26	0.3	0.8	0.9
27	0.3	1.0	0.3
28	0.6	2.3	0.6
29	0.5	2.5	0.6
30	—	0.3	0.1
31	1.0	12.0	65.0

The main features in the spectra of these compounds are oxygen-containing ions, obtained as a result of the fragmentation of the β-bond in relation to the oxygen atom, and the ions corresponding to $(M—H_2O)^+$ [79]. The member C_{31} is present in the largest amount, while the rest occurs in insignificant quantities. The ions 339$^+$ (65% of the base peak) and 141$^+$ (11%) correspond to the fragmentation of the most abundant member C_{31}, in which the hydroxyl group should be in position 9 (Scheme 1).

The very intensive peak at m/e 111 indicates a fragmentation during which the positive charge of the ion formed is stabilized through resonance; hence, the most probable position of the double bond in the predominant member is C-6. This has been confirmed by comparing the mass spectra of unsaturated and saturated secondary alcohols, isolated from the same wax. The mass spectrum of the saturated alcohols shows that here also hentriacontan-9-ol is the predominant member. Owing to the lack of a double

$$H_3C-(CH_2)_{21} \left. \begin{array}{c} \\ \end{array} \right| CH \left. \begin{array}{c} \\ \end{array} \right| CH_2-CH=CH-(CH_2)_4-CH_3$$

with branches: $\rightarrow 141^+$, $\rightarrow 111^+$, and $339^+ \leftarrow$, OH

$$H_3C-(CH_2)_{21} \left. \begin{array}{c} \\ \end{array} \right| CH \left. \begin{array}{c} \\ \end{array} \right| CH_2-CH_2-CH_2-(CH_2)_4-CH_3$$

with branches: $\rightarrow 143^+$, $\rightarrow 113^+$, and $339^+ \leftarrow$, OH

Scheme 1. Mass-spectral fragmentation of unsaturated and saturated secondary alcohols from rose flower wax.

bond and the possibility of stabilization by resonance, however, the ratio of the ions 143^+ and 113^+, corresponding to the ions 141^+ and 111^+ of the predominant unsaturated secondary alcohol, is different. The ion 113^+ is much less abundant than the ion 143^+, while the ions 111^+ and 141^+ are equally abundant in the spectrum of the unsaturated alcohols.

According to literature data, unsaturated secondary alcohols have not been found as components of plant waxes so far.

Simultaneously with us, saturated alcohols (primary and secondary) in *Rosa damascena* Mill. have been studied by Wollrab [52]. In this case, too, just like with the hydrocarbons and the acids, there are differences, especially in the amounts of the individual members, which we ascribe to the same reasons as mentioned for the hydrocarbons and acids. In certain other data, however, there is an agreement between our and Wollrab's results, namely secondary alcohols are found only in the free state, the secondary alcohol C_{31} is markedly prevalent and the hydroxyl group is in position 9. Moreover, the position of the hydroxyl group was demonstrated in a different manner: Wollrab used a mass spectral study of the ketones obtained by oxidation of the secondary alcohols, whereas we employed direct mass spectral investigation of the secondary alcohols.

5. COMPOSITION AND STRUCTURE
OF THE LONG-CHAIN FATTY KETONES

The establishment of carbonyl compounds in waxes is of great importance because of the interest attached to the biogenesis of plant wax components, and the biogenesis of normal hydrocarbons in particular. As shown, the latter are contained in a considerable amount in the wax of the Bulgarian oil-bearing rose.

According to literature data, palmitone has been found in the wax from *Sandalum album* [60]. Nonacosan-15-one has been isolated from the leaves of *Brassica oleracea* [61]. According to Kreger [62], the presence of asymmetrical ketones has not been reliably established in plant waxes. Later on, nonacosan-10-one, however, was found in the surface lipids of *Brassica oleracea* leaves [63].

The product isolated by us from the benzene–ether and ether fractions during column chromatography of rose bud and rose flower waxes had, after recrystallization from alcohol, m.p. 76–77°C [64]. The IR data — strong absorption at 1720 cm^{-1} — indicated the presence of ketones. The negative result of the attempted oxidation of this product with silver oxide, as well as resistance to saponification confirmed the presence of a ketone.

The ketonic character was also confirmed by the preparation of an oxime, m.p. 51.8–52.5°C. Its IR spectrum had maxima due to the azomethine group at 1640 cm^{-1} and to the hydroxyl group at 3610 cm^{-1}, just like in the case of the oxime of palmitone.

According to its melting point and that of its oxime, the ketone isolated by us was close to ginnone, nonacosan-10-one, a ketone obtained from ginnol (nonacosan-10-ol) found in the wax of *Ginkgo biloba* L. This prompted us to carry out a Beckmann rearrangement of the oxime. The amide obtained had m.p. 82.5–84°C, a value very close to the melting point of the amide from ginnone. The amide thus obtained was further hydrolyzed. In an attempt at identifying the acid part by paper chromatography according to the method of Kaufmann and Nitsch [65], we were surprised to get numerous spots. With the aid of standards — normal acids with even and odd number of carbon atoms — the acids C_{10}, C_{12}, C_{14}, C_{16}, C_{18}, C_{20}, C_{22}, C_{17} and C_{21} were identified. Also the odd-numbered acids C_{13} and C_{15} were identified only by their R_f-values (without standards).

NMR spectroscopy demonstrated the presence of ketones with relatively long alkyl groups. The presence of a methyl group adjacent to the carbonyl group was excluded.

Since it is impossible to obtain more than two acids by the Beckmann rearrangement of the oxime of one ketone, it follows from our first result that not less than 6 ketones must be contained in the product isolated by us.

Taking into consideration the great significance of the reliable establishment of the presence of a homologous series of ketones in waxes, as well as the determination of their structures to elucidate the biogenesis of hydrocarbons in plant waxes (the hypotheses of Chibnall *et al.* [66] and of Kreger [62]), we continued our investigations on the composition and structure of ketones in rose flower wax [62a]. Since direct gas-liquid chromatography of the ketones (which would have yielded the most reliable results on their individual composition) was not possible at that time because of the high boiling point (above 400°C), we reduced the ketones to hydrocarbons and identified them by gas-liquid chromatography. We also carried out a mass spectral investigation of the ketone mixture. The results of the gas-liquid chromatography of the hydrocarbons obtained from the reduction of the ketones are presented in Table XVII.

Table XVII

Gas-liquid Chromatography Data
on the Quantitative Composition
of Ketones in Rose Flower Wax, mole-%

Number of C-atoms	Ketones	Number of C-atoms	Ketones
17	0.4	27	6.8
18	0.2	28	2.8
19	3.4	29	8.3
20	1.0	30	2.8
21	2.9	31	55.5
22	1.0	32	2.6
23	2.3	33	3.2
24	1.2	34	1.2
25	2.4	35	0.8
26	2.2		

The results in Table XVII show that the wax contains a homologous series of all the 19 ketones in the C_{17}–C_{35} range with even and odd numbers of carbon atoms. The ketones with an odd number of carbon atoms, particularly C_{31}, C_{29}, C_{27}, C_{19} and C_{33}, are present in a considerably greater amount than those with an even number of carbon atoms. We noticed in the gas-liquid chromatogram a splitting of the peak C_{33}, and chromatography of a larger sample of the mixture showed a similar splitting of the peaks C_{22}, C_{30} and C_{32}. This splitting of the peaks can only be caused by the presence of branched chain hydrocarbons (ketones, originally) containing the same number of carbon atoms. It cannot be due to the unsaturated hydrocarbons because, prior to gas-liquid chromatography, the mixture was purified from unsaturated compounds on a silica gel–silver nitrate column.

The data on the mass spectral investigation of the ketones at a low ionizing energy are presented in Table XVIII. These data confirm the results obtained by gas-liquid chromatography for the presence of a homologous series in the range quoted above. As the fragmentation under electron impact of higher ketones has not been studied so far, we assumed that the

Table XVIII

Mass Spectral Data of Ketones of Rose Flower Wax

Number of C-atoms	$\dfrac{(M-15)^+}{M^+}$	Structure of carbon chain
17	0	Normal
18	3.1	Branched and normal
19	3.9	Branched and normal
20	1.9	Branched and normal
21	0	Normal
22	3.5	Branched and normal
23	0	Normal
24	1.8	Branched and normal
25	6.2	Branched and normal
26	14.3	Branched and normal
27	3.4	Branched and normal
28	1.4	Branched and normal
29	0	Normal
30	6.2	Branched and normal
31	0	Normal
32	32.0	Mainly branched

ketones would behave similarly to higher paraffins [28]. It has been shown that paraffins with a straight chain give a very intensive molecular peak, while the peak $(M-15)^+$ is lacking and the relationship $\dfrac{(M-15)^+}{M^+}$ is close to zero. When a methyl group is present as a side chain, the ratio of the abundances $\dfrac{(M-15)^+}{M^+}$ is about 3. When two and more methyl groups are present, this ratio is higher. For five of the ketones studied by us (Table XVIII) this ratio is zero, so that we can assume that the ketones C_{17}, C_{21}, C_{23}, C_{29} and C_{31} have a normal chain and are not admixed with branched-chain ketones. For all the other ketones the ratio $\dfrac{(M-15)^+}{M^+}$ is greater than zero, an indication for the presence of ketones with side chain methyl groups. Moreover, the percentage of branched chain ketones appears to be considerable.

The high ratio $\dfrac{(M-15)^+}{M^+} = 32$ for the ketone C_{32} shows with certainty that its main component is the branched chain ketone, probably containing a quaternary carbon atom.

In continuation of our investigations we made a comparative study of the ketones in waxes from rose buds and rose flower [67]. The gas chromatographic data on the individual composition of the hydrocarbons obtained from the hydrogenation of the ketones in both waxes, as well as data from the mass spectral study of the ketones carried out with a high ionizing energy, indicated that there occurred no considerable changes in the qualitative and quantitative compositions of the ketones during the development of the bud into flower. The main component is $C_{30}H_{62}CO$ (molecular weight 450). The mass spectral data show that it is not n-hentriacontan-16-one (palmitone), but an isomer with a different position for the carbonyl group. According to Beynon et $al.$ [68], for asymmetrical ketones a stronger intermolecular reaction $M^+ + H$ is more characteristic than for symmetrical ketones. In point of fact, the ratio $M/M + 1$ for palmitone is 3, while in the case of our ketone, this ratio is 2.66.

To determine the position of the carbonyl group, the peaks for α- and β-splitting were sought. While in palmitone α-splitting produced a maximum at m/e 239 (the transition $450 \rightarrow 239$ was confirmed by a metastable peak with m/e 127.5), in our case this peak was absent, while at the same time peaks with m/e 337 and m/e 141 (the transition $450 \rightarrow 337$ was confirmed by the metastable peak 252.2) were present. This α-splitting may only be explained by the following structure of the ketone studied: $C_8H_{17} - CO - C_{22}H_{45}$. Actually, peaks with m/e 113 (C_8H_{17}) and with m/e 309 ($C_{22}H_{45}$) are found in the spectrum, which also are due to the α-splitting.

The β-splitting likewise confirms this structure. There are peaks at m/e 352 and m/e 156 in the spectrum, while in the case of palmitone, this splitting leads to a fragment with m/e 254. The two carbon chains are normal, which follows from the slight intensity of the peaks $(M^+ -15)$ and $(M^+ -29)$ as compared with the molecular peak. The weak peaks at m/e 239 (α-splitting) and m/e 254 (β-splitting) allow the assumption that the ketone mixture studied contains about 1–2% palmitone.

The mass spectral data at high ionizing energy confirm that in the cases of mixtures consisting of normal and branched-chain ketones, the latter contain a methyl group as a side chain. Moreover, these data now indicate more definitely that the branched ketones C_{30}, C_{28}, C_{27} and C_{26} contain this group in the C-2 position (isopropyl group). The mass spectral study again confirmed that the C_{32} ketone is most markedly branched.

The presence of asymmetric ketones in plant waxes was reliably confirmed by our investigations on the structure of the ketones in rose flower wax. Moreover, ketones with a branched chain were found for the first time. A comparison of our results of the individual composition of the unsaturated secondary alcohols, saturated secondary alcohols and ketones (Tables XV, XVI and XVII) in rose flower wax indicate that members with an odd number of carbon atoms are the dominant ones in all three homologous series. In addition, the homologue C_{31} is present markedly in the largest amount in all three homologous series. Moreover, the mass spectral investigations of the position of the functional group demonstrate that it is in the prevalent unsaturated secondary alcohol, in the corresponding saturated alcohol, as well as in the ketone, equally in position 9. This gives us serious grounds to consider that a biogenetic relationship is possible between these compounds. Our results from the studies of the ketones, and especially the lack of ketones with a CO-group in position 2, are in disagreement with the scheme of Kreger [69] for the formation of C_{29} ketone in plant waxes by ω-oxidation of palmitone, followed by β-oxidation, decarboxylation and reduction.

A comparison of the position of the functional group in the homologous series mentioned above with the position of the double bond in linoleic acid, which is contained in the same wax in a considerable amount (Table XIII), permits the suggestion that the latter may be a precursor in their formation (Scheme 2).

$$HOOC-(CH_2)_7-CH=CH-CH_2-CH=CH-(CH_2)_4-CH_3$$

$$CH_3-(CH_2)_{21}-\underset{OH}{CH}-CH_2-CH=CH-(CH_2)_4-CH_3$$

$$H_3C-(CH_2)_{21}-\underset{OH}{CH}-CH_2-CH_2-CH_2-(CH_2)_4-CH_3$$

$$H_3C-(CH_2)_{21}-\underset{O}{C}-CH_2-CH_2-CH_2-(CH_2)_4-CH_3$$

Scheme 2. Comparison of the structures of the predominant unsaturated secondary alcohol, saturated secondary alcohol and ketone from rose flower wax with the structure of linoleic acid.

6. COMPOSITION AND STRUCTURE
OF THE LONG-CHAIN FATTY DIOLS

Thin-layer chromatography of benzene–alcoholic and alcoholic eluates from column chromatography of unsaponified rose flower wax revealed spots which corresponded to substances more polar than the primary alcohols detected in the wax so far. One of them had the same R_f value as that of higher aliphatic glycols obtained by the oxidation of olefins from rose flower with performic acid and subsequent hydrolysis. This substance was isolated by preparative thin-layer chromatography [70].

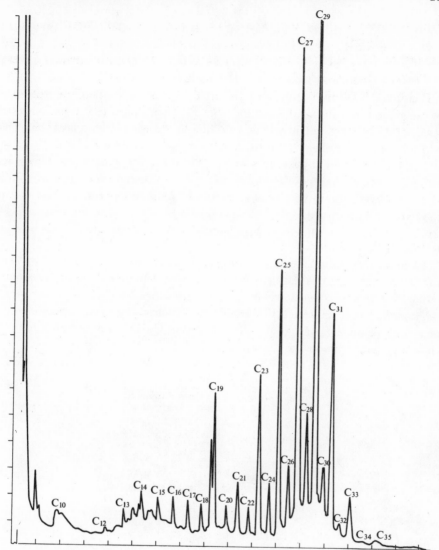

Fig. 7. Gas-liquid chromatography of paraffins obtained by the reduction of glycols

After recrystallization, the compound melted at 71–72 °C. Its IR spectrum showed maxima due to a secondary hydroxyl group at 1100 cm^{-1} and 3640 cm^{-1}, as well as an intensive band corresponding to hydrogen bonds in the region 3200–3500 cm^{-1}, indicating diol groups. The NMR spectrum of this fraction had signals for CH$_3$-protons at 0.9 δ, a CH$_2$ signal centred at

1.3 δ, CH_2CHOH (m) at 1.4 δ, OH (s, br, 2H) at 2.1 δ and CHOH (m 2H) at 3.45 δ. The NMR spectrum of the acetyl derivative showed signals for CH_3 (tr, $J = 6.5$ Hz) at 0.85 δ, CH_2 at 1.28 δ, CH_2CHOAc (m) at 1.47 δ, OAc (2s, 6H) at 2.05 δ and 2.06 δ and CHOAc at 5.02 δ (m, 2H).

Gas-liquid chromatography of the hydrocarbons obtained by reduction of the glycols according to Downing et al. [71] has shown that a homologous series of diols is present in which, just like in the case of hydrocarbons, the odd-numbered members are prevalent in the C_{19}–C_{33} interval (Fig. 7).

The mass spectrum of the fraction confirmed the presence of a homologous series of straight-chain diols. The observation by Beynon et al. [68] that the most intensive ions in the mass spectrum of diols arose from α-cleavage to the hydroxyl groups served as a basis for its interpretation. The mass spectrum also showed hydrocarbon fragments C_nH_{2n+1} and C_nH_{2n-1}, as well as M—18 ions.

The mass spectrum further confirmed that diols with an odd number of carbon atoms were the major constituents with the diol C_{29} being predominant. This fact was established by a comparison of the mass spectrum of diols with that of their acetyl derivatives. Accurate spectral measurements at a high resolution of the M^+ of the C_{29} and C_{31} homologues also showed that they corresponded to diols (Table XIX).

Table XIX

Mass Spectral Fragments Subjected
to High Resolution Analysis

m/e	Experimental mass	Deduced empirical formula	Calculated mass
468	468.4888	$C_{31}H_{64}O_2$	468.4906
440	440.4552	$C_{29}H_{60}O_2$	440.4593
	440.3615	$C_{30}H_{48}O_2$	440.3654
353	353.3763	$C_{24}H_{49}O$	353.3783
334	334.3583	$C_{24}H_{46}$	334.3599
325	325.3469	$C_{22}H_{45}O$	325.3470

The mass spectrum of the diol fraction was sufficient to deduce the structure of the predominant C_{29} diol. The high abundance of the ions M—115 at m/e 325 (10% of the base peak at m/e 69) and M—87 at m/e 353 (10%) was an indication for a γ-position of the two hydroxyl groups, i.e. the compound is nonacosan-5,8-diol (Scheme 3).

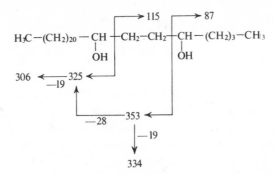

Scheme 3. Mass spectral fragmentation of nonacosan-5,8-diol.

A further proof of this structure is the ratio of the abundances of the peaks at m/e 115 (9.7%), 101 (9.7%), 87 (51.6%) and 73 (9.7%), which is exclusively in favour of the ion 87. Further fragmention of the ions m/e 325 and 353, with a loss of mass 19, results in the ions 306 (10.6%) and 334 (9.7%), respectively. This pattern of fragmentation is supported by the presence of metastable peaks at m/e 289 and 317 for the transitions 325 → 306 and 353 → 334, respectively, and also by the accurate mass measurement of the ions of m/e 353, 334 and 325 (Table XIX). The ion of m/e 325 is also derived from m/e 353 by the loss of m/e 28.

The fact that the mass spectrum gives evidence for the presence of hentriacontanediol with a 6, 9-position of the hydroxyl group also merits attention (peaks at m/e 339 (M—129, 2.8%) and m/e 367 (M—101)).

The ester fraction isolated by column chromatography from rose flower wax was saponified in order to establish whether diols were present in an esterified form. Thin-layer chromatography of the isolated neutral product did not show the presence of diols.

An investigation of the wax from rose buds was carried out in a similar manner. It showed that this wax also contained diols. According to the IR, NMR and mass spectral data, there is no considerable difference in the qualitative and quantitative compositions of the diols from rose buds or rose flower, as we have observed in the case of the other components of these two waxes.

So far no long-chain γ-diols have been found in natural waxes of plant and animal origin and, in general, in natural products. Stürke [72] reported the isolation of a diol from a Carnauba wax which was characterized as pentacosanediol, but the positions of the hydroxyl groups were not given. Later on, Murray and Schoenfeld [73] identified C_{22}, C_{24} and C_{28} α, ω-diols in the same wax. Downing *et al.* [58] studied in detail the composition of the unsaponifiable part of wool-, bee- and Carnauba waxes. From all three waxes fractions of diols were isolated which, according to the authors, were α, β- in wool wax, α, ω- in Carnauba wax, and their type in the bee wax was not specified. Downing [58] found α, β-diols in the unsaponifiable part of *Vernix caseosa*. Mazliak [75] isolated a fraction of α, ω-diols from the skin wax of an apple variety. Dodova Angelova and Ivanov [76] identified α, β- and α, ω-diols also in the skin wax of certain apple varieties, chiefly as homologues with an even number of carbon atoms. In 1967 Vulfson *et al.* [77] found butane-1,4-diol in lipids from yeast.

It is well known that in plant waxes acids, primary alcohols and aldehydes are present mainly with an even number of carbon atoms, and the biogenetic relationship between them has been experimentally proved. Other straight-chain components of plant waxes, such as hydrocarbons, secondary alcohols and ketones are present as homologues mainly with an odd number of carbon atoms and a biogenetic relationship exists between them, too. To the latter compounds now one should add γ-diols. It is interesting that γ-diols, just like secondary saturated and unsaturated alcohols in rose flower wax, are present only in the free state. The fact that α, β- and α, ω-diols occur in plant waxes chiefly with an even number of carbon atoms, whereas the γ-diols present have an odd number of carbon atoms, suggests a different pattern of their biogenesis.

7. COMPOSITION AND STRUCTURE
OF THE LONG-CHAIN ALIPHATIC LACTONES

Thin-layer chromatography of an ether fraction from the column chromatography of unsaponified wax showed the presence of two new types of compounds, which migrated between the primary and secondary aliphatic long-chain alcohols. One of these new fractions was found to be a homologous series of unsaturated secondary alcohols [59] (see p. 241). The second unknown substance was isolated also by means of preparative thin-layer chromatography on silica gel–gypsum [78].

The IR spectrum of this material showed an absorption band at 1785 cm^{-1}, corresponding to a carbonyl group of a five-membered lactone ring, as well as a maximum at 1150 cm^{-1} due to a C–O bond. The ratio of the peaks for the methyl and methylene groups at 1380 cm^{-1} and 1470 cm^{-1} was typical for straight long-chain compounds.

Signals for the protons of methyl and methylene groups in a straight chain were present in the NMR spectrum of the substance at 0.8 δ and

1.2 δ, respectively. The overlapping triplet and multiplet for protons of the two CH_2 groups in the lactone ring were in the range 2.08 δ to 2.56 δ. The multiplet of the CH group of the lactone ring appeared at 4.3 δ.

The IR and NMR spectral data have shown that the material isolated must have the structure of a lactone of a γ-hydroxy acid, with a relatively long aliphatic chain. The mass spectral data presented in Table XX confirm this assumption and show the presence of a homologous series of lactones with a general formula:

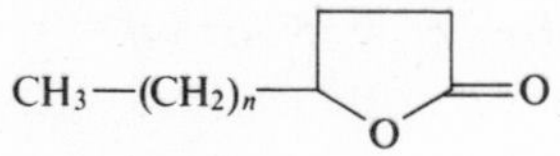

where $n = 17, 18, 19, 20, 21, 22$ and 23. The main fragment was the ion with a mass of 85 (100% abundance), which is due to the α-cleavage of the lactone ring. The $M-H_2O$ fragments are typical of straight chain γ-lactones having more than 3 carbon atoms in the side chain, while the $M-2H_2O$ fragments characterize lactones having more than 6 carbon atoms [79]. Evidence for the $M-18 \rightarrow M-36$ transition was the presence of metastable peaks at m/e 341, 327 and 313, corresponding to the most abundant lactones C_{26}, C_{25} and C_{24}. There were also peaks due to the $M-CO_2$ ions.

Table XX

Mass Spectral Data of Lactones of Bulgarian Rose Wax

C_n	M	%	$M-H_2O$	%	$M-2H_2O$	%	M—85	%
C_{22}	338	0.1	320	0.3	302	0.02	253	0.1
C_{23}	352	0.2	334	0.6	316	0.03	267	0.1
C_{24}	366	3.0	348	11.0	330	3.0	281	0.5
C_{25}	380	2.0	362	11.0	344	4.0	295	1.0
C_{26}	394	6.0	376	39.0	358	12.0	309	1.0
C_{27}	408	0.3	390	2.0	372	0.5	323	0.5
C_{28}	422	0.2	404	1.0	386	0.3	357	1.0

In order to prove whether there is a relationship in the chain lengths of the lactones represented in larger amounts and the saturated higher fatty acids isolated from the same wax, a mass spectrum of the acids was taken. Molecular peaks corresponding to the acids C_{22}, C_{23}, C_{24}, C_{25}, C_{26}, C_{27} and C_{28} were present, the most abundant being those of the even-numbered acids C_{24} (9.4% of the base peak) and C_{26} (1.3%). The peak of the odd-numbered acid C_{27} (1.3%) was also abundant. The fact that the most abundant lactones correspond to the most abundant acids leads to the assumption that there exists a direct biogenetic relationship between these two classes of rose wax components. It is logical to assume that the corresponding hydroxy acids should also be present in the rose wax.

A comparison between the structures of the predominant members of the series of unsaturated secondary alcohols [59], saturated secondary alcohols [57] and ketones [67] found in the rose wax, on the one hand, and the most abundant lactone, γ-hexacosanolactone, on the other, reveals a structural analogy between them (Scheme 4).

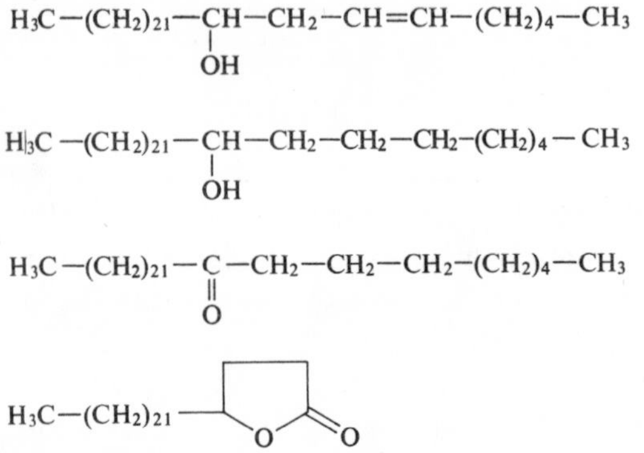

$$H_3C-(CH_2)_{21}-\underset{\underset{OH}{|}}{CH}-CH_2-CH=CH-(CH_2)_4-CH_3$$

$$H_3C-(CH_2)_{21}-\underset{\underset{OH}{|}}{CH}-CH_2-CH_2-CH_2-(CH_2)_4-CH_3$$

$$H_3C-(CH_2)_{21}-\underset{\underset{O}{\|}}{C}-CH_2-CH_2-CH_2-(CH_2)_4-CH_3$$

Scheme 4. Comparison of the structures of unsaturated secondary alcohols, saturated secondary alcohols, ketones and lactones from rose flower wax.

So far, lactones have not been found in Rosaceae. However, γ-lactones with a shorter chain have been found in other plants, such as strawberries [80, 81] and apricots [82].

8. COMPOSITION AND STRUCTURE
OF THE CYCLIC COMPOUNDS

A. Aromatic Compounds: Benzoic Acid and 2-Phenylethanol

When the free acids from rose flower wax, isolated under mild conditions (by means of 5% NaHCO₃ at 50°C), were kept for a long period of time at room temperature, colourless needles with m.p. 119–120°C appeared on the surface of the acids. The appearance of crystals and the m.p. led to the supposition that the substance could be benzoic acid. Since the presence of benzoic acid in plant wax was a possibility unexpected by us, we isolated fresh amounts of free acids by treating the wax with 5% NaHCO₃. After acidification with HCl, the free acids were extracted with pure ether free of any aromatic compound.

The fraction of free acids thus isolated was subjected to sublimation and they yielded a sublimate, having the same m.p. as in the preceding case. The IR spectrum confirmed the presence of an aromatic acid (maxima at 1700, 1610, 1590, 1500 and 690 cm^{-1}), and the spectrum was found to be fully identical with that of an authentic sample of benzoic acid; mixed m.p. determination showed no depression.

According to the references available, the presence of benzoic acid has not been shown so far in the flower of the oil-bearing rose. Its presence in the wax, and hence in the concrete from the flowers of the Bulgarian oil-bearing rose, may be one of the factors in the therapeutic effect of the concrete when it is used in the production of preparation in dermatology, cosmetics and stomatology.

In one of our earlier papers on the composition of the acids of the wax obtained from rose flower, we used paper chromatography in a non-polar phase [49]. In addition to the spots of the saturated fatty acids, we also observed a spot which we assumed to be due to unsaturated hydroxy-acid.

Later on, by using the possibilities offered by thin-layer chromatography, we made an attempt to isolate that most polar substance accompanying the free acids of rose flower wax. For this purpose, we effected the methylation of a free acid sample with diazomethane. The acids were then subjected to thin-layer chromatography on silica gel, prior to and after methylation.

The results indicated that the substance of interest to us had a lower R_f-value than that of hydroxy fatty acids. In addition, while the R_f-values of the acids changed (after methylation they were close to the front of the solvent), the substance studied retained its R_f-value. This was the first indication that it was not an acid.

The IR spectral data showed the presence of a free hydroxyl (maximum at 3640 cm^{-1}), aromatic CH (3040, 3070 and 3090 cm^{-1}), monosubstituted aromatic ring (maxima at 1610, 1590, 1503, 740 and 705 cm^{-1}), aliphatic CH (2955 and 2880 cm^{-1}) and aliphatic CH_2 (1450 and 1430 cm^{-1}).

The NMR spectrum contained one proton signal at δ 2.06 (OH); two triplets at δ 2.76 (CH_2Ph) and δ 3.74 (CH_2OH); one singlet at δ 7.18 (5 Ph protons). The results from the IR- and NMR spectra gave us grounds to suggest that the substance studied should be 2-phenylethanol. This was confirmed by a comparison of the IR- and NMR spectra of the compound isolated with those of authentic 2-phenylethanol, as well as by the data of thin-layer chromatography.

The purity of the chromatographically pure 2-phenylethanol was checked by means of gas-liquid chromatography. It showed that 2-phenylethanol constituted 98.9% of the substance isolated. The two other insignificant peaks corresponded to citronellal (0.5%) and geraniol (0.6%).

It is known that 2-phenylethanol is contained in the flowers of the oil-bearing rose and it is one of the main components of the absolute from rose flower concrete, since it is soluble in ethanol. Its presence in rose flower wax, even though in insignificant amounts (0.57% of the wax) may be explained by a possible absorption by the other wax components.

B. Polycyclic Compounds

Column chromatography of the unsaponified wax of rose flower, followed by thin-layer chromatography using various solvent systems also gives spots indicating the presence of unknown substances, present in insignificant amounts, in addition to the compounds already established in the wax. In an effort to carry out a detailed study of the rose flower wax, we also underus as well as by other authors [51]. These results seemed to suggest that the compounds we isolated had cyclic structure. The positive reactions of the substances with Liebermann–Burchard or Salkovsky reagents confirmed the IR data on their cyclic structure.

According to literature data, many steroids and terpenoids have been isolated from plants so far, but they are found in superficial waxes only on very rare occasions [83]. Thus the detection of polycyclic compounds in took the identification of these micro-component substances, taking into consideration the greater possibilities offered by modern research methods.

In view of the very low contents of the unknown substances, a larger amount of the wax was treated. The substances in question were present mainly in the eluates obtained with benzene, benzene–ethanol and ethanol during column chromatography. By means of preparative thin-layer chromatography pure substances were isolated. The IR spectra of all of the isolated substances were recorded in potassium bromide, in carbon tetrachloride or in carbon disulfide.

Data of the IR spectra of the isolated products — maxima with low intensity at 735 cm^{-1} for methylene groups, more than 4 in a straight chain, ratio of methyl and methylene groups non-typical of compounds with a straight chain, in some cases 1 : 1, 1.5 : 1 and 2 : 1, presence of 5-membered and 6-membered lactone rings, and the simultaneous presence of several types of carbonyl groups — came as a surprise, inasmuch as hitherto only compounds with open chain had been found in the wax of rose flower by rose flowers is of great interest. So far only mono- and sesquiterpene compounds have been found in this plant material. Moreover, the therapeutic action of rose flower and of the products obtained from it [84] may be connected with the presence of compounds having a cyclic structure (triterpene and steroid type).

(i) *Pentacyclic dihydroxytriterpenoid.* One of the substances isolated, which was present in relatively larger amount, became the object of our initial study. Its IR spectrum showed a maximum of weak intensity at 735 cm^{-1}, 1 : 1 ratio of the methyl and methylene groups, and maxima of weak intensity for a double bond at 1645 cm^{-1} and 1012 cm^{-1}. Maxima at 1050 cm^{-1} and at 3640 cm^{-1} (in carbon tetrachloride and carbon disulfide) were also present. The NMR data were typical of polycyclic compounds (e.g. steroids and triterpenes). The mass spectrum of this compound had $M^+ = 442$, corresponding to the molecular formula $C_{30}H_{50}O_2$. The typical peaks in the upper part of the spectrum were $M^+ - H_2O$ (*m/e* 424), $M^+ - 2H_2O$ (*m/e* 406), $M^+ - H_2O - CH_3$ (*m/e* 409), and $M^+ - 2H_2O - CH_3$ (*m/e* 391). According to all mass spectral data the substance is a pentacyclic dihydroxytriterpenoid, similar to ψ-taraxasterol or betuline. An indication of its similarity to betuline-type compounds is the peak for a vinyl double bond in the IR spectrum (3098 cm^{-1}). The first hydroxyl group is in the cycle A or B (possibly in position 3, typical of triterpenes and steroids). An indication of this are peaks at *m/e* 207 and *m/e* 189 (base peak).

The second hydroxyl group is at another part of the molecule. It is not primary because there is no $M^+ - 31$ peak ($M^+ - CH_2OH$). According to the high $M - H_2O$ peak, the hydroxyl group must be secondary or tertiary.

(ii) *Ursolic acid.* In order to isolate one of the more polar substances, we somewhat modified the method used. The non-saponified wax was dissolved in light petroleum and the solution repeatedly extracted with methanol. The residue of the methanolic extract was chromatographed on a silica gel column. A positive reaction for triterpene compounds was found in the fractions eluted with benzene — ether (5 : 1). A chromatographically pure substance was isolated from them by preparative thin-layer chromatography. Its R_f-value coincided with that of standard ursolic and oleanolic acids; the m.p. (from EtOH) was 286–287°C.

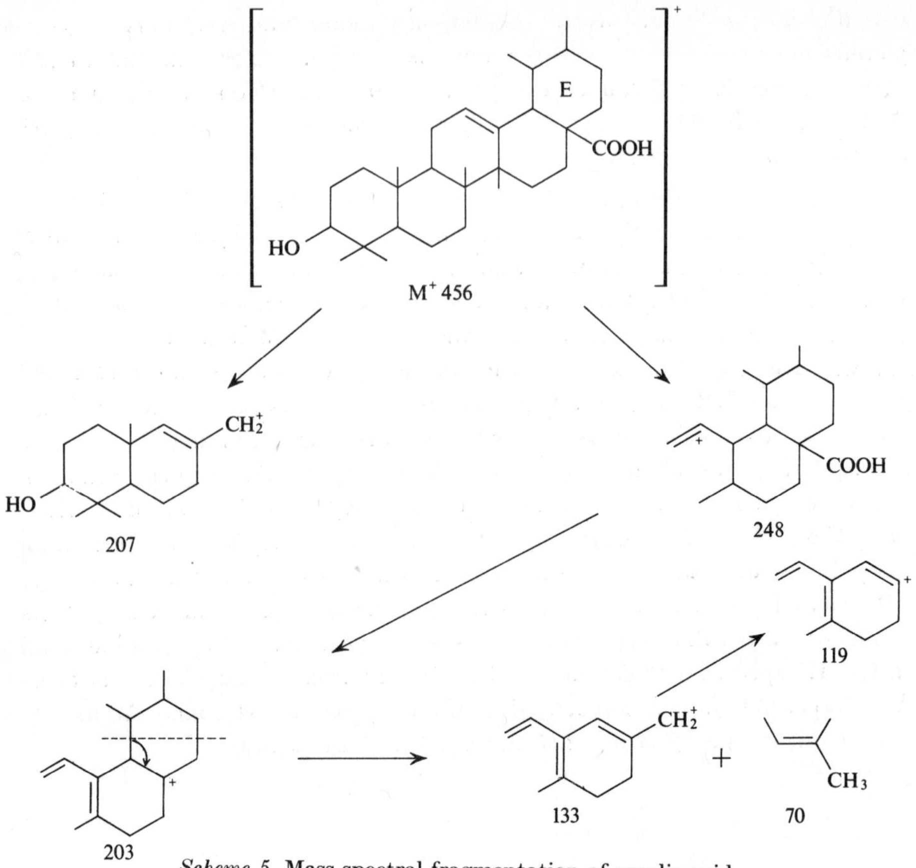

Scheme 5. Mass spectral fragmentation of ursolic acid.

The IR data were in agreement with the assumption of a triterpene acid possessing a double bond and a hydroxyl group in position 3. Mass spectroscopy indicated a molecular peak at m/e 456, and two main fragments of m/e 207 (45% abundance) and m/e 248 (100%), resulting from a retro Diels–Alder fragmentation (Scheme 5), typical of Δ^{12}-oleanenes and Δ^{12}-ursenes [86, 87]. Ions corresponding to the fragments at m/e 438 ($M - H_2O$) and m/e 423 ($M - H_2O - CH_3$) were also present. The ion of m/e 248, after the loss of mass 45 (COOH), resulted in the ion of m/e 203 (60%) (for 248 → 203, a metastable peak at m/e 166.5). The very high abundance of the ion of m/e 203 confirmed the position of the −COOH group at C_{17} [88]. A very intense peak at m/e 133 was also present, resulting from the ion of m/e 203, after the loss of mass 70 (for 203 → 133, a metastable peak at 87.5). In

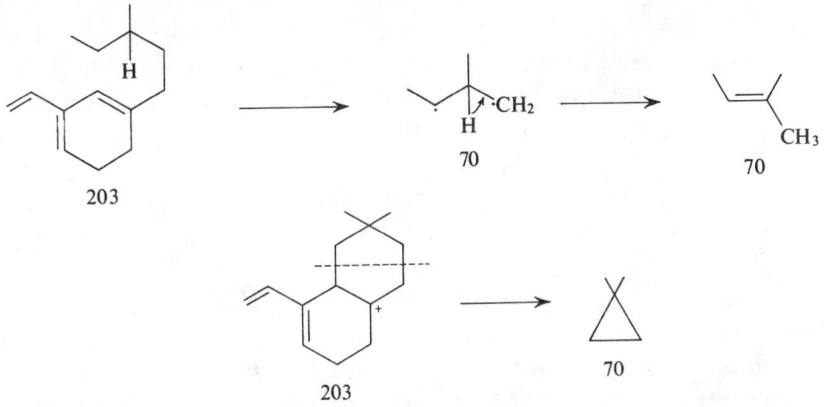

Scheme 6. Mass spectral fragmentation of ions of *m/e* 203 from ursolic and oleanolic acids.

Budzikiewicz's paper [86] the structure of the fragment ion of *m/e* 70 is not discussed. Moreover, there are no data on the mass spectral differentiation between ursene and oleanene compounds. In our opinion, the fragment 70 is formed as a result of a transfer of a hydrogen atom from C_{20}, leading to a stable olefinic structure (Scheme 6). A fragmentation of this type in the case of oleanolic acid would lead to an unstable cyclopropane ion with a mass of 70, due to the presence of a quaternary carbon atom in the E ring. The difference in the stabilization of fragment 70 should lead to a considerable difference in the abundance of the ion of *m/e* 133 in the case of ursolic acid and oleanolic acid. The mass spectra of standard ursolic and oleanolic acids confirmed the correctness of our assumption. There is no ion of *m/e* 70 in the spectrum of oleanolic acid. The fragment 133 is much more abundant in the case of ursolic acid (53%) than in that of oleanolic acid (20%). Conversely, the ion 203 is more abundant in the mass spectrum of oleanolic acid (85%) in comparison with the same ion from ursolic acid (60%). In addition, the more abundant ion of *m/e* 133 in the case of ursolic acid corresponded to the more abundant 119 ion. The mass spectrum of the substance isolated from rose flower concrete, fully coincided with that of authentic ursolic acid. This was also confirmed by the NMR data. In the NMR spectrum in $CDCl_3$ of ursolic acid and of our product the signal of the protons of the methyl groups of C_{29} and C_{30} at δ 0.85 was a doublet, while the same signal in the NMR spectrum of oleanolic acid was a singlet.

The presence of ursolic acid has not been established in rose flowers heretofore. Zimmermann [89] found this acid in the leaves of certain other species of Rosaceae. The presence of ursolic acid in the flower of the oil-bearing rose (*Rosa damascena* Mill.) may be of significance in elucidating the active principle of this rose and of the products obtained from it.

We believe that the considerable difference in the abundance of the fragments 133, 203 and 70 in the mass spectra of ursolic acid and oleanolic acid, established by us, can be used for their mass specure differentiation. This may be of great importance in cases where only a very small amount of the product studied is available and identification by other techniques is impossible.

(*iii*) *Callitrisic acid and sterols* [90]. Thin-layer chromatograms of benzene and benzene–ether fractions obtained by column chromatography of rose flower wax showed the presence of spots of unknown substances with positive Liebermann–Burchard reaction. One of them was isolated from the benzene–ether fraction. According to its R_f value, it was situated between the spots of references of betuline and ursolic acid. The IR spectra showed, besides the maxima for CH_3 and CH_2 groups in a ratio inherent to cyclic terpenoids, the presence of a trisubstituted benzene ring (710, 760, 830, 1510, 1610 cm^{-1}, also 3000–3100 cm^{-1}), carboxyl group (1710 cm^{-1}, also 2400–2800 cm^{-1}) and hydroxyl group (3200–3600 cm^{-1}). The mass spectra showed M$^+$ of m/e 300. High resolution measurement gave the formula $C_{20}H_{28}O_2$. Among all the compounds having this formula, dehydroabietic acid and callitrisic (4-epidehydroabietic) acid are the only ones in accordance with the IR data of the isolated substance.

A mass spectral investigation of diterpenes of the type of podocarpa-8,11,13-trienoic acid (in ester form), carried out by Enzel and Wahlberg [91] showed a difference between the mass spectra of dehydroabietic and 4-epide-hydroabietic acids. It appeared mainly in the abundances of the ions M–15 (m/e 285). In the case of 4-epidehydroabietic acid, this ion is nearly as abundant as the base peak at 239 (100%), whereas in the mass spectrum of dehydro-abietic acid the same ion (M –15) is only 20%. Enzel and Wahlberg, however, do not discuss the question of the possible mass spectral differentiation of these two acids on the basis of the difference in the abundances of the ion M–15 (m/e 285). We suggest that this difference can be used to establish the configuration at C_4 of the diterpene acids of unkown stereochemistry. The intense loss of a methyl group at C_{10} in the case of compounds with *axial* COOH (as 4-epidehydroabietic acid) is probably caused by a partial compensation of the resulting positive ion at C_{10} by the carbonyl group of the COOH. According to the Dreiding model of 4-epidehydroabietic acid, the distance between the carbonyl group of the COOH at C_4 and the methyl group at C_{10} is equal to the C–C bond length. It allows the mentioned compensation of the positive charge. In the case of the *equatorial* acid (as dehydroabietic acid) that distance is greater, and no compensation can be expected.

The pattern of fragmentation (Scheme 7) thus fully coincides with the structure of 4-epidehydroabietic acid. This pattern is proved by high resolution measurement and by the presence of metastable peaks, confirming each of the transitions mentioned below:

for M^+ 300 → 285 m^* at m/e 270.3
for M^+ 285 → 239 m^* at m/e 200.3
for M^+ 239 → 197 m^* at m/e 162.3.

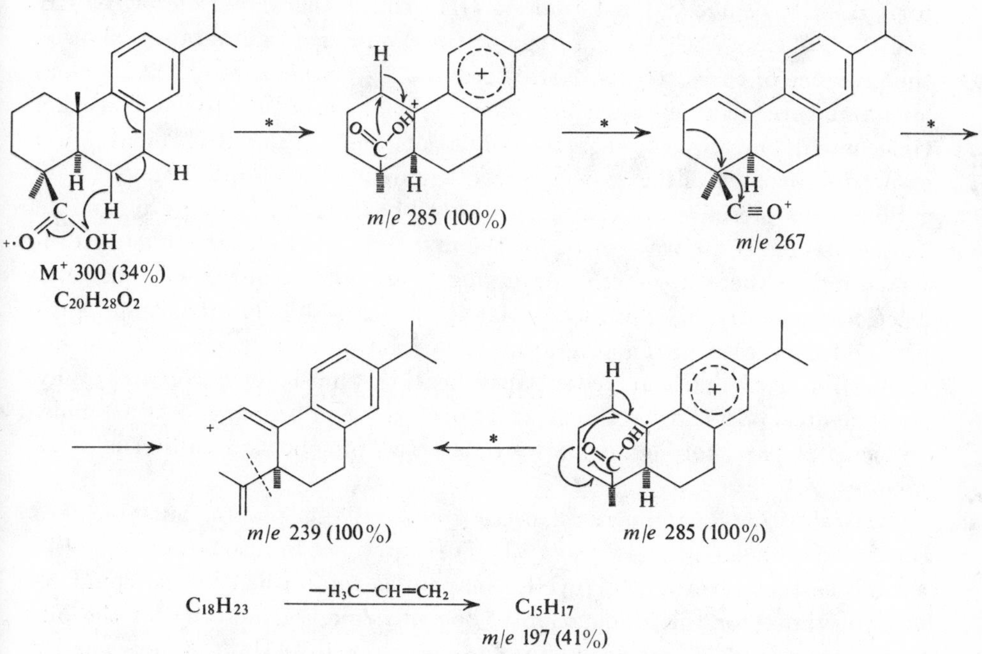

Scheme 7. Mass spectral fragmentation of callitrisic acid.

The high resolution measurement data enabled us to explain the origin of the ion with m/e 197 and thus to expand the scheme proposed.

Callitrisic acid was established as a natural product by Carman and Deeth [92] as a component of the resins of *Callitris collumelaris*. It was found in the resins of other *Callitris* species by Gough [93] and by Ghuah and Ward [94]. Up to now, callitrisic acid has not been found in Rosaceae.

From a biogenetic point of view, the presence of a diterpenic compound (callitrisic acid) in the Bulgarian rose concrete is not so unexpected, since monoterpene [18] and triterpene [85] compounds have been found so far.

Another substance unknown up to now to occur in Rosaceae was isolated by means of thin-layer chromatography from the benzene fraction of the rose wax. It showed positive Liebermann–Burchard reaction. In comparative thin-layer chromatography its R_f value coincided with that of β-sitosterol used as reference. The IR spectrum had the characteristic maxima for β-sitosterol. The NMR spectrum contained the methylene eminence, characteristic of sterols, signals for CH_3 at 0.6 δ, 0.77 δ and 0.92 δ, a multiplet for $CH-OH$ centred at 3.4 δ (*axial* OH group) and signals for $CH=CH$ and $>C=CH$ in the 5–5.25 δ region. Gas-liquid chromatography showed the presence of three sterols: β-sitosterol (62.3%), stigmasterol (29.1%) and an admixture of an unidentified sterol which, according to its retention time, might be campesterol. After silylation, the gas-liquid chromatogram showed no change either in the percentage or in the retention time.

Since the presence of sterols in the oil-bearing rose concrete, and in Rosaceae in general, was stated for the first time, it was interesting to establish whether there are sterols occurring in an ester form as well. The ester fraction of the rose absolute was isolated by means of column chromatography and thin-layer chromatography. The fraction gave a positive Liebermann–Burchard reaction. After saponification, thin-layer chromatography of the neutral part showed the presence of sterols and primary fatty alcohols. In the acid part, terpene acids were detected (ursolic and callitrisic acids mainly).

β-Sitosterol and stigmasterol occur frequently in plants, but they are rarely found in superficial waxes [83]. Their presence in rose flower concrete, as well as that of other polycyclic compounds established by us, could be of importance for the elucidation of the physiological activity of the oil-bearing rose and of the products obtained from it [95]. It is noteworthy that dehydroabietic acid, an epimer of callitrisic acid, has an antinicotinic activity [96].

Thus far only mono- and sesquiterpene compounds have been found in Bulgarian rose flower concrete. The results obtained by us have shown for the first time that it contains also di- and triterpene compounds, although only as micro-components.

As the summarized result of our investigation on the wax from rose flower, the presence of the following cyclic compounds has been established: benzoic acid, 2-phenylethanol, ursolic acid, callitrisic acid, a pentacyclic dihydroxytriterpene of betuline type, β-sitosterol and stigmasterol.

IV. COMPOSITION
OF ABSOLUTE FROM ROSE FLOWER CONCRETE
AND THE STRUCTURES OF ITS COMPONENTS

1. GENERAL CHARACTERIZATION OF THE ABSOLUTE

The composition of absolute from Bulgarian rose flower concrete has not been investigated in detail so far. The same applies to the composition of the absolute produced in Morocco in significant amounts in the past few years. An industry of products from roses has been developing in that country, using a rose supposed to be also *Rose damascena* Mill., which has undergone an evolution under the effect of the special local climatic conditions [97].

The only data in the literature on the absolute from the Bulgarian oil-bearing rose refer to some of its physical constants [98]. According to these data, it represents a viscous liquid of a green-brown colour. It has a strong fragrance, typical of the rose, which is mild and more permanent than that of the rose oil produced by hydrodistillation.

Specific gravity	0.9682–0.9916
Optical rotation	$+9°40'-+14°25'$
Refractive index	1.50633–1.51566
Acid number	3.5–11.2
Ester number	19.6–30.9
Ester number after acetylation	211.9–243.2
(acetylation number)	
Total alcohols as geraniol	69.3–81.8%

As can be seen, the absolute from the Bulgarian oil-bearing rose is dextro-rotatory, whereas the rose oil produced by means of steam distillation is laevo-rotatory. The substances causing dextro-rotation are obviously non-volatile with steam, because when an absolute is distilled by steam a laevo-rotatory distillate is obtained ($-0°54'$ to $-2°42'$).

It is rather logical to expect that the chemical composition of the absolute, not studied methodically so far, should be close to that of rose oil, on whose composition extensive investigations have been carried out. According to data published by Gildemeister and Hoffmann [4], Bulgarian rose oil contains the following components: ethanol, 2-phenylethanol, geraniol, nonyl-aldehyde, carvone, farnesol and aliphatic hydrocarbons (8–10%). It was reported that the hydrocarbons C_{17}, C_{19}, C_{20} and C_{21} [11, 12], as well as the unsaturated hydrocarbon eicosene-10 [13] are also present in the stearoptene from rose oil. It has been established that rose oil also contains acetaldehyde, salicylaldehyde, propylaldehyde, citral, cinnamaldehyde and phenylacetaldehyde [14, 15]. Later on, the composition of rose oil stearoptene was defined more accurately [47, 99]. It was found that the saturated hydrocarbons were in the C_{14} to C_{23} range, C_{19} being prevalent, while the unsaturated olefinic hydrocarbons were in the C_{15} to C_{21} range, with C_{19} as the predominant one. Traces of methanol and nonyl alcohol were also present in rose oil, as well as traces of acetic acid and valeric acid, both free and bound as esters [16].

In 1959 a new component of a cyclic structure, named "rose oxide", was isolated from Bulgarian rose oil. It possessed a specific rose odour. Initially, a structure with a tetrahydrofuran ring was ascribed to it, but later on it was found that it was (methyl-2-propen-1)-yl-2-methyl-4-tetrahydropyran.

Being very important in contributing to the rose odour, great interest has been attached to its synthetic preparation [100, 101, 102]. In addition, also the aliphatic terpene hydrocarbon myrcene has been found in Bulgarian rose oil [103].

A standard for rose oil, based on experimental data collected from many years of rose oil analysis, has been elaborated in Bulgaria, concerning chiefly its physico-chemical constants [3]:

1. Mobile transparent liquid.
2. Yellow to yellow-green colour.
3. Odour, typical of rose oil.
4. Specific gravity at 30°C 0.848–0.861.
5. Refractive index at 25°C 1.4530–1.640.
6. Number of polarization in 100 mm tube −2.2° to −4.8°.
7. Freezing point 16.5°–23.5°C.
8. Ester number 7.2–17.2.
9. Acid number 0.92–3.75.
10. Saponification number 8.0–21.0.
11. Ester number after acetylation 197–233.3.
12. Free alcohols, as geraniol 62.9–75.5%.

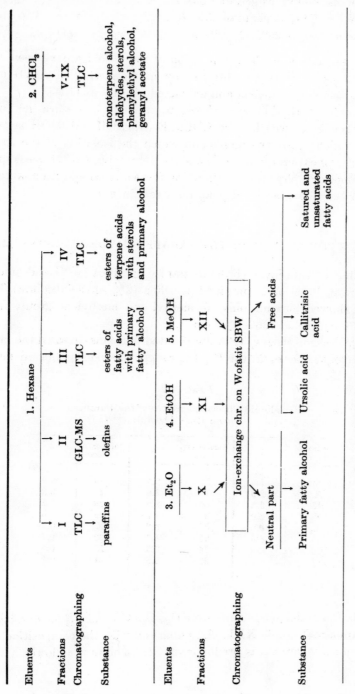

Fig. 8. Group chromatographic analysis of absolute

13. Alcohols, bound, as geraniol 2.0–4.7%.

14. Total alcohols, as geraniol 65.8–78.2%.

15. Stearoptene 15–23%.

Our investigations on the composition of the absolute have been carried out with 22 g of absolute, obtained by us from 41 g of concrete from Bulgarian rose flower, picked and extracted also by us [104].

The sample of absolute was chromatographed on a silica gel column. Elution was effected with hexane, $CHCl_3$, Et_2O, EtOH and MeOH as detailed in Fig. 8 which shows the manner in which the isolation of the fractions and the identification of the components were done. On the basis of thin-layer chromatography, the fractions of the same composition were combined; they are denoted by Roman numerals in Fig. 8.

2. COMPOSITION OF THE PARAFFIN HYDROCARBONS

According to thin-layer chromatography on silica gel G and silica gel–silver nitrate, Fraction I contained paraffins (2% of the absolute). The IR spectrum showed maxima only for methyl and methylene groups at 1385 cm^{-1}, 1470 cm^{-1} and 2860–3000 cm^{-1}.

Gas-liquid chromatography of the isolated paraffins revealed the presence of a homologous series in the C_{11}–C_{33} range. The odd-numbered members

Table XXI

Gas-liquid Chromatography of the Paraffins
from Rose Absolute

Number of C-atoms	%	Number of C-atoms	%	Number of C-atoms	%
11	1.8	18	2.5	26	0.9
X_1	2.9	19	3.6	27	0.8
13	5.3	20	2.8	28	0.2
X_2	2.0	21	18.4	29	0.6
X_3	3.6	22	2.2	X_5	0.2
15	6.6	23	24.7	30	0.7
16	2.8	24	3.3	X_6	0.6
17	8.1	25	5.8	31	0.3

prevailed. The main components were C_{23}, C_{21}, C_{17} and C_{15} (decreasing order of their amounts) (Table XXI). A comparison with the composition of rose wax paraffins, where C_{27} is predominant [43], shows that lower molecular weight paraffins prevail in the absolute. This can be expected, taking into account the manner in which the absolute is obtained. A comparison with the composition of stearoptene from rose oil, where C_{19} is predominating, reveals that in the steam distillation of rose flower hydrocarbons with still lower molecular weight are distilled over.

The peaks indicated with X are probably due to branched-chain paraffins.

3. COMPOSITION OF THE OLEFINIC HYDROCARBONS

According to the IR data, Fraction II (5.3% of the absolute) contained unsaturated hydrocarbons (maxima not only for CH_3 and CH_2, but also for CH=CH at 1650 cm^{-1} and 3020 cm^{-1}). The fraction gave a blue colour with Liebermann–Burchard reagent. This reaction gave us grounds to assume that in this fraction, in addition to the expected unsaturated hydrocarbons found in the stearoptene from Bulgarian rose oil so far [47] and in the wax from concrete, also terpene hydrocarbons were present. Gas-liquid chromatography, carried out under conditions suitable for terpene hydrocarbons, showed peaks coinciding with those of authentic α-pinene,

Table XXII

Gas-liquid Chromatography of the Olefins
from Rose Absolute

Number of C-atoms	%	Number of C-atoms	%	Number of C-atoms	%
X_1	0.1	X_{13}	0.1	X_{23}	0.4
p 13	0.5	18	0.8	X_{24}	1.3
X_2	0.1	p 18	0.4	23	13.2
X_3	0.1	X_{14}	0.1	X_{25}	0.2
X_4	0.2	19	25.7	X_{26}	0.3
X_5	0.1	p 19	8.4	24	0.9
p 14	0.6	X_{15}	0.1	X_{27}	0.1
X_6	0.1	20	0.8	X_{28}	0.9
X_7	0.1	X_{16}	0.8	25	3.0
X_8	0.4	X_{17}	1.5	X_{29}	0.2
X_9	0.2	X_{18}	1.8	X_{30}	0.3
p 15	1.5	21	3.5	27	3.2
X_{10}	0.1	p 21	7.7	X_{31}	0.3
X_{11}	0.1	X_{19}	3.3	29	3.0
X_{12}	0.1	X_{20}	0.2	X_{32}	0.1
p 16	0.5	X_{21}	0.3	31	0.5
17	2.7	22	1.7		
p 17	4.5	X_{22}	0.2		

camphene, sabinene, β-phellandrene, limonene and γ-terpinene. In the total mixture of olefinic hydrocarbons, the terpene hydrocarbons were present in insignificant quantities: α-pinene 0.5%, camphene 0.2%, sabinene 0.5%, limonene 0.5%, β-phellandrene 1.5% and γ-terpinene 1.2%. In order to identify the rest of the peaks, gas-liquid chromatography was combined with mass spectrometry. The results given in Table XXII showed that a homologous series of olefins in the C_{12}–C_{31} range was present in Fraction II, with the odd-numbered members prevailing. Most abundant were: C_{19}, C_{23}, C_{21}, C_{27}, C_{29} and C_{25}. Among the even-numbered members C_{22} was predominant. A comparison with the rose wax olefins shows that lower molecular olefins prevail in the absolute.

In this respect a greater analogy is found with the olefinic hydrocarbons of stearoptene, where also C_{19} is predominant.

The peaks marked with p in the Table are due to lower paraffins which have remained as contaminations in the olefin fraction, since owing to their low molecular weight they are hard to elute. Several of the first peaks, designated with X, belong to the already established monoterpene hydrocarbons. Some of the other peaks, also marked by X, are probably due to isomeric hydrocarbons with different positions of the double bond, as well as to diene hydrocarbons found by us in rose flower wax [48].

4. COMPOSITION OF THE ESTER FRACTIONS

Thin-layer chromatography of Fraction III (0.03% of the absolute) showed a spot coinciding in its R_f value with a standard of higher fatty acid ester. The IR spectrum of the isolated pure substance confirmed the presence of an ester (maxima at 1745 cm^{-1} and 1260 cm^{-1}). After the saponification of the ester, thin-layer chromatography of the acid and neutral parts indicated the presence of esters of higher fatty acids with primary fatty alcohols. Their insignificant amounts in the absolute of rose flower, although they are markedly present in the wax, should be due to their lower solubility in ethanol owing to their higher molecular weight.

Another ester component (according to its IR data) was isolated from Fraction IV. It gave a positive Liebermann–Burchard reaction (red colour). Thin-layer chromatography of the acid and the neutral parts obtained after saponification of this ester fraction revealed the presence of terpene acids (mainly ursolic and callitrisic acids), found by us as micro-components in rose flower wax, and primary fatty alcohols and sterols. Therefore, there are two types of esters present in the absolute: esters of higher fatty acids with primary fatty alcohols and sterols, and esters of terpenic acids with primary fatty alcohols and possibly likewise with sterols. The insignificant quantity of the isolated ester fraction (0.07% of the absolute) did not allow a more detailed investigation.

5. COMPOSITION OF THE FRACTIONS CONTAINING TERPENE ALCOHOLS AND OTHER LOW MOLECULAR COMPOUNDS

Thin-layer chromatography of Fractions V–IX (60.8% of the absolute) eluted with $CHCl_3$ showed spots giving positive reactions with the Liebermann–Burchard reagent (red colour). Their R_f values coincided with those of authentic monoterpene alcohols (geraniol, nerol), phenylethyl alcohol and β-sitosterol. These fractions were combined and analyzed by means of IR spectroscopy. Maxima were found for CH_3 and CH_2 groups (1380 cm^{-1}, 1470 cm^{-1} and 2800–3000 cm^{-1}), for benzene ring (710, 760, 1510, 1610, 1525, 3020 and 3070 cm^{-1}), for OH group (1050, and 3200–3500 cm^{-1}), and for C=O group (1715–1735 cm^{-1}). Gas-liquid chromatography confirmed the thin-layer chromatographic results concerning the main components of the Bulgarian rose absolute, which are well known: phenylethyl alcohol, cironellol, geraniol, nerol, citral, nonylaldehyde and geranyl acetate.

Thin-layer chromatography of Fraction X (7.5% of the absolute), eluted with ether, showed the presence of a spot with an R_f value corresponding to a primary fatty alcohol; further spots were situated between those of authentic betuline and ursolic acid. Some of the spots gave red colour with the Liebermann–Burchard reagent. The IR spectrum had indications of a very complex composition: presence of OH group, benzene ring, COOH group and lactone ring. Fractions XI (8.8%) and XII (1.2% of the absolute), eluted with EtOH and MeOH, respectively, showed an analogous composition.

6. COMPOSITION AND STRUCTURE OF THE FREE FATTY ACIDS

Fractions X, XI and XII were combined. Free acids were isolated by means of ion-exchange resin Wofatit SBW and then methylated with diazomethane. The esters of fatty acids were separated from those of the terpene acids by preparative thin-layer chromatography. Thin-layer chromatography on silica gel G–silver nitrate of the methyl esters of the fatty acids showed the presence of esters of saturated and unsaturated acids with one, two and three double bonds.

The composition of the free acids was established both by gas-liquid chromatography of their methyl esters on a polar and non-polar phase and by mass spectrometry of the acids themselves. The gas-liquid chromatography data, given in Table XXIII, revealed the presence of a homologous

Table XXIII

Gas-liquid Chromatography of the Methyl Esters
of the Total Free Acids

Number of C-atoms	%	Number of C-atoms	%
10	0.1	18	15.6
11	0.1	18 : 1	3.8
12	0.3	19	0.2
13	0.2	18 : 2	0.6
14	2.8	20	4.7
15	0.8	18 : 3	0.4
16	58.0	21	0.5
16 : 1	1.8	22	2.4
17	4.5	23	1.5
16 : 2	0.6	24	1.2
		25	0.1
		26	1.0

series in the C_{10}–C_{26} range, in which the members with even number of carbon atoms predominated. Palmitic acid was the most abundant among the saturated acids, and oleic acid among the unsaturated ones. The percentage of the saturated acids in the total mixture of free acids was 66.3%, according to thin-layer chromatography.

The mass spectral data (Table XXIV) of the isolated fatty acids made it possible to draw certain conclusions on the structure of the carbon chain. Furthermore, the mass spectrum showed that the acid range was much wider, extending from C_9 to C_{32}. The most predominant members were the same as those detected by gas-liquid chromatography. In comparison with the content of fatty acids in rose wax [51], more lower members are found in the rose absolute.

In the mass spectrum, ions typical for higher fatty acids M^+ and $M-COOH$, as well as ions due to hydrocarbon fragments occurred. The most prominent re-arrangement ion with m/e 60 (67.5% of the base peak at m/e 43) was an indication that the major part of the acids had a straight

Table XXIV

Mass Spectral Data on the Free Acids of Rose Absolute

Number of C-atoms	M %	M—2 %	M—45 %	M—15 %	M—15 / M %	Carbon chain
9	2.8	0.0	15.7	8.2	3.7	Normal and branched
10	2.8	0.6	8.2	11.2	5.1	Normal and branched
11	3.2	0.7	6.4	12.8	5.8	Normal and branched
12	1.6	0.5	3.7	16.5	9.9	Normal and branched
13	3.7	0.5	2.9	6.0	1.7	Normal and branched
14	2.5	0.6	2.3	18.0	7.2	Normal and branched
15	2.8	0.6	3.0	7.5	2.3	Normal and branched
16	41.0	0.8	1.6	8.9	0	Normal
17	1.0	0.6	1.7	5.3	0.5	Normal
18	27.8	0.9	2.2	2.0	0.7	Normal and branched
19	2.2	0.4	1.2	1.0	0.6	Normal and branched
20	8.3	0.4	1.2	0.8	0.1	Normal
21	1.4	0.2	0.8	0.3	0.2	Normal
22	3.0	0.6	0.7	1.0	0.3	Normal
23	1.2	0.2	0.5	0.9	0.8	Normal and branched
24	44.5	0.3	0.4	0.9	0.2	Normal
25	0.8	0.0	0.5	0.7	0.8	Normal and branched
26	1.7	0.2	0.3	0.5	0.3	Normal
27	0.6	0.5	0.3	0.5	0.9	Normal and branched
28	1.2	0.4	0.1	0.5	0.4	Normal
29	0.6	0.2	0.2	0.5	0.9	Normal and branched
30	0.8	0.0	0.5	0.2	0.3	Normal
32	0.3	0.0	0.0	0.0	0.0	Normal

chain (Scheme 8). The comparatively abundant ion of m/e 74 (10.5%) might be due to the presence of branched-chain acids — a methyl group in α-position.

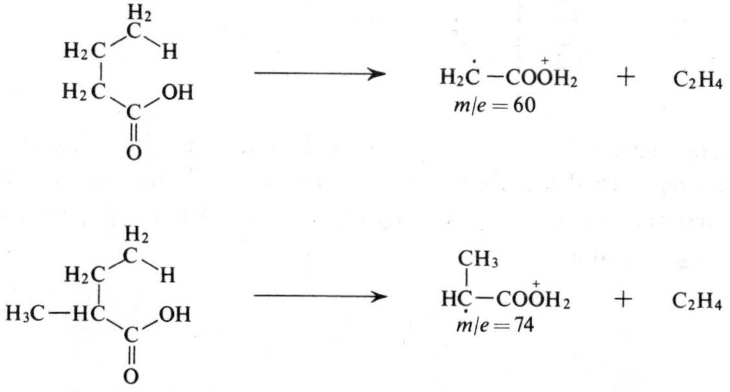

Scheme 8. Mass spectral fragmentation of normal and α-methyl-branched fatty acids.

The ratio $\dfrac{M-15}{M^+}$ characterizes the degree of branching of the carbon chain [62a]. As seen from Table XXIV it is the members C_{12}, C_{14}, C_{11} and C_{10} which contain a methyl group as a side chain in the highest proportion. It is an interesting fact that there is greater branching in the case of the odd-numbered acids above the member C_{19}.

No α-methyl-branched long-chain fatty acids have been found in plants so far. Such an acid with a relatively short chain (α-methyl-butyric acid) is present in the essence from strawberries.

7. COMPOSITION AND STRUCTURE
OF THE LONG-CHAIN PRIMARY ALCOHOLS

After the removal of the fatty acids from Fraction X, a substance having the same R_f value as a primary fatty alcohol, used as standard, was isolated by preparative thin-layer chromatography. The IR spectrum confirmed the presence of OH group (maxima at 1050 cm^{-1} and 3640 cm^{-1}). The isolated primary alcohols were acetylated and analyzed by gas-liquid chromatography (Table XXV). As shown in the Table, the alcohols occur

Table XXV

Gas-liquid Chromatography of the Alcohols of Rose Absolute

Number of C-atoms	%	Number of C-atoms	%	Number of C-atoms	%
10	0.9	19	1.2	24	11.0
14	0.9	20	17.9	25	2.8
15	1.2	21	4.7	26	6.8
16	0.5	22	39.2	27	2.5
17	1.2	23	3.8	28	4.3
18	1.2				

in a homologous series in the C_{10}–C_{28} range. In this case, just like in rose wax, the even-numbered members prevail, yet the predominant ones have lower molecular weights (C_{22}, C_{20} and C_{24}) than the alcohols preponderant in rose wax (C_{28}, C_{24} and C_{22}).

8. CYCLIC COMPOUNDS

After removal of the fatty acids and the primary alcohols from the ether, ethanol and methanol fractions, very small quantities of material remained. In thin-layer chromatography they gave red spots when sprayed with Liebermann–Burchard reagent. Two of them proved to be identical with ursolic acid [85] and callitrisic acid [90], already found by us as micro-components of the wax. In addition, two cyclic compounds were isolated: one with a 5-membered lactone ring, and the other with a 6-membered lactone ring (based on the IR spectra). The structures of these compounds are not yet elucidated.

Our investigations on the composition of the absolute from Bulgarian oil-bearing roses are mainly of a qualitative nature. However, they offer an idea about the quantities of some groups of compounds: hydrocarbons, alcohols, acids and others, as well as about the ratio of the individual members of the various homologous series. It should be borne in mind, however, that during the treatment of the absolute some components of this complex mixture may undergo certain changes, such as oxidation (aldehydes) and partial polymerization (unsaturated hydrocarbons, unsaturated fatty acids), as well as a loss of or decrease in the amounts of volatile components during isolation.

Special emphasis should be placed on the fact that during the study of the absolute from concrete of the oil-bearing rose, we have established for the first time that monoterpene mono- and dicyclic hydrocarbons: α-pinene, camphene, sabinene, β-phellandrene, limonene and γ-terpinene are present in Bulgarian rose flower. All these hydrocarbons are substances with a pleasant fragrance, and in spite of their low quantities, they doubtlessly contribute to the typical and unique odour of the Bulgarian rose oil and absolute. According to literature data, monoterpene hydrocarbons have been found in the Moroccoan rose, too [97].

In the absolute from the Bulgarian rose, we have also been the first to establish the presence of α-methyl branched fatty acids and this is their first proven occurrence in a natural product.

We believe that monoterpene hydrocarbons, as well as the α-methyl fatty acids are not inherent to the absolute only. Most probably they are present in other products of the oil-bearing rose as well; for instance, mono-terpene hydrocarbons occurring in rose oil. One of the reasons why they have now been found in the absolute is that a bigger sample of it has been treated. This has made possible the concentration of some of the micro-components by column chromatography in the corresponding fractions. Moreover, the

components possessing a more polar nature pass into the absolute during
the separation of the concrete into wax and absolute.

As is seen, the study of the composition of the absolute from the Bulgarian
rose flower has led to an extension of the range of homologous series of
paraffins, olefins, alcohols and fatty acids, present in the oil-bearing rose,
due to the identification of lower members. The main reason for this is the
higher solubility in ethanol of the members with a lower molecular weight.

V. BIOGENESIS OF THE LONG-CHAIN COMPONENTS
OF NATURAL WAXES

The experimental results obtained by us and discussed so far gave us
grounds to draw certain conclusions and inferences on the biogenesis of
the long-chain components of natural waxes. Current data indicate that this
problem is very complicated and still not fully elucidated. An evaluation of
the biogenetic significance of the results reported by us would be difficult
without giving first a picture of the present state of knowledge about the
biogenesis of these compounds.

1. BIOGENESIS OF NORMAL LONG-CHAIN HYDROCARBONS

The authors who first identified some components of plant waxes, were
also the first to suggest hypotheses for their formation. As early as 1929,
Clenshaw and Smedly-Maclean [105] established the presence of hentriacontane in spinach leaves. They proposed a head-to-head condensation
mechanism of palmitic acid to account for its formation. Simultaneously
with them Channon and Chibnall [61] found nonacosane and nonacosan-15-
one in cabbage leaves and assumed a similar mechanism for their biosynthesis: head-to-head condensation of pentadecanoic acid [61] (Scheme 9).

From that time on, C_{29} compounds occurring in cabbage leaves became
the basis for discussion on the biosynthesis of wax components, and *Brassica
oleracea* the main plant for experiments, for the solution of this question.
However, somewhat later Channon and Chibnall discarded their hypothesis,
since the C_{15} acid had not been found in nature. Moreover, the intermediate
products assumed, such as the corresponding ketones, secondary alcohols
and olefins were found only in a very limited number of cases at that time.
In 1934 Chibnall and Piper [35] proposed another scheme on the basis of
results obtained by them in studying animal and plant waxes. It possessed,
however, the same weak points, since it operated with a hypothetical

$$C_{13}H_{27}-CH_2-COOH \quad + \quad HOOC-CH_2-C_{13}H_{27} \longrightarrow$$

$$\longrightarrow C_{13}H_{27}-CH_2-CO-CH_2-C_{13}H_{27} \longrightarrow$$

$$\longrightarrow C_{13}H_{27}-CH_2-\underset{\underset{OH}{|}}{CH}-CH_2-C_{13}H_{27} \longrightarrow$$

$$\longrightarrow C_{13}H_{27}-CH_2-CH=CH-C_{13}H_{27} \longrightarrow$$

$$\longrightarrow C_{13}H_{27}-CH_2-CH_2-CH_2-C_{13}H_{27}$$

Scheme 9. Scheme of Channon and Chibnall for the biogenesis of long-chain normal hydrocarbons [61].

unsaturated acid and could not explain the formation of tritriacontan-17-ol and the corresponding ketone, found by Kreger [69].

Striving to explain the formation of this alcohol and ketone, Kreger again returned to the condensation mechanism and evolved a new scheme [69], according to which tritriacontan-17-one and the tritriaconten- 17-ol may be obtained as a result of the condensation of two molecules of stearic acid. As is seen, this scheme involves the intermediary formation of methyl ketones (Scheme 10).

$$CH_3-(CH_2)_{16}-COOH \quad + \quad HOOC-(CH_2)_{16}-CH_3$$

$$\downarrow$$

$$CH_3-(CH_2)_{16}-CO-(CH_2)_{16}-CH_3$$

$$\downarrow \text{Double } \omega\text{-oxidation}$$

$$HOOC-CH_2-CH_2-(CH_2)_{14}-CO-(CH_2)_{14}-CH_2-CH_2-COOH$$

$$\downarrow \beta\text{- Oxidation}$$

$$HOOC-CH_2-CO-(CH_2)_{14}-CO-(CH_2)_{14}-CO-CH_2-COOH$$

$$\downarrow \text{Decarboxylation}$$

$$CH_3-CO-(CH_2)_{14}-CO-(CH_2)_{14}-CO-CH_3$$

$$\downarrow \text{Reduction}$$

$$CH_3-CH_2-(CH_2)_{14}-CO-(CH_2)_{14}-CH_2-CH_3$$

Scheme 10. Scheme of Kreger for the formation of tritriacontan-17-one [62].

18*

$$CH_3-(CH_2)_{13}-CH_2-COOH \longrightarrow CH_3-(CH_2)_{13}-COOH$$

$$2\,CH_3-(CH_2)_{13}-COOH \longrightarrow CH_3-(CH_2)_{13}-CO-(CH_2)_{13}-CH_3 \longrightarrow$$

$$\longrightarrow CH_3-(CH_2)_{13}-\underset{\underset{OH}{|}}{CH}-(CH_2)_{13}-CH_3 \longrightarrow$$

$$\longrightarrow CH_3-(CH_2)_{13}-CH_2-(CH_2)_{13}-CH_3$$

Scheme 11. Formation of C_{29}-hydrocarbon from palmitic acid through head-to-head condensation mechanism.

Later on, using methyl ketones labelled in the carbonyl group, we demonstrated that they were not intermediates in the formation of paraffins from higher fatty acids [106].

Other schemes, more or less probable, have also been proposed for the biogenesis of the wax components. It has been shown with the aid of labelled atoms that the precursors of the straight-chain wax components are the fatty acids. It is now an established fact that the activated acetate is transformed into palmitic acid through malonylcoenzyme A, which yields the remaining 14 carbon atoms [107]. It has likewise been found that the labelled acetate is incorporated in *n*-heptane in *Pinus jefrei* [108] and that growing cabbage leaves rapidly incorporate the exogenous labelled acetate in their surface lipids [109]. However, the explanation of the biosynthetic pathways of wax components with a long-chain (C_{20}–C_{40}) still presents considerable difficulties. For a better understanding of the biosynthesis of these compounds we are greatly indebted to Kolattukudy for his consistent and tenacious investigations by means of labelled atoms.

In his studies Kolattukudy obtained experimental results which are at variance with a head-to-head condensation mechanism as proposed in its initial form. According to that mechanism, the *n*-C_{29} hydrocarbon is formed from palmitic acid after its preliminary transformation into pentadecanoic acid (Scheme 11).

From this pathway it would follow that palmitic acid fully loses its carboxylic carbon atom, while Kolattukudy's results show that in all *n*-C_{29} compounds of *Brassica oleracea* the whole carbon chain of palmitic acid is included.

The same hypothesis, applied to the biosynthesis of the *n*-C_{31} alkane requires that the *n*-C_{16} acid 1-^{14}C should yield a product, whose activity should be half of that of the product obtained from *n*-C_{16} acid *U*-[14]C. The

$$2 \text{ CH}_3-(\text{CH}_2)_{14}-\overset{\text{x}}{\text{C}}\text{OOH} \longrightarrow \text{CH}_3-(\text{CH}_2)_{14}-\overset{\text{x}}{\text{C}}\text{O}-(\text{CH}_2)_{14}-\text{CH}_3 \longrightarrow$$

$$\longrightarrow \text{CH}_3-(\text{CH}_2)_{14}-\overset{\text{x}}{\text{C}}\text{H}_2-(\text{CH}_2)_{14}-\text{CH}_3$$

$$2 \overset{\text{x}}{\text{C}}\text{H}_3-(\text{CH}_2)_{14}-\text{COOH} \longrightarrow \overset{\text{x}}{\text{C}}\text{H}_3-(\text{CH}_2)_{14}-\text{CO}-(\text{CH}_2)_{14}-\overset{\text{x}}{\text{C}}\text{H}_3 \longrightarrow$$

$$\longrightarrow \overset{\text{x}}{\text{C}}\text{H}_3-(\text{CH}_2)_{14}-\text{CH}_2-(\text{CH}_2)_{14}-\overset{\text{x}}{\text{C}}\text{H}_3$$

Scheme 12. Expected results from experiments with 1-^{14}C-and U-^{14}C-labelled palmitic acid.

results of experiments carried out with spinach and pea leaves [110], however, have shown that the activities are the same in both cases (Scheme 12).

In addition, the intact carbon chains of the C_{16} and C_{18} acids are incorporated into *n*-nonacosan-15-one. Experiments for the time course of incorporation of labelled acetate into the C_{29} compounds of *Brassica oleracea* indicate that the specific activity of the alkane is always the highest, followed by that of the ketone. The secondary alcohol has a much lower specific activity. All this is in contradiction with the precursor–product relationship of the condensation mechanism [109, 111]. Moreover, all attempts to establish interconversion between the C_{29} compounds of *Brassica oleracea* failed.

On the basis of this experimental evidence against the head-to-head condensation mechanism, in 1966 Kolattukudy put forward an elongation–decarboxylation mechanism in an attempt at elucidating the results from experiments with labelled atoms [112] (Scheme 13).

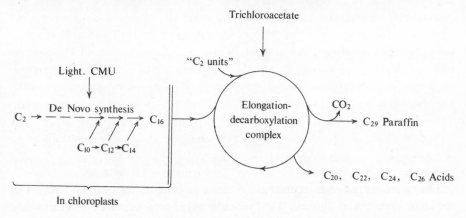

Scheme 13. Elongation–decarboxylation mechanism of alkane biosynthesis.

According to this hypothesis, the acetate is transformed into palmitic acid in the chloroplasts. Later on the n-C_{16} acid, linked to coenzyme A or to an acyl-carrier protein (ACP) becomes a substrate of the enzyme complex for elongation-decarboxylation, and after the elongation of the C_{16} acid to C_{30} or to C_{32}, the product undergoes decarboxylation to give the paraffin C_{29} or C_{31}.

This hypothesis is in good agreement with certain facts established by Kolattukudy, namely, that trichloroacetate at low concentrations definitely inhibits the synthesis of paraffins and long-chain fatty acids, whereas the synthesis of common fatty acids, C_{16} and C_{18}, remains unaffected. Conversely, the synthesis of the common fatty acids (C_{16} and C_{18}), which is dependent on photosynthetic processes, is stimulated by light and is inhibited by 3-(4-chlorophenyl)-1,1-dimethylurea (CMU). The synthesis of alkanes is unaffected by light and CMU. The exogenous radioactive precursors introduced which label the alkanes, also label the long-chain fatty acids in the leaves of spinach, pea or cabbage [109, 110].

The fact that stearic acid 18–^{14}C is incorporated in the n-C_{17} paraffin is evidence in favour of a direct decarboxylation process [113]. Likewise, the labelled C_{16} acid yields the C_{15} alkane, accompanied by C_{17} alkane which, in turn, suggests elongation prior to decarboxylation.

In spite of numerous experimental results which may well be explained by the elongation–decarboxylation mechanism, there are also others which do not agree with it. Thus, for instance, the exogenous labelled acid C_{30} cannot be incorporated into the C_{29} paraffin of *Brassica oleracea*. Owing to this, the conclusion about the direct decarboxylation of the acids to paraffins is still considered as insufficiently reliable. In addition, some doubt in that mechanism arises also from results reported by Macey and Barber [53]. These authors compared the wax composition of certain pea and cabbage mutants. In cabbage, the C_{15} acid, which is characteristic of the normal glaucus form, is markedly less in the mutant forms and this corresponds well with the decrease in the C_{29} compounds. In the case of two pea mutants, the decrease in the amount of the C_{32} acid reflects the decrease in the quantity of the C_{31} hydrocarbon; two other mutants, however, give an entirely different relationship, thus a direct precursor–product relationship is missing here [114].

Moreover, Kolattukudy visualizes the formation of nonacosan-15-one in cabbage leaves by the oxidation of the C_{30} acid at the C_{16} carbon atom. In 1970 Macey and Barber [115] established, however, that in addition to nonacosan-15-one, also nonacosan-14-one (about 16% of the ketone mixture) was present. These researchers assumed that these two ketones may be the products of the following condensation reactions:

$$C_{15} \text{ acid} + C_{15} \text{ acid} \rightarrow \rightarrow \rightarrow \text{nonacosan-15-one.}$$
$$C_{14} \text{ acid} + C_{16} \text{ acid} \rightarrow \rightarrow \rightarrow \text{nonacosan-14-one.}$$

In this way the necessity of taking into account also the condensation mechanism in the biogenesis of wax components has emerged again. It is only by some condensation mechanism that the biogenesis of corinemycolic acid

$$CH_3-(CH_2)_{14}-\underset{\underset{OH}{|}}{CH}-\underset{\underset{C_{14}H_{29}}{|}}{CH}-COOH$$

in the wax from *Mycobacterium tuberculosis* may be explained [114].

Obviously, this compound may be formed by the condensation of two molecules of palmitic acid and subsequent hydrogenation.

Recently, Kolattukudy has returned again to the idea of the condensation mechanism, by putting forward an acceptor–donor mechanism. This is actually a head-to-head condensation, yet occurring between two different (unequal) fatty acids, with specific decarboxylation of one of the acids (Scheme 14).

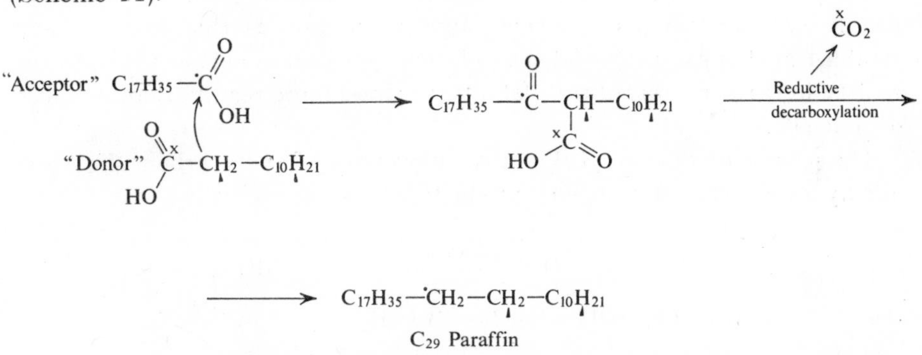

Scheme 14. Acceptor–donor condensation mechanism for the synthesis of alkanes.

Direct experimental evidence for the specific decarboxylation of the donor acid has been obtained by Albro and Dittmer in recent years by studying olefins from *Sarcina lutea* (116–119). They have established the presence of unsaturated hydrocarbons with methyl groups in iso- and antiiso positions at both ends of the chain, and they believe that hydrocarbons of such a type may only be obtained by a condensation pathway. Based on their *in vivo* and *in vitro* experimental results, they assume an acceptor–donor mechanism for the formation of olefins [120] (Scheme 15). They find that palmitaldehyde is rapidly incorporated into the hydrocarbon under suitable conditions [120].

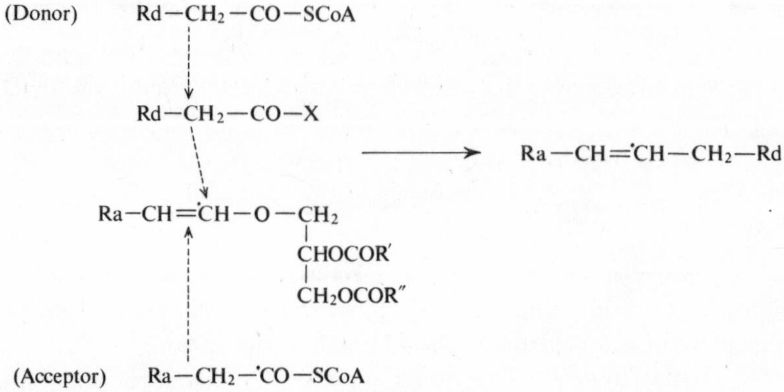

(Donor) $Rd-CH_2-CO-SCoA$

$Rd-CH_2-CO-X$

                                        $\longrightarrow$ $Ra-CH{=}CH-CH_2-Rd$

$Ra-CH{=}CH-O-CH_2$
$\qquad\qquad\qquad\quad |$
$\qquad\qquad\qquad\ CHOCOR'$
$\qquad\qquad\qquad\quad |$
$\qquad\qquad\qquad\ CH_2OCOR''$

(Acceptor) $Ra-CH_2-CO-SCoA$

Scheme 15. Acceptor–donor condensation mechanism for the synthesis of olefins in *Sarcina lutea.*

Moreover, they succeeded in isolating an intermediate product and identified it as a neutral plasmalogene. In confirmation of this scheme, they established that exogenous labelled plasmalogene takes part as the acceptor moiety in the synthesis of the olefin three times more readily than palmitic acid itself.

The scheme by Stumpf [121] for the biogenesis of hydrocarbons, in which aldehydes are the intermediary products, is also noteworthy:

$$R-CH_2-CH_2-COOH \xrightarrow[-CO_2]{\alpha\text{-oxidation}} R-CH_2-CHO \longrightarrow$$

$$R-CH_2-CH_2-OH \longrightarrow R-CH{=}CH_2 \longrightarrow R-CH_2-CH_3$$

The main argument for this mechanism was the fact that α-oxidizing enzymes have been found in leaves of plants. According to the mechanism, there is a biogenetic relationship between paraffins and olefins. An experimental result, reported by Kolattukudy is also in support of such a pathway; it was found that in *Brassica oleracea*, fed with labelled acetate, the aldehyde fraction showed a considerable decrease in radioactivity, while paraffins, ketones and secondary alcohols had increased activity. Moreover, aldehydes have been found in many plants. In our opinion, Stumpf's mechanism can explain only with difficulty why aldehydes with an even number of carbon atoms are dominant in plant waxes as it supposes transformation of the even-numbered acid into an aldehyde by means of α-oxidation and subsequent decarboxylation.

2. BIOGENESIS OF LONG-CHAIN KETONES AND SECONDARY ALCOHOLS

Some of the possible pathways for the formation of ketones and secondary alcohols have already been interpreted when discussing the biogenesis of the hydrocarbons. It has been pointed out that, according to Channon and Chibnall's scheme of 1929, secondary alcohols and ketones are intermediates in the formation of hydrocarbons. We quoted also Kolattukudy's considerations to explain the formation of nonacosan-15-one by oxidation of the elongated C_{30} acid. It is seen that most of the hypotheses have tried to account for the presence of symmetric ketones, and more explicitly, of nonacosan-15-one in *Brassica oleracea*. However, in recent years, asymmetric ketones have also been found in waxes both by us [62a, 64, 67] and by Macey and Barber [115]. This has led to new difficulties in the elucidation of the biogenesis of the wax components, and has given rise, as we have already seen, to recurrence again to a mechanism based on condensation processes.

In relation to the biogenesis of secondary alcohols and the question to what extent they are precursors of paraffins, it is of interest to discuss certain results obtained by Wollrab and by us almost simultaneously, when studying the composition of the wax from the oil-bearing rose.

Wollrab found hentriacontan-9-ol as the prevalent homologue of secondary alcohols, and hentriacontane, as the predominant representative of normal paraffins present in the same source [31]. On the basis of these results, he assumed a biogenetic relationship between secondary alcohols and hydrocarbons. Our investigations on the composition of the wax in Bulgarian rose flower confirmed Wollrab's result on the content of secondary alcohols, hentriacontan-9-ol being the prevalent homologue [57], moreover we have shown that also a homologous series of ketones with hentriacontan-9-one as the dominant homologue was present [67]. In view of Wollrab's result, that C_{31} is the prevalent paraffin, we assumed a biogenetic relationship among these three classes of compounds: secondary alcohols, ketones and paraffins.

Later on our own investigations indicated, however, that of the paraffins it was not C_{31}, but C_{27} which was predominating [43]. At the same time,

Wollrab identified the olefins hentriacont-7-ene and nonacos-5-ene in the wax from rose flower and assumed that the secondary alcohols hentriacontan-9-ol and nonacosan-7-ol, present in the wax, could be formed from the olefins mentioned above by their hydroxylation in allylic position [31].

Recently, in the wax from rose flower we have also established the presence of a homologous series of unsaturated secondary alcohols, hentriaconten-9-ol being the predominant component, with the probable position of the double bond at C-6 [59].

It is our belief that the simultaneous presence of unsaturated secondary alcohols, saturated secondary alcohols and ketones with hentriaconten-9-ol, hentriacontan-9-ol and hentriacontan-9-one, respectively, being the predominant members in the wax, is convincing evidence for a biogenetic relationship of these compounds. The detection of hentriaconten-9-ol makes even more possible the pathway proposed by Wollrab for the formation of secondary alcohols from unsaturated hydrocarbons. Further, it is obvious that the oxidation of hentriacontan-9-ol would result in the formation of hentriacontan-9-one. Such a pathway for the formation of ketones is in support of the assumption that they are not intermediates in the biosynthesis of paraffins. This conclusion has also been confirmed by the negative result obtained by us in feeding rose bush branches with hentriacontan-9-one, labelled in the carbonyl carbon atom, as an attempted precursor to hentriacontane [106].

3. BIOGENESIS OF LONG-CHAIN ALDEHYDES AND PRIMARY ALCOHOLS

It has been established that both of primary alcohols and aldehydes present in plant waxes, the members with an even number of carbon atoms are prevalent. For a long time it has been known that the same holds true also for the fatty acids in the waxes. This fact has given grounds to assume that the fatty acids are precursors of the primary alcohols and aldehydes. Later on, by means of ^{14}C-labelled compounds, it has been found that the acids C_2-C_{18} are transformed into fatty alcohols [122, 109]; further, on the basis of the correlation between the chain length of the aldehydes and alcohols it is accepted that the aldehydes could be intermediates of the reduction process of acids to primary alcohols [123].

The results obtained by us in a study of the aldehydes and acids in three decorative roses showed a complete correlation among them concerning the most prevalent homologues in one of the roses. In the two other, acids, present in considerable amounts, correspond to the aldehydes of the same chain length present also in considerable amounts [124, 125]. Two possibilities of the formation of aldehydes are under discussion: direct reduction of the carboxyl group of the acid, or α-oxidation of the acid to the α-keto-acid and subsequent decarboxylation [126, 127]. According to Kolattukudy, the latter mechanism is improbable, because it would result in aldehydes with odd-numbered carbon atoms, and this is inconsistent with all the experimental results on the composition of aldehydes in plant waxes obtained so far. Kolattukudy [128] has demonstrated the transformation of a fatty acyl-coenzyme A into a fatty alcohol, catalyzed by acyl-coenzyme A reductase and aldehyde reductase.

It should be noted that in the course of our investigations on the composition of waxes from decorative roses [124] we established that along with saturated aldehydes, unsaturated aldehydes were also present in them. Such compounds had not been detected in plant waxes previously. The unsaturated aldehydes $C_{18:1}$ and $C_{18:2}$ have been identified. They are probably formed by the same pathway as the saturated ones, but from the corresponding unsaturated C_{18} (oleic and linoleic) acids. Hence, it is very probable that they contain the double bonds in the same positions as oleic acid and linoleic acid, respectively.

4. BIOGENESIS OF LONG-CHAIN DIOLS

In addition to primary and secondary alcohols, even though more rarely and not in large amounts, diols have also been found in the waxes; they are α, ω- [122, 73] and α, β-diols [71, 129]. Dodova-Angelova and Ivanov have identified both α, β- and α, ω-diols in the wax from apples [76]. The predominance of members with an even number of carbon atoms in α, β- and α, ω-diols gives grounds to assume that they are biogenetically related to the long-chain fatty acids. It is presumed that the biosynthesis of the α, ω-diols takes place through ω-oxidation of the corresponding acids and subsequent reduction of the two carboxyl groups. As for α, β-diols, it is believed that they are products of a reduction of α-hydroxyacyl-coenzyme A [123].

As already stated, we have recently established for the first time the presence of α, γ-diols in the wax from concrete of the Bulgarian oil-bearing rose. This is also the first case of finding this type of compound in plant waxes [70]. The fact that in the α, β- and α, ω-diols found so far the even-numbered members prevail, whereas in the case of the α, γ-diols homologues with odd-numbered carbon atoms are predominant, gives us grounds to assume that the biogenetic pathway of the formation of the latter is different from those of the α, β- and α, ω-diols. Since in the wax from rose flower we established the presence of a homologous series of dienes with conjugated double bonds, we believe that they can be precursors of the α, γ-diols. In our opinion, the transformation of the dienes with conjugated double bonds into α, γ-diols could take place by a biogenetic pathway analogous to that assumed for the formation of secondary alcohols from olefins, which has already been discussed in the section on secondary alcohols:

$$R-CH_2-CH=CH-CH=CH-CH_2-R' \longrightarrow$$

$$\longrightarrow R-CH_2-\underset{\underset{OH}{|}}{CH}-CH_2-CH=CH-CH_2-R' \longrightarrow$$

$$\longrightarrow R-CH_2-\underset{\underset{OH}{|}}{CH}-CH_2-CH_2-\underset{\underset{OH}{|}}{CH}-CH_2-R'$$

The intermediate products in this biogenetic pathway are unsaturated secondary alcohols with an $n + 3$ position of the hydroxyl group to the double bond; as already stated, in the case of the unsaturated secondary alcohols, hentriaconten-9-ol with a double bond probably at position 6 is the prevalent homologue.

5. BIOGENESIS OF LONG-CHAIN PARAFFINS WITH AN EVEN NUMBER OF CARBON ATOMS AND OF FATTY ACIDS WITH AN ODD NUMBER OF CARBON ATOMS

The detailed studies on the composition of waxes, made possible through the application of the modern methods of analysis (mainly thin-layer chromatography, gas chromatography and mass spectrometry) have led to the discovery of new classes of long-chain compounds usually present in small amounts, in these natural products. Thus, while in the past it was believed that in nature, and more precisely in plant waxes, only even-numbered acids and odd-numbered hydrocarbons could be found, gas chromatography has reliably confirmed the usual presence, although in small amounts, also of odd-numbered acids and even-numbered hydrocarbons.

As it has been emphasized in Section V.1, the problem of the biogenesis of odd-numbered hydrocarbons (the main components of many plant waxes) is not yet fully elucidated, in spite of persistent and profound investigations by many researchers. Owing to this, the biogenesis of odd-numbered acids and even-numbered hydrocarbons has been little discussed so far. Even in the latest review articles on the biogenesis of plant waxes by Kolattukudy [123] and Hamilton [130], the biogenesis of even-numbered hydrocarbons and odd-numbered acids is not treated at all.

According to reference data [131], odd-numbered acids are formed by the same pathway as the even-numbered ones, but in their synthesis propionyl-ACP (acyl-carrier protein) takes part instead of the malonylcoenzyme A. As far as the biogenesis of the hydrocarbons with an even number of carbon atoms is concerned, there is practically only one mechanism, which has been suggested by Wanless et al. [132] (Scheme 16).

$R-CH_2-CH_2-CH_2-COOH$ $\xrightarrow{\ \beta-Oxidation\ }$ $R-CH_2-CO-CH_2-COOH$

$\downarrow$ $\alpha-Oxidation$ $\qquad\qquad\qquad\qquad\qquad\qquad$ $\downarrow$ $-CO_2$

$R-CH_2-CH_2-CO-COOH$ $\qquad\qquad\qquad$ $R-CH_2-CO-CH_3$

$\downarrow$ $-CO_2$ $\qquad\qquad\qquad\qquad\qquad\qquad\qquad$ $\downarrow$ Reduction

$R-CH_2-CH_2-CHO$ $\qquad\qquad\qquad\qquad$ $R-CH_2-CH_2-CH_3$

$\downarrow$

$R-CH_2-CH_2-COOH$

$\downarrow$ $\beta-Oxidation$

$R-CO-CH_2-COOH$ $\xrightarrow{\ -CO_2\ }$ $R-CO-CH_3$ $\xrightarrow{\ Reduction\ }$ $R-CH_2-CH_3$

R contains an even number of carbon atoms

Scheme 16. Biosynthesis of even-numbered and odd-numbered paraffins according to Wanless et al. [132].

These authors assume that a long-chain even-numbered acid is the precursor of both even-numbered and odd-numbered hydrocarbons. Through β-oxidation and decarboxylation it gives rise to the formation of odd-numbered hydrocarbons; by α- and subsequent β-oxidation followed by decarboxylation even-numbered hydrocarbons are formed.

The weak point of this scheme is the assumption that methyl ketones are intermediate compounds both in the formation of odd-numbered and even-numbered paraffins. However, it has been established with the aid of labelled atoms that methyl ketones do not play the part of intermediary products in the biosynthesis of the paraffins [106].

On the basis of the results obtained for the individual composition [43] of the long-chain hydrocarbons in the wax from the oil-bearing rose flower, we presumed a biogenetic relationship between paraffins and olefins. Further on, we established a correlation between the predominant odd-numbered and even-numbered olefins. Thus C_{25}, C_{27} and C_{29} are dominant of the odd-numbered olefins, while C_{24}, C_{26} and C_{28}, respectively, of the even-numbered ones. On the basis of these facts we assumed that the even-numbered olefins and their next higher odd-numbered homologues possess a common precursor and, in the course of the biosynthesis, the olefins having an odd number of carbon atoms undergo shortening of the chain by one carbon atom, resulting in the formation of the corresponding even-numbered olefin. Later on, studying the composition of the hydrocarbons of three decorative roses [133], we established a similar relationship both in the case of the paraffins and olefins. Among the odd-numbered homologues, C_{27} is the prevalent member of the paraffins in all three roses. The hydrocarbons C_{23}, C_{25} and C_{29} are also present in considerable amounts. Among the even-numbered paraffins C_{24}, C_{26} and C_{28} are predominant. Of the olefins C_{25}, C_{27} and C_{29} occur preponderantly of the odd-numbered ones, while C_{24}, C_{26} and C_{28} among the even-numbered ones. This relationship in the amounts of the even- and odd-numbered hydrocarbons seems to be of a more general nature. We observed a similar correlation also in the hydrocarbons of the brown algae *Cistoseira barbata*, studied by us [134], as well as in the paraffins of 12 apple varieties, studied by Ivanov and Dodova-Angelova [135], in six cultivars of *Satsuma mandarin* studied by Nordby and Nagy [136], as well as in various tissues of Duncan grapefruit, investigated by Nagy *et al.* [137].

Taking into account, on the one hand, the possibility of odd-numbered paraffins being formed by direct decarboxylation of the higher fatty acids, as demonstrated by Kolattukudy [111], and on the other, the ω-oxidation of higher fatty acids in living cells, reported by Verkade [138], we assumed that the correlation between the amounts of even- and odd-numbered hydrocarbons, established by us, as well as the biosynthesis of the even-numbered hydrocarbons, could be explained by the intermediate formation of an α, ω-dicarboxylic acid or by the ω-oxidation of the odd-numbered paraffin obtained, according to Scheme 17.

It is not for the first time that the possibility of ω-oxidation during the biogenesis of the components of plant waxes is discussed. Kreger [69] likewise assumes a double ω-oxidation in the scheme of the formation of triacontan-17-ol and tritriacontan-17-one, suggested by him.

In support of our scheme it should be emphasized that a homologous series of α, ω-dicarboxylic acids in the C_{16}–C_{26} range has been found in the Japanese wax from *Rhus succedanea* [139], predominantly with even-numbered members (C_{20} and C_{22} being present in the largest amounts), whereas the odd-numbered ones occur in very small amounts. Moreover, Kolattukudy lately established that the terminal methyl group of externally

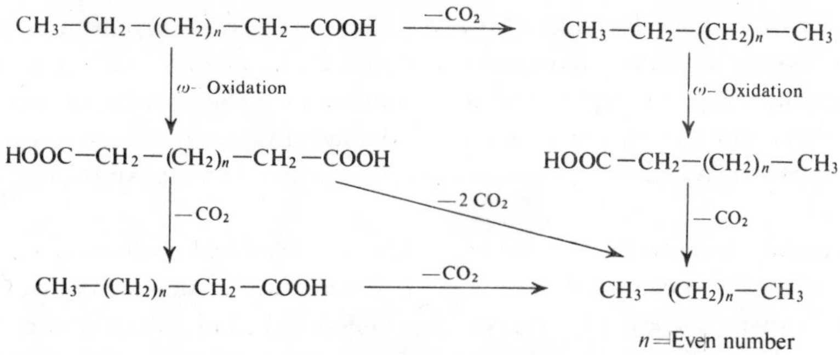

CH$_3$—CH$_2$—(CH$_2$)$_n$—CH$_2$—COOH $\xrightarrow{-CO_2}$ CH$_3$—CH$_2$—(CH$_2$)$_n$—CH$_3$

$\downarrow$ ω- Oxidation $\downarrow$ ω- Oxidation

HOOC—CH$_2$—(CH$_2$)$_n$—CH$_2$—COOH   HOOC—CH$_2$—(CH$_2$)$_n$—CH$_3$

$\downarrow$ $-CO_2$ $-2 CO_2$ $\downarrow$ $-CO_2$

CH$_3$—(CH$_2$)$_n$—CH$_2$—COOH $\xrightarrow{-CO_2}$ CH$_3$—(CH$_2$)$_n$—CH$_3$

$n =$ Even number

Scheme 17. Biosynthesis of even-numbered paraffins and odd-numbered fatty acids according to Stoianova-Ivanova *et al.* [133, 125].

introduced normal hentriacontan-1-^{14}C was oxidized to —COOH in tissue cuts free of bacteria [140].

The pathway for the formation of the even-numbered paraffins proposed by us thus provides an explanation also for the biosynthesis of odd-numbered acids, found most frequently, just as for the even-numbered hydrocarbons occurring in insignificant amounts. It is obvious from the scheme that the latter may be formed by ω-oxidation from the odd-numbered paraffins, as well as by decarboxylation of the dicarboxylic acids. In the latter case it is sufficient to assume, as it is most probable, that the decarboxylation does not take place, at both ends simultaneously, but it occurs consecutively. It is evident that the decarboxylation of one carboxyl group will thus result in an acid with an odd number of carbon atoms, and of the second will give rise to a hydrocarbon with an even number of carbon atoms. In accordance with this assumption are the results of the study of the acid compositions of the three decorative roses [125], where the even-numbered acids C$_{22}$ and C$_{24}$, present in the largest amounts, are matched by considerable amounts of the odd-numbered C$_{21}$ and C$_{23}$ acids. Furthermore, a similar correspondence between the odd- and even-numbered homologues has also been found in the case of those components (aldehydes and alcohols) of the oil-bearing and decorative roses, whose biogenetic relationship with the higher fatty acids has already been proved. Thus, considering the homologous series of the aldehydes in all three decorative roses [124], the prevailing even-numbered acids, C$_{22}$ and C$_{24}$ are in correspondence with the most widely represented even-numbered aldehydes (C$_{22}$ and C$_{24}$); of the odd-numbered compounds the C$_{21}$ and C$_{23}$ aldehydes predominate. A similar relationship between the amounts of odd- and even-numbered members has also been observed by us in the homologous series of the primary alcohols in the wax from the oil-bearing rose [57].

The pathway of the formation of even-numbered hydrocarbons and odd-numbered acids in plant waxes suggested by us should, naturally, be verified experimentally by using labelled compounds. The results of experiments carried out by other authors with labelled substances so far, however, have not presented facts, to our knowledge, which would contradict our proposition.

At the same time when this scheme for even- and odd-numbered alkane biosynthesis was proposed, Khan and Kolattukudy demonstrated the enzymic transformation of exogenous labelled C_{32} acid into C_{31} and C_{30} alkanes, and into C_{31} acid. Thus experimental evidence has been found to show that odd- and even-numbered alkanes have a common precursor [141].

The study of the composition of rose wax, carried out by us and the detection of new classes of long-chain compounds present as micro-components, poses a number of new biogenetic questions; the biogenesis of long-chain hydrocarbons with conjugated double bonds, of unsaturated secondary alcohols, and of α,γ-diols — all established by us for the first time as wax components. The biogenesis of unsaturated secondary alcohols, however, as well as that of dienes with conjugated double bonds requires additional investigations, in order to establish reliably the positions of the double bonds.

REFERENCES

1. MALEEV, A., STOIANOV, S., NESHEV, G., "Bolgarskoe rosovoe maslo", p. 7. Pharmakologicheskie i klinicheskie issledovania, Pharmachim. Bulgaria, 1973.
2. TOPALOV, V., "Compte-rendu du 3e Congrès international des huiles essentielles", p. 264. Plovdiv, 1964.
3. NICOLOV, N., OGNIANOV, I., "Compte-rendu du 3e Congrès international des huiles essentielles", p. 27. Plovdiv, 1964.
4. GILDEMEISTER, E., HOFFMANN, F., "Die Ätherische Öle", Vol. V, Akademie Verlag, Berlin, 1959, p. 228.
5. GUENTHER, E., "The Essential Oils", Vol. V, van Nostrand Comp. Inc., Princeton, New Jersey, 1959, p. 3.
6. MARKOVNIKOFF, W., REFORMATSKI, A., J. prakt. Chem., 47, 293 (1893).
7. RAIKOV, P., Z. Chem., 22, 149 (1898).
8. IVANOV, D., IVANOV, CHR., OGNIANOV, I., Compt. rend. Acad. bulg. Sci., 6, 13 (1953); 6, 25 (1953).
9. IVANOV, D., IVANOV, CHR., MARECOV, N., OGNIANOV, I., Compt. rend. Acad. bulg. Sci. 7, 25 (1954).
10. IVANOV, D., IVANOV, CHR., OGNIANOV, I., Compt. rend. Acad. bulg. Sci., 6, 9 (1953).
11. IVANOV, D., IVANOV, CHR., STOIANOVA-IVANOVA, B., Compt. rend. Acad. bulg. Sci., 6, 29 (1953).
12. IVANOV, D., IVANOV, CHR., STOIANOVA-IVANOVA, B., Compt rend. Acad. bulg. Sci., 7, 17, (1954).

13. STOIANOVA-IVANOVA, B., IVANOV, D., *Compt. rend. Acad. bulg. Sci.*, *10*, 193 (1957).
14. PANAYOTOV, I., IVANOV, D., *Perf. Essent. Oil Record*, *49*, 231 (1958).
15. PANAYOTOV, I., IVANOV, D., *Perf. Essent. Oil Record*, *49*, No. 8 (1958).
16. IVANOV, D., PANAYOTOV, I., TCHORBADJIEV, S., BELICHEVA, V., *Perf. Essent. Oil Record*, *51*, No. 11 (1960).
17. IVANOV, D., MARECOV, N., PAVLOVA, ST., IVANOVA, L., *Commun. Dept. Chemistry, Bulg. Acad. Sci.*, *4*, 277 (1956).
18. GUENTHER, E., "The Essential Oils", Vol. V, D. van Nostrand Compt. Inc., Princeton, New Jersey, 1952. p. 32.
19. GILDEMEISTER, E., HOFFMANN, F., "Die Ätherische Öle", Vol. V, Akademie Verlag, Berlin, 1959.
20. NAVES, Yv. R., MAZUYER, G., "Les parfums naturels." Paris, 1939. p. 269.
21. WALBAUM, H., ROSENTHAL, A., "Ber. Schimmel A. G. Jubil. Ausg.", 1969., p. 195.
22. GLICHITCH, L. S., NAVES, Y. R., *Parfums de France*, *11*, 163 (1933).
23. NAVES, Y. R., MAZUYER, G., "Les parfums naturels", Paris, 1939, p. 271.
24. PROPHETE, M. H., *Bull. Soc. Chim.*, *39*, 1600 (1926).
25. IVANOV, D., IVANOV, CHR., STOIANOVA-IVANOVA, B., *Compt. rend. Acad. bulg. Sci.*, *8*, 33 (1955).
26. NAVES, Y. R., MAZUYER, G., "Les parfums naturels", Paris, 1939, p. 166.
27. CHIBNALL, A. C., EL MANGOURI, H. A., PIPER, S. H., *Biochem. J.*, *58*, 506 (1954).
28. WOLLRAB, V., STREIBL, M., ŠORM, F., *Coll. Czechoslov. Chem. Commun.*, *30*, 1654 (1965).
29. STRANSKY, K., STREIBL, M., ŠORM, F., *Coll. Czechoslov. Chem. Commun.*, *33*, 417 (1968).
30. WOLLRAB, V., *Coll. Czechoslov. Chem. Commun.*, *33*, 1584 (1968).
31. WOLLRAB, V., *Phytochemistry*, *8*, 623 (1969).
32. STOIANOVA-IVANOVA, B., KOUSMANOVA, M., *Compt. rend. Acad. bulg. Sci. 17*, 941 (1964).
33. STOIANOVA-IVANOVA, B., MLADENOVA, K., *Rivista Italiana EPPOS*, *49*, 526 (1967).
34. SMULLIN, C., *J. Amer. Oil Soc.*, *35*, 180 (1958).
35. CHIBNALL, A. C., PIPER, S. H., *Biochem. J.*, *28*, 2209 (1934).
36. KOLATTUKUDY, P. E., LIU, T. J., *Biochem. Biophys. Res. Commun.*, *41*, 1369 (1970).
37. SAUSSURE, TH., *Ann.* (2), *13*, 337.
38. BLANCHET, R., *Ann.*, *7*, 154 (1833).
39. FLÜKIGER, P. A., *Z. Chem.*, *126* (1870).
40. ULLMAN, F. R., "Enzyklopedie der technischen Chemie", Vol. VIII, 1931, p. 771.
41. FLÜCKIGER, P. A., *Pharm. Chem.*, *2*, 412 (1888).
42. "Bericht von Schimmel et Co.", October, 1890.
43. MLADENOVA, K., STOIANOVA-IVANOVA, B., *Compt. rend. Acad. bulg. Sci.*, *26*, 901 (1973).
44. ROUSSEVA-ATANASOVA, N., IANAK, I., *J. Chromatography*, *21*, 207 (1966).
45. WOLLRAB, V., STREIBL, M. ŠORM, F., *Chem. Ind.*, *1872* (1967).
46. STOIANOVA-IVANOVA, B., NIKOLOVA, D., TZVETKOVA, V., *Compt. rend. Acad. bulg. Sci.*, *18*, 141 (1965).
47. STOIANOVA-IVANOVA, B., IGNATOVA, E., *Rivista Italiana EPPOS*, *51*, 375 (1969).
48. STOIANOVA-IVANOVA, B., MLADENOVA, K., MALOVA, I., *Phytochemistry*, *10*, 2525 (1971).
49. STOIANOVA-IVANOVA, B., KOLAROVA, E., *Compt. rend. Acad. bulg. Sci.*, *15*, 151 (1962).
50. STOIANOVA-IVANOVA, B., MLADENOVA, K., *Rivista Italiana EPPOS*, *50*, 72 (1968).
51. STOIANOVA-IVANOVA, B., MLADENOVA, K., *Rivista Italiana EPPOS*, *52*, 575 (1970).
52. WOLLRAB, V., *Coll. Czechoslov. Chem. Commun.*, *34*, 867 (1969).
53. MACEY, M. J. K., BARBER, H. N., *Phytochemistry*, *9*, 5 (1970).

54. STOIAUOVA-IVANOVA, B., HADJIEVA, P., *Compt. rend. Acad. bulg. Sci.*, *18*, 145 (1965).
55. BASHKIREV, A. N., KOMSOLKIN, V. V., SOKOVA, K. M., ANDREEVA, T. P., "Methodi analisa organicheskih soedinenii nefti, ih smesei i proisvodnih", Sb. 1, Izd. AN SSSR, 1960, p. 170.
56. KAUFMANN, H. P., DAS, B., *Fette, Seifen, Anstrichmittel*, *63*, 614 (1961).
57. STOIANOVA-IVANOVA, B., HADJIEVA, P., GERGOVA, S., *Rivista Italiana EPPOS*, *52*, 673 (1970).
58. DOWNING, D. T., KRANZ, K. E., MURRAY, K. E., *Austral. J. Chem.*, *13*, 80 (1960).
59. HADJIEVA, P., STOIANOVA-IVANOVA, B., *Compt. rend. Acad. bulg. Sci.*, *26*, 77 (1973).
60. CHIBNALL, A. C., PIPER, S. H., EL MANGOURI, H. A., WILLIAMS, E. F., IYENGAZ, V. V., *Biochem. J.*, *31*, 1981 (1937).
61. CHANNON, H. I., CHIBNALL, A. C., *Biochem. J.*, *23*, 168 (1929).
62. KREGER, D. R., "Encyclopaedia of Plant Physiology", Springer Verlag, Berlin, 1958. Vol. *10*, p. 249.
62a. STOIANOVA-IVANOVA, B., HADJIEVA, P., POPOV, S., *Phytochemistry*, *8*, 1549 (1969).
63. PURDY, S. H., TRUTER, E. V., *Proc. Roy. Soc. B.*, *158*, 553 (1963).
64. STOIANOVA-IVANOVA, B., HADJIEVA, P., MLADENOVA, K., *Rivista Italiana EPPOS*, *49*, December (1967).
65. KAUFMANN, H. P., NITSCH, W., *Fette, Seifen, Anstrichmittel*, *56*, 154 (1955).
66. CHIBNALL, A. C., PIPER, S. H., POLLARD, A., SMITH, J. A. B., WILLIAMS, E. F., *Biochem. J.*, *25*, 2095 (1931).
67. STOIANOVA-IVANOVA, B., MLADENOVA, K., POPOV, S., *Phytochemistry*, *10*, 1391 (1971).
68. BEYNON, J. H., LESTER, G. R., SAUNDERS, K. A., WILLIAMS, A. E., *Trans. Faraday Soc.*, *57*, 1259 (1961).
69. KREGER, D. R., *Recueil Trav. Bot. Nederl.*, *41*, 603 (1948).
70. STOIANOVA-IVANOVA, B., HADJIEVA, P. TAMAS, J., *Phytochemistry*, *13*, 1523 (1974).
71. DOWNING, D. T., KRANZ, Z. H., MURRAY, K. E., *Austral. J. Chem.*, *14*, 619 (1961).
72. STÜRKE, H., *Ann.*, *223*, 283 (1884).
73. MURRAY, K. E., SCHOENFELD, R., *Austral. J. Chem.*, *8*, 424 (1955).
74. DOWNING, D. T., *Austral. J. Chem.*, *18*, 1287 (1965).
75. MAZLIAK, P., *Phytochemistry*, *1*, 79 (1962).
76. DODOVA-ANGELOVA, M., IVANOV, CHR., *Compt. rend. Acad. bulg. Sci.*, *22*, 1039 (1969).
77. VULFSON, N. S., GOLOVKINA, L. S., VAVER, V. A., PROKASOVA, N. V., BERGELSON, L. D., *Isv. Acad. Nauk SSSR, Ser. Chim.*, *11*, 2415 (1967).
78. HADJIEVA, P., STOIANOVA-IVANOVA, B., DANIELI, B., *Chemistry and Physics of Lipids*, *12*, 60 (1974).
79. BEYNON, J. H., SAUNDERS, R. A., WILLIAMS, A. E., "The Mass Spectra of Organic Molecules", Elsevier, 1968., pp. 254. 142.
80. WILLHALM, B., PALLUY, E., WINTER, M., *Helv. Chim. Acta*, *49*, 65 (1966).
81. TRESSL, R., DRAWERS, F., HEIMANN, W., *Z. Naturforsch., B.*, *24*, 1202 (1969).
82. TANG, C. S., YENINGS, G., *J. Agr. Food Chem.*, *16*, 252 (1968).
83. HAMILTON, S., HAMILTON, R. J., "Materials and Technology, Encyclopaedia", London, 1972., p. 238.
84. MICHAILOV. P., BEROVA, N., *Parfumerie und Kosmetik*, *47*, 293 (1966).
85. HADJIEVA, P., STOIANOVA-IVANOVA, B., DANIELI, B., *Annali di Chimica*, *62*, 670 (1972).
86. BUDZIKIEWICZ, H., WILSON, J. M., DJERASSI, C., *J. Am. Chem. Soc.*, *85*, 3688 (1963).
87. KARLINER, J., DJERASSI. C., *J. Org. Chem.*, *31*, 1945 (1966).

88. BUDZIKIEWICZ, H., DJERASSI, C., WILLIAMS, D. H., "Structure Elucidation of Natural Products by Mass Spectrometry", Vol. II, Holden-Day, San Francisco, 1964, p. 124.
89. ZIMMERMANN, J., Helv. Chim. Acta, 27, 332 (1944).
90. HADJIEVA, P., STOIANOVA-IVANOVA, B., Rivista Italiana, EPPOS, 57, April (1975).
91. ENZEL, C., WAHLBERG, J., Acta Chem. Scand., 23, 871 (1969).
92. CARMAN, R. M., DEETH, H. C., Austr. J. Chem., 20, 2789 (1967).
93. GOUGH, L. J., Tetrahedron Letters, 295 (1968).
94. GHUAH, Y. S., WARD, A. D., Austral. J. Chem., 22, 1333 (1969).
95. STOIANOVA-IVANOVA, B., DANIELI, B. HADJIEVA, P., Rivista Italiana, EPPOS, 53, 138 (1971).
96. SUZUKI, A., ASANO, M., OHKUBO, CH., TAMURA, S., Agr. Biol. Chem., 36, 2051 (1972).
97. IGOLEN, G., La France et ses parfums, 70, 339 (1970).
98. GUENTHER, E.,. "The Essential Oils", Vol. V, van Nostrand Comp. Inc., Princeton, New Jersey, 1953, p. 34.
99. STOIANOVA-IVANOVA, B., DINKOV, D., HRIVNAC, M., Rivista Italiana, EPPOS, 51, 315 (1969).
100. OHLOFF, G., KLEIN, E., SCHENK, G. O., Angew. Chem., 73, 578 (1961).
101. NAVES, Y. R., TULLEN, P., Helv. Chim. Acta, 44, 1867 (1961).
102. MARC, J., JAQUET, B., Bull. Soc. Chim. France, 1983 (1963).
103. NISHIMURA, K., SAKAI, T., OGAWA, M., HIROSE, Y., Bull. Chem. Soc. Japan, 37, 1407 (1964).
104. STOIANOVA-IVANOVA, B., HADJIEVA, P., UBIK, K., TZUTZULOVA, A., Rivista Italiana, EPPOS, 56, Novembre (1974).
105. CLENSHAW, E., SMEDLY-MACLEAN, J., Biochem. J., 23, 107 (1929).
106. MONDESHKY, L. M., MAREKOV, N. L., STOIANOVA-IVANOVA, B., ZOLOTOVITCH, G., Compt. rend. Acad. bulg. Sci., 24, 1055 (1971).
107. LINEN, F., Federation Proc., 20, 941 (1961).
108. SANDERMAN, W., SCHWERS, W., BEINHOFF, O., Chem. Ber., 93, 2266 (1960).
109. KOLATTUKUDY, P. E., Biochemistry, 4, 1844 (1965).
110. KOLATTUKUDY, P. E., Plant Physiol., 43, 375 (1968).
111. KOLATTUKUDY, P. E., Biochemistry, 5, 2265 (1966).
112. KOLATTUKUDY, P. E., Phytochemistry, 6, 963 (1967).
113. HAN, I., CHAN, H. W. S., CALVIN, M., J. Am. Chem. Soc., 91, 5156 (1969).
114. WARTH, A. H., "The Chemistry and Technology of Waxes", Reinhold Publ., New York, 1957.
115. MACEY, M. J. K., BARBER, H. N., Phytochemistry, 9, 13 (1970).
116. ALBRO, P. W., DITTMER, J. C., Biochemistry, 8, 394 (1969).
117. ALBRO, P. W., DITTMER, J. C., Biochemistry, 8, 953 (1969).
118. ALBRO, P. W., DITTMER, J. C., Biochemistry, 8, 1913 (1969).
119. ALBRO, P. W., DITTMER, J. C., Biochemistry, 8, 3317 (1969).
120. ALBRO, P. W., MEEHAN, D. T., DITTMER, J. C., Biochemistry, 9, 1893 (1970).
121. STUMPF, P. K., "Plant Biochemistry" (Ed. J. Bonner and J. E. Varner) Academic Press, New York, 1965. p. 322.
122. MAZLIAK, P., Ph. D. Thesis, Univ. of Paris, France, 1963.
123. KOLATTUKUDY, P. E., Ann. Rev. Plant Physiology, 21, 163 (1970).
124. MLADENOVA, K., STOIANOVA-IVANOVA, B., Compt. rend. Acad. bulg. Sci., 28, 335 (1975).
125. MLADENOVA, K., STOIANOVA-IVANOVA, B., KOCHOVA, V., Commun. Depart. Chem., 8, No. 1, 128 (1975).
126. MARTIN, R. O., STUMPF, P. K., J. Biol. Chem., 234, 2548 (1959).
127. HITCHCOCK, C., MORIS, L. J., JAMES, A. T., Eur. J. Biochem., 3, 419 (1968).
128. KOLATTUKUDY, P. E., Lipids, 5, 259 (1970).
129. NICOLAIDES, N., J. Am. Oil Chem. Soc., 42, 691 (1965).
130. HAMILTON, S., HAMILTON, R. J., "Plant Waxes, Materials and Technology, Encyclopaedia", Longmans, London, 1972, p. 192.

131. DAGLEY, S., NICHOLSON, D. E., "An Introduction to Metabolic Pathways" (in Russian), Publ. House "Mir", Moscow, 1973, p. 165.
132. WANLESS, G. G., KING, W. H., RITTER, J. J., *Biochem. J.*, *59*, 684 (1955).
133. STOIANOVA-IVANOVA, B., MLADENOVA, K., *Compt. rend. Acad. bulg. Sci.*, *27*, 1239 (1974).
134. STOIANOVA-IVANOVA, B., MLADENOVA, K., *Compt. rend. Acad. bulg. Sci.*, *25*, 767 (1972).
135. IVANOV, CH., DODOVA-ANGELOVA, M. S., *Compt. rend. Acad. bulg. Sci.*, *22*, 751 (1969).
136. NORDBY, H. E., NAGY, S., *Phytochemistry*, *14*, 183 (1975).
137. NAGY, S., NORDBY, H. E., LASTINGER, J. C., *Phytochemistry*, *14*, 2443 (1975).
138. VERKADE, . E., *Fette, Seifen, Anstrichmittel*, *46*, 521 (1939).
139. LAMBERTON, J. A., *Austral. J. Chem. 14*, 323 (1969).
140. KOLATTUKUDY, P. E., *Plant Physiology 44*, 315 (1969).
141. KHAN, A. A., KOLATTUKUDY, P. E., *Biochem. Biophys. Res. Commun.*, *61*, 1379 (1974).

GY. LITKEI

CHALCONE EPOXIDES
IN FLAVONOID CHEMISTRY

I. INTRODUCTION

For some time past, the investigation of the oxidation reactions of chalcones has been a vigorously studied field of flavonoid chemistry. Under both *in vitro* and *in vivo* conditions, 2'-hydroxychalcones of lower state of oxidation may give rise to different flavonoids having a higher oxidation number.

The results of flavonoid chemistry were summarized in the 1960s in several monographs [1–12]. In recent years it has been shown that 2'--hydroxychalcones are intermediates in flavonoid biogenesis [13–21]. Several authors have suggested that the various flavonoids are formed in plants through chalcone epoxides [22–27]. Epoxides are also considered to play the part of intermediates in the mechanism of several reactions (e.g., the Algar–Flynn–Oyamada reaction), but the literature contains hardly any information on the chemistry of chalcone epoxides.

Although some epoxides had already been isolated from plants [6] and the chemistry of compounds containing an oxirane ring was well known [28–31], recent interest in the chemical investigation of chalcone epoxides was aroused by the researches of Bognár, started in the sixties.

The present paper summarizes results in the chemistry of chalcone epoxides and of the Algar–Flynn–Oyamada oxidation, achieved during the last decade (1963 – 1973).

II. CHALCONE EPOXIDES IN FLAVONOID CHEMISTRY

1. OXIDATION OF CHALCONES

A. Oxidation by Peroxides and Peracids

(i) *Role of the hypothetical epoxide intermediates.* Chalcones containing no hydroxyl substituent are oxidized by alkaline hydrogen peroxide to chalcone epoxides; this process, called the Weitz–Scheffer reaction, has long been known [32, 33].

$$\text{Ar}-\overset{\overset{\text{O}}{\|}}{\text{C}}-\overset{\overset{\text{O}}{}}{\text{CH}}-\text{CH}-\text{Ar}'$$

$$\underset{\substack{\text{Weitz–Scheffer-reaction}}}{\text{Ar}-\overset{\overset{\text{O}}{\|}}{\text{C}}-\text{CH}=\text{CH}-\text{Ar}'} \quad \xrightarrow{\text{H}_2\text{O}_2/\text{OH}^-} \qquad \xleftarrow{\text{OH}^- \text{ or } \text{H}^+} \quad \underset{\substack{\text{Darzens-reaction}}}{\text{Ar}-\overset{\overset{\text{O}}{\|}}{\text{C}}-\text{CH}_2-\text{Hlg} + \text{OHC}-\text{Ar}'}$$

Epoxides are also formed in the base- or acid-catalyzed [34] condensation of phenacyl halides and aromatic aldehydes (Darzens reaction).

In the course of the alkaline hydrogen peroxide oxidation of 2'-hydroxy-chalcones or flavanones, the products are 3-hydroxyflavanones, 3-hydroxy-flavones and other compounds (Algar–Flynn–Oyamada reaction). The same derivatives are obtained by the condensation of 2-hydroxyphenacyl halides and aromatic aldehydes (Gowan–Hayden–Wheeler reaction). 2'-Hydroxy-chalcone dibromides react with alkalis to give flavones, 3-hydroxyflavones or aurones (Emilewicz–von Kostanecki reaction or Rasoda–Limaye reaction). It is a common feature of these reactions that, depending on the substituents in rings A and B of the chalcone and on the reaction conditions, aurones are also formed.

The mechanism of the Algar–Flynn–Oyamada [5, 35, 36], Gowan–Hay-den–Wheeler [37], Rasoda–Limaye [38], and Emilewicz–von Kostanecki [39–41] reactions was explained postulating 2'-hydroxychalcone epoxide as an intermediate. The role of this hypothetical common intermediate of the reactions has not been proved; only 3-hydroxyflavanone is known as an intermediary product.

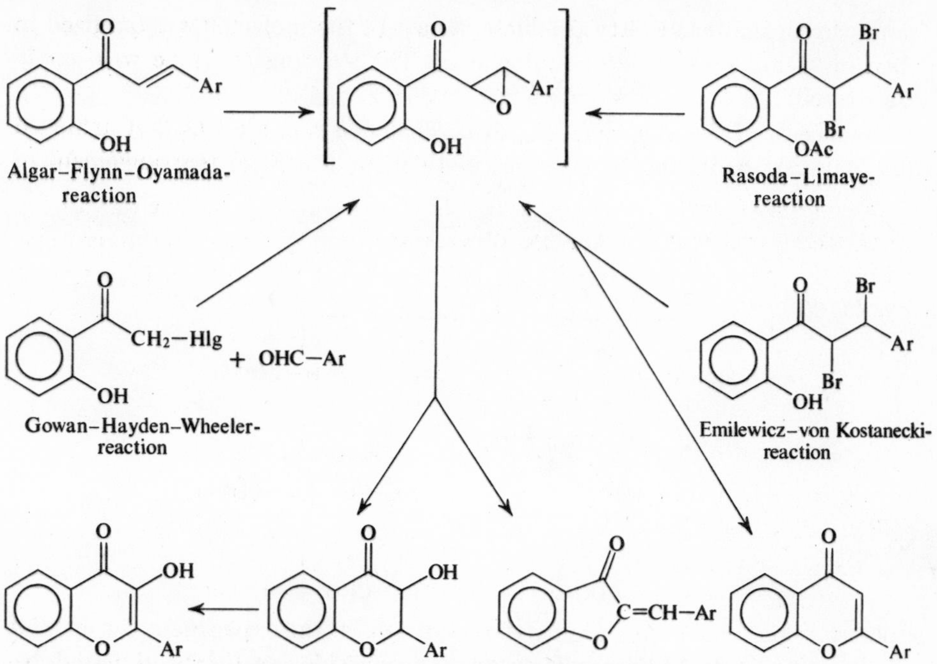
Ar
OH
Algar–Flynn–Oyamada-reaction
O
Ar
OH
Br
Ar
Br
OAc
Rasoda–Limaye-reaction
CH₂–Hlg
+ OHC–Ar
OH
Gowan–Hayden–Wheeler-reaction
Br
Ar
Br
OH
Emilewicz–von Kostanecki-reaction
OH
Ar
OH
Ar
C=CH–Ar
Ar

The formation of 2′-hydroxychalcone epoxides was similarly supposed [42] in the oxidation of *o*-hydroxydibenzoylmethanes by peracids, also affording 3-hydroxyflavone.

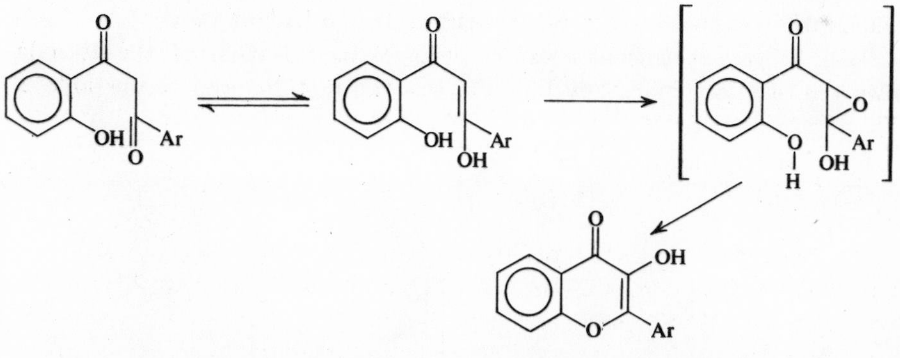
OH
Ar
OH
Ar
OH
O
O
Ar
H
OH
OH
Ar

(*ii*) *2′-Hydroxychalcone epoxides*. 2′-Hydroxy-5′-methyl-4-methoxychalcone epoxide was first prepared by Verma and Bokadia [43], in a very poor yield, by the oxidation of chalcone with monoperphthalic acid.

Yokoyama and Nohara [44] having made a detailed study of the oxidation of chalcones with perbenzoic acid found that phenyl migration occurred and, through intermediary products, a part of the molecule was oxidized to benzoic acid, benzaldehyde and phenol. The starting chalcone was partly recovered.

Synthesis of the unstable 2′-hydroxychalcone epoxide was first achieved by Ramakrishnan and Kagan [45] in 1970, by the Fries rearrangement of

phenyl epoxycinnamate. Under the conditions of the experiment the epoxide is converted into 3-hydroxyflavanone. The epoxide can also be prepared, besides other products, by the m-chloroperbenzoic acid oxidation of 2′-hydroxychalcone [45]. The isomeric flavanone fails to react with peracids.

2′-Hydroxychalcone epoxide is an unstable compound; even light occasions its conversion to 2′-hydroxydibenzoylmethane and 3-hydroxyflavanone; when exposed to air, it is transformed to 3-hydroxyflavone.

(iii) *2′-Acetoxychalcone epoxides.* Using a modification of the Rasoda–Limaye reaction, Marathey [46, 47] was the first to prepare unstable 2′-

acetoxychalcone epoxide analogues from 2'-acetoxychalcone dibromides with sodium carbonate, through the intermediate α-bromo-β-hydroxydihydrochalcone (bromohydrin). Similarly, the corresponding aurone was obtained from 2'-acetoxy-5',6'-benzo-4-methoxychalcone dibromide.

Later, other researchers [38, 48–50] also synthesized 2'-acetoxychalcone epoxides through the bromohydrins. Fischer and Arlt [49] found that the action of water on an *erythro*-chalcone dibromide results in the *erythro*-bromohydrin only if ring B of the molecule contains an electron-releasing substituent in the *para* position. When using aqueous sodium carbonate, the intermediates could not be isolated, only 3-hydroxyflavanones were obtained. On the other hand, the bromohydrin with sodium acetate in acetone solution gave *trans*-2'-acetoxy-4-methoxychalcone epoxide; the latter was converted by sodium carbonate to the 3-hydroxyflavanone.

The bromohydrin derivative was synthesized by Bien *et al.* [48] from 2'-
-hydroxychalcone and N-bromoacetamide (NBA) in aqueous tetrahydrofuran
solution, in the presence of a catalytic amount of perchloric acid. The reaction, however, was accompanied by bromination in the aromatic nucleus.

In similar circumstances, 2'-hydroxychalcones undergo only nuclear
bromination resulting in 2'-hydroxy-3,5-dibromochalcones. If the 2'-hydrox-
yl group is protected by acetyl or benzyl substitution and if the molecule
contains a *p*-methoxy substituent, the bromohydrins, and from these, the
trans- 2'-OR-chalcone epoxides (R = CH_3CO; $CH_2C_6H_5$) are obtained.

Treatment with acetyl hypobromite (AHB) in chloroform gives α-bromo-
β-acetoxydihydrochalcones; no nuclear bromination occurs [48].

According to the investigations of Zimmerman and Ahramjian [51], the
mechanism of the Darzens condensation also involves the halohydrin.

The first step consists of the formation of a carbanion from the phenacyl halide, followed by the addition of the aldehyde, resulting in the halohydrin and finally in the *trans*-epoxide.

Ballester and Blanco [52] synthesized 2′,4′,6′-trimethoxy-3-nitrochalcone epoxide from the diastereomeric chlorohydrins in the presence of alkali.

In the course of the alkaline peroxide oxidation of 2′-acetoxy- or -benzoyl-oxychalcones the protective group was split off [35] and, similarly to the Algar–Flynn–Oyamada reaction, the formation of chalcone epoxide could not be detected. Gormley et al. [53, 54] oxidized 2′-tosyloxychalcones in alkaline medium at room temperature to obtain 2′-tosyloxy-chalcone epoxides. However, Wurm [75] recently obtained only 3-hydroxyflavanones in this reaction.

(*iv*) *2′-Methoxychalcone epoxides.* In 1932 Baker and Robinson [55], then Algar and McKenna [56] synthesized 2′-methoxychalcones by the methylation of 2′-hydroxychalcones. Alkaline hydrogen peroxide oxidation of the products gave 2′-methoxychalcone epoxides in high yields.

Removal of the protective methyl group from the epoxides is difficult, thus the conversion of these compounds to flavonoids cannot be studied.

These experiments were almost forgotten until the 1960s when biosynthetic studies and work on the elucidation of reaction mechanisms again focused attention on chalcone epoxides.

(v) *2'-OR-chalcone epoxides.* ($R = CH_2C_6H_5$; CH_2OCH_3). A paper by Bognár and Stefanovski [57] in 1962 gave fresh impetus to the research of chalcone epoxides. It was found that the hydroxyl group in 2'-hydroxy-chalcones could be protected by a benzyl or *p*-nitrobenzyl group, and alkaline peroxide oxidation of the resulting 2'-OR-chalcone gave a stable 2'-OR-chalcone epoxide ($R = CH_2C_6H_5$ or $p\text{-}NO_2- C_6H_4-CH_2$) in high yields.

ArCH₂Hlg/OH⊖   H₂O₂/OH⊖   HCl Ar = p NO₂—C₆H₄   H⊕ Ar = C₆H₅

Treatment of these epoxides with acid reagents makes possible the preparation of 3-hydroxyflavanone or the chlorohydrin [1-(2'-OR-phenyl)-2-hydroxy-3-chloro-3-phenylpropan-1-one].

These results have shown that chalcone epoxides are important intermediates in flavonoid chemistry, but they can be prepared only if the 2'-hydroxyl group of the chalcone is protected by a group stable to alkali.

The most widely used oxidizing agents for chalcones are hydrogen peroxide [32, 33, 58], sodium peroxide [59], sodium hypochlorite [60] and *t*-butyl hydroperoxide [249, 345, 346]. The bases applied are alkali hydroxides [32, 36, 61], triethylamine, ammonium hydroxide [62], sodium tungstate [63] or tetramethylammonium hydroxide [64].

As shown by kinetic studies [64], the rate of epoxide formation in alkaline hydrogen peroxide depends on the pH (Fig. 1).

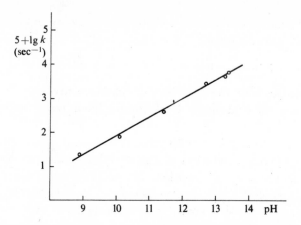

Fig. 1. Dependence of the rate of oxidation of 2'-benzyloxychalcone as a function of the pH

The oxidation takes place also at rather low pH values, but it occurs most rapidly at pH 12–14. Kinetic studies revealed that the rate of oxidation is also influenced by the substituent in ring B of the chalcone. A linear correlation was found between the Hammet σ_p^* value of the substituent and the rate of oxidation (Fig. 2).

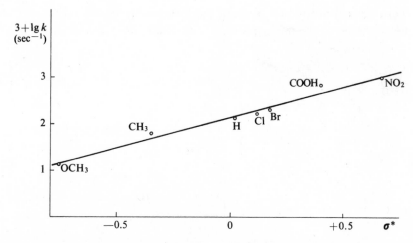

Fig. 2. Dependence of the rate of oxidation of 2'-benzyloxy-4-R-chalcones as a function of the σ^* substituent constant

Electron-withdrawing substituents enhance the reaction rate, and the chalcone epoxide is readily formed. As recently shown by Khandual *et al.*

[65], in the oxidation with chromic acid the substituents in ring B of the chalcone have an opposite effect:

$$4\text{-}OCH_3 > 3\text{-}OCH_3 > 2\text{-}OCH_3 > 4\text{-}Cl > H > 3\text{-}NO_2 > 4\text{-}NO_2$$

These results indicate that the oxidation mechanism involves the electrophilic attack of chromic acid on the C=C double bond, resulting in epoxide formation.

It has been found that 2'-benzyloxychalcone epoxides are only formed in the alkaline peroxide oxidation if the starting chalcone has no free hydroxyl group in the p- or p' position. In the presence of such a group, the chalcone is degraded by hydrogen peroxide [66]. However, as Dean and Podimuang [67] have shown, 2',6'-dimethoxy-4'-hydroxychalcone does give the epoxide.

The inactivating effect of the free hydroxyl group in alkaline solution may be due to the formation of phenoxide or enolate ion [67].

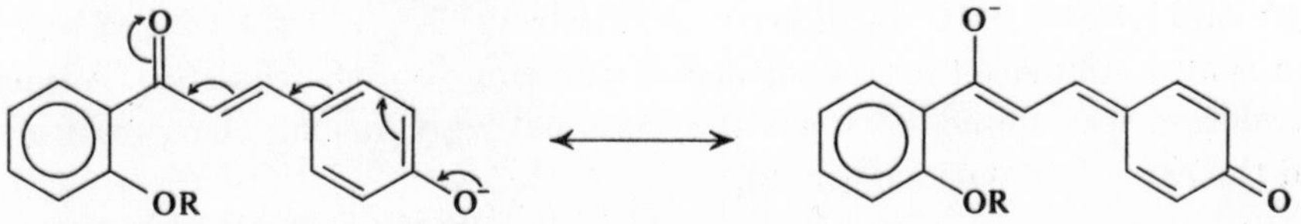

According to Bunton and Minkoff [68], the oxidation of α,β-unsaturated ketones starts with the nucleophilic attack of a hydroperoxide anion, giving rise to a carbanion:

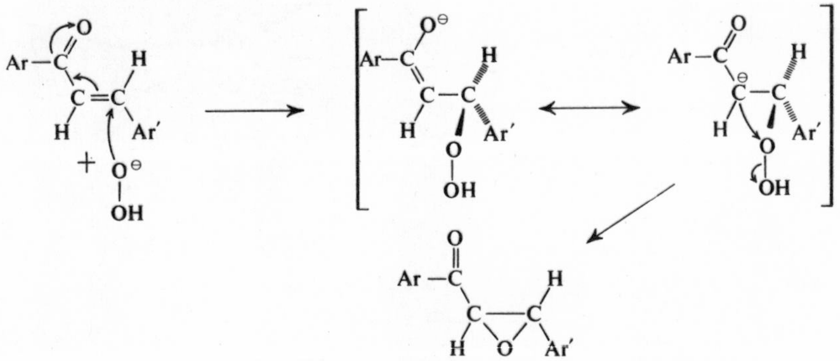

However, overlap control by the carbonyl group can only take effect if the acyl group is coplanar with the C-2 and C-3 atoms, thus electron delocalization is possible and *cis* addition [69] may result in the formation of the *trans* epoxide.

According to kinetic studies, the electron character of the substituent in ring B has influence on the *cis* addition (Fig. 2). The presence of an electron-attracting group favours nucleophilic attack by the peroxide anion on the β-carbon atom.

Temple [70] found that the reaction rate is also influenced by the rate of formation of the peroxide anion which, in turn, depends on the pH (Fig. 1), as follows:

$$H_2O_2 + OH^- \rightleftharpoons OOH^- + H_2O.$$

In contrast with the alkaline oxidation of benzalacetones [70], the oxidation of 2′-OR-chalcones gives epoxides only; no side reactions occur. Epoxide formation, however, is determined by steric and other constitutional factors of the molecule [66]. 2,6-Disubstituted chalcones, similarly to chalcone analogues containing a naphthyl group instead of ring B, are oxidized very slowly. Anthracene and pyrene analogues do not react even at high temperatures. Similarly, no epoxide is formed if ring B of the molecule is replaced by a 2-pyrrolyl-, N-methyl-2-pyrrolyl- [66] or a 1-phenyl-pyrazolyl [59] group. As has been found recently, 3,5-di-*t*-butylchalcones do not give epoxides either; the molecule suffers oxidative degradation yielding 3,5-di-*t*-butylbenzoic acid [71].

The electron character of the α-substituent in the chalcone may also influence epoxide formation; thus an α-nitro group will promote [72, 73], whereas an α-methoxyl group hinders [74] epoxide formation.

A great number of chalcone epoxides have been synthesized by the alkaline hydrogen peroxide oxidation of 2′-OR-chalcones and their analogues. The protective groups used are benzyl [43, 50, 57, 66, 72, 73, 76–92], methoxymethylene [83, 84, 87, 93–96] or tosyl [53, 54, 75].

The 2′-substituted chalcone epoxides are stable, well-crystallized compounds. The oxirane ring, mainly in *p*-methoxy-substituted chalcone epoxides, is opened on warming the compounds in ethanol solution [91], and an α-hydroxy-β-ethoxydihydrochalcone is obtained. As shown by Parthasarathy and Sharma [97], chalcone epoxides may undergo photo-oxidative decomposition on standing; thus irradiation with a mercury lamp of a methanolic solution of 2'-benzyloxy-3,4,4'-trimethoxychalcone epoxide led to decomposition to 2-benzyloxy-4-methoxybenzoic acid and veratraldehyde [97].

$$ \longrightarrow \quad Ar-COOH \; + \; CO \; + \; Ar'CHO $$

B. Oxidation in the Presence of Metal Ions

Japanese researchers [98, 99] made a detailed study of the oxidation reactions of 2'-hydroxy-4-methoxychalcones in glacial acetic acid, with manganese(III) acetate and lead(IV) acetate as the oxidizing agents. With either agent, the main product of the reaction was the *cis* and *trans* aurone derivative. It is suggested that the first product of the oxidation is Ar—O—Mn(OAc)$_2$, after which homolysis of the oxygen – metal bond gives rise to the Ar-O· radical and manganese(II) acetate. Attack by the radical on the α-carbon atom may directly give the aurone derivative.

Oxidation occurs only in the presence of a 4-methoxy substituent. Oxidizing 2'-benzyloxy-4,4'-dimethoxychalcone in a similar way, the product was a mixture of 1-(2'-benzyloxy-4'-methoxyphenyl)-2-acetoxy-3-(4-methoxyphenyl)propane-1,3-dione and *erythro*-2,3-diacetoxy-1-(2'-benzyloxy--4'-methoxyphenyl)-3-(4-methoxyphenyl)propan-1-one [99].

R = CH₂C₆H₅

Recently it has been found [100] that the first step of the oxidation gives β-hydroxychalcone as an intermediate and a benzyl derivative is also a product of the reaction.

Roux *et al.* [101] oxidized α-methoxychalcones with lead(IV) acetate in glacial acetic acid to obtain a mixture of 2-(α-acetoxy-4-methoxybenzyl)--2,4,6-trimethoxy- and 2-hydroxy-2-(α-hydroxy-4-methoxybenzyl)-4,6-dimethoxycoumaran-3-one; the latter was further oxidized to 2-acetoxy-2-(4-methoxybenzoyl)-4,6-dimethoxybenzo[b]furan-3[2H]-one.

In the experiments of Dean and Podimuang [67] 2',4-dihydroxychalcones were oxidized with potassium ferricyanide; formation of the resulting aurones was thought to involve a free radical mechanism.

Pelter *et al.* [102] reported that 4'-hydroxyflavones were additional products of the oxidation reaction; they found that chalcones containing a 4-methoxy substituent did not react.

Recently Roux *et al.* [101, 103] studied the alkaline $K_3Fe(CN)_6$ oxidation of 2',4-dihydroxy-4', 6'-dimethoxychalcone in the presence of 3,5-dimethoxyphenol. The free radical mechanism of the reaction was proved by the formation of aurone and a benzofuran derivative. It is suggested that the free radical is formed first on the 2'-hydroxyl group, and its attack on the α, β

double bond results in a resonance-stabilized radical; this can give benzo-furan with the phenoxyl radical, or is transformed into aurone by the oxidative loss of the C-2 hydrogen atom.

Under similar conditions, 2'-methoxymethoxy-4-hydroxy-4',6'-dimeth-oxychalcone does not react with alkaline $K_3Fe(CN)_6$.

The first successful use of thallium(III) acetate in methanol for the oxida-tion of chalcones was achieved by Ollis *et al.* [104–106]. It was found that the chalcones were converted with some rearrangement into 1,2-diaryl-3,3-dimethoxypropan-1-one, which is a transient product decomposed by acids to deoxybenzoin:

$$Ar-\overset{O}{\underset{\|}{C}}-CH=CH-Ar' \longrightarrow Ar-\overset{O}{\underset{\|}{C}}-\underset{\underset{CH(OCH_3)_2}{|}}{CH}-Ar' \xrightarrow{H^+} Ar-\overset{O}{\underset{\|}{C}}-CH_2-Ar'$$

The oxidation of 2'-hydroxychalcones gives flavones and coumaranones. The formation of the latter compounds shows that the intermediate of the reaction is the dimethylacetal derivative, which is converted to coumara-none [106].

If the 2'-hydroxyl group is protected, oxidation to flavone cannot occur; thus the reaction product is 1-(2'-benzyloxy-4'-methoxyphenyl)-2-(4-methoxyphenyl)-3,3-dimethoxypropan-1-one, from which removal of the protective group gives 4',7-dimethoxyisoflavone as the sole isolable product [105]. 6,7,2'-Trimethoxy-3',4'-methylenedioxyisoflavone (milldurone) and 4,7-dimethoxy-3',4'-methylenedioxyisoflavone (lettadurone) were synthesized similarly in satisfactory yields, though longer reaction times (3 days) were necessary.

In the meantime McKillop *et al.* [107, 113] found that chalcones in methanol solution, in the presence of perchloric acid or boron trifluoride etherate, are rapidly oxidized by thallium(III) nitrate (TTN) to the dimethylacetal derivatives. The method was applied by Farkas *et al.* [108, 109] to the oxidation of 2'-hydroxychalcones; in this way isoflavones were directly prepared in satisfactory yields (30–80%). The conversion was not accompanied by side reactions.

Gottsegen [110] and Antus [111] used the TTN oxidation to achieve the successful total synthesis of a number of naturally occurring isoflavones and flavonoids of novel type.

The mechanism of the oxidation by thallium(III) nitrate probably involves thallylation on the carbonyl group, being the site of the greatest electron density. The complex thus formed has a highly polarized positive β-carbon atom, thus addition of the nucleophilic methanol becomes possible [106, 111].

Simultaneously with this step, the initially co-ordinative thallium–oxygen linkage becomes a covalent bond; this is followed by heterolysis of the oxygen–thallium bond and aryl migration.

According to recent investigations [112] the course of the TTN oxidation is changed by the presence of a 5'-substituent in the chalcone molecule: aryl migration does not occur and a semiquinone derivative is obtained. This effect, however, can be suspended by acetylation of the 2'-hydroxyl group.

R = CH$_3$; CH$_2$C$_6$H$_5$

Hörhammer et al. [114] successfully achieved the oxidation of 2',3,6-trihydroxy-4-methoxychalcone to the 2'-hydroxy-4-methoxy-3,6-dioxochalcone analogue by means of Fremy salt.

No oxidation or rearrangement takes place if there is an inactivating substituent such as an NO$_2$ group in ring A or B of the chalcone. Further, substituents sensitive to oxidation (e.g. OH, NH$_2$) must be protected [107].

Oxidations in the *para* positions can also be effected in flavones.

C. Enzymic Oxidation

Rathmell and Bendall [115] investigated the hydrogen peroxide oxidation of 2',4',4-trihydroxychalcone in the presence of horseradish peroxidase catalyst; the optimal pH was found to be 7.5 and the reaction gave, with the consumption of one atom oxygen and presumably by free radical mechanism, 3,7,4'-trihydroxyflavone and 4',6-dihydroxy-2-(α-hydroxybenzyl) coumaranone. The latter product readily transforms into aurone in a non-enzymic reaction.

In 1960 Seshadri and Thakur [116] isolated a quinochalcone (carthamone), which gave carthamin on reduction.

Carthamone   Carthamine

They found that oxidation of carthamin in the presence of peroxidase gave the quinochalcone. Peroxidase oxidation attempted later by Obara and Onodera [117] did not yield the quinochalcone, but using nitric acid as oxidizing agent, 2′,3′,6′-trihydroxychalcones readily gave the corresponding quinochalcones, either in alcohol or in glacial acetic acid.

2. CONVERSIONS OF 2′-OR-CHALCONE EPOXIDES

A. Reactions with Hydrogen Halides

Bognár and Stefanovski ·[57] treated 2′-benzyloxychalcone epoxide with hydrogen chloride in ether, or with hydrogen bromide and hydrogen iodide in acetic acid, or with hydrogen iodate in acetone, to obtain 3-hydroxyflavanone in each case. When hydrogen chloride in ether was used, 1-(2′-benzyloxyphenyl)-2-hydroxy-3-chloro-3-phenylpropan-1-one (the chlorohydrin) was also present as a by-product formed in 10% yield. Substituted 2′-benzyloxychalcone epoxides with HCl in ether gave, depending on the substitution pattern of the starting epoxide, 3-hydroxyflavanones, chlorohydrins, or 1,3-diarylpropan-1,2-diones, and in some cases mixtures of the chlorohydrins and 3-hydroxyflavanones [89, 90].

Seshadri et al. [78] showed that the 1,2-diones were formed from the chlorohydrins in a secondary reaction; they also detected the formation of small amounts of formyldeoxybenzoins and isoflavones in these reactions.

According to Chopin and Durual [77], epoxides carrying ro substituent in ring B give only 3-hydroxyflavanones when treated with hydrogen chloride in glacial acetic acid.

2'-Benzyloxy-2,4-dichloro-, -4-nitro-, and -4-carboxychalcone epoxides do not react with HCl in ether, even after long reaction times [90]. This indicates that these p-substituents deactivate the oxirane ring, thus they hinder the reaction [33, 94].

Examination of the reaction products has shown that if the substituent in ring B has a positive Hammett σ_p value ($\sigma \geq 0$), the 3-hydroxyflavanone derivative will be produced, whereas if it is negative ($\sigma < 0$), the reaction results only in the cleavage of the oxirane ring without removal of the protective group, and the main product will be the chlorohydrin [89, 90].

When the σ constant is between $+ 0.3$ and $- 0.3$, the reaction follows both courses: the 3-hydroxyflavanone and chlorohydrin derivatives are obtained together. If the phenyl rings A or B are replaced by a five- or six-membered heteroaromatic or condensed ring system, the reaction product is always the chlorohydrin.

Indian [80] and French [50] researchers reported that a substituent in position 4' in ring A of the chalcone molecule did not influence the direction of the reaction; the only product isolated was the 3-hydroxyflavanone derivative. On the other hand, in the presence of a 4-methoxy substituent, Seshadri et al. [78] found the chlorohydrin to be the sole product.

Recent investigations [92] have shown that the electron character of a 5'-substituent can modify the course of the reaction. Thus on treatment with HCl in ether, 2'-benzyloxy-5'-methoxy- as well as -5'-methylchalcone epoxides give 3-hydroxy-6-methoxy- and -6-methylflavanone, respectively, whereas 2'-benzyloxy-5'-chlorochalcone epoxide affords the corresponding chlorohydrin.

As shown by the results, depending on the Hammett σ value of the 5'-substituent, and in contrast with the effect of ring B described above, if $\sigma \leq 0$, the product is 3-hydroxyflavanone, and when $\sigma > 0$, the chlorohydrin is obtained. Yet the presence of a $\sigma < 0$ substituent in ring B can suspend this directing influence of the C-5' substituent, e.g. 2'-benzyloxy-4,5'-dimethoxychalcone epoxide gives the chlorohydrin as the only isolable product. The directing influence of a C-5' substituent is also seen in the chalcone $\rightleftharpoons$ flavanone isomerization [118]

Epoxide derivatives containing methoxy groups in the 3,5- or 6'-positions did not give crystalline products in this reaction. Hydrogen chloride in ether caused darkening of the reaction mixture and thin-layer chromatography revealed the presence of several ill-defined compounds. Seshadri et al. [82] suggested the formation of polymeric products and also the occurrence of other reactions.

Oyamada and Baba [93] reported that 2'-methoxymethoxychalcone epoxides with methanolic hydrochloric acid invariably gave 3-hydroxyflavanones, independently of the substituents present. A similar result was obtained by Enebäck [94], who used sulfuric acid in methanol. On the other hand, Chopin and Pineau [84, 95] found later that in the presence of a p-methoxy substituent the protective group is split off, the oxirane ring suffers cleavage, and 3-hydroxyflavanone is formed in a low yield (8%) only.

Recently the conversions of 2-nitrochalcone epoxides with HCl in ether have also been investigated [119, 120]; the reaction was found to yield 1,3-dihydroxy-2-phenylquinoline-4[1H]-one.

(i) Structure determination of chlorohydrins. Cleavage with hydrochloric acid of the oxirane ring of a chalcone epoxide may give an α-hydroxy-β-chloroethane or α-chloro-β-hydroxyethane derivative and, depending on whether the ring opening occurs with inversion or retention, an erythro or a threo-chlorohydrin may result.

Earlier House [121] proved that the chlorohydrins obtained from the epoxides of α, β-unsaturated ketones had α-hydroxy-β-chloroketone structure; the formation of the analogous chlorohydrins from 2'-substituted chalcone epoxides was supposed by Bognár and Stefanovski [57].

An example for elucidating the structure of chlorohydrins is shown in the case of the product obtained from 2'-methoxychalcone epoxide [122, 123]. This chlorohydrin can be prepared from the epoxide with HCl in ether, or with tin(IV) chloride in anhydrous benzene. When hydrogen bromide is used, a bromohydrin is obtained, but this is unstable and suffers decomposition on standing, with the loss of HBr.

Halohydrins lose hydrogen halide at elevated temperatures (140–150 °C) to give a halogen-free compound. In the case of the above chlorohydrin, this product proved to be 1-(2'-methoxyphenyl)-3-phenyl-propane-1,2-dione, identical with the compound made by Enebäck and Gripenberg [124] from the corresponding chalcone epoxide with alkali.

Sodium acetate in ethanol gave two chlorine-free products which were separated by fractional crystallization. Physical properties showed one of them to be identical with the above dione prepared by thermal treatment and the other, having a positive ferric chloride colour reaction, was the enolic desmotropic form of the former.

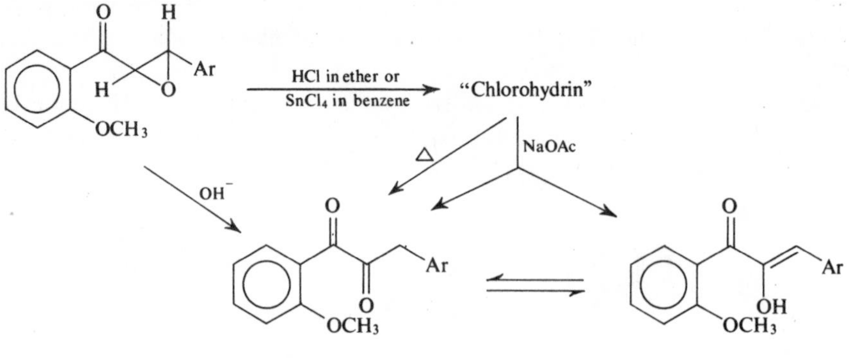

HCl in ether or SnCl₄ in benzene → "Chlorohydrin"

Δ   NaOAc

OH⁻

The structures of these products were also proved by the reaction with o-phenylenediamine; both tautomers gave 2-(2'-methoxyphenyl)-3-benzylquinoxaline in high yield.

The reaction product was also identical when the dione or its enolic tautomer was treated with phenylhydrazine: a well crystallized, osazone-type bis-phenylhydrazone was obtained.

$$Ar'-\overset{O}{\underset{}{C}}-\overset{O}{\underset{}{C}}-CH_2-Ar$$

$$Ar'-\overset{O}{\underset{}{C}}-\overset{OH}{\underset{}{C}}=CH-Ar$$

In a study of the conversions of chlorohydrins prepared from different substituted chalcone epoxides, Chopin and Durual [50] obtained only 1,2-diones on treatment with sodium acetate in glacial acetic acid. 2'-Benzyl-oxychalcone epoxide with tin(IV) chloride gave the chlorohydrin [57], whereas 3- or 4-methoxy-substituted epoxides did not yield a homogeneous, isolable product [50]. The mixture obtained, however, could be converted into the 1,2-dione with sodium acetate in acetic acid.

The transformation experiments afford evidence that the chlorohydrins are really α-hydroxy-β-chloro derivatives, since the elimination of hydrogen chloride results in a compound with its two oxygens being attached to neighbouring carbon atoms. This structure is unequivocally proved by the formation of the quinoxaline derivative [122, 123].

In the knowledge of these reactions, the structure of the halogen-free product obtained from 1-(2'-p-nitrobenzyloxybenzoyl)-2-phenylethylene-chlorohydrin with sodium acetate, was successfully elucidated. Earlier this compound had been supposed to be the corresponding cis-chalcone epoxide [57]. Thermal decomposition of the chlorohydrin gave the same substance as treatment with sodium acetate. The product reacted with o-phenylene-diamine to yield a quinoxaline derivative. The infrared spectrum showed the absence of hydroxyl groups, and the ferric chloride colour test was negative. Thus the chalcone which had been thought a cis-chalcone epoxide was shown to be 1-(2'-p-nitrobenzyloxyphenyl)-3-phenylpropane-1,2-dione [122, 123].

Further evidence supporting the structure of this substance was obtained by reaction with acetic anhydride and pyridine, when the dione and the chlorohydrin derivative equally gave the monoacetate of the enolic form. This experiment also showed that hydrogen chloride elimination from the chlorohydrin could occur under the conditions of acetylation.

Cleavage of the ring of trans-epoxides leading to chlorohydrin may take place with inversion on the C-3 atom (trans cleavage), or with retention of the configuration (*cis* cleavage) to give an *erythro-* and *threo*-chlorohydrin, respectively.

Opening of the oxirane ring with retention is thought by Wasserman and Aubrey [125] to follow $S_N i$ mechanism., occurring through an oxonium ion pair, with participation of the carbonyl group.

On the other hand, House and Ryerson [126] have suggested that the protonated oxirane ring may open directly, according to the "fourcentre" mechanism, with retention, and without participation of the carbonyl group.

According to the interpretation of Brewster [127], *cis* opening of the oxirane ring can only take place if the formation of a carbonium cation is possible.

The formation of the *erythro* chlorohydrin, involving inversion and *trans* cleavage, is a proton-catalyzed $S_N 2$ reaction. The oxygen of the epoxide molecule binds the proton by a co-ordinate linkage, then attack by the chloride anion on C-3 loosens the C-3-O bond and results in its rupture.

Erythro chlorohydrins are formed in alcoholic hydrochloric acid [121], and undergo cyclization to *trans* epoxide when acted upon by alkali [128, 129].

On the other hand, *threo* chlorohydrins cannot give *cis* epoxides, since this is prevented by the *syn* configuration of the bulky phenyl and benzoyl

groups, thus 1,2-*anti* elimination of hydrogen chloride may lead, through the enolic form, to the 1,2-dione derivative.

Since the chlorohydrins gave 1,2-dione derivatives with the elimination of hydrochloric acid [122], it follows that cleavage by HCl in ether or by tin(IV) chloride of the oxirane ring of 2'-OR-chalcone epoxides gives the *threo*-α-hydroxy-β-chloro derivative. This was also supported by the NMR studies of Reichel and Neubauer [129]. The coupling constant of the *erythro* chlorohydrins is 4 Hz, while that of *threo* isomers is 2 Hz.

(*ii*) *Cyclization of epoxides to 3-hydroxyflavanones.* As shown by experiment, treatment with HCl in ether of *trans*-2'-benzyloxychalcone epoxides gave the *threo* chlorohydrin only if the Hammett σ_p value of the substituent in ring B was negative. In the opposite case the protective group was split off as well, and cyclization gave rise to 3-hydroxyflavanone as the main product.

This latter reaction may be rationalized by supposing that the first step is

(a) cleavage of the protective group, or

(b) opening of the oxirane ring and the formation of chlorohydrin, or

(c) elimination of the protective group and cleavage of the oxirane ring, followed by cyclization to 3-hydroxyflavanone.

These assumptions, however, can be rejected, since the benzyl group is not split off either from 2'-benzyloxychalcone or from the chlorohydrin under the experimental conditions used, and thus a cyclic compound cannot be produced [57, 90].

In explaining the formation of the cyclized product, Bognár and Stefanovski [57] suggested that the protective group is split off simultaneously with the cleavage of the oxirane ring, as a result of internal nucleophilic substitution. The process starts with the coordinate binding of a proton. An electron-attracting substituent in ring B ($\sigma \geq 0$) enhances affixing of the proton, thus nucleophilic attack by the ethereal C-2' oxygen and cleavage of the protective group may ensue.

If ring B contains an electron-releasing substituent ($\sigma < 0$), the electron density on the β-carbon atom is increased and internal nucleophilic attack is hindered; therefore, a *threo* chlorohydrin is produced, either by the "four-centre" mechanism [126], or by *cis* addition as suggested by Brewster [127].

The following experimental facts may be cited in support of the notion about the decisive directing role of the nucleophilicity of the ethereal C-2′ oxygen and the electron density on the β-carbon atom.

(*a*) Enebäck [94] and Oyamada [93] found that 2′-methoxymethoxy-chalcone epoxides invariably give 3-hydroxyflavanones, independently of the nature of the substituent in ring B. This shows that the electron-releasing methoxymethylene group increases the nucleophilicity of the ethereal C-2′ oxygen, thus the cyclic product is readily formed; however, the possibility of previous elimination of the acid-sensitive methoxymethylene group cannot be excluded, either.

(*b*) A *p*-nitrobenzyl blocking group decreases the electron density on the ethereal C-2′ oxygen atom, therefore cyclization cannot take place; only the oxirane ring is opened and, according to Bognár and Stefanovski [57], these derivatives give chlorohydrins.

(*c*) The influence of C-5′ substituents in the epoxides described above can also be explained in terms of the nucleophilic character of the C-2′ ethereal oxygen. An electron-withdrawing substituent will reduce the nucleophilicity, thus attack by the chloride anion and formation of the chlorohydrin will be predominant, whereas an electron-releasing substituent will favour internal nucleophilic attack. The latter effect may, however, be modified by a substituent in ring B, thus electron density on the β-carbon atom must at any rate be taken into account when considering the reaction route [92].

(*d*) As in some cases (when σ is between $+ 0.3$ and $- 0.3$) both the chlorohydrins and the cyclized products (3-hydroxyflavanones) are formed, two competing reactions must run parallel [66].

(*e*) It was found [72] that the presence of an electron-attracting group attached to the α-carbon atom of the epoxide molecule also facilitates elimination of the protective group and the occurrence of cyclization. Thus 2′-benzyloxy-α-nitrochalcone epoxide gives, probably through the 3-hydroxy-3-nitroflavanone derivative, 3-hydroxyflavone [72]. The process is not influenced by the ring B substituent [73].

R = CH₂C₆H₅

The opening of the epoxide ring and cyclization to flavanone may take place with inversion or retention. If the cyclization occurred with retention, the *trans diaxal* C-2-H and C-3-OH groups of the newly formed 3-hydroxy-3-nitroflavanone would be favoured in an elimination reaction [128]; the result of the *trans* elimination of water would be 3-nitroflavone.

This latter reaction is also informative as regards the stereochemical course of the cyclization of 2′-benzyloxychalcone epoxides with acids.

Since actually nitrous acid and not water is eliminated, it follows that the ring formation takes place with inversion on the C-3 atom.

Bognár and Stefanovski [57] also supposed inversion during the forma
tion of the pyranone ring from 2'-benzyloxychalcone epoxide. In the course
of this reaction chalcone epoxides give the more stable 3-hydroxyflavanone
with *trans* configuration and (2a) : (3a) conformation.

The structure of 3-hydroxyflavanone and the reaction mechanism are
also confirmed by the chemical and spectral properties of the product.

2′-Benzyloxychalcone epoxides give the same 3-hydroxyflavanones as obtained in the alkaline hydrogen peroxide oxidation of 2′-hydroxychalcones.

The structure of the product prepared by the latter reaction was proved by Bognár and Rákosi [130] and also by other authors [131].

Trans-3-hydroxyflavanone derivatives cannot be dehydrated, but they are readily dehydrogenated [131]. This is the evidence for the *trans axial-equatorial* steric positions of C-2-H and C-3-OH, whereas C-2-H and C-3-H are *trans diaxial*, favouring elimination [130–132]. The latter statement was confirmed by NMR studies reported by Clark-Lewis *et al.* [133].

The isomeric C-2-H, C-3-H-*cis*-3-hydroxyflavanone is unstable; as shown by Indian researchers [134], it is readily isomerized to the more stable *trans* derivative.

B. Cleavage of the Oxirane Ring by Acidic Agents

In the reaction with hydrochloric acid in ether, the reactivity of 2′-benzyloxychalcone epoxides and the course of the conversion are primarily determined by the electron structure of the oxirane ring and by the substituents present. This fact has been amply corroborated in several other reactions. Such studies were made with differently substituted 2′-benzyloxy-4-R-chalcone epoxides (R = OCH_3, $\sigma = -0.27$; R = H, $\sigma = 0$; R = NO_2, $\sigma = 0.78$), and it was found [91] that a part of 2′-benzyloxy-4-methoxychalcone epoxide is converted to 2′-benzyloxy-α-hydroxy-β-ethoxy-4-methoxydihydrochalcone even by simple recrystallization from ethanol.

$+ C_2H_5 - OH$

$R = CH_2C_6H_5$

This conversion can be made complete by warming in the presence of sulfuric acid. Thus treatment with methanol and sulfuric acid of 2'-benzyl-oxy-4-methoxy-,-4-methyl- and -4-isopropylchalcone epoxides gave the corresponding dihydrochalcones, whereas 2'-benzyloxy- or 2'-methoxy-methoxychalcone epoxides yielded the 3-hydroxyflavanones [66]. Very little or no conversion was obtained with 2'-benzyloxy-4-nitro- and -2,4-dichlorochalcone epoxides. Similarly, 2'-methoxymethoxy-4-nitro- and -2,4-dichlorochalcone epoxides, containing an acid-sensitive protective group, do not react with methanolic sulfuric acid, either. A stabilizing effect of the p-nitro group has also been shown in other reactions of chalcones [135].

On the other hand, the presence of a p'-nitro group facilitates the opening of the oxirane ring [136]. Yet, fission of the oxirane ring of *trans*-4-nitro-chalcone epoxides can be readily accomplished with thiophenol to give α-thiophenylchalcone through intermediary products.

$$Ar-\overset{O}{\underset{\|}{C}}-CH-CH-C_6H_4-p-NO_2 \xrightarrow{C_6H_5SH} Ar-\overset{O}{\underset{\|}{C}}-CH-\overset{OH}{\underset{|}{C}H}-Ar' \xrightarrow{HCl/AcOH}$$

$$\underset{SC_6H_5}{}$$

$$\rightarrow Ar-\overset{O}{\underset{\|}{C}}-CH-\overset{Cl}{\underset{|}{C}H}-Ar' \xrightarrow{(C_2H_5)_3N} Ar-\overset{O}{\underset{\|}{C}}-C=CH-C_6H_4-p-NO_2$$

$$\underset{SC_6H_5}{} \qquad \underset{SC_6H_5}{}$$

The presence of a 4-methoxy substituent also renders the chlorohydrin unstable; recrystallization from ethanol or reaction with sodium acetate do not result in dehydrohalogenation, but the same dihydrochalcone is obtained as from the epoxide [91].

In contrast with earlier results reported by Enebäck [94], Pineau and Chopin [95] have recently found that treatment with H_2SO_4 in methanol of 2'-methoxymethoxy-4-methoxychalcone epoxide, a compound sensitive to acids, results only in methanolysis and removal of the blocking group; cyclization to 3-hydroxyflavanone is slight (6%). The latter reaction probably occurs through the dihydrochalcone derivative produced in a secondary process; evidence for this is the cyclization of the dihydrochalcone to 3-hydroxy-4-methoxyflavanone, achieved by Pineau and Chopin [84] by means of polyphosphoric acid or concentrated sulfuric acid.

Aubry and Chopin [96] also found that chalcone epoxides having a 2'-methoxymethoxy protective group react with acids first undergoing protonation in the oxirane ring, followed by fission; the next step is the removal of the blocking group. If ring B is unsubstituted and ring A has the resorcine substitution pattern, the products are 3-hydroxyflavanones. It can be assumed that the protonated oxirane ring is opened by S_N2 attack of water or methanol to give the product with *threo* conformation; this is then followed by attack of the 2'-phenolate anion leading to *trans*-3-hydroxyflavanone. If the *erythro* isomer was also formed, this should give rise to *cis*-3-hydroxyflavanone.

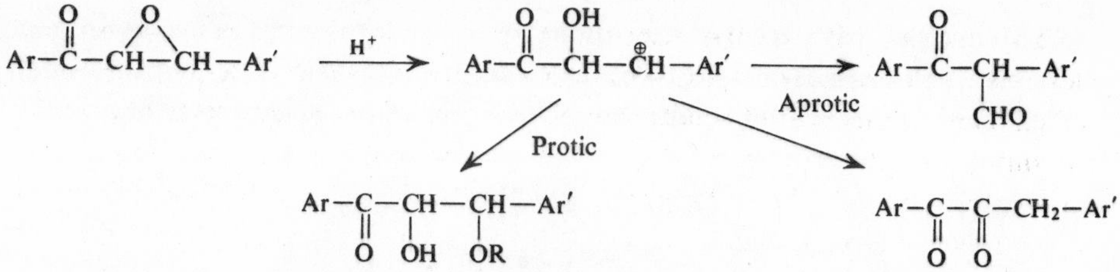

$$Ar-\overset{\overset{O}{\|}}{C}-\overset{}{C}H-\overset{}{C}H-Ar' \xrightarrow{H^+} Ar-\overset{\overset{O}{\|}}{C}-\overset{}{C}H-\overset{\oplus}{C}H-Ar' \longrightarrow[\text{Aprotic}]{} Ar-\overset{\overset{O}{\|}}{C}-\overset{}{C}H-Ar'$$

(Epoxide above CH—CH; OH on second CH)

Protic → $Ar-\overset{\overset{O}{\|}}{C}-\overset{}{C}H-\overset{}{C}H-Ar'$ (OH, OR)

Aprotic → $Ar-\overset{\overset{O}{\|}}{C}-\overset{\overset{O}{\|}}{C}-CH_2-Ar'$

In strongly acidic medium attack with S_N1 mechanism by the 2′-phenolate anion on the transient carbonium cation is also a possibility. In this case the formation of both *cis*- and *trans*-3-hydroxyflavanone is expected. As shown by experiment, the way of conversion of 2′-methoxymethoxychalcone epoxides is also determined by the solvent used [95]. With acid reagents in an aprotic solvent the carbanion is converted to 1,2-dione derivatives or formyldeoxybenzoins, whereas in protic solvents it is rather solvolysis that will predominate:

2′-Benzyloxychalcone epoxides containing no methoxy substituent react with hydrogen chloride in alcohol or in glacial acetic acid, as well as with sulfuric acid in methanol, to give 3-hydroxyflavanone, but 4-methoxy-substituted derivatives afford the chlorohydrin or dihydrochalcone derivative [57, 81, 95].

When 2′-benzyloxy-4-methoxychalcone epoxide is treated with glacial acetic acid in alcohol, the product is the monoacetate. Its structure is confirmed by synthesis of the same compound from the chlorohydrin with silver acetate.

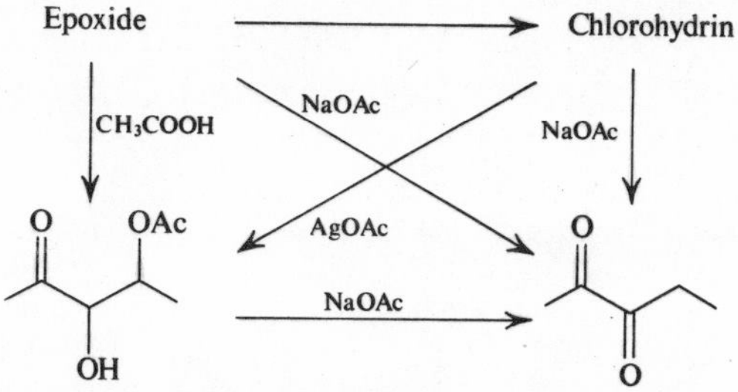

Epoxide ⟶ Chlorohydrin

(CH₃COOH ↓ ; NaOAc ; NaOAc ↓ ; AgOAc ; NaOAc)

Enebäck [94] synthesized α-methoxychalcones by the methylation of 1,2-diones; removal of the protective group then gave 2-benzyl-2-methoxy-coumaran-3-one.

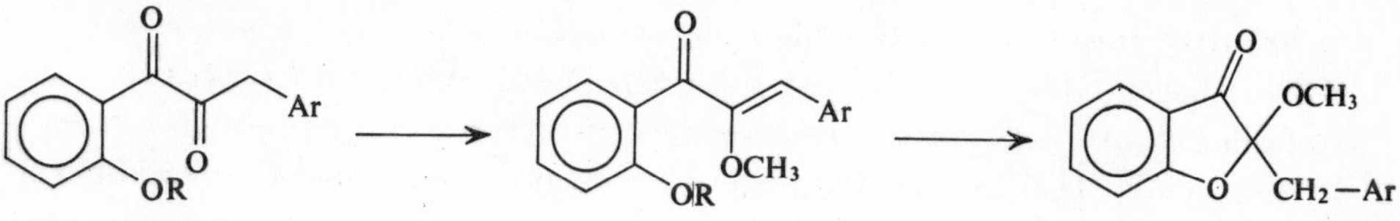

Chopin *et al.* [81] treated the dione or its chlorohydrin with hydrogen chloride in glacial acetic acid to obtain 2-hydroxy-2-benzylcoumaran-3-one which can be dehydrated to aurone, or rearranged in the presence of alkali to coumaran-2-one.

The conversion to 2-hydroxy-2-benzylcoumaranone is influenced by the substituents in the molecule [81].

2'-Benzyloxy-4-methoxychalcone epoxide is acetylated by acetic anhydride in pyridine to a diacetate which is identical with the product obtainable from the chlorohydrin with silver acetate and acetic anhydride.

The diacetate is also accessible by acetylation of the glycol monoacetate. When the epoxide is acetylated with acetic anhydride in the presence of sodium acetate, the α-acetoxychalcone derivative is a by-product formed in 10% yield, besides the diacetate. This compound is probably produced by the elimination of acetic acid from the glycol monoacetate under the influence of sodium acetate [91].

A similar result was reported by Clark–Lewis and Jeminson [85]. The α-acetoxychalcone derivative can also be prepared from the chlorohydrin and dione by means of acetic anhydride in pyridine.

The above authors [85] achieved the cyclization of 6′-methoxy- α-acetoxy-chalcones to aurones.

R = CH₂C₆H₅

If the substituent constant in ring B is greater than zero ($\sigma > 0$), the oxirane ring is not cleaved by acetic anhydride; thus 2′-benzyloxy.- or -4-nitrochalcone epoxides do not react with acetic anhydride. These experiments also show that the presence of an electron-releasing substituent in p-position in ring B is one of the conditions required for opening of the oxirane ring. Such a substituent renders this ring unstable promoting its fission and the formation of a carbonium ion of transient existence; this ion undergoes further conversion suffering attack from an alcoholate. Acetate or chloride ion, or occasionally with the elimination of a proton.

Formation of the carbonium ion favours *cis* addition [121], thus the products expected are the *threo* derivatives. NMR studies by Pineau and Chopin [95] have recently shown that the *erythro* isomers are also produced in various reactions.

The poor stability and the reactivity with nucleophilic reagents of chlorohydrins with 4-methoxy substituents can also be attributed to the effect of the electron-releasing group.

Recent studies have shown [92, 96] that the stability of the oxirane ring is also effected by a 6'-methoxy substituent. 2'-Benzyloxy-6'-methoxy-chalcone epoxide reacted with hydrogen chloride in methanol and, without removal of the protective group, 2'-benzyloxy-α-hydroxy-β,6'-dimethoxy-dihydrochalcone was obtained. As shown by NMR spectroscopy, the product was the isomer having *threo* configuration. The same compound can be prepared with sulfuric acid in methanol. In the case of 6'-methoxychalcone epoxide containing the acid-sensitive methoxymethoxy protective group, methanolic sulfuric acid removed this group, and opening of the oxirane ring gave rise to 2'α-dihydroxy-6'β-dimethoxydihydrochalcone.

Such 6'-methoxydihydrochalcone derivatives were cyclized by French researchers [84, 95, 96] to 3-hydroxyflavanones.

The special reactions of 6'-methoxy-substituted chalcone epoxides are probably due to steric factors.

The stability of the oxirane ring towards nucleophilic agents depends particularly on the substituent present in ring B; in the case of $\sigma > 0$, the oxirane ring is stable and is not cleaved by nucleophilic reagents, or rather it is possible but vigorous conditions are required; a substituent constant $\sigma < 0$ renders the epoxide ring unstable.

C. Cleavage of the Oxirane Ring by Alkaline Agents

Baker and Robinson [55] reported that alkaline treatment of 2'-methoxy-chalcone epoxides gave directly the benzilic acid derivative; in the experiments of Enebäck and Gripenberg [124], α-hydroxychalcones were also obtained. This unstable enolic form may readily be converted in the presence of piperidine to the more stable 1,2-dione, which then gives the benzilic acid.

Analogously, 2′-methoxymethoxy- or 2′-benzyloxychalcone epoxides also afford α-hydroxychalcones; removal of the protective group results in 2-hydroxy-2-benzylcoumaranones and subsequent dehydration yields aurones [81, 92, 94].

Collins and Neville [137] studied the rearrangement of isotopically labelled chalcone epoxides and found that the carbonyl groups of the intermediary 1,2-diketone were not equivalent. By converting p-substituted epoxides, they have shown that the 2-hydroxy-2,3-diphenylpropionic acid derivative is produced by migration of the benzyl group in ring B [138].

According to Dodwadmath and Wheeler [33], if the epoxide contains a nitro substituent in ring B, treatment with alcoholic alkali does not give a benzilic acid derivative.

Irish authors [53, 54] reported that alkali in nitrogen atmosphere effects the cleavage of the protective group from 2'-tosyloxychalcone epoxide and 3-hydroxyflavanone is obtained; in the presence of air the product is 3-hydroxyflavone.

If the epoxide has also a 6'-methoxy substituent, the reaction leads to a mixture of 3-hydroxy-5-methoxyflavanone and 4-methoxyaurone.

Treatment with alkali of 2'-acetoxy-[38, 46–48, 50] or 2'-hydroxychalcone epoxides [43, 45] also results in 3-hydroxyflavanone.

The conversion of 2'-methoxymethoxychalcone epoxides with urea in the presence of alkali was investigated [139, 140]; the products obtained were 5-(2'-methoxymethoxyphenyl)-5-benzylhydantoins. It has been assumed that the intermediate of transitory existence was a 1,2-dione derivative which reacted with urea after rearrangement to benzilic acid. The yield of the hydantoin derivative depends on the nature of the substituent in the epoxide.

Treatment with thiourea gives 5-phenyl-5-benzyl-2-thionhydantoin in an analogous reaction [139]. When no alkali is present, the epoxides react with thiourea and guanidine to give 2-amino-4-aryl-5-(α-hydroxybenzyl) triazoles and 2-amino-4-benzoyl-5-phenylimidazolines, respectively [141].

Opening of the epoxide ring was also investigated with morpholine and piperidine [142, 143]. It has been found that secondary amines effect fission of the oxirane ring by S_N2 mechanism, affording *d,l-erythro-α-hydroxy-β-amino-β-phenylpropiophenone* [144].

A detailed study was made of the reactions of chalcone epoxides with hydroxylamine [145, 146]. In alkaline medium 4-hydroxyisoxazolines, whereas in weak acidic solution the intermediate 1-aryl-2-benzylethylene-oxide oximes are obtained.

The intermediary oxime may give 4-hydroxyisoxazoline in both alkaline and acid medium [147].

Bodforss [148] and others [123, 142, 149, 150–154] investigated the reactions of chalcone epoxides with hydrazine hydrate and phenylhydrazine. These reactions afforded 3,5-diphenylpyrazole derivatives through the intermediary 4-hydroxypyrazolines.

In some cases the corresponding 4-hydroxypyrazoline could be isolated [123, 151–154], and it was dehydrated to the pyrazole by thermal treatment [154], or in the presence of acid [153, 155, 156]. According to recent studies [144], chalcone epoxide analogues give only 3,5-diphenylpyrazoles. Also in the presence of alkali, epoxides afford only 3,5-diphenylpyrazoles on treatment with hydrazine hydrate or phenylhydrazine [157].

Cromwell [142] reported that *cis*- and *trans*-chalcone epoxides did not react in the same way with phenylhydrazine. The *cis* isomer was less reactive and it gave the pyrazole whereas the *trans* compound afforded a stable 4-hydroxypyrazoline in a much quicker reaction; *cis* elimination of water from this product can be achieved only with difficulty.

Erythro- and *threo*-chlorohydrins also react with hydrazine hydrate; the products are the stereoisomeric 4-hydroxypyrazolines [123, 151, 173].

From *threo*-chlorohydrins the same stereoisomeric 4-hydroxypyrazolines are obtainable as from *trans*-chalcone epoxides [151, 153].

D. Reduction of Chalcone Epoxides

2'-Methoxychalcone epoxide can be selectively reduced with 1 mole of hydrogen, resulting only in cleavage of the oxirane ring [122, 123]. The same compound is obtained when the chlorohydrin derivative is hydrogenated under identical conditions; only the halogen atom is removed and 1-(2′-methoxyphenyl)-2-hydroxy-3-phenylpropan-1-one is produced.

On catalytic hydrogenation with 2 moles of hydrogen, both the epoxide and chlorohydrin give the same product, 1-(2′-methoxyphenyl)-1,2-dihydroxy-3-phenylpropane. The same diol can be synthesized by converting the epoxide with lithium aluminium hydride in ether solution [122, 123].

It has been found that the epoxide ring is opened by hydrogenation to give a hydroxyl group on the α-carbon atom neighbouring the carbonyl group. This is proved by the fact that reductive dehalogenation of the chlorohydrins with α-hydroxy-β-chloro structure gives the same α-hydroxyketone or *vic.*-diol as the reduction of the epoxides.

Bhrara *et al.* [78] hydrogenated 2′,4′-dibenzyloxy-4-methoxychalcone epoxide in glacial acetic acid to obtain formononetin and 2,4-dihydroxyphenyl-β-acetoxy-α-hydroxy-β-(4-methoxyphenyl)ethyl ketone.

The LiAlH$_4$ reduction of 2′-benzyloxychalcone epoxides also gave the 1,2-diols in the experiments of Bokadia *et al.* [43, 158] and Chopin and Piccardi [159, 160]. NMR spectroscopy showed that the products were the *erythro* isomers. However, when the reduction was effected with KBH$_4$, a 7 : 3 mixture of the *trans-erythro* and *trans-threo* epoxyalcohols could be obtained [159, 160].

When a mixture of LiAlH$_4$ and AlCl$_3$ (1 : 7) is used as the reducing agent of 2′-benzyloxychalcone epoxide, the protective group is split off and 2,3-*trans*-3,4-*trans*-flavan-3,4-diol is formed [43, 158]. According to recent investigations [160], the 2,3-*trans*-3,4-*cis* isomer is also a product of the reduction.

Both flavan isomers are also accessible by acid treatment of the isomeric epoxyalcohols [160].

Catalytic hydrogenation of *cis-* or *trans-*2-nitrochalcone epoxides is a new route for synthesizing 2-hydroxy-2-phenylquinolines [142].

E. Reactions with Lewis Acids

In synthesizing the unsubstituted chalcone epoxide, Weitz and Scheffer [58] reported in 1921 that the product was isomerized by hydrochloric acid to a β-ketoaldehyde.

Later it was shown that real structure of the product was 1,3-diphenyl-1,2-propanedione [161], yet treatment with sulfuric acid in acetic acid gave indeed, the β-ketoaldehyde derivative.

The fact that chalcone epoxide afforded this β-ketoaldehyde derivative held out promises of a new isoflavone synthesis.

Starting with an epoxide, Baker and Robinson [55] were the first to synthesize a deoxybenzoin and its formyl derivative, in 1932. 2'-Methoxychalcone epoxide or the dione obtained from it was treated with alkali; the resulting glycolic acid derivative was decarboxylated. Subsequent oxidation afforded o-methoxydeoxybenzoin. Formylation and removal of the protective group led to isoflavone, although in a poor yield.

Algar and McKenna [56] applied the method of Weitz and Scheffer [58] to synthesize o-methoxyformyldeoxybenzoin, but the yield of isoflavone was very low (4%), since demethylation also caused splitting off of the formyl group, thus the main product was o-hydroxydeoxybenzoin. It was shown that hydrogen bromide in acetic anhydride or acetic acid, as well as hydrogen iodide in acetic acid gave no isoflavone at all; only aluminium chloride was effective.

These methods did not find wide application since they afforded the isoflavone in a rather laborious way and in low yields. Chalcone epoxides containing the less stable benzyl protecting group appeared more promising for the preparation of isoflavone derivatives.

Treatment of a solution of 2'-benzyloxy-4-methoxychalcone epoxides in glacial acetic acid with hydrogen bromide [80] or concentrated sulfuric acid [89, 91] results in simultaneous removal of the blocking group, and 4'-methoxyisoflavones are obtained in a much better yield.

A number of years ago House et al. [126, 162] investigated the isomerization of chalcone epoxides to formyldeoxybenzoins by means of boron trifluoride etherate. This method was adopted by Indian authors [27, 80]

22*

and other researchers [50, 80, 91] for the successful synthesis of isoflavones from 2′-OR-chalcone epoxides.

The reaction with concentrated acid or boron trifluoride etherate represents an advantageous new isoflavone synthesis as the previous steps can be readily achieved in almost quantitative yield.

Application of the method to variously substituted chalcone epoxides has revealed that 2′-benzyloxychalcone epoxides with conc. H_2SO_4 or HBr in acetic acid, or with boron trifluoride etherate may give not only isoflavones, but also 3-hydroxyflavanones, depending on the substituent of the starting epoxide [80, 89, 90].

In the course of these reactions neither the appearance of deoxybenzoin derivatives nor the simultaneous formation of isoflavone and flavanone derivatives could be detected. The epoxides containing C-3, C-5- or C-6′-methoxy substituent in ring B and A, respectively, gave a reaction mixture whose composition could not be established, similarly to the reaction with hydrogen chloride in ether; the same applies to derivatives carrying a condensed or heterocyclic ring instead of ring B [89]. As in the case of hydrochloric acid, the reaction route depends on the Hammett σ_p values of the substituents. According to experimental evidence, the epoxides give isoflavones only if ring B has an electron-releasing substituent ($\sigma < 0$). If $\sigma > 0$, solely 3-hydroxyflavanones are obtained.

Several authors reported [50, 77, 79, 80] that if ring A of the epoxide contained a 4′-methoxy substituent and ring B was unsubstituted, treatment with boron trifluoride etherate afforded only 3-hydroxyflavanone. However, the same reagent gave rise to 3-hydroxyflavanones and isoflavones in the presence of an electron-releasing ($\sigma < 0$) and electron-attracting ($\sigma > 0$) C-5' substituent, respectively [92].

A comparison of the experiments made with Lewis acids and hydrochloric acid has shown that the chalcone epoxides giving chlorohydrins with HCl in ether, yield isoflavone derivatives with boron trifluoride etherate or concentrated sulfuric acid.

2'-Benzyloxy- or 2'-methoxymethoxychalcone epoxides carrying a 6'-methoxy substituent, did not give an isolable product with boron trifluoride etherate [92]. Recently Gormley and O'Sullivan [54] allowed 2'-tosyloxy-6'-methoxychalcone epoxide to react with boron trifluoride etherate at low temperature to obtain 2-tosyloxy-6-methoxyformyldeoxybenzoin. However, removal of the protective group from this product did not yield the isoflavone derivative, as the formyl group was also split off under the reaction conditions applied; thus 2-hydroxy-6-methoxydeoxybenzoin was produced.

R = tosyl

Conversion to a slight extent of 2'-benzyloxy-4-methoxychalcone epoxides to formyldeoxybenzoin or isoflavone derivatives was demonstrated by Bhrara et al. [78], effecting the reaction with HCl in ether, HBr in acetic acid, and also with glacial acetic acid. These compounds are formed, however, only as by-products, the main products being the corresponding chlorohydrin, 1,2-dione or glycol monoacetate derivatives.

The *threo*-chlorohydrin resulting from 2'-benzyloxy-4-methoxychalcone epoxide can be converted with boron trifluoride etherate to 4'-methoxyisoflavone; the yield is 30% [66].

The reactions of chalcone epoxides with Lewis acids widened the field of possible uses of the epoxides, and opened the way to new syntheses of different 3-hydroxyflavanones and isoflavones. Several natural isoflavones have been synthesized from the appropriately substituted chalcone epoxide with boron trifluoride etherate; examples are: daidzein [27], formononetin [27, 50, 78], cabreuvin, 7,8,3',4'-tetramethoxyisoflavone [80], 3'-hydroxy-formononetin [88], pseudobaptigenin [27], afrormosin, cabreuvin [82, 163], 7,4'-dimethylangolensin [27], and 3",4"-dihydrodurmillone [164].

3. REARRANGEMENT REACTIONS OF FLAVONOIDS INVOLVING ARYL OR AROYL MIGRATION

In flavonoid chemistry several reactions are known which lead to derivatives of different type and oxidation number, formed by aryl or aroyl migration. Interest is also attached to these rearrangement reactions from the biogenetic point of view since they may represent models of the formation of the different flavonoids from a common precursor in the plant.

A. Rearrangements of Cyclized Compounds

As early as 1926, Freudenberg and Carrara [165] showed that treatment of 5,6,3',4'-tetramethylcatechin with phosphorus trichloride gave an isoflavene derivative. They found that the reaction involved aryl migration.

Later Clark–Lewis and Korytnyk [166] prepared 2-ethoxyisoflavan from flavan-3-tosyl ester.

Lithium aluminium hydride reduction of 3-hydroxyflavan derivatives led — probably via the epoxides [167] — to 2,3-diarylpropan-1-ol; the reaction involves benzyl migration.

Oxidation of flavanone with lead tetraacetate gives, among other products, isoflavone [168].

Dean and Podimuang [67] synthesized the corresponding 2-methyliso-flavone by dehydrating 2-(α-hydroxybenzyl)-2,4,6-trimethylcoumaran-3-one with sulfuric acid. This rearrangement is characterized by benzoyl migration.

A detailed study was made of the benzilic acid rearrangement of 3-hydroxyflavanone derivatives effected by alkali, which gives, among other products, 3-benzalcoumaran-2-ones [70, 169]. Neville et al. [137, 138] show-

ed by isotopic studies that this rearrangement takes place with benzyl migration.

B. Rearrangements of Chalcones

In recent years, oxidation experiments with thallium(III) acetate in methanol, made by Ollis *et al.* [104–106] have shown that 1,2-diaryl-3,3-dimethoxypropan-1-ones can be prepared by the rearrangement of chalcones (p. 309).

Using ^{14}C-labelled chalcone, it was shown that the rearrangement involved aryl migration [106].

C. Conversions of Chalcone Epoxides

The isomerization by acids of chalcone epoxides to formyldeoxybenzoin derivatives may take place with aryl- or aroyl migration. This rearrangement comprises the transient formation of a carbonium cation, after opening of the oxirane ring.

Evidence against aryl migration is the experimental fact that on cleavage of the oxirane ring by acids, the hydroxyl group is found in every case attached to the α-carbon atom [89].

House [170] and others [106] used unsubstituted chalcone epoxide label-led with ^{14}C in the α-position to prove aroyl migration unequivocally. The [α-^{14}C]-formyldeoxybenzoin derivatives were prepared by means of Lewis acids from [β-^{14}C]-4'-methoxy-, -4,4'-dimethoxy- and -2',4'-dimethoxy-chalcone epoxides by Grisebach and Barz [171]; these reactions also afforded evidence for the migration of the aroyl group. The deoxybenzoins were identified after deformylation as the 2,4-dinitrophenylhydrazones. It was found that the formyldeoxybenzoin made from 2',4'-dimethoxychalcone epoxide failed to undergo deformylation even under rather vigorous condi-tions. Chopin and Piccardi [86] treated 2',4'-dibenzyloxy-4-methoxy-[β-^{14}C]-chalcone epoxide with boron trifluoride etherate followed by de-benzylation with hydrochloric acid in acetic acid to obtain directly 7-hydroxy-4'-methoxy-[3-^{14}C]-isoflavone.

$R = R' = CH_2C_6H_5$

Considering the fact of aroyl migration, House [172] suggested the follow-ing possibilities to explain the formation of formyldeoxybenzoin, the final product of the reaction is shown on p. 346.

Route 1 can at once be excluded, as it has been shown [172] that unsatu-rated esters do not give formyldeoxybenzoins under similar conditions. Decision between routes 2 and 3 may also elucidate whether the reaction is an intramolecular or intermolecular process. By the parallel conversions of unsubstituted chalcone epoxide and p,p'-disubstituted chalcone epoxides, House [172] has proved unambiguously that the rearrangement is an intramolecular reaction. He has also shown that using an equivalent amount of the reagent (boron trifluoride etherate), reaction route 4 is also operative, and a fluorohydrin is formed, from which the formyldeoxybenzoin is obtainable.

$$Ar-\overset{\overset{O}{\|}}{C}-\overset{H}{\underset{\underset{O}{H}}{C}}-Ar' \longrightarrow Ar-\overset{\overset{O}{\|}}{C}-O-\overset{H}{\underset{\underset{H}{\|}}{C}}=\overset{Ar'}{C} \quad \textbf{1}$$

$$Ar-\overset{\overset{O}{\|}}{C}{}^{\oplus} + \overset{CH=CH-Ar'}{\underset{OH}{}} \longrightarrow Ar-\overset{\overset{O}{\|}}{C}-CH-Ar' \quad \underset{CHO}{}$$

$$\textbf{2}$$

$$Ar-\overset{\overset{O}{\|}}{C}-\overset{H}{\underset{\underset{H}{\overset{\oplus}{O}}}{C}}-Ar'$$

$$\overset{Ar}{\underset{\underset{OH}{CH-CH-Ar'}}{\overset{O}{C}}} \quad \textbf{3}$$

$$Ar-\overset{\overset{O}{\|}}{C}-\overset{H}{\underset{\underset{OH}{H}}{C}}-\overset{X}{\underset{H}{C}}-Ar' \longrightarrow \overset{Ar\quad O}{\underset{\underset{OH\quad X}{CH-C-Ar'}}{C}}\overset{H}{}$$

$$\textbf{4}$$

Kinetic measurements have shown [126] that the rate of conversion of *p*-substituted chalcone epoxides to formyldeoxybenzoins depends on the Hammett σ value of the substituent. An electron-releasing substituent ($\sigma < 0$) increases the rate of isomerization, which is in agreement with the studies made with 2'-benzyloxy-4-R-chalcone epoxides [90], and the reaction yields formyldeoxybenzoin or isoflavone derivatives. If the substituent is electron-attracting ($\sigma \geq$), the rate of isomerization is lower and the 2'-benzyloxy-4-R-chalcone epoxides do not give isoflavones, but only 3-hydroxyflavanones [90].

The kinetic studies [126] also revealed that in the reaction of the epoxides with boron trifluoride etherate, the decomposition of the primary boron complex is followed by a slow rate-determining process:

$$\underset{H}{\overset{H}{\underset{\|}{C}}}\overset{O}{\underset{C}{}} + (C_2H_5)_2\overset{(+)}{O}-BF_3^{(-)} \underset{Rapid}{\rightleftharpoons} \overset{H}{\underset{C}{C}}\overset{(+)}{O}-BF_3^{(-)} \underset{Slow}{\rightleftharpoons} \overset{H}{\underset{\overset{\oplus}{C}}{C}}-OBF_3^{\ominus}$$

The two-directional reactions of 2'-benzyloxy-4-R-chalcone epoxides with Lewis acids indicate that the course of the conversion and thus the reaction

mechanism is determined by the stability of the complex formed. If the
complex is stable, the oxirane ring is opened simultaneously with the nucleophilic attack by the C-2′ ethereal oxygen, and the product is 3-hydroxy-
flavanone.

In the opposite case, when the conversion of the complex with opening of the
oxirane ring is a rapid process, the intramolecular aroyl migration takes
place through an intermediary product, and this is followed by debenzylation
and the formation of isoflavone [66]. Since the aroyl migration also occurs
in the chlorohydrins, the intermediary products can be the corresponding
fluorohydrins.

However, the formation of fluorohydrin could not be detected during the reaction, probably it reacts directly with the excess of boron trifluoride etherate to give the isoflavone derivative [172].

The experiments have also shown that the reaction route is governed by the nucleophilicity of the C-2′ ethereal oxygen atom. If the ($\sigma < 0$) effect of the substituents in ring A increases the nucleophilic character of this atom, the opening of the oxirane ring is accompanied by simultaneous cyclization to 3-hydroxyflavanone. In the opposite case the oxirane ring is cleaved and the end-product of the rearrangement reaction is an isoflavone derivative [92].

Elucidation of the isomerization reactions of chalcone epoxides leading to isoflavones has also importance from the point of view of flavonoid biogenesis. As the acid-catalyzed rearrangement takes place with aroyl migration in contrast with aryl migration occurring in the biogenetic process, it follows that the formation of isoflavones from chalcones in the plant does not involve the chalcone epoxide intermediate, or if it does, the reaction route must be different.

4. STRUCTURE STUDY OF CHALCONE EPOXIDES

The direction of the conversions with acid reagents of 2′-substituted chalcone epoxides is decisively influenced by the electron structure of the molecule, particularly of the oxirane ring. The various substituent effects and the electron distribution in the molecule may be studied by spectroscopic methods [173–175] and by quantum chemical calculations [176, 177].

Lutz and Weiss [178] have stated that the oxidation by alkaline hydrogen peroxide of both *cis*- and *trans*-chalcones gives stable *trans*-chalcone epoxides. The *cis* isomer is the unstable form, which was first prepared by Wasserman and Aubrey [179] from 1,3-diarylpropyne(2)-1-one.

$$\longrightarrow \quad Ar-\overset{\overset{\displaystyle O}{\|}}{C}-\overset{\overset{\displaystyle H}{|}}{C}\underset{\underset{\displaystyle O}{\diagdown\diagup}}{\quad}\overset{\overset{\displaystyle H}{|}}{C}-Ar'$$

According to IR and NMR evidence, the epoxides made by alkaline oxidation are all *trans* isomers [89, 90], therefore the spectroscopic work has been restricted to these stable compounds. The aim of the investigation was to study the following problems:

(*a*) the formation and stability of the conformers;

(*b*) the interaction of the oxirane ring and the carbonyl group;

(*c*) interactions through conjugation between the oxirane ring and the aromatic system.

A. Spectroscopic Studies

Cromwell [142] used spectroscopic methods to prove the existence of hyperconjugational interaction between the oxirane ring and the α-carbonyl group. The binding electrons of the epoxide ring may interact with the π electrons, enhancing the polarization of the carbonyl group. The electron structure of the oxirane ring as pictured by Cromwell [142] is illustrated in Fig. 3.

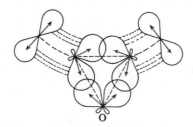

Fig. 3. Structure of the oxirane ring

It has been shown [180] that a steric prerequisite of ensuing conjugation is that the orientation of the bonds be perpendicular to the plane of the three-membered ring, i.e. the axes of the p_π orbitals of the interacting groups must be parallel to, and in nearly symmetric arrangement with the "bent bond" binding electrons (Fig. 3).

Cromwell and Graff [180] characterized hyperconjugation by the following resonance structures:

Several authors have reported the infrared spectroscopic investigation of chalcone epoxides [142, 181]. These studies dealt mainly with the carbonyl stretching vibration; the influence of the steric effect of the 2'-OR group on the conjugation and on the appearance of the characteristic bands of the oxirane ring was not examined.

According to the IR spectra, the ν_{CO} values of 2'-OR-chalcones plotted against the σ^* values of the 4-R substituents give a linearly increasing connection, when recorded either in the solid state (KBr) or in solution (CCl$_4$) (Figs 4, 5).

These correlations show that the oxirane ring is in conjugation with both the carbonyl group and the aromatic ring, and a substituent in ring B may modify the electron distribution, and therefore the reactivity, of the epoxide molecule.

As recently shown by Sohár and Sipos [182], a similar linear relationship exists between the wave number values of the carbonyl stretching vibration in 4'-substituted chalcone epoxides and the electron affinity of the substituent. In the presence of a 4'-R-substituent, a connection is expected between the electronegativity of the substituent and the ν_{CO} or $\nu_{Ar-C(O)}$ values, since this part of the molecule has the same structure as in the corresponding acetophenone or chalcone, where such relationships have been detected repeatedly [183–186].

As shown by measurement, the $\nu_{Ar-C(O)}$ value of 4-R-chalcone epoxides in the range 1200–1300 cm^{-1} is not affected by the electronegativity of the substituent.

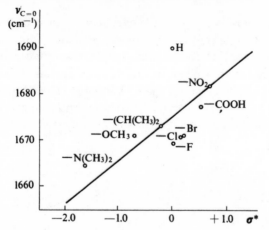

Fig. 4. Dependence of ν_{CO} as a function of σ^* in 2′-benzyloxy-4-R-chalcone epoxides (KBr)

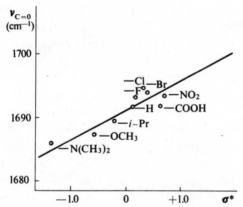

Fig. 5. Dependence of ν_{CO} as a function of σ^* in 2′-benzyloxy-4-R-chalcone epoxides (in CCl_4)

The ν_{CO} *vs.* σ^* values obtained in solids did not give a linear relationship. This is in agreement with the results of Cromwell *et al.* [142, 181] showing that in the solid state *trans*-4-R-chalcone epoxides exist in the non-conjugated *gauche* form.

According to Soviet authors [187], the dipole moments of *p*- and *p′*-substituted chalcones also indicate the *gauche* conformer to be the stable form.

When the spectra are recorded in solution, a double carbonyl band can be assigned, which is indicative of an equilibrium of conformers [142, 181].

The more intense band with the higher frequency must be due to the *gauche* rotational isomer, while the band of lower frequency can be assigned to the *cisoid* form. The latter is the conjugated form. When the wave number values of higher frequency appearing in the double carbonyl bands in carbon tetrachloride are plotted against the σ^* values of the 4-R group — as it was done in the case of the KBr spectra — no characteristic distribution is obtained. This indicates the existence of the non-conjugated *gauche* form.

gauche   *cisoid*

According to the experiments — and at variance with the statements of Cromwell *et al.* [181] — the dependence on the substituent of the ν_{CO} band assigned to the conjugated *cisoid* form with lower frequency cannot be given unequivocally, since the bands often appear as "shoulders", thus their exact positions cannot always be determined. A different result is obtained (Figs 4 and 5), if a bulky 2'-OR substituent is present. The ν_{CO} values as a function of the σ^* of the 4-R-substituents in ring B revealed a linear relationship in the spectra taken both in the solid form and in solution, and only one band can be assigned to carbonyl. The experimental facts can be explained by supposing that, owing to the steric effect of the 2'-OR group, these compounds exist in the *cisoid* conformation in the solid state also. Because of the same steric effects, only one of the conformers, the conjugated one, is present in solution; no equilibrium of the conformers is attained.

In the case of 2',6'-disubstituted chalcone epoxides, also only one carbonyl band can be observed. It is surprising, however, that the carbonyl frequency of 2'-benzyloxy-6'-methoxychalcone epoxide is found at 1714 cm^{-1}. This is indicative of the formation of the non-conjugated *gauche* form. Since the corresponding 2'-benzyloxy-6'-methoxychalcone does exist also in the conjugated form (ν_{CO} 1662), it appears that steric effects suspend coplanarity in these epoxides, this being signalled by a considerable increase of the carbonyl stretching frequencies.

The interaction between the oxirane ring and the aromatic system can also be studied by examining the oxirane bands of chalcone epoxides. The epoxide bands can be assigned in the regions 1200–1300 cm^{-1} and 800–910 cm^{-1}, which are assumed to correspond to the symmetric ($\nu_{s(ring)}$) and asymmetric ($\nu_{as(ring)}$) stretching vibrations, respectively, of the oxirane ring [188].

The following band regions are characteristic of *trans* chalcone epoxides:

I[cm^{-1}]	II[cm^{-1}]	III[cm^{-1}]	IV[cm^{-1}]	V[cm^{-1}]
1400 ± 10	1230 ± 20	890 ± 15	790 ± 15	590 ± 20

On the basis of analogies, bands II and III are the symmetric and asymmetric vibrations, respectively, of the oxirane ring. Band I is probably a coupled vibration, whereas bands IV and V can be assigned to the deformation vibration of the oxirane ring [188]. It has been found that the 4-R-substituents of ring B characteristically influence the appearance of bands II

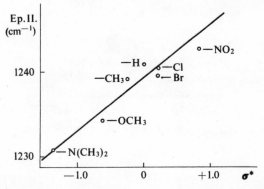

Fig. 6. Dependence of $\nu_{s(ring)II}$ as a function of σ^* in 4-R-chalcone epoxides (in CCl$_4$)

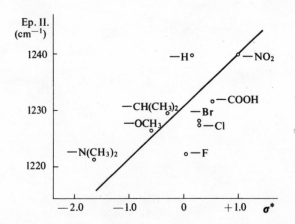

Fig. 7. Dependence of $\nu_{s(ring)II}$ as a function of σ^* in 2′-benzyloxy-4-R-chalcone epoxides (in CCl$_4$).

and III. No such effect is observed in the case of the other bands. Similarly, the presence of a 4'-R substituent in ring A is of no consequence.

The wave number values of band II of 4-R- and 2'-benzyloxy-4-R-chalcone epoxides plotted against σ^* of the R substituent show a linearly increasing relation (Figs 6 and 7).

Similar relations are obtained for the $\nu_{as(ring)III}$ bands (Figs 8 and 9), but the relation has a linearly decreasing trend.

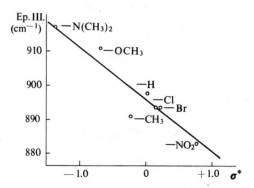

Fig. 8. Dependence of $\nu_{as(ring)III}$ as a function of σ^* in-4-R-chalcone epoxides (in CCl_4)

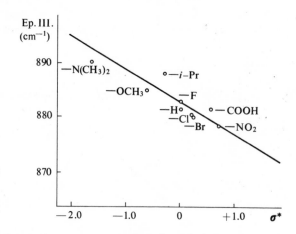

Fig. 9. Dependence of $\nu_{as(ring)III}$ as a function of σ^* in 2'-benzyloxy-4-R-chalcone epoxides (in CCl_4)

The $\nu_{s(ring)II}$ and $\nu_{as(ring)III}$ vibrations of the oxirane ring according to Tobin [188] are shown in Fig. 10.

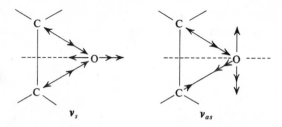

Fig. 10. The $\nu_{s(ring)II}$ and $\nu_{as(ring)III}$ vibrations of the oxirane ring

In interpreting the relations of opposite trend, one must take into account the "bent bond" character of the linkages in the oxirane ring [142, 180] and the fact that quantum chemical calculations show maximum electron density in the outer sphere of the ring, and minimum electron density inside the ring [189–191].

It may be assumed that with increasing electron-attracting character of the substituent in ring B, the electron density about the oxygen atom is reduced, the lone electron pairs are drawn inside the ring and, exerting some binding character, they stabilize the ring. As a consequence of the higher electron density, the forces inhibiting the essentially "breathing" $\nu_{s(ring)II}$ vibration become stronger, thus the frequency of the vibration is increased (Figs 6, 7). On the other hand, for $\nu_{as(ring)III}$ the force inhibiting the vibration is reduced since the electron density along the direction of the movement of the oxygen atom is decreased, thus the frequency of the vibration becomes lower (Figs 8, 9). The correctness of these assumptions have been substantiated by quantum chemical calculations [176, 177].

The results of IR spectroscopy are in agreement with recently published NMR and mass spectrometric data [182, 192, 193].

B. Quantum Chemical Calculations

The spectroscopic studies have afforded information about the conformation of 2'-OR-chalcone epoxides and about the conjugational relationship between the oxirane ring system and the carbonyl group [173–175]. As shown by synthetic work, the direction of the reactions of 2'-OR-chalcone epoxides is decided by the electron distribution determined by the 4-R substituent. These statements have been confirmed by the determination of the quantum chemical parameters [176, 177] of chalcone epoxides with different Hammett σ_p values ($\sigma = 0$; -0.27; 0.78).

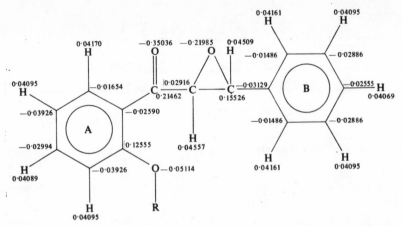

Fig. 11. Net $(\sigma + \pi)$ charge distribution of 2'-benzyloxychalcone epoxide (in -e units)

Figure 11 shows the total $(\sigma + \pi)$ net charge distribution of 2'-benzyloxy-chalcone epoxide calculated by the method of Del Re *et al.* [194–196] and by the ω-SCF LCAC MO method [197–199].

According to the calculated values, the oxygen atom of the oxirane ring has a higher negative charge (-0.21985) than the 2'-C ethereal oxygen (0.05114). It means that with acid reagents the protonation of the epoxide oxygen is more likely, and further reaction takes place only when this protonation has been accomplished. The charge densities on the α- and β-carbon atoms of the oxirane ring are extremely different (0.02916 and 0.15526, respectively). These data are in agreement with the experimental facts which showed that the opening with hydrochloric acid of the oxirane ring of chalcone epoxides gives solely the α-hydroxy-β-chloro derivatives (chlorohydrins) [122, 123]. According to charge density calculations it is evident that the chloride anion attacks the β-carbon atom.

The characteristic quantum chemical indices listed in Table I $(f_i; \pi_{ii}; SS_i; FE_i^{HOMO}; FE_i^{LEMO})$ indicate that the α-carbon atom is favoured in the case of electrophilic, whereas the β-carbon for nucleophilic attack. This is in agreement with the empirical facts. Chalcone epoxides do not give benzal-coumaranones (aurones) by direct cyclization, since nucleophilic attack can only occur on the β-carbon atom.

4-R-substituents in ring B characteristically influence, according to their character, the charge distribution $(\sum^{\sigma+\pi} Q_i)$ and quantum chemical indice of the atoms of the oxirane ring (Table I). It is found that the carbon atoms

CHALCONE EPOXIDES IN FLAVONOID CHEMISTRY

Table I

Calculated Quantum Chemical Indices of 2'-Benzyloxychalcone Epoxides

R	H			OCH₃			NO₂		
	α	β	γ	α	β	γ	α	β	γ
$\sum\limits^{\sigma+\pi} Q_i$	0.02916	0.15526	0.21985	0.00559	0.14716	0.21956	0.04762	0.16030	0.21905
f_i	0.53322	0.41175	0.93664	0.54191	0.40368	0.93585	0.53022	0.41283	0.93329
πi_i	0.63188	0.53093	0.00695	0.63660	0.52167	0.00721	0.64214	0.53179	0.00744
$SS_i[\beta_0^{-1}]$	1.52488	1.00294	1.29389	1.67489	0.98991	1.31125	1.45658	1.00566	1.28294
FE_i^{HOMO}	0.73979	0.40288	0.37259	0.74440	0.32378	0.32766	0.72070	0.41728	0.37806
FE_i^{LEMO}	0.54729	0.65814	0.00061	0.52134	0.66931	0.00105	0.55864	0.58646	0.00008

$\sum\limits^{\sigma+\pi} Q_i$ — total net charge

f_i — free valence index

πi_i — atomic autopolarizability

SS_i — superdelocalizability

FE_i^{HOMO} — frontal electron density on the highest occupied molecular orbital

FE_i^{LEMO} — frontal electron density on the lowest empty molecular orbital of the epoxide ring are most negative if a 4-methoxy substituent is present; with a 4-nitro substitution the charge density is decreased. These data also show quantitatively that the oxirane ring is in conjugational interaction with the aromatic ring B. At the same time the data support the infrared spectroscopic results (Figs 6–9), according to which the tendency of the $\nu_{s(ring)II}$ and $\nu_{as(ring)III}$ bands is determined by the charge density on the oxygen atom in the oxirane ring. Calculations indicate that increasing electron-attraction results in lower electron density about the oxygen atom, and this is accompanied by a characteristic change of the bands of the oxirane ring.

As seen from Table I, the Hammett σ value of the 4-R-substituent also affects the charge density $(\sum^{\sigma+\pi} Q_i)$ of the β-carbon atom of the oxirane ring. When the $OCH_3 \rightarrow NO_2$ substituent exchange is made, the charge density on the β-carbon atom drops from 0.14716 to 0.16030, resulting in increased proneness to nucleophilic attack. The same inference can be drawn from the other reactivity indices (Table I), which substantiate the different mechanisms of the reactions with acids of 2'-benzyloxy-4-R-chalcone epoxides, mentioned earlier. It has been supposed [89, 90] that the course of the reaction and the end-products are decided by the charge density on the β-carbon atom, as it conclusively affects the possibility of internal nucleophilic attack by the 2'-C ethereal oxygen. A higher charge density on the β-carbon atom $(\sigma < 0)$ inhibits nucleophilic attack, whereas decreasing charge density $(\sigma > 0)$ will favour the same; subsequent cyclization can give the 3-hydroxyflavanone derivative. Calculations have confirmed the correctness of these assumptions, and have also shown that quantum chemical computations can be successfully applied to such investigations of flavonoid chemistry.

The work done on chalcone epoxides has both theoretical and practical significance. The epoxides are starting materials in the synthesis of the members of many classes of the flavonoid compounds.

By proper choice of the reagent and of the substituents in the epoxide molecule, the different flavonoid derivatives can, in most cases, be prepared in satisfactory yields.

Similarly, many conversions of the reactive oxirane ring are also possible, thus, e.g., heterocyclic derivatives can be synthesized.

Another important field is the investigation of the little studied chalcone aziridines, the analogues of the epoxides. A comparison of the chemical properties of 2'-OR-chalcone aziridines ($R = CH_2C_6H_5$; CH_2OCH_3) with the epoxides [200–202] reveals differences in their reactions, yet aziridines are also suitable starting materials for the synthesis of the cyclic 3-amino-flavanones.

III. OTHER EPOXIDES IN FLAVONOID CHEMISTRY

1. FLAVENE EPOXIDES

Interest is attached to flav-3-ene epoxides because of their significance in the synthesis of flavan-3,4-diols and other derivatives [203, 204]. *Cis*-flav-3-ene epoxide was postulated as an intermediate in the synthesis of 2,3-*cis*-3,4-

trans-flavan-3,4-diol from 2′-hydroxychalcone dibromide. It is supposed that the chalcone dibromide is cyclized to *trans*-3-bromoflavanone; this is reduced to *trans-trans*-3-bromoflavan-4-ol, which gives the flavan-3,4-diol derivative with acetic anhydride and potassium acetate through an intermediary *cis*-epoxide.

Cis-flav-3-ene epoxide was successfully isolated by Vickars [205].

2,3-*Trans*-3,4-*cis*-flav-3-ene epoxide was made by Bolger *et al.* [203], by treatment of 2,3-*cis*-3,4-*trans*-4-acetoxy-3-bromoflavan with methanolic potassium hydroxide.

The oxidation of flav-3-ene with peracetic acid [206] or hydrogen peroxide in the presence of potassium hydrogen carbonate in benzonitrile also gives 2,3-*trans*-3,4-*cis*-flav-3-ene epoxide [207]. The success of this latter oxidation depends to a large extent on the nature of the substituents in ring A.

2. AURONE EPOXIDES

The synthesis and conversions of aurone epoxides were studied in detail by Wheeler and his group [208–211]. It was found that depending on the reaction conditions and the substituents, the products are 3-hydroxyflavones, 2-aroylcoumaranones or 4-hydroxy-3-phenylcoumarines.

Since 3-hydroxyflavone is obtainable from aurone epoxides, it indicates that this compound can be formed from aurone dibromide with alkali through the epoxide as intermediate.

3. FLAVINDOGENIDE EPOXIDES

In recent years several publications have dealt with the synthesis [212, 213] and possible conversions [214–216] of 3-arylideneflavanone epoxides. On treatment with Lewis acids they give benzoxepine-3,5-dione; their reduction with lithium aluminium hydride and subsequent dehydration affords naturally occurring haematoxylin derivatives [214].

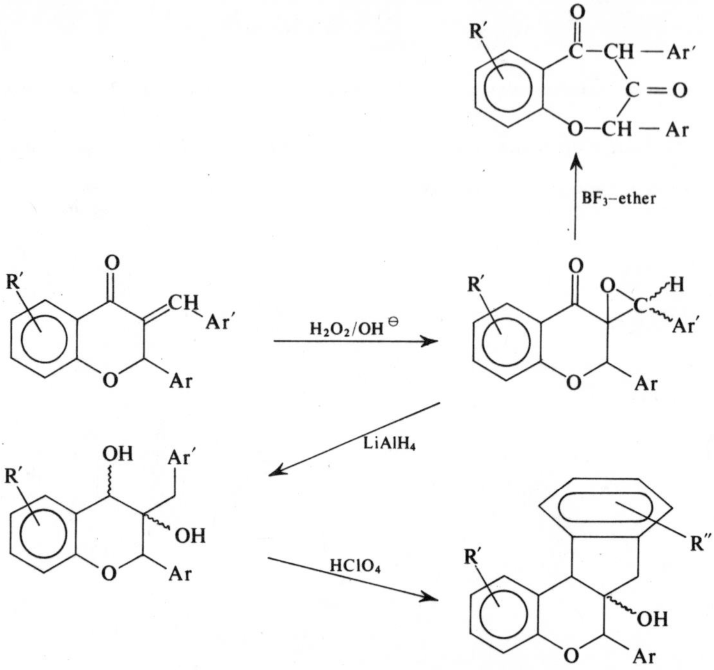

$$R' \quad \overset{O}{\underset{}{\text{C}}}-\text{CH}-\text{Ar}'$$
$$\text{C}=\text{O}$$
$$\text{O}-\text{CH}-\text{Ar}$$

↑ BF$_3$–ether

R′ ... $\overset{O}{=}$ ... CH Ar′ / O Ar $\xrightarrow{\text{H}_2\text{O}_2/\text{OH}^{\ominus}}$ R′ ... O, C–H, Ar′ / O Ar

LiAlH$_4$

R′ ... OH Ar′ / OH / O Ar $\xrightarrow{\text{HClO}_4}$ R′ ... R″ / OH / O Ar

3-Arylidenechromanone epoxides are structurally related to 3-arylidene-flavanone epoxides. Using such compounds, Farkas *et al.* [217] achieved the synthesis of the racemic form of natural eucomol.

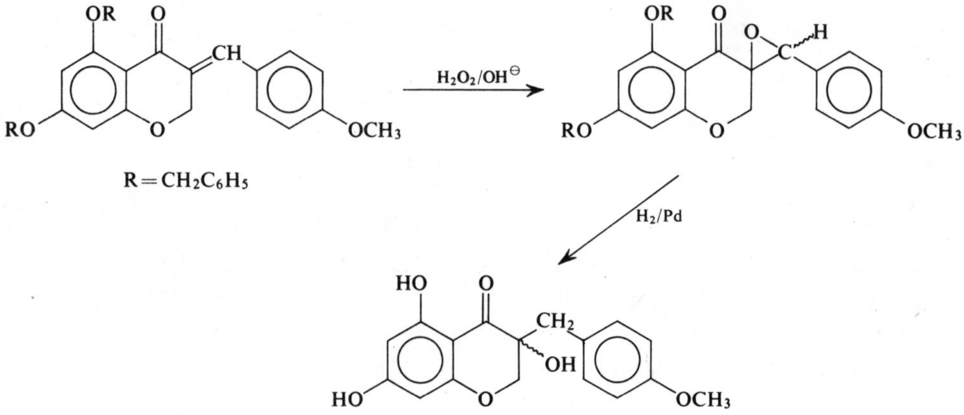

OR O ... CH / RO O OCH$_3$ $\xrightarrow{\text{H}_2\text{O}_2/\text{OH}^{\ominus}}$ OR O O C–H / RO O OCH$_3$

R = CH$_2$C$_6$H$_5$

H$_2$/Pd

HO O CH$_2$ OH / HO O OCH$_3$

IV. THE ALGAR–FLYNN–OYAMADA REACTION

3-Hydroxyflavanones and 3-hydroxyflavones play an important part in flavonoid chemistry. They are very widespread in nature in the form of glycosides, and under laboratory conditions they can be converted to many different derivatives.

Several synthetic procedures are known for the preparation of these two types of compounds; the most important ones are listed below.

1. SYNTHESIS OF 3-HYDROXYFLAVANONES

Oxidation of flavanones or 2'-hydroxychalcones with one of the following reagents
   -- Fenton's reagent [218]
   --- lead tetraacetate [168, 219]
   -- potassium permanganate [220]
   --- alkaline hydrogen peroxide [36, 61, 221]
   -- iodine and silver acetate [222];
treatment of 3-bromoflavanone with silver acetate [223];
reaction of 2'-hydroxy-α-methoxychalcone with acid [168, 224];
treatment of 2'-acetoxychalcone dibromide with
   — silver acetate [38]
   -- acetone and sodium carbonate [38];
from 2'-hydroxychalcone dibromide with alkali [225, 226];
synthesis from o-hydroxyphenacyl halide and aromatic aldehyde in the presence of alkali [37];
reduction of 3-hydroxyflavones with
   — Raney nickel [227]
   —,zinc and hydrochloric acid
   — sodium hydrogen sulfite and sodium carbonate [228];
treatment of 2'-OR-chalcone epoxide with acid [57, 90];
reaction of 2',α-dihydroxy-β-methoxydihydrochalcone with acid [95, 96];
from 3-aminoflavanone with acid [229].

2. SYNTHESIS OF 3-HYDROXYFLAVONES

Reaction of isonitrosoflavanone with acid [230];
from aurones with
   alcoholic potassium hydroxide [231]
   hydrogen cyanide [37];

treatment of ω-methoxyacetophenone with acid anhydride [232];
dehydrogenation of 3-hydroxyflavanone by means of

- Pd/C and cinnamic acid [233, 234]
- alkaline hydrogen peroxide [62, 233]
- air in alkaline solution [235, 236]
- air in acid medium [228]
- potassium carbonate [227]
- bismuth acetate [237]
- iodine, potassium acetate and acid [131]
- N-bromosuccinimide [238, 239]
- dimethyl sulfate and potassium carbonate [240]
- sodium sulfite and alkali [241, 242]
- magnesium bisulfite or calcium bisulfite [243, 244];

reaction of o-hydroxydibenzoylmethane with formic acid [42];
conversion of flavindogenides with alkaline hydrogen peroxide [36].

Only a few of the methods listed find use in the practical synthesis of 3-hydroxyflavanones or 3-hydroxyflavones. The usual method of preparation for these two types of compound is the oxidation with alkaline hydrogen peroxide of the appropriate 2'-hydroxychalcone or flavanone derivative, reported in 1934 by Algar and Flynn [36] and, independently, by Oyamada [61]. This important reaction has found widespread application and is known in the literature as the Algar–Flynn–Oyamada (AFO) reaction [245].

The reaction product obtained in the experiments of these authors was the 3-hydroxyflavone. Murakami and Iris [62], and later Reichel and Stendel [221] isolated 3-hydroxyflavanone, the intermediate of the reaction, and showed that 3-hydroxyflavone was formed from this by further oxidation.

The AFO reaction also proved suitable for the synthesis of 3-hydroxy-flavone glycosides from chalcone glycosides [221, 246–248].

Several authors [249–251] reported the condensation of *o*-hydroxyace-tophenones with an aromatic aldehyde in the presence of alkaline hydrogen peroxide or sodium peroxide [249]; this modified AFO reaction takes place without the isolation of the intermediates.

In 1948 Geissman and Fukushima [35] attempted the total synthesis of natural kaempferol by the alkaline oxidation of 2'-hydroxy-4'4,6'-trime-thoxychalcone; instead of the expected product, however, 4,4',6-trime-thoxybenzalcoumaran-3-one (an aurone) was obtained.

H₃CO ... O ... H₃CO ... OH ... OCH₃

H₂O₂/OH⁻

H₃CO ... O ... OH ... H₃CO ... O ... OCH₃ ... H₃CO ... O ... C=CH ... OCH₃ ... H₃CO ... O

The fact that the AFO reaction may also afford an aurone derivative was often ignored initially; this gave rise to conflicting publications about the structures of the oxidized products [252–254].

Systematic investigations showed later that aurones are formed only from chalcones which contain a 6'-methyl or 6'-methoxy substituent [255]. However, if a 4-hydroxyl group is also present in the chalcone molecule, only 3-hydroxyflavanone or 3-hydroxyflavone is obtained instead of the aurone derivative [236, 255–259]. Similarly, the 3-hydroxyflavone is the oxidation product from 2',4-dihydroxy-6'-carbethoxymethoxychalcone [260].

Venturella and Bellino [261] reported that not only the 4-hydroxyl, but also the 2-hydroxyl group is responsible for the course of the reaction. On the other hand, a 6'-substituted chalcone containing a C-2- or C-4-methoxyl group also gave, under the conditions of the AFO reaction, the corresponding 3-hydroxyflavanone and 3-hydroxyflavone derivatives [259, 261] apart from the main product aurone.

Later it was found that 6'-substituted-2,3- or -3,4-dihalogenchalcones also afford aurone and 3-hydroxyflavone derivatives [262, 263], whereas 2-, 3- or 4-nitro-6'-methoxychalcones fail to undergo oxidation [263].

Recently Dean *et al.* [264] have shown that under the circumstances of the AFO reaction of 2'-hydroxy-2-nitrochalcones, hydrogen peroxide does not take part in the process, but the base effects the cyclization of the starting material, through the flavanone carbanion, to the corresponding 10-hydroxy-2-methyl-11H-[1]-benzopyrano[3, 2b]-indole-11-one.

Similar derivatives are obtained from 6′-methoxy-2-nitrochalcones [264]. On the other hand, 2′,6′-dihydroxy-3′- or -5′-nitrochalcones yield aurones [265].

If no C-6′-substituent is present, chalcones containing nitro [265–267], acetamido [268, 269], dimethylamino [266], sulfonyl [270], sulfonamido [75], carboxyl [47, 271], *p*-phenyl [272], benzoyl group [273] or halogen atom [274–278] in ring A or B, as well as chalcone analogues with heterocyclic or condensed ring [279–283], and the vinylogues of chalcones [67], all afford the corresponding 3-hydroxyflavone as a result of the AFO reaction.

Farkas *et al.* [285] used polyhydroxychalcones with protected hydroxyl groups except for the C-2′-OH; thus oxidation with 5–30% hydrogen peroxide in the presence of 10–20% sodium hydroxide or sodium peroxide gave the 3-hydroxyflavones in the best yields (20–40%).

The course of the AFO oxidation is not unambiguous in 2-methoxy- or 2,6-dimethoxychalcones, since the aurone derivatives are also formed [284]. However, 2,6-dimethyl- or -dihydroxychalcones give the corresponding 3-hydroxyflavones [2, 67].

In the course of further studies, Wheeler *et al.* [286–288] found that the oxidation of 3′-methoxychalcones afforded, in addition to the 3-hydroxy-flavone, 2-benzyl-2-hydroxycoumaran-3-one ("hydrated aurone") as a result of a secondary reaction, and the main product was 2-arylbenzofuran-3--carboxylic acid.

To explain the formation of the latter products, the following possibilities were considered [288].

In the course of the AFO oxidation of 2-hydroxyfurfurylideneacetophenones, A. Rao and N. Rao [289] observed the formation of coumaran-3-ones or 2-(2-furyl)-3-hydroxychromones, depending on the substituent.

Adams [71] oxidized 2',4-dihydroxychalcone; the product, besides the 3-hydroxyflavone, was 2-(4-hydroxyphenyl)benzofuran-3-carboxylic acid in 32% yield. If ring B carries alkyl groups, the reaction is specific and the 3-hydroxyflavone is obtained as the sole product.

The AFO reaction is not limited to 2'-hydroxychalcone derivatives: it also occurs with the isomeric flavanones [61, 62, 221, 290, 291]. Yet, these reactions fail to take place if a C-2' or C-5 hydroxyl group is present [284]; notwithstandingly, recently Chopin and Dellamonica [344] obtained an aurone by the alkaline hydrogen peroxide oxidation of 5-hydroxy-3',4'-dimethoxy-7-neohesperidosylflavanone.

3. THE EARLY CONCEPT OF THE AFO REACTION

The sometimes controversial experimental facts resulting from the AFO reactions required an explanation; several concepts were put forward to interpret the results.

Algar and Flynn [36] supposed that the intermediate of the reaction was the corresponding chalcone epoxide or peroxide. This assumption was adopted by Geissman and Fukushima [35], and they also explained the aurone formation.

According to this concept, in chalcone epoxides containing a C-6' substituent, steric effects would induce the phenolate anion to attack on the α-instead of the β-carbon atom; the intermediary product would thus be a 2-hydroxy-2-benzylcoumaran-3-one derivative, which could give aurone by the elimination of water.

This hypothesis was accepted by most researchers, although proving the existence of the chalcone epoxide intermediate remained unsuccessful.

In the previous chapters we dealt in detail with the synthesis and conversion of 2'-OR-chalcone epoxides. Such epoxides can be prepared under the conditions of the AFO reaction and, owing to the presence of the 2'-protective group, they are stable compounds. On removal of the blocking group, the flavonoid derivatives which are the products of the AFO reaction can also be obtained. However, these further reactions were effected under conditions other than those of the AFO reaction, therefore all this afforded only indirect evidence for the possible intermediate role of chalcone epoxides.

In 1942 Reichel and Stendel [221] interpreted the mechanism of the AFO reaction by assuming that the chalcone gives a mesomeric anion when acted upon by the alkali; on this a hydroperoxide anion is added. Intramolecular cationotropic hydroxyl migration and the addition of a proton gives rise to a glycol derivative; subsequent elimination of a hydroxide ion then affords 3-hydroxyflavanone. In the presence of a suitable acceptor (H_2O_2 or O_2), the hydrogen anion with its electron pair is detached from the C-2 atom, followed by proton elimination from C-3; the final result is thus 3-hydroxyflavone.

Reichel's concept excluded the intermediary formation of a chalcone epoxide, but failed to explain how aurones are produced.

24*

In 1965 Dean and Podimuang [67] also rejected that chalcone epoxides
are intermediates, since they found that the internal deactivating effect of
the phenolate anion produced in alkaline medium from hydroxychalcones
hinders the attack of the peroxide anion, thus no chalcone epoxide can be
formed.

It was shown that 4'-or 4- and 2-hydroxychalcones do not give an epoxide
with alkaline hydrogen peroxide, but the molecule suffers decomposition by
slow oxidation. At the same time 2',2-dihydroxychalcone is readily oxidized
to 2',3-dihydroxyflavanone; the deactiviting effect of the phenolate anion
does not prevail.

It was considered further evidence that in the oxidation of 2'-hydroxy-2,5',
6-trimethylchalcone, if the intermediate were the epoxide, the steric effect
of the C-2 and C-6 substituents would compel the phenolate anion to attack,
rather, the α-carbon atom, thus the product should be an aurone. In reality,
however, only the 3-hydroxyflavone derivative was obtained.

Similarly, only flavonols were the products of the oxidation of 2'-4-dihydroxy-3,5-di-*t*-butylchalcones [71]. On the other hand, the oxidation of 3,5-di-*t*-butylchalcone did not give the epoxide either, but the compound was oxidized to 3,5-di-*t*-butyl-4-hydroxybenzoic acid. Therefore, it was suggested [67] that oxidation in the course of the AFO reaction is either preceded by cyclization (I), or both reactions occur simultaneously (II) to yield the endproduct 3-hydroxyflavanone.

(I)

(II)

This concept comprises the 2'-hydroxychalcone ⇌ flavanone isomerization, and the simultaneous nucleophilic attack by the peroxide anion.

Dean and Podimuang [67] found that the oxidation of 2',6'-dimethoxy-4'-hydroxychalcone, in contrast with the case of 4'-hydroxychalcone, gave the epoxide; this indicated that in C-6'-substituted derivatives — for steric reasons —, the phenolate anion produced in alkaline medium does not inactivate the carbonyl group, thus attack by the peroxide anion may give rise to the formation of the epoxide.

The formation of aurone was rationalized as follows [67]. "One consideration is that the rotation of the carbonyl group out of the plane of the phenolic ring increases the distance of the phenolic oxygen atom from the β-position more than that from the α-position; another is the steric repulsion between the 6'-substituent and the carbonyl oxygen, which favours the product with the smaller heterocyclic ring."

At the same time it was reported [6] that at higher temperatures when steric effects cease to operate, the oxidation products are only 3-hydroxyflavones, and no aurones are obtained.

An attempt was also made to explain the formation of the 3-hydroxyflavone produced in the oxidation of 2',4-dihydroxy-3,4',6'-trimethoxychalcone. According to Dean [6, 67], this reaction is due to the effect of the 4-phenolate anion.

This argument is controversial, since the inactivating effect of the 4-phenolate anion on the chalcone carbonyl group is left out of consideration. If this is also taken into account, in accordance with the oxidation of 4-hydroxychalcone, then epoxide cannot be formed at all. The assumption is also refuted by the fact that the oxidation of 2',3-dihydroxy-4',6'-dimethylchalcone also gives flavonol, although the effect of the 3-phenolate anion is different from that of the 4-phenolate anion.

It has been proved that the AFO reaction does not occur by free radical mechanism [67]; this mechanism is involved only in the oxidation of 4-hydroxychalcones to aurones. Oxidation by free radical mechanism results in aurones even from such chalcones which always yield the 3-hydroxyflavone under the conditions of the AFO reaction [67, 98, 99, 101, 103].

4. STRUCTURE INVESTIGATION
OF 2'-SUBSTITUTED CHALCONES

The literature contains many references to the structure investigation of unsubstituted chalcones, yet little information is available concerning the structure of 2'- or 2',6'-disubstituted chalcones. These two groups of derivatives have several distinctly characteristic chemical properties. The elucidation of their structural problems is at the same time a contribution to the explanation of the AFO reaction mechanism.

Rotational Isomerism of Chalcones

A number of experimental facts provide evidence for the conjugational interaction between the carbonyl group and the double bond, as well as the aromatic ring [184].

In chalcones two geometric isomers, and for each, two conformations (rotamers) favouring conjugation can be conceived. These are shown below with the appropriate relative interatomic distances and van der Waals radii [292–294].

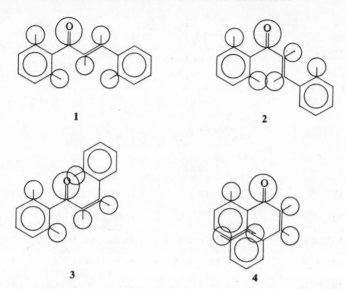

The relative stability of the conformers is determined by factors of steric and rotational hindrance [292, 293]. The 3,4-*cis*-isomers are unstable, although a *trans*-chalcone can be converted to a *cis*-chalcone [295, 296].

There have been several IR spectroscopic studies [293, 297, 298] and dipole moment measurements [293, 294] concerning the rotational isomerism in solution of chalcones substituted in the 4- and 4'-position. It was found that *trans*-chalcones exist in solution in the *trans*-s-*cis* (**1**) and *trans*-s-*trans* (**2**) conformations, while in the solid state the *trans*-s-*cis*- (**1**) conformation is present. This is proved by the IR spectra obtained in solution, which have double carbonyl stretching vibration bands in the region 1630–1700 cm^{-1}; the band with the higher frequency is assigned to structure **1**. At equilibrium conformer **1** is preponderant as this arrangement is favoured by both steric factors and conjugation [293, 297]. This has also been confirmed by X-ray diffraction measurements [299, 300].

In 2'- and 2',6'-substituted chalcones the space requirement of the substituents may influence the conditions of rotational isomerism, since rotation about the aryl–CO bond may give rise here to further conformational isomerism. As shown by Table II and Fig. 12, the structure of the region between 1570 and 1700 cm^{-1} is different if the spectrum is recorded in KBr (or in liquid film) as compared with the spectra in solution [174]. The solution spectra show band splitting, or the appearance of a new "shoulder", except 2'-benzyloxy-6'-methoxychalcone (**10**) and 2'-hydroxy-6'-methoxychalcone (**11**). This reveals that in solution 2'-substituted chalcones may also be

Table II

Characteristic Frequencies of 2′- and 2′,6′-Substituted Chalcones in the
Region 1570–1700 cm^{-1}

Product	R	R_1	KBr (cm^{-1})	CCl$_4$ (cm^{-1})	CHCl$_3$ (cm^{-1})
5	H	H	1642	1583; 1570; 1642; 1619; 1587	1642; 1619; 1585
6	CH$_3$	H	1660; 1647sh	1611; 1580; 1663; 1648sh; 1606; 1584	1657; 1640sh; 1603; 1580
7	CH$_2$OCH$_3$	H	1664; 1650sh	1613; 1582; 1665; 1643sh; 1604; 1578	1660; 1641sh; 1600; 1577
8	COCH$_3$	H	1670; 1639	1609; 1580; 1672; 1640; 1608; 1578	1667; 1642; 1604; 1575
9	CH$_2$C$_6$H$_5$	H	1657	1610; 1590; 1660; 1643sh; 1604; 1576	1655; 1640; 1601; 1575
10	CH$_2$C$_6$H$_5$	OCH$_3$	1662	1631; 1598; 1662; 1630; 1610sh; 1598	1650; 1630sh; 1597
11	OCH$_3$	OH	1640; 1630	1593; 1578; 1640; 1626; 1585	1638; 1623sh; 1580

present as both *trans*-s-*cis* and *trans*-s-*trans* rotational isomers. The band
with higher frequency (1640–1680 cm^{-1}) may be assigned to the vibration
of the *trans*-s-*cis* form, whereas the adsorption of lesser intensity, and often
appearing as a "shoulder" between 1620 and 1650 cm^{-1}, must be due to
the carbonyl stretching vibration of the *trans*-s-*trans* form.

The intense broad band between 1580 and 1620 cm^{-1} can be assigned to
the stretching vibrations of the C=C bond (these vibrations probably
conceal the skeletal vibration bands of the mono- and disubstituted aromatic rings). The sharp band between 1570 and 1585 cm^{-1} is due to the
skeletal vibration of the monosubstituted B-ring [301].

The common occurrence of the rotamers is also proved by the fact that the
ν_{CO} bands assigned to the *trans*-s-*cis* form undergo, in general a smaller
shift than the corresponding bands of the *trans*-s-*trans* form, when the
solvent CCl$_4$ is replaced by CHCl$_3$ [302].

The experience that chalcones which carry a bulky OR substituent in the
2′-position (R = H; CH$_3$; CH$_2$OCH$_3$; CH$_2$C$_6$H$_5$) can exist in solution in both
the s-*cis* and s-*trans* forms, may afford information about the possible
conformations of *trans*-2′-OR-chalcones.

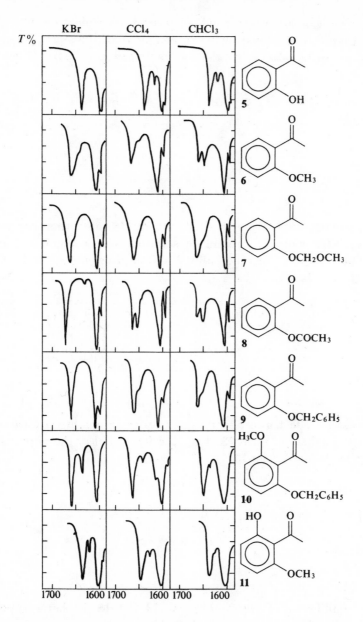

Fig. 12. Spectra of 2′-substituted chalcones in the region 1600–1700 cm⁻¹

Since rotation about the bond connecting the aromatic ring and the carbonyl C-atom is hindered owing to conjugation, the steric position of the 2'-OR group in relation to the carbonyl can be illustrated by formulae **12** and **13**.

If the compounds were to exist in form **12** only, then solely the s-*cis* conformation could be present in solution, and a single ν_{CO} absorption would be observed since the bulky 2'-OR group would sterically hinder the formation of **14**.

This steric effect also operates to a lesser extent in the case of **12**, and it is the smallest in form **13**. Thus the formation of the s-*trans* conformer **15** can be deduced from **13**.

The equilibrium of the conformers (**13** ⇌ **15**) is characterized by the corresponding ν_{CO} absorptions (Fig. 12).

It is known [303–305] that 2'-hydroxychalcone derivatives can form very strong chelates between the hydroxyl and carbonyl groups even in the solid state; this also confirms the existence of **13** and **15**. According to Sabata and Rout [303] the resonance form **16** should also be considered for 2'-substituted chalcones, which constitutes further evidence for the existence of rotamer **13**.

16

Form **16** is stabilized by Coulomb interaction. The experiments provided evidence for such an effect [174]. It was found that the ν_{CO} frequency was also influenced by the character of group R. As shown by Table II, the polarity decrease of ν_{CO} as a function of the character of group R is the following:

$$H < CH_3 < CH_2C_6H_5 < CH_2OCH_3 < COCH_3 .$$

The decrease of the polarity of the carbonyl group, i.e. the frequency, is more pronounced if a less electron-donating substituent is present.

In the case of 2',6'-disubstituted chalcones no essential change in the band structure can be observed within the region of the carbonyl stretching vibration. A band is found at about 1630 cm^{-1} in both the solid state and solution, but this is due to the skeletal stretching vibration of the vicinally trisubstituted aromatic ring [301]. As shown by experience, the formation of rotamers cannot be detected in these disubstituted chalcone derivatives; probably they exist only in the *trans*-s-*cis* conformation (**17**).

17

The appearance of the s-*trans* form is hindered by the steric factors discussed above. The carbonyl stretching vibration frequencies of 2'-6'-disubstituted chalcones show also that conjugation between the carbonyl group and the aromatic ring is not suspended by the introduction of the newer substituent on account of its possible steric effect, in contrast with the case of the corresponding epoxide. Any decrease in coplanarity would cause a marked increase in the carbonyl stretching vibration frequency (about 1690 cm^{-1}) as has been shown by Dinya [185] in the corresponding aceto-phenones. Enebäck [94] demonstrated by UV spectroscopy that in 2'-6'-disubstituted chalcones, steric factors do not effect the coplanarity of the aroyl group. In non-ionized derivatives this is due to hydrogen-chelate formation.

The effect of the substituent was also studied in p- and p'-substituted chalcones by spectroscopic and dipole moment measurements [293, 297, 298, 306, 307]. It was found that the ν_{CO} and Hammett σ_p values of 4-sub-stituted chalcones are in a linear relation [297, 298]. This connection can also be demonstrated by the determination of the pK_{BH^+} values of 2'-benzyloxy-4-R-chalcones [308].

At the same time, the nature of the substituent in the p-position also influences the formation of rotational isomers [298].

Spectroscopic studies afford evidence for the possible structures of 2'- and 2',6'-disubstituted chalcones. It has been established that in the former case there is an equilibrium between the s-cis and s-$trans$ conformers, either in solution or in the solid state, but the 2',6'-disubstituted chalcones exist — owing to steric effects — only in the s-cis conformation.

The facts that the stable form of 2',6'-disubstituted chalcones is the s-cis conformation and that substituents do not suspend the conjugational inter-action between the carbonyl group and aromatic ring, indicate a necessity of confirming or revising Dean's hypothesis [67] of the oxidation reactions of chalcones.

5. OXIDATION STUDIES WITH 2'-HYDROXYCHALCONE
AND FLAVANONE

In the course of a study of the oxidation reactions of 2'-hydroxychalcone and flavanone, Reichel and Stendel [221] found by isolation of the products that the amount of the base is of decisive importance in the AFO reaction. In the presence of 0.001 M alkali and hydrogen peroxide, 2'-hydroxy-chalcone is more rapidly isomerized to flavanone, than oxidized to 3-hy-droxyflavanone. At higher alkali concentrations, however, the conversion to 3-hydroxyflavanone is the quicker process. It was also shown that the direct oxidation of flavanone does not take place; this reaction only occurs with 2'-hydroxychalcone.

It is known [309] that the components of the AFO reaction have character-istic and different UV spectra. This property gave the opportunity to study the oxidation reaction by UV spectrophotometry [64, 310, 311].

A. The Chalcone ⇌ *Flavanone*
Equilibrium in Alkaline Medium

According to measurements made in different pH ranges, at low pH values oxidation does not occur at all, but, as a result of the 2′-hydroxychalcone ⇌ flavanone isomerization, an equilibrium characteristic of the given pH value is attained. As shown in Fig. 13, at pH 9.57 2′-hydroxychalcone as well as flavanone gives an equilibrium mixture of identical composition, and hydrogen peroxide does not take part in the reaction.

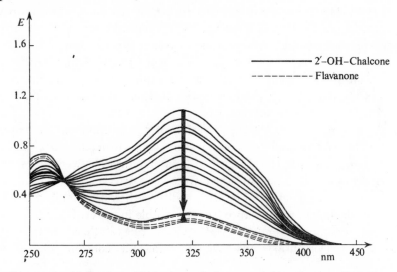

Fig. 13. Isomerization of 2′-hydroxychalcone and flavanone at pH 9.57

The experiments have shown that at various pH values in each case the determining factor and the first phase of the reaction is the 2′-hydroxychalcone ⇌ flavanone isomerization, i.e. the formation of the equilibrium mixture.

Similar results are published by Ferreira *et al.* [101], who found that 2′-hydroxy-α-methoxychalcones or the isomeric flavanones are not oxidized by hydrogen peroxide in the presence of sodium acetate, only the equilibrium is shifted favouring chalcone formation.

The composition of the equilibrium mixture has been determined at different pH values by several researchers [118, 309, 312]. It has been shown that at pH 8–10 the equilibrium is on the side of flavanone, whereas at higher pH values 2′-hydroxychalcone is predominant.

The 2'-hydroxychalcone $\rightleftarrows$ flavanone or flavanone $\rightleftarrows$ 2'-hydroxychalcone isomerization at pH > 9.75 is accompanied by the appearance of a new band at 420 nm in the UV spectrum. Its change with time is indicative of the attainment of an equilibrium.

Exactly the same results are obtained when starting either with 2'-hydroxychalcone or flavanone, in the presence or absence of hydrogen peroxide. The new band appearing at 420 nm is due to dissociation or the formation of phenolate anion [94, 309].

The occurrence of dissociation, the formation of phenolate anion is also proved by the identical spectra recorded in tetramethylammonium hydroxide. This is significant, as in the presence of tetramethylammonium hydroxide complex formation and any secondary reaction can be excluded.

As shown by the spectroscopic studies, in the realm of higher pH values the dissociation of 2'-hydroxychalcone is a rapid process, whereas the conversion of the dissociation product or the attainment of an equilibrium can be followed readily by spectroscopy.

In order to determine the composition of the equilibrium mixture, the properties of the so-called "chalcone sodium salt", formed from 2'-hydroxychalcone or flavanone in the presence of sodium hydroxide, were investigated. This "chalcone sodium salt" obtained from 2'-hydroxychalcone with sodium hydroxide in aqueous ethanol or with sodium ethoxide in anhydrous ethyl alcohol is a dark yellow substance, barely soluble in water. It is more readily soluble in organic solvents, e.g. it can be recrystallized from toluene. As shown by elementary analysis, the molecule contains one atom of sodium [66].

The IR spectrum of the "chalcone sodium salt" has a band which can be assigned to the carbonyl group; at the same time regions indicating a cyclized product can also be found. The compound can be deuterated, and the spectra reveal that besides 2'-OD-chalcone, flavanone is also present. On dilution the "chalcone sodium salt" is converted to flavanone, either in aqueous or alcoholic solution.

The spectral and other properties of the "chalcone sodium salt" indicate that the dissociation of 2'-hydroxychalcone in strongly alkaline medium is accompanied by a structural change, as suggested by Dean [67]. The appearance of a band at 420 nm, excitable with the less energy, is indicative of conjugation. This structural change is also seen from the NMR spectra. Comparison of the NMR spectra of 2'-hydroxychalcone (Fig. 14) and the "chalcone sodium salt" (Fig. 15) shows considerable shift of the aromatic protons in the latter.

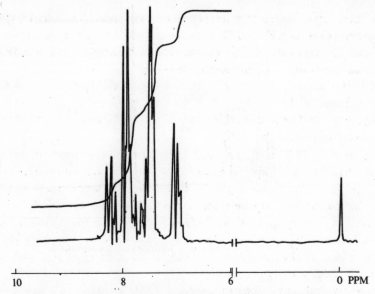

Fig. 14. NMR spectrum of 2′-hydroxychalcone (DMSO-d$_6$)

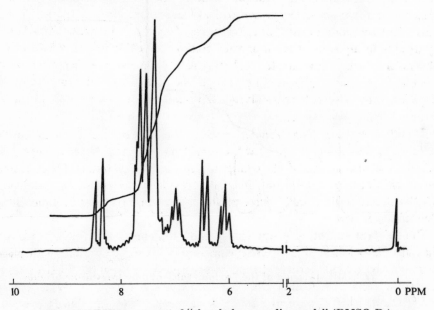

Fig. 15. NMR spectrum of "the chalcone sodium salt" (DMSO-D$_6$)

A similar change is observed in the case of o-hydroxyacetophenone (Fig. 16) and the sodium salt (Fig. 17) made from it.

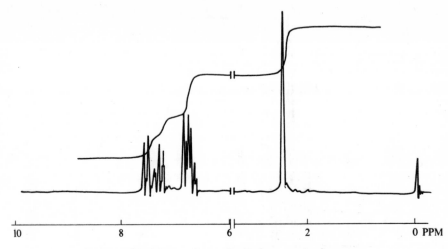

Fig. 16. NMR spectrum of *o*-hydroxyacetophenone

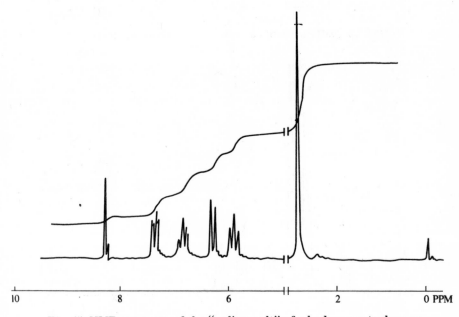

Fig. 17. NMR spectrum of the "sodium salt" of *o*-hydroxyacetophenone

According to the experimental results, above pH 9.75 the equilibrium mixture is formed after the dissociation of the phenolic hydroxyl group; its composition is determined by the pH of the medium.

This shows that the pH-dependent stability of the "chalcone sodium salt" determines any further conversion. In strongly alkaline medium the equilibrium is shifted towards the "chalcone sodium salt" and there is little dissociation; at lower pH values or on dilution, however, flavanone is formed or the equilibrium mixture of 2'-hydroxychalcone and flavanone, corresponding to the given pH value, is obtained. This explains the ring cleavage of flavanones in alkaline medium [313, 314], and isomerization of 2'-hydroxychalcone in dilute alkali solution [315]. In the course of the equilibrium isomerization of α-methoxychalcones to 3-methoxyflavanones, Ferreira et al. [101] also observed that α,β-unsaturated ketones in the presence of a base are stabilized by resonance.

B. Formation of 3-Hydroxyflavanones

As shown by spectroscopic studies, the oxidation reaction begins only after the equilibrium mixture has been formed (Figs 18 and 19). This process can be followed spectroscopically, though results of studying the reaction order point to a complex process.

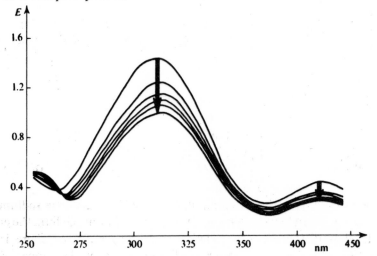

Fig. 18. 2'-Hydroxychalcone in the presence of 0.01 N NaOH and H$_2$O$_2$ (first part of the reaction)

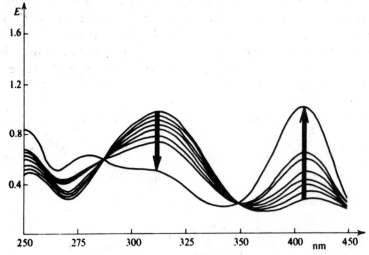

Fig. 19. 2'-Hydroxychalcone in the presence of 0.01 N NaOH and H$_2$O$_2$ (second part of the reaction)

According to TLC and preparative studies [221], the oxidation reaction is determined by the amount of the alkali present. Slight oxidation takes place in the presence even of a catalytic amount (0.01 mole) of sodium hydroxide; both 2'-hydroxychalcone and flavanone give thus 3-hydroxyflavanone. If the quantity of the alkali is increased (0.1–0.5 mole), the presence of 3-hydroxyflavone can also be detected, though the main product is still 3-hydroxyflavanone. One mole of sodium hydroxide is not sufficient for completing the reaction; for this at least three moles of alkali are required.

In the presence of even greater amounts of alkali, decomposition also occurs accompanied by secondary and other oxidation reactions. Thus Cummins *et al.* [288] isolated and identified the derivatives of benzoic acid and of *o*-hydroxyacetophenone produced in the oxidation.

The fact that 2'-hydroxychalcone is oxidized to 3-hydroxyflavanone only at higher pH values (pH > 9.75) shows that the corresponding chalcone epoxide cannot be an intermediate in the AFO reaction since the oxidation to 2'-benzyloxychalcone epoxide does occur at lower pH values as well. At the same time, structural changes may take place in alkaline medium, and this — in agreement with the epoxidation reaction mechanism proposed — by Bunton and Minkoff [68] — will hinder chalcone epoxide formation.

When the oxidation reactions are carried out in the presence of tetramethylammonium hydroxide, the composition of the reaction mixture is similar to that obtained with sodium hydroxide; also the use of tetramethylammonium hydroxide leads to the characteristically pH-dependent equilibrium reaction mixture, either from 2'-hydroxychalcone or flavanone. If an excess of tetramethylammonium hydroxide is used, the equilibrium is shifted towards the dissociated chalcone but, as shown by spectroscopy and TLC, similarly as in alkaline medium, a cyclized product is also present in the reaction mixture. The oxidation reaction is slow in dilute solution, whereas in concentrated solutions, in the presence of at least three moles of tetramethylammonium hydroxide, oxidation occurs very rapidly.

The investigations have shown [64] that the oxidation of 2'-hydroxychalcone or flavanone to 3-hydroxyflavanone is primarily determined by the amount of the base present. This proves that the mechanism of the oxidation reaction is similar to the α-oxidation of aliphatic ketones, which is also decided by the pH of the medium and the quantity of the base used.

There are many references in the literature concerning the mechanism of the α-oxidation of different aliphatic ketones effected in acid or alkaline medium [316–320]. According to these, the reaction is controlled by the rate of the reversible enolization of the carbonyl group [316, 317, 320], this being a function of the alkali concentration. The oxidation takes place through the enolic form. The enolization initiated by the metal ion is a slow process, but ensuing oxidation occurs rapidly. This was proved by Ellis [323] using the example of oxidizing a ketone and its magnesium enolate. Recently the enolization of acetophenones has also been demonstrated and studied [321, 322].

The oxidation of chalcones, similarly to that of aliphatic ketones, may occur through the enolized form, which is here the enolized flavanone derivative.

These investigations supported Dean's hypothesis [67] and showed at the same time that chalcone epoxide is not an intermediate in the AFO reaction. This has also been confirmed by Philbin *et al.* [74, 324] during a study of the oxidations of 2'-hydroxy-α-methoxy-(or methyl-)-chalcones. They found that if ring A in the chalcone has the phloroglucinol substitution pattern, the reactions give 2-(α-hydroxybenzyl)-2-methoxycoumaran-3-one, whereas in the absence of the 6'-substituent flavonols are produced.

During the oxidation of α-methylchalcone, the intermediary 3-methyl-3-hydroxyflavanone is not converted to 3-hydroxyflavone [325]. A study of the stereochemical properties of the coumaranones produced in the oxidation has shown that they are *erythro* isomers. If the intermediate were the *trans*-chalcone epoxide, cyclization involving inversion at the α-carbon atom would result in *threo*-coumaranone.

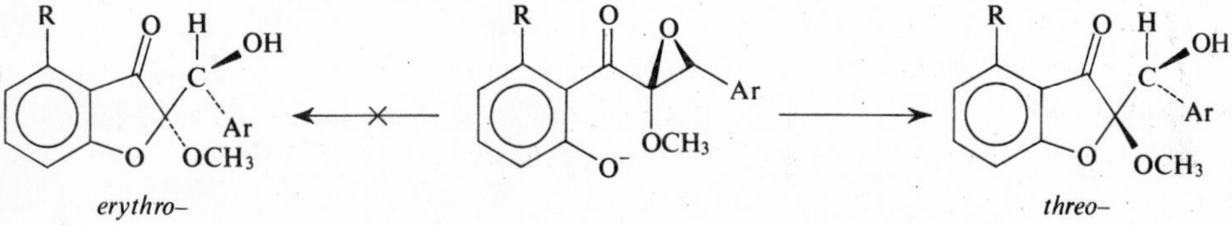

erythro– *threo–*

Further evidence is offered by the fact that the AFO oxidation of 2'-tosyloxy-α-methoxychalcone does not give an epoxide. The formation of an epoxide intermediate is also excluded by the fact that the methanolysis of aurone epoxides results in coumaranones with *erythro* and *threo* configuration, whereas the product of the AFO reaction of α-methoxychalcones is only the *erythro* isomer.

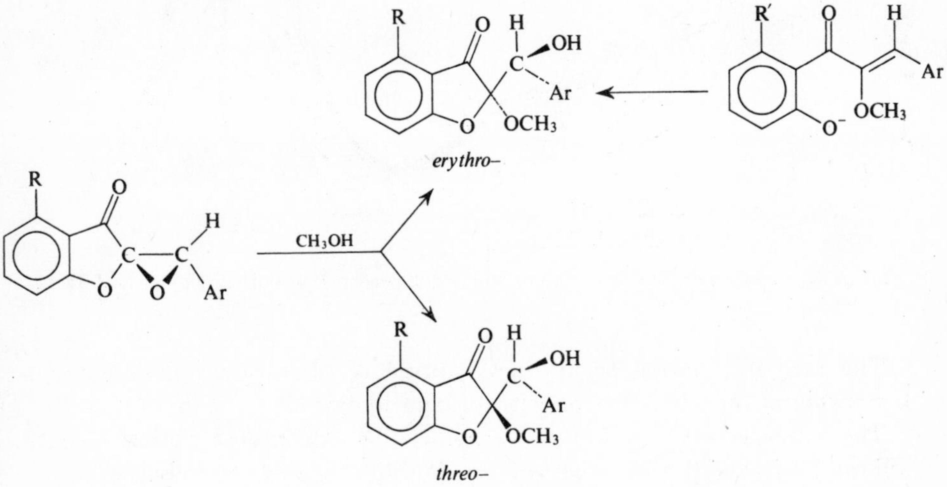

erythro–

CH₃OH

threo–

25*

C. Formation of 3-Hydroxyflavones

The intermediate of the AFO reaction is 3-hydroxyflavanone which is oxidized in the presence of the base to 3-hydroxyflavone. The base is a catalyst in the autocatalytic oxidation [221].

According to experiment, 3-hydroxyflavanone gives in a secondary reaction a 3-hydroxyflavone which binds the base. During the reaction an unstable intermediate ("sodium salt") is formed, which contains two atoms of sodium according to elementary analysis [64].

UV spectroscopy has shown that 3-hydroxyflavanone is dehydrogenated above pH 10.5 to 3-hydroxyflavone. The factor responsible for this conversion is not the hydrogen peroxide, but the pH of the medium. It was found that the reaction occurred only in the presence of 0.5 mole of oxygen [326, 327].

The dehydrogenation can be followed spectroscopically, as a new band appears at 410 nm (Fig. 20), which points to a dissociation or enolization process, similar to the case of 2'-hydroxychalcone.

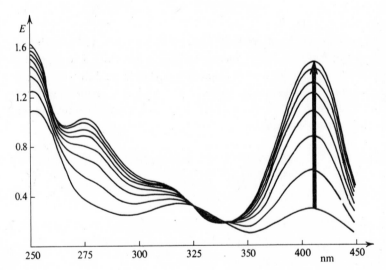

Fig. 20. Conversion of 3-hydroxyflavanone in the presence of 0.01 N NaOH (pH 12.13)

The dehydrogenation occurs in the presence of tetramethylammonium hydroxide in the same way as with sodium hydroxide.

The intermediate "sodium salt", which has an intense yellow colour, affords 3-hydroxyflavone with acid or on dilution. The intermediate is unstable; on standing in the presence of alkali and hydrogen peroxide it under-goes oxidative decomposition.

The IR spectrum of the "sodium salt" is diffuse and it has not the charac-teristics of flavone spectra. The compound is converted by deuterium oxide to 3-OD-flavone.

In the early interpretation of the oxidation of 3-hydroxyflavanone it was supposed, considering the stereochemical aspects [131, 132], that 3-hydroxy-flavone may result from the *trans* elimination of the *diaxial* hydrogen atoms. However, the spectroscopic results, the formation of the intermediary "sodium salt" and its properties cannot be unequivocally explained by this early concept of the reaction mechanism.

Weissberger *et al.* [328–333] elucidated the mechanism of the conver-sion of benzoin to benzil in alkaline medium. The process starts with enoliza-tion, which depends on the amount of the alkali (1). Further conversion may occur through the ene-diolate (2), followed by irreversible oxidation (3).

$$\underset{\substack{|\\Ar-CH-C-Ar'}}{\overset{OH\ \ O}{}} + \ OH^- \ \rightleftharpoons \ \underset{\substack{|\ \ \ |\\Ar-C=C-Ar'}}{\overset{OH\ O^-}{}} + \ H_2O \qquad \textbf{1}$$

$$\underset{\substack{|\ \ \ |\\Ar-C=C-Ar'}}{\overset{OH\ O^-}{}} + \ OH^- \ \rightleftharpoons \ \underset{\substack{|\ \ \ |\\Ar-C=C-Ar'}}{\overset{O^-\ O^-}{}} + \ H_2O \qquad \textbf{2}$$

$$\underset{\substack{|\ \ \ |\\Ar-C=C-Ar'}}{\overset{O^-\ O^-}{}} \ \xrightarrow[+\ O_2]{-2\,e} \ \underset{\substack{\|\ \ \ \|\\Ar-C-C-Ar'}}{\overset{O\ \ \ O}{}} + \ H_2O_2 \qquad \textbf{3}$$

It has also been shown that formation of the ene-diolate is hindered by the presence of an *o*-methoxy substituent [328, 329].

Recently the conversions of aromatic α-ketones, in alkali have been the subject of several investigations, and in some cases the formation of the free radical anion **4** has also been demonstrated by ESR spectroscopy [334–337].

$$\underset{\substack{|\ \ \ |\\Ar-C=C-Ar'}}{\overset{O^{\cdot}\ O^-}{}} \qquad \textbf{4}$$

The stability of the free radical anion is largely determined by the sub-stitution pattern in the aromatic ring and by the reaction conditions [334].

The conversion by alkali of 3-hydroxyflavanone to 3-hydroxyflavone is structurally analogous to the formation of benzil from benzoin. The occur-rence of enolization, which depends on the alkali concentration, was proved spectroscopically; isolation of the intermediary "sodium salt" and the examination of its properties gave evidence for the formation of the enediolate (2) [64]. The presence of the free radical anion could not be detected by ESR measurements [66]; this can be due to a very low concentration of free radicals, or their rapid further reaction.

Dávid, Bognár and Rákosi [338] determined the pH-dependent rate constants of the oxidation of 3-hydroxyflavanone in alkaline medium (Table III).

Table III

The pH-Dependent Rate of Oxidation
of 3-Hydroxyflavanone and Percentage
of 3-Hydroxyflavone
in the Equilibrium System [327]

pH	$k(sec^{-1} \cdot 10^{-2})$	3-Hydroxyflavone, %
9	0.145	26
10	0.577	86.4
11	3.460	100
1 N NaOH	very quick	100

3-Aminoflavanone possessing basic character is oxidized to 3-aminoflavone and hydrolyzed to 3-hydroxyflavone at lower pH values and more rapidly than 3-hydroxyflavanone (Table IV).

Table IV

The pH-Dependent Rate Constants
of the Oxidation of 3-Aminoflavanone
and the Percentage
of 3-Aminoflavone Produced [327]

pH	$k(sec^{-1} \cdot 10^{-2})$	3-Aminoflavone, %
8.2	0.239	66
9.2	0.39	72.8
10.3	1.03	86.4
11.1	6.93	93.5
11.8	40.00	100
0.1 N NaOH	very quick	100

It was found that in the pH range 8–12 a mixture of 3-aminoflavone and 3-hydroxyflavone, whereas above pH > 11 only 3-aminoflavone was formed.

UV spectroscopic studies revealed that the hydrolysis of 3-amino-flavanone precedes oxidation.

The irreversible oxidation of 3-hydroxyflavanones to 3-hydroxyflavones, similarly to the dehydrogenation of α-hydroxycarbinols (acylcarbinols), may occur through the ene-diolate, or ene-diolate anion, and the product is the corresponding dicarbonyl derivative, or its more stable tautomeric form, the 3-hydroxyflavone, which is present in alkaline medium in ionic form [66] as shown by UV spectroscopic evidence.

The hydroperoxide formed in the dehydrogenation reaction was detected by Reichel and Stendel [221] by means of the enzyme catalase. It can be supposed that during the dehydrogenation of 3-aminoflavanone enolate formation is promoted by the α-amino group, thus the reaction may occur at lower pH values and more rapidly [327].

As the dehydrogenation of 3-hydroxyflavanone occurs with tetramethyl-ammonium hydroxide in the same way as with alkali, the suggestion that 3-hydroxyflavone is formed in the AFO reaction by reduction of the metal ion, can be excluded.

It has been proposed by Pelter et al. [102] that chalcones or flavanones in plants give an enolic intermediate when acted upon by metal ions, and the oxidative elimination of the metal ion may lead to the corresponding 3-hydroxyflavone.

6. OXIDATION EXPERIMENTS WITH
2'-HYDROXY-6'-METHOXYCHALCONE
AND 5-METHOXYFLAVANONE

It has been reported in the literature [35, 255] that the expected product of the AFO reaction of 6'-methoxy-substituted 2'-hydroxychalcones is the corresponding aurone derivative.

The change of the UV spectrum of 2'-hydroxy-6'-methoxychalcone or 5-methoxyflavanone in the presence of sodium hydroxide or tetramethyl-ammonium hydroxide is similar to that of the spectra of 2'-hydroxychalcone or flavanone [64].

In the presence of a base, the chalcone ⇌ flavanone equilibrium mixture is formed, but the appearance of the band at 420 nm, characteristic of the dissociation of the hydroxyl group, is not unambiguous; at the same time there is a hypsochromic shift of the original band at 320 nm to 295 nm. (A hypsochromic shift is also observed with 2'-hydroxychalcone, but this amounts only to 12 nm.) A similar difference is found in the spectra of the corresponding 2-hydroxyacetophenones in the presence of a base.

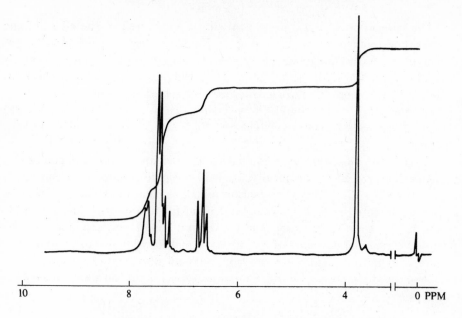

Fig. 21. NMR spectrum of 2′-hydroxy-6′-methoxychalcone

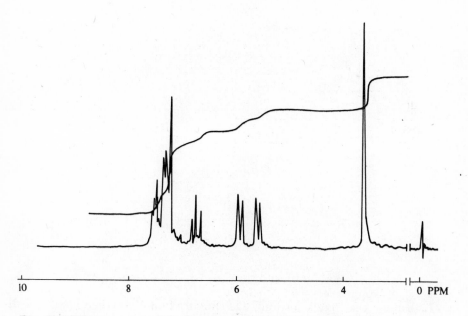

Fig. 22. NMR spectrum of the "sodium salt" of 2′-hydroxy-6′-methoxychalcone

This alteration of the UV spectra can be attributed to the effect of the 6'-methoxy substituent. According to Enebäck [94], the coplanarity of 2'-hydroxy-6'-methoxychalcone ceases in alkaline medium since protolysis breaks down the hydrogen chelate. Thus the spectral change of the non-conjugated system differs from that of conjugated chalcones.

On the other hand, the NMR spectrum of the "sodium salt" (Fig. 22) from 2'-hydroxy-6'-methoxychalcone (Fig. 21) shows a similar shift as observed in the "sodium salt" of 2'-hydroxychalcone (Fig. 15).

Though the oxidation experiments conducted under different conditions can be followed spectroscopically, they do not give homogeneous end-products. As shown by TLC, the reaction mixtures contain as many as four to six components [64, 66]. Isolation and identification showed the main products to be 4-methoxyaurone and 3-hydroxy-5-methoxyflavanone, accompanied by smaller amounts of 3-hydroxy-5-methoxyflavone and 2-hydroxy-6-methoxybenzoic acid. The reaction mixture also contains the starting chalcone and the corresponding flavanone, especially if the alkali concentration is low.

Likewise, the oxidation of 2',4-dihydroxy-3,4',6'-trimethoxy-3',6-di-methylchalcone gives at least four products [339].

Oxidation experiments in the presence of tetramethylammonium hydroxide gave the same results as the use of sodium hydroxide, with the only difference that 2-hydroxy-6-methoxybenzoic acid, produced by oxidative decomposition of the molecule, was obtained in a higher quantity. Variation of the reaction conditions (solvent, molar ratio of the base) slightly modified the proportion of the main products, but the reaction was never unambiguous.

At variance with Dean's results [6, 67], the use of higher temperatures did not result in a straight reaction either; aurone derivative was obtained in each case [64, 66].

It appears that aurone formation is a secondary process in the AFO reaction of 6'-methoxy-substituted chalcones.

Spectroscopic as well as preparative studies have revealed that 3-hydroxy-5-methoxyflavanone on treatment with a base is only partly dehydrogenated to give the corresponding flavonol; the main product of the reaction is 4-methoxyaurone. This fact shows that, in agreement with the references cited above [328, 329], the formation of the ene-diolate (2) or free radical anion (4) is hindered by the presence of an o-methoxy substituent, thus the rate of flavonol formation is reduced, and the preferred reaction product is the aurone.

Aurone formation was explained through the chalcone epoxide by Geissman and Fukushima [35] and Dean and Podimuang [67], but the two hypotheses differed as regards the further conversion of the epoxide. According to the first, the intermediate is 2-hydroxy-2-benzylcoumaranone, whereas in Dean's opinion it is 2-(α-hydroxybenzyl)-coumaranone.

Gripenberg and Juselius [169, 340] found that 5-methoxyflavanone derivatives could be converted to the corresponding aurones through 2-hydroxy-
2-benzylcoumaranone derivatives; however, there is spectroscopic and
chromatographic evidence that, under the conditions of the AFO reaction,
3-hydroxy-5-methoxyflavanone does not give 2-hydroxy-2-benzyl-4-methoxycoumaranone, and no 4-methoxyaurone can be obtained from the
latter. This experimental evidence shows that the mechanism of the AFO
reaction involving the chalcone epoxide as an intermediate, as proposed by
Geissman and Fukushima [35], is incorrect.

Recently, Donnelly *et al.* [312, 341] have also proved that no epoxide is
formed during the oxidation. In a study of the properties of α-phenylchalcones (5) "it was considered that coulombic repulsion of the α-phenyl group
by the phenoxide ion would outweigh the steric effect of a 6'-methoxyl
group and lead to preferential cyclization at the β-carbon atom to give
chromanones."

The base-catalyzed cyclization and oxidation reaction of 2'-hydroxy-α-
phenylchalcone (5) occurs readily (Table V).

Table V

Conversion of α-Phenylchalcones
at Different pH-Values (Yields, %)

Product	pH 8	pH 9	pH 10	pH 11
5	84	60	0	14.5
6	16	40	100	53.6
7	0	0	0	31.9

At a higher pH the oxidation takes place also with atmospheric oxygen
(Table VI), which is due to the effect of the α-phenyl group promoting
enolization.

Table VI

Conversion of α-Phenylchalcones to 3-Hydroxyflavanones
(pH 13.2; Yield of **7**, %)

Product	Time, h.	O₂	Air	N₂	AFO
7	24	73	53	0	68

The alkaline hydrogen peroxide oxidation of chalcone **8** gives a 1 : 1 mixture of 2,3-dihydro-2-hydroxy-2,3-diphenylnaphtho[2,1-b]piran-1-one (**9**) and 2-(α-hydroxybenzyl)-2-phenylnaphtho[2,1-b]furan-1-[2H]-one (**10**). This reaction is not selective even at elevated temperatures.

α-Hydroxybenzylcoumaranones have also been obtained in the oxidation of other chalcones [115, 342], which are converted by alkali to the corresponding aurones. It can be supposed that under the conditions of the AFO reaction the γ-pyrone ring of the primary product 3-hydroxy-5-methoxy-flavanone is opened by the alkali; the 2-(α-hydroxybenzyl)-4-methoxy-coumaranone formed then by cyclization is dehydrated to yield 4-methoxy-aurone (see p. 400).

Japanese researchers [343] have shown by X-ray analysis that the aromatic character and planarity of the γ-pyrone ring is changed on the effect of a substituent in position 5. Such a substituent renders the ring thermodynamically unstable. This also supports the concept of the formation of the more stable aurones from 5-methoxyflavanonols with alkali.

This hypothetical mechanism may also explain the experimental fact that the AFO reaction of 4-hydroxy-substituted 6′-methoxychalcone does not lead to aurone formation [236, 255–259]. Evidently, in this case the electron-donating *p*-hydroxyl group in ring B promotes the enolization of the carbonyl group and the formation of the ene-diolate (2); the *o*-methoxyl group remains in this case without effect, therefore only 3-hydroxyflavone is obtained as the final product.

Recently Ferreira *et al.* [101] found that the steric effect of the substituent in 6′-methoxychalcones is of little importance. They do not exclude the possibility of the oxidation occurring by free radical mechanism, when the 6′-methoxyl group stabilizes the 2′-phenoxy radical.

The elucidation of the mechanism of the AFO reaction may help in clarifying other reaction routes, such as that of the Rasoda–Limaye and Gowan–Hayden–Wheeler reactions. It is a common feature in all the three reactions that in the presence of a 6′-methoxy substituent the final product is the aurone derivative instead of the corresponding 3-hydroxyflavone. 3-Hydroxyflavanone is assumed to be a common intermediate in these reactions; this may give not only 3-hydroxyflavone and aurone, but also the other products obtained in the course of AFO reactions, such as "hydrated aurone", 2-arylbenzofuran-3-carboxylic acid, etc.

REFERENCES

1. "The Chemistry of Flavonoid Compounds" (Ed. T. A. Geissman), Pergamon Press, Oxford—London—New York—Paris, 1962.
2. "Chemistry and Biochemistry of Plant Pigments" (Ed. T. W. Goodwin), Academic Press, London—New York, 1965.
3. "Fortschritte der Chemie organischer Naturstoffe" (Ed. L. Zechmeister), Springer-Verlag, Wien, *13*, 1 (1956); *14*, 186 (1957); *16*, 1 (1958); *17*, 1 (1959); *20*, 165 (1962); *25*, 150 (1967); *27*, 158 (1969); *28*, 1 (1970).
4. "Recent Developments in the Chemistry of Natural Phenolic Compounds, Proceedings of the Plant Phenolics Group Symposium" (Ed. W. D. Ollis), Pergamon Press, Oxford—London—New York—Paris, 1961.
5. "Recent Progress in the Chemistry of Natural and Synthetic Colouring Matters and Related Field" (Ed. T. S. Gore, B. S. Joshi, S. V. Sunthankar, B. D. Tilak), Academic Press, New York—London. 1962.
6. "Naturally Occurring Oxygen Ring Compounds" (Ed. F. M. Dean), Butterworths, London, 1963.
7. "Biogenesis of Natural Compounds" (Ed. P. Bernfeld), Pergamon Press, Oxford—London—New York—Paris, 1963.
8. DAVIES, D. D., GIOVANELLI, J., REES, T. P., "Plant Biochemistry", Blackwell Sci. Publ., Oxford, 1964.
9. "Chemical Plant Taxonomy" (Ed. T. Swain), Academic Press, London—New York, 1963.
10. "Biochemistry of Phenolic Compounds" (Ed. J. B. Harborne), Academic Press, London—New York, 1964.
11. HARBORNE, J. B., "Comparative Biochemistry of the Flavonoids", Academic Press, London, 1967.
12. MABRY, T. J., ALSTON, R. E., RUNECKLES, V. C., "Recent Advances in Phytochemistry", Appleton-Century-Crofts, New York, 1968.
13. GRISEBACH, H., BRANDNER, G., *Experientia*, *18*, 400 (1962).
14. GRISEBACH, H., *Planta Medica*, *1962*, 385.
15. PATSCHKE, L., HESS, D., GRISEBACH, H., *Z. Naturforsch.*, *19b*, 1114 (1964).
16. PATSCHKE, L. GRISEBACH, H., *Z. Naturforsch.*, *20b*, 399 (1965).
17. GRISEBACH, H., KELLNER, S., *Z. Naturforsch.*, *20b*, 446 (1965).
18. GRISEBACH, H., BILHUBER, W., *Z. Naturforsch.*, *22b*, 746 (1967).
19. WONG, E., *Biochim. Biophys. Acta*, *111*, 358 (1965).
20. WONG, E., *Phytochemistry*, *5*, 463 (1966).
21. WONG, E.. *Phytochemistry*, *7*, 1751 (1968).
22. IMASEKI, H., WHEELER, R. E., GEISSMAN, T. A., *Tetrahedron Letters*, *1965*, 1785.
23. GRISEBACH, H., DOERR, N., *Z. Naturforsch.*, *15b*, 284 (1959).
24. GRISEBACH, H., *Z. Naturforsch.*, *14b*, 802 (1959).
25. BOGNÁR, R., *Acta Phys.-Chim. Debrecina*, *6*, 99 (1959—60).
26. GRISEBACH, H., OLLIS, W. D.. *Experientia*, *17*, 4 (1961).

27. GROVER, S. K., JAIN, A. C., SESHADRI, T. R., *Indian J. Chem.*, *1*, 517 (1963).
28. PAQUIN, A.M., "Epoxidverbindungen und Epoxidharze", Springer-Verlag, Berlin—Göttingen—Heidelberg, 1958.
29. BUCHANAN, J. G., SABLE, H. Z., Stereoselective Epoxide Cleavages, in "Selective Organic Transformations", Vol. 2. (Ed. B. S. Thyagarajan), Wiley-Interscience, New York, 1972.
30. BERTI, G., Stereochemical Aspects of the Synthesis of 1,2-Epoxides, in "Topics in Stereochemistry", Vol. 7. (Ed. N. L. Allinger, E. L. Eliel), John Wiley and Sons, 1972.
31. MALINOVSZKIJ, M. G., "Okiszi olefinov i ih proizvodnije", Goshimizdat, Moscow, 1961.
32. WEITZ, E., SCHEFFER, A., Ber., *54*, 2327 (1921).
33. DODWADMATH, R. P., WHEELER, T. S., *Proc. Ind. Acad. Sci. 2A*, 438 (1935); *C. A.*, *30*, 1770 (1935).
34. SIPOS, GY., SCHÖBEL, GY., *J. Chem. Soc. (C)*, *1970*, 1154.
35. GEISSMAN, T. A., FUKUSHIMA, D. K., *J. Am. Chem. Soc.*, *70*, 1686 (1948).
36. ALGAR, J., FLYNN, J. P., *Proc. Roy. Irish Acad.*, *42B*, 1 (1934).
37. GOWAN, J. E., HAYDEN. P. M., WHEELER, T. S., *J. Chem. Soc.*, *1955*, 862.
38. LIMAYE, D. B., *Rasayanam*, 2, 53 (1955).
39. DONNELLY, J. A., DORAN, H. J., MURPHY, J. J., *Tetrahedron*, *29*, 1037 (1973).
40. DONNELLY, J. A., DORAN, H. J., *Tetrahedron*, *31*, 1565 (1975).
41. DONNELLY, J. A., DORAN, H. J., *Tetrahedron*, *31*, 1791 (1975).
42. FLETCHER, H., PHILBIN, E. M., THORNTON, P. D., WHEELER, T. S., *Tetrahedron Letters*, *1959*, 9.
43. VERMA, B. L., BOKADIA, M. M., *J. Indian Chem. Soc.*, *42*, 399 (1965).
44. YOKOYAMA, T., NOHARA, F., *Bull. Chem. Soc. Japan*, *38*, 1498 (1965).
45. RAMAKRISHNAN, V. T., KAGAN, J., *J. Org. Chem.*, *35*, 2898 (1970).
46. MARATHEY, M. G., *Science and Culture (India)*, *20*, 135 (1954).
47. MARATHEY, M. G., *J. Org. Chem.*, *20*, 563 (1955).
48. BIEN, S., BER, M., FLOHR, E., *Israel J. Chem.*, *5*, 51 (1967).
49. FISCHER, F., ARLT, W., *Chem. Ber.*, *97*, 1910 (1964).
50. CHOPIN, J., DURUAL, P., *Bull. Soc. Chim. France*, *1965*, 3350.
51. ZIMMERMAN, H. E., AHRAMJIAN, L., *J. Am. Chem. Soc.*, *82*, 5459 (1960).
52. BALLESTER, M., BLANCO, D. P., *J. Org. Chem.*, *23*, 652 (1958).
53. GORMLEY, T. R., O'SULLIVAN, W. J., PHILBIN, E. M., WHEELER, T. S., *Chem. and Ind.*, *1962*, 1863.
54. GORMLEY, T. R., O'SULLIVAN, W. J., *Tetrahedron*, *29*, 369 (1973).
55. BAKER, W., ROBINSON, R., *J. Chem. Soc.*, *1932*, 1798.
56. ALGAR, J., MCKENNA, J., *Proc. Roy. Irish Acad.*, *49*, 225 (1944); *C. A.*, *38*, 5502 (1944).
57. BOGNÁR, R., STEFANOVSKI, J., *Tetrahedron*, *18*, 143 (1962); *Magyar Kém. Foly.*, *68*, 296 (1962).
58. WEITZ, E., SCHEFFER, A., Ber., *54*, 2344 (1921).
59. FINAL, I. L., MAHMUD, S. Z., *J. Chem. Soc.* (C), *1971*, 2534.
60. MARMOR, S., *J. Org. Chem.*, *28*, 250 (1963).
61. OYAMADA, T., *J. Chem. Soc. Japan*, *55*, 1256 (1934); *C. A. 29*, 4358 (1935); *Bull. Chem. Soc. Japan*, *10*, 182 (1935).
62. MURAKAMI, M., IRIS, T., *Proc. Imp. Acad. (Tokyo)*, *11*, 229 (1935); *C. A.*, *29*, 6598 (1935).
63. MULCHANDANI, N. B., CHADHA, M. S., *Chem. and Ind.*, *1964*, 1554.
64. LITKEI, GY., BOGNÁR, R., DINYA, Z., DÁVID, É. R., "Topics in Flavonoid Chemistry and Biochemistry, Proceedings of the Fourth Bioflavonoid Symposium, Keszthely, 1973". (Ed. L. Farkas, M. Gábor, F. Kállay), Akadémiai Kiadó, Budapest, 1975, p. 110.
65. KHANDUAL, N. C., SATPATHY, K. K., NAYAK, P. L., *J. Chem. Soc. Perkin II.*, *1974*, 328.
66. LITKEI, GY., A kalkonok és a kalkon-epoxidok a flavonoidok kémiájában, Kand. ért., Debrecen, 1973—74. (Chalcones and Chalcone Epoxides in the Chemistry of Flavonoids, Chem. Cand. Thesis, Debrecen, 1973—74. In Hungarian.)
67. DEAN, F. M., PODIMUANG, V., *J. Chem. Soc.*, *1965*, 3978.

68. BUNTON, C. A., MINKOFF, G. J., *J. Chem. Soc.*, *1949*, 665.
69. ZIMMERMANN, H. E., SINGER, L., THYAGARAJAN, B. S., *J. Am. Chem. Soc.*, *81*, 108 (1959).
70. TEMPLE, R. D., *J. Org. Chem.*, *35*, 1275 (1970).
71. ADAMS, J. H., *J. Org. Chem.*, *32*, 3992 (1967).
72. SAKHOVA, M. K., LITKEI, GY., SAMOKHVALOV, G. J., *Dokl. Acad. Nauk.*, *151*, 1120 (1963).
73. BUDAGIANTS, M. J., SAKHOVA, M. K., SAMOKHVALOV, G. J., *Zh. Org. Khim.*, *5*, 1857 (1969).
74. BRADY, B. A., O'SULLIVAN, W. I., PHILBIN, E. M., *Chem. Commun.*, *1970*, 1435.
75. WURM, G., *Arch. Pharm.*, *306*, 299 (1973).
76. ROW, L. R., SASTRY, C. V., *Tetrahedron*, *19*, 1371 (1963).
77. CHOPIN, J., DURUAL, P., *C. R. Acad. Sci. Paris*, *257*, 700 (1963).
78. BHRARA, S. C., JAIN, A. C., SESHADRI, T. R., *Tetrahedron*, *20*, 1141 (1964).
79. DURUAL, P., CHADENSON, M., CHOPIN, J., *Bull. Soc. Chim. France*, *1964*, 11.
80. BHRARA, S. C., JAIN, A. C., SESHADRI, T. R., *Tetrahedron*, *21*, 963 (1965).
81. CHOPIN, J., DURUAL, P., CHADENSON, M., *Bull. Soc. Chim. France*, *1965*, 3572.
82. JAIN, A. C., SARPAL, P. D., SESHADRI, T. S., *Indian J. Chem.*, *3*, 369 (1965).
83. CHOPIN, J., PINEAU, J. P., *C. R. Acad. Sci. Paris*, *265*, 1001 (1967).
84. PINEAU, C., CHOPIN, J., *Bull. Soc. Chim. France*, *1967*, 1471.
85. CLARK-LEWIS, J. W., JEMINSON, R. W., *Aust. J. Chem.*, *20*, 149 (1967).
86. CHOPIN, J., PICCARDI, G., VILLE, A., *C. R. Acad. Sci. Paris*, *267*, 728 (1968).
87. CHOPIN, J., PICCARDI, G., *C. R. Acad. Sci. Paris*, *267*, 1336 (1968).
88. JAIN, A. C., SESHADRI, T. R., *Indian J. Chem.*, *7*, 305 (1969).
89. LITKEI, GY., BOGNÁR, R., *Kémiai Közlemények*, *34*, 249 (1970).
90. LITKEI, GY., BOGNÁR, R., DINYA, Z., *Acta Chim. Acad. Sci. Hung.*, *71*, 403 (1972).
91. BOGNÁR, R., LITKEI, GY., *Acta Chim. Acad. Sci. Hung.*, *67*, 83 (1971).
92. LITKEI, GY., BOGNÁR, R., *Acta Chim. Acad. Sci. Hung.*, *77*, 93 (1973).
93. OYAMADA, T. BABA, H., *Bull. Chem. Soc. Japan*, *39*, 507 (1966).
94. ENEBÄCK, E., *Soc. Sci. Fennica Comm. Phys. Math.*, *28*, 1 (1963).
95. PINEAU, J. P., CHOPIN, J., *Bull. Soc. Chim. France*, *1971*, 3678.
96. AUBRY, C., CHOPIN, J., *Bull. Soc. Chim. France*, *1971*, 4503.
97. PARTHASARATHY, M. R., SHARMA, D. K., *Indian J. Chem.*, *12*, 1009 (1974).
98. KUROSAWA, K., *Bull. Chem. Soc. Japan*, *42*, 1456 (1969).
99. KUROSAWA, K., HIGUCHI, J., *Bull. Chem. Soc. Japan*, *45*, 1132 (1972).
100. KUROSAWA, K., MORIYAMA, A., *Bull. Chem. Soc. Japan*, *47*, 2717 (1974).
101. FERREIRA, D., BRANDT, E. V., VOLSTEEDT, F. R., ROUX, D. G., *J. Chem. Soc. (Perkin I.)*. *1975*, 1437.
102. PELTER, A., BRADSHAW, J., WARREN, R. F., *Phytochemistry*, *10*, 835 (1971).
103. VOLSTEEDT, F. R., FERREIRA, D., ROUX, D. G., *J. Chem. Soc. Chem. Comm.*, *1975*, 217.
104. OLLIS, W. D., ORMAND, K. L., SUTHERLAND, I. O., *Chem. Commun.*, *1968*, 1237.
105. OLLIS, W. D., ORMAND, K. L., REDMAN, B. T., ROBERTS, R. J., SUTHERLAND, J. O., *J. Chem. Soc. (C)*, *1970*, 125.
106. OLLIS, W. D., ORMAND, K. L., SUTHERLAND, I. O., *J. Chem. Soc. (C)*, *1970*, 119.
107. McKILLOP, A., SWANN, B. P., TAYLOR, E. C., *Tetrahedron Letters*, *1970*, 5281.
108. FARKAS, L., GOTTSEGEN, A., NÓGRÁDI, M., ANTUS, S., *Chem. Commun.*. *1972*. 825.
109. FARKAS, L., NÓGRÁDI, M., GOTTSEGEN, Á., ANTUS, S., *J. Chem. Soc. (Perkin I.)*, *1974*, 305.
110. GOTTSEGEN, Á., Természetes eredetü izoflavánok és homoizoflavánok szintézise, Kandidátusi értekezés, Budapest, 1973. (The Synthesis of Natural Isoflavans and Homoisoflavans. Chem. Cand. Thesis, Budapest, 1973, In Hungarian.)
111. ANTUS, S., Private communication.
112. FARKAS, L., NÓGRÁDI, M., ANTUS, S., MÁK, M., MKE Vegyészkonferencia előadás vázlatok. Pécs, 1973.
113. McKILLOP, A., TAYLOR, E. C., Chem. in Britain, *9*, 4 (1972).
114. HÖRHAMMER, L., WAGNER, H., RÖSLER, H., KECKEISEN, M., FARKAS, L., *Tetrahedron*, *21*, 969 (1965).
115. RATHMELL, W. G., BENDALL, D. S., *Biochem. J.*, *127*, 125 (1972).
116. SESHADRI, T. R., THAKUR, R. S., *Curr. Sci.*, *29*, 54 (1960).

117. OBARA, H., ONODERA, J., *Chem. Letters, 1974,* 1357.
118. GROUILLER, A., THOMASSERY, P., PACHECO, H., *Bull. Soc. Chim. France, 1973,* 3448.
119. SPENCE, T. W. M., TENNANT, G., *J. Chem. Soc. (D), 1970,* 1100.
120. SWORD, J. P., *J. Chem. Soc. (C), 1971,* 820.
121. HOUSE, H. O., *J. Org. Chem., 21,* 1306 (1956).
122. BOGNÁR, R., LITKEI, GY., *Acta Phys. Chim. Debrecina, 8,* 25 (1962).
123. BOGNÁR, R., LITKEI, GY., *Magyar Kém. Foly., 70,* 445 (1964).
124. ENEBÄCK, C., GRIPENBFRG, J., *Acta Chem. Scand., 11,* 866 (1957).
125. WASSERMAN, H. H., AUBREY, N. E., *J. Am. Chem., Soc., 78,* 1726 (1956).
126. HOUSE, H. O., RYERSON, G. D., *J. Am. Chem. Soc., 83,* 979 (1961).
127. BREWSTER, J. H., *J. Am. Chem. Soc., 78,* 4061 (1956).
128. BECKER, H., "Einführung in die Elektrontheorie Organisch-Chemische Reaktionen", Berlin, 1961.
129. REICHEL, L., NEUBAUER, A., *Z. Chem., 8,* 423 (1968).
130. BOGNÁR, R., RÁKOSI, M., *Chem. and Ind., 1956,* 188; *Acta Chim. Acad. Sci. Hung., 14,* 369 (1958).
131. MAHESH, V. B., SESHADRI, T. R., *Proc. Indian Acad. Sci., 41A,* 210 (1955).
132. CLARK-LEWIS, J. W., *Rev. Pure Appl. Chem., 12,* 96 (1962).
133. CLARK-LEWIS, J. W., JACKMAN, L. M., WILLIAMS, L. R., *J. Chem. Soc., 1962,* 3858.
134. RAO, C. B., VENKATESWARLU, V., *Tetrahedron, 20,* 551 (1964).
135. LITKEI, GY., BOGNÁR, R., *Acta Phys. Chim. Debrecina, 17,* 239 (1971).
136. CHANDA, B. K., KAR, J. N., BEHERA, G. B., ROUT, M. K., *J. Indian Chem. Soc., 48,* 867 (1971).
137. COLLINS, C. J., NEVILLE, O. K., *J. Am. Chem. Soc., 73,* 2471 (1951).
138. HENDLEY, E. C., NEVILLE, O. K., *J. Am. Chem. Soc., 75,* 1955 (1953).
139. ENEBÄCK, C., ALBERTY, J. E., *Arzneim. Forsch., 10,* 1231 (1965).
140. ENEBÄCK, C., *Acta Chem. Scand., 12,* 1528 (1958).
141. McGUINNERS, D. S., *J. Org. Chem., 27,* 4691 (1962).
142. CROMWELL, N. H., *Rec. Chem. Progr., 19,* 215 (1958).
143. BELJAJEV, V. F., *Zh. Org. Khim., 5,* 352 (1969).
144. ZHIGACHEV, V. E., SMUSHKEVICH, Y. I., MELNIKOV, N. A., *Tr. Mosk. Khim. Tekhnol. Inst., 66,* 120 (1970).
145. WIDMANN, O., *Ber., 49,* 2778 (1916).
146. ROTH, H. J., SCHWARZ, H., *Arch. Pharm., 294,* 769 (1961).
147. NEUBAUER, A., Private communication.
148. BODFORSS, S., *Ber., 51,* 192 (1918).
149. JÖRLANDER, H., *Ber., 49,* 2786 (1916).
150. WIDMANN, O., *Ber., 49,* 2781 (1916).
151. LITKEI, GY., NEUBAUER, A., BOGNÁR, R., *Magyar Kém. Foly., 78,* 359 (1972).
152. NEUBAUER, A., BOGNÁR, R., LITKEI, GY., *Chem., Ges., 16,* 60 (1969).
153. NEUBAUER, A., LITKEI, GY., BOGNÁR, R., *Tetrahedron, 28,* 3241 (1972).
154. CROMWELL, N. H., *J. Am. Chem. Soc., 76,* 5752 (1954).
155. TISHCHENKO, I. G., STANISHEWSKII, L. S., KAVALEVA, A. F., OSIPOVA, S. N., *Vest. Acad. Nauk. Belarus. SSR., Ser. Khim. Nauk., 1970,* 89.
156. FREUDENBERG, K., STOLL, W., *Ann., 440,* 38 (1924).
157. SHARMA, T. S., SAXENA, M. K., BOKADIA, M. M., *Indian J. Chem., 9,* 794 (1971).
158. SHARMA, T. C., BOKADIA, M. M., VERMA, B. L., *Chem. and Ind., 1966,* 599.
159. CHOPIN, J., PICCARDI, G., *C. R. Acad. Sci. Paris, 267,* 895 (1968).
160. PICCARDI, G., CHOPIN, J., *Bull. Soc. Chim. France, 1971,* 230.
161. MOUREU, H., *Compt. Rend., 186,* 380, 503 (1928).
162. HOUSE, H. O., REIF, D. J., *J. Am. Chem. Soc., 77,* 6525 (1955).
163. JAIN, A. C., Szinteticseszkije issledovanija v rjadu Flavonoidov: Thesis doktora him. nauk., Moscow, 1967.
164. JAIN, A. C., ROHTAGI, V. K., SESHADRI, T. R., *Indian J. Chem., 11,* 98 (1973).
165. FREUDENBERG, K., CARRARA, G., COHN, E., *Ann., 446,* 87 (1926).
166. CLARK-LEWIS, J. W., KORYTNYK, W., *J. Chem. Soc., 1958,* 2367.
167. CLARK-LEWIS, J. W., RAMSAY, G. C., *Aust. J. Chem., 18,* 389 (1965).
168. CAVILL, G. W. K., DEAN, F. D., GOOKIN, A. M., MARSHALL, B. M., ROBERTSON, A., *J. Chem. Soc., 1954,* 4573.

169. GRIPENBERG, J., *Acta Chem. Scand.*, 7, 1323 (1953).
170. HOUSE, H. O., *J. Am. Chem. Soc.*, 76, 1235 (1954).
171. GRISEBACH, H., BARZ, W., *Chem. Ber.*, 97, 1688 (1964).
172. HOUSE, H. O., *J. Am. Chem. Soc.*, 78, 2298 (1956).
173. DINYA, Z., LITKEI, GY., BOGNÁR, R., MÁTYÁS, GY., *Magyar Kém. Foly.*, 78, 504 (1972).
174. DINYA, Z., LITKEI, GY., *Acta Chim. Acad. Sci. Hung.*, 75, 161 (1973).
175. DINYA, Z., LITKEI, GY., BOGNÁR, R., MÁTYÁS, GY., ROCHLITZ, SZ., JÉKEL, P., *Acta Chim. Acad. Sci. Hung.*, 77, 323 (1973).
176. DINYA, Z., LITKEI, GY., *Magyar Kém. Foly.*, 78, 630 (1972).
177. DINYA, Z., LITKEI, GY., *Acta Chim. (Budapest)*, 77, 211 (1973).
178. LUTZ, R. E., WEISS, J. O., *J. Am. Chem. Soc.*, 77, 1814 (1955).
179. WASSERMAN, H. H., AUBREY, N. E., *J. Am. Chem. Soc.*, 77, 590 (1955).
180. CROMWELL, N. H., GRAFF, M., *J. Org. Chem.*, 17, 414 (1952).
181. CROMWELL, N. H., SCHUMACHER, F. H., ADELFANG, J. L., *J. Am. Chem. Soc.*, 83, 974 (1961).
182. SOHÁR, P., SIPOS, GY., *Acta Chim. Acad. Sci. Hung.*, 67, 365 (1968).
183. TSUKERMAN, S. V., KUTYULJA, L. A., LAVRUSHIN, V. F., *Nguyen, M. T., Zh. Fiz. Khim.*, 42, 1930 (1968).
184. DINYA, Z., BOGNÁR, R., *Kémiai Közlemények*, 37, 1 (1972).
185. DINYA, Z., *Acta Chim. Acad. Sci. Hung.*, 72, 323 (1972).
186. DINYA, Z., BOGNÁR, R., *Acta Chim. Acad. Sci. Hung.*, 73, 453 (1972).
187. ORLOV, V. D., KOROTKOV, S. A., TISHCHENKO, V. N., LAVRUSHIN, V. F., *Zh. Strukt. Khim.*, 14, 567 (1973).
188. TOBIN, M. C., *Spectrochim. Acta*, 16, 1108 (1960).
189. PARKER, R. E., ISAACS, N. S., *Chem. Rew.*, 59, 737 (1959).
190. FROST, A. A., ROUSE, R. A., *J. Am. Chem. Soc.*, 90, 1965 (1968).
191. CLARK, D. T., *Theoret. Chim. Acta (Berlin)*, 10, 111 (1968).
192. ITAGAKI, Y., NAKANISHI, E., *Bull. Chem. Soc. Japan*, 41, 522 (1968).
193. TURNER, A. B., LUTZ, R. E., MCFARLANE, N. S., BOYKIN, D. W., *J. Org. Chem.*, 36, 1107 (1971).
194. DEL RE, G., *J. Chem. Soc.*, 1958, 4031.
195. DEL RE, G., PULLMAN, B., YONEZAVA, T., *Biochim. Biophys. Acta*, 75, 153 (1963).
196. BERTHOD, H., GIESSNER-PRETTRE, C., PULLMAN, B., *Theoret. Chim. Acta (Berlin)*, 8, 212 (1967).
197. WHELAND, G. W., MANN, D. E., *J. Chem. Phys.*, 17, 264 (1949).
198. BERGSON, G., Arkiv för Kemi, 19, 181 (1962).
199. JANSSEN, M. J., SANDSTRÖM, J., *Tetrahedron*, 20, 2339 (1964).
200. BOGNÁR, R., LITKEI, GY., SZIGETI, P., *Acta Chim. Acad. Sci. Hung.*, 68, 421 (1971).
201. LITKEI, GY., BOGNÁR, R., SZIGETI, P., TRAPP, V., *Acta Chim. Acad. Sci. Hung.*, 73, 95 (1972).
202. LITKEI, GY., BOGNÁR, R., ANDÓ, J., *Acta Chim. (Budapest)*, 76, 95 (1973).
203. BOLGER, B. J., MARATHE, K. G., PHILBIN, E. M., WHEELER, T. S., *Tetrahedron*, 23, 341 (1967).
204. BROWN, B. R., SHAW, N. S., *Chem. Commun.*, 1971, 1579.
205. VICKARS, M. A., *Tetrahedron*, 20, 2873 (1964).
206. CLARK-LEWIS, J. W., BAIG, M. I., *Aust. J. Chem.*, 24, 2581 (1971).
207. CLARK-LEWIS, J. W., MCGARRY, É. J, ILSLEY, A. H. *Aust. J. Chem.* 27, 8651 (1974).
208. FITZMAURICE, W. E., GEISSMAN, T. A., O'SULLIVAN, W. I., PHILBIN, E. M., WHEELER, T. S., *Chem. and Ind.*, 1955, 652.
209. GOWAN, J. E., PHILBIN, E. M., WEHLER, T. S., *Sci. Proc. Roy. Dublin Soc.*, 27, 185 (1956).
210. GEOGHEGAN, M., O'SULLIVAN, W. I., PHILBIN, E. M., WHEELER, T. S., *Tetrahedron*, 22, 3203 (1966).
211. GEOGHEGAN, M., O'SULLIVAN, W. I., PHILBIN, E. M., *Tetrahedron*, 22, 3209 (1966).
212. DOHERTY, J. R., KEANE, D. D., MARATHE, K. D., O'SULLIVAN, W. I., PHILBIN, E. M., *Tetrahedron Letters*, 1968, 441.
213. KEANE, D. D., O'SULLIVAN, W. I., PHILBIN, E. M., SIMONS, R. M., TEAGUE, P. C., *Tetrahedron*, 26, 2533 (1970).
214. DRESCHER, K., HOFMANN, H., FRÖMING, K. H., *Chem. Ber.*, 101, 2494 (1968).

215. DOHERTY, J. R., KEANE, D. D., O'SULLIVAN, W. I., PHILBIN, E. M., *Chem. and Ind., 1969*, 586.
216. HOFMANN, H., WESTERNACHER, H., *Chem. Ber., 102*, 205 (1969).
217. FARKAS, L., GOTTSEGEN, A., NÓGRÁDI, M., *Tetrahedron Letters, 1968*, 4099; *Tetrahedron, 26*, 2787 (1970).
218. MAHESH, V. B., SESHADRI, T. R., *J. Chem. Soc., 1955*, 2503.
219. OYAMADA, T., *J. Chem. Soc. Japan, 64*, 331 (1943); C. A., *41*, 3797 (1947)
220. KURTH, E. F., HERGERT, H. L., ROSS, J. D., *J. Am. Chem. Soc.,* 77, 1621 (1955).
221. REICHEL, L., STENDEL, J., *Ann., 553*, 83 (1942).
222. GOEL, O. P., NARASIMHACHARI, N., SESHADRI, T. R., *Proc. Indian Acid. Sci., 39A*, 254 (1954).
223. ZEMPLÉN, G., BOGNÁR, R., *Ber., 76*, 452 (1943).
224. MOLHO, D., CHOPIN, J., CHANDERSON, M., *Bull. Soc. Chim. France, 1959*, 454.
225. OYAMADA T., *Ann., 538*, 44 (1939).
226. PENDSE, H. K., LIMAYE, S. D., *Rasayanam, 2*, 90 (1955); C. A. *50*, 11334 (1956).
227. KUBOTA, T., *J. Chem. Soc. Japan, 59*, 1153 (1938).
228. PEW, J. C., *J. Am. Chem. Soc., 70*, 3031 (1948).
229. BOGNÁR, R., RÁKOSI, M., *Liebigs Ann. Chem., 693*, 225 (1966).
230. KOSTANECKI, S., SZABRANSKI, W., *Ber., 37*, 2819 (1904).
231. AUWERS, K. G., MÜLLER, K., *Ber., 41*, 4233 (1908).
232. ALLAN, K., ROBINSON, R., *J. Chem. Soc., 1924*, 2192.
233. KOTAKE, M., KUBOTA, T., *Ann., 544*, 253 (1940).
234. LINDSTEDT, G., *Acta Chem. Scand., 4*, 772 (1950).
235. OYAMADA, T., *J. Chem. Soc. Japan, 55*, 755 (1934).
236. JANES, N. F., MORGAN, J. W., *J. Chem. Soc., 1960*, 2560.
237. GUIDER, J. M., SIMPSON, T. H., THOMAS, D. B., *J. Chem. Soc., 1955*, 170.
238. BOGNÁR, R., RÁKOSI, M., *Acta Chim. Acad. Sci. Hung., 8*, 309 (1955).
239. GHIYA, B. J., MARATHEY, M. G., *Indian J. Chem., 3*, 420 (1965); C. A., *64*, 1921 (1966).
240. HERGERT, H. L., COAD, P., LOGAN, A. V., *J. Org. Chem., 21*, 304 (1956).
241. KURTH, F. E., HERGERT, H. L., ROSS, J. D., *J. Am. Chem. Soc.,* 77, 1621 (1955).
242. GROUILLER, E. M.. BROUSSE, E., PACHECO, H., *Bull. Soc. Chim. France, 1969*, 2889.
243. KURTH, E. F., *Ind. Eng. Chem., 45*, 2096 (1953).
244. BOBROV, A. V., MUTOVINA, M. G., TYUKOVKINA, M. A., DEVYATKO, V. G., LAPTEVA, K. J., *Khim. Drev., 10*, 85 (1971); C. A., 77, 19486 (1972).
245. GOWAN, J. E., WHEELER, T. S., "Name Index of Organic Reactions", Longmans, London, 1962.
246. BARGELLINI, G., OLIVERIO, A., *Ber., 75*, 2083 (1942).
247. REICHEL, L., MARCHAND, J., *Ber., 76*, 1132 (1943).
248. BRANDE, E. A., TIMMOUS, C. T., *J. Chem. Soc., 1955*, 3766.
249. MARATHEY, M. G., *J. Sci. Ind. Res. (India), 20B*, 40 (1961).
250. OZAWA, H., OKUDA, T., MATSUMOTO, S., *J. Pharm. Soc. Japan, 71*, 1178 (1958).
251. SMITH, M. A., NEUMANN, R. N., WEBB, R. A., *J. Heterocycl. Chem., 5*, 425 (1968).
252. BARGELLINI, G., *Atti X. Congr. intern. chim., 3*, 32 (1939); C. A. 34, 1018 (1940).
253. OLIVERIO, A., SCHIAVELLO, A., *Gazz. Chim. Ital., 80*, 788 (1950).
254. OLIVERIO, A., MARINI-BETTOLO, G. B., BARGELLINI, G., *Gazz. Chim. Ital., 78*, 363 (1948); C. A., *43*, 1772 (1949).
255. NARASIMHACHARI, N., SESHADRI, T. R., *Proc. Indian Acad. Sci., 30A*, 216 (1949).
256. ANAND, N., IYER, T., VENKATARAMAN, K., *Proc. Indian Acad. Sci., 30A*, 120 (1949).
257. ARCOLEO, A., BELLINO, A., CASINOVI, C., VENTURELLA, P., *Ann. Chim. (Rome) 47*, 75 (1957); C. A., *51*, 1051 (1957).
258. ARCOLEO, A., BELLINO, A., VENTURELLA, P., *Ann. Chim. (Rome), 47*, 658 (1957); C. A., *52*, 1154 (1958).
259. VENTURELLA, P., BELLINO, A., *Ann. Chim. (Rome), 50*, 202 (1960); C. A., *54*, 22610 (1960).
260. YAN, C. F., UONG, T., CHEN, F. C., *Hua Hsueh, 4*, 135 (1973); C. A., *81*, 120382 (1974).
261. VENTURELLA, P., BELLINO, A., *Ann. Chim. (Rome), 50*, 1510 (1960); C. A., *55*, 9412 (1961).

262. KADIVAL, M. V., HIAYAKAONAWAR, J. G., BADIGAR, V., RAJAGOPAL S., J. Pract. Chem., 17, 1 (1962).
263. BELLINO, A., VENTURELLA, P., Atti Acad, Sci., Lettere Arti Palermo, 21, 17 (1962).
264. DEAN, F. M., PATAMPONGSE, C., PODIMUANG, V., J. Chem. Soc. (Perkin I.) 1974, 583.
265. SESHADRI, S., TRIVEDI, P. L., J. Org. Chem., 25, 841 (1960).
266. REICHEL, L., HEMPEL, G., Ann., 625, 184 (1959).
267. SIPOS, GY., JEKL, J., Acta Univ. Szeged, Acta Phys.-Chem., 10, 57 (1964).
268. RAVAL, A. A., SHAH, N. M., J. Org. Chem., 22, 304 (1957).
269. SARMA, O. N., SRIMMANARAYAMA, G., RAO, N., SUBBA, V., Curr. Sci., 39, 133(1970).
270. WURM, G., LACHMANN, C., Arch. Pharm., 307, 695 (1974).
271. SHAH, D. N., PARIKH, S. K., SHAH, N. M., J. Am. Chem. Soc., 77, 2223 (1955).
272. HSU, K. K., SHI, J. Y., J. Chin. Chem. Soc. (Taipei), 20, 51 (1973).
273. AMIN, K. C., AMIN, G. C., J. Indian Chem. Soc., 36, 126 (1959); 38, 391 (1961).
274. PARIKH, S. R., SHAH, N. M., J. Indian Chem. Soc., 36, 729 (1959).
275. CHEN, F. C., CHANG, C. T., J. Chem. Soc., 1958, 146.
276. CHANG, C. T., CHEN, F. C., CHEN, T. S., HSU, K. K., UENG, T., HUNG, M., J. Chem. Soc., 1961, 3414.
277. CHANG, C. T., CHEN, F. C., J. Chem. Soc., 1961, 3155.
278. CHRISTIAN, C. M., AMIN, G. C., Acta Chim. Acad. Sci. Hung., 21, 391 (1959).
279. RAUT, K. B., WENDER, S. H., J. Org. Chem., 25, 50 (1960).
280. VENTURELLA, P., BELLINO, A., PIOZZI, F., Farmaco Ed. Sci., 26, 591 (1971).
281. THAKAR, K. A., DESHPANDE, G. D., J. Indian Chem. Soc., 49, 1029 (1972).
282. RAO, A. V., RAO, N. V., Indian J. Chem., 7, 1091 (1969).
283. CORVAISIER, A., Bull. Soc. Chim. France, 1962, 528.
284. NARASIMHACHARI, N., RAJAGOPALAN, D., SESHADRI, T. R., Proc. Indian Acad. Sci., 37A, 705 (1953).
285. FARKAS, L., HÖRHAMMER, L., WAGNER, H., RÖSLER, H., GURNIAK, R., Chem. Ber., 97, 610 (1964).
286. CUMMINS, B., DONNELLY, D. M. X., PHILBIN, E. M., SWIRSKI, J., WHEELER, T. S., WILSON, R. K., Chem. and Ind., 1960, 348.
287. DONNELLY, D. M. X., EADES, J. F. K., PHILBIN, E. M., WHEELER, T. S., Chem. and Ind., 1961, 1453.
288. CUMMINS, B., DONNELLY, D. M. X., EADES, J. F., FLETCHER, H., O'CINNEIDE, F., PHILBIN, E. M., SWIRSKI, J., WHEELER, T. S., WILSON, R. K., Tetrahedron, 19, 499 (1963).
289. RAO, A. V. S., RAO, N. V. S., Indian J. Chem., 7, 1091 (1969).
290. ROW, L., RAO, C. S., Current Sci. (India), 25, 393 (1956); C. A., 52, 2849 (1958).
291. FARKAS, L., VERMES, B., NÓGRÁDI, M., Chem. Ber., 99, 3222 (1966).
292. MIQUEL, J. F., Bull. Soc. Chim. France, 1961, 1369.
293. ARBUZOV, B. A., JULDASEVA, L. K., ANONIMOVA, J. V., SAGIDULLIN, R. R., CERNOVA, A. V., FAZLIEV, D. F., Izv. Acad. Nauk, (Ser. Khim.), 6, 1258 (1969).
294. MAURET, M. P., BLARDET, D. M., MARONI, M. P., Bull. Soc. Chim. France, 1971, 903.
295. LUTZ, R. E., JORDAN, R. H., J. Am. Chem. Soc., 72, 4090 (1950).
296. MENGER, F. M., SMITH, J. H., J. Am. Chem. Soc., 91, 4211 (1969).
297. TSUKERMAN, S. V., SUROV, J. N., LAVRUSHIN, V. F., Zh. Obs. Khim., 38, 524, 2411 (1968).
298. DZURILLA, M., KRISTIAN, P., Coll. Czechoslov. Chem. Commun., 35, 417 (1970).
299. RABINOVICH, D., J. Chem. Soc. (B), 1970, 11.
300. RABINOVICH, D., SCHMIDT, G. M., J. Chem. Soc. (B), 1970, 1427.
301. VARSÁNYI, GY., "Vibrational Spectra of Benzene Derivatives", Akadémiai Kiadó, 1969.
302. NOACK, K., Spectrochim. Acta, 18, 1625 (1962).
303. SABATA, B. U., ROUT, M. K., J. Indian Chem. Soc., 41, 74 (1964).
304. SOHÁR, P., SZÉLL, T., DUDÁS, T., Acta Chim. Acad. Sci., Hung. 70, 355 (1971).
305. ORLOV, V. D., BOROBOJ, I. A., LAVRUSHIN, V. F., Zh. obsch. khim., 1973, 642.
306. DHAR, D. N., SINGHAL, D. V., Spectrochim. Acta, 26A, 1171 (1970).
307. VAN DE SANDE, C., SERUM, J. W., VANDEWALLE, M., Org. Mass. Spectrometry, 6, 1333 (1972).
308. DÁVID, É. R., LITKEI, GY., BOGNÁR, R., Acta Phys.-Chim. Debrecina, 17, 215(1971).

309. Dávid, É. R., Bognár, R., *Acta Phys.-Chim. Debrecina*, 7, 141 (1961).
310. Litkei, Gy., Dávid, É. R., Vizsgálatok az Algar-Flynn-Oyamada-reakció körében. MTA Flavonoid Munkabizottságának II. Kollokviuma, Mátrafüred, 1973. (Investigations of the Algar-Flynn-Oyamada Reaction. Lecture at the 2nd Scientific Session of the Working Committee for Flavonoid Research of the Hungarian Academy of Sciences, Mátrafüred, 1973. In Hungarian.)
311. Litkei, Gy., Bognár, R., Dinya, Z., Dávid, É. R., Oxidation Experiments in the Group of Flavonoide. Four Bioflavonoid Symposium, Keszthely, 1973.
312. Donnelly, D. M. X., Kavanagh, P. J., Gunning, P. J. M., Interconversions in the Neoflavonoids and in the Isoflavonoids. Fourth Bioflavonoid Symposium, Keszthely, 1973.
313. Schröder, K. L., Darstellung von Chalconen und Flavanonen durch Umsetzung von 2-Hydroxy-acetophenonderivaten mit Benzaldehidderivaten unter milden und physiologischen Bedingungen, Diss. Humboldt-Universität, Berlin, 1967.
314. Grouiller, A., Thomassery, P., Pacheco, H., *C. R. Acad. Sci. Paris. (Ser. C.)*, 280, 991 (1975).
315. Löwenbein, L., *Ber.*, 57, 1515 (1924).
316. Speakman, T. P., Waters, W. A., *J. Chem. Soc.*, 1955, 40.
317. Corey, E. J., Schaefer, J. P., *J. Am. Chem. Soc.*, 82, 918 (1960).
318. Heubest, H. B., Jones, D. N., Slater, G. P., *J. Chem. Soc.*, 1961, 4472.
319. Littler, J. S., *J. Chem. Soc.*, 1962, 827.
320. Wiberg, K. B., Geer, R. D., *J. Am. Chem. Soc.*, 87, 5202 (1965).
321. Bell, R. P., Earls, D. W., Timimi, B. A., *J. Chem. Soc. (Perkin II.)* 1974, 811.
322. Gilbert, T. J., Johnson, C. D., *J. Am. Chem. Soc.*, 96, 5846 (1974).
323. Ellis, I. W., *Chem. Commun.*, 1970, 406.
324. Cullen, W. P., Donnelly, D. M. X., Keenan, A. K., Lavin, T. P., Melody, D. P., Philbin, E. M., *J. Chem. Soc. (C)*, 1971, 2848.
325. Rao, A., Subla, V., *Curr. Sci.*, 43, 477 (1974).
326. Dávid, É. R., Kalkon ⇌ flavanon átalakulás spektrofotometriás vizsgálata, Egyetemi doktori értekezés, Debrecen, 1962. (Spectrophotometric Study of the Chalcone ⇌ Flavanone Interconversion. Doctoral Thesis, Debrecen, 1962. In Hungarian.)
327. Dávid, É. R., Az ultraibolya spektrofotometria alkalmazása a flavonoid kutatásban, Kand. ért., Debrecen, 1975. (The Use of Ultraviolet Spectrophotometry in Flavonoid Research. Chem. Cand. Thesis, Debrecen, 1975. In Hungarian.)
328. Weissberger, A., *J. Chem. Soc.*, 1935, 223.
329. Weissberger, A., Strassner, E., Mainz, H., Schwarze, W., *Ann.*, 478, 112 (1930).
330. Weissberger, A., Mainz, H., Strassner, E., *Ber.*, 62, 1942 (1929).
331. Weissberger, A., Bach, H., *J. Chem. Soc.*, 1935, 226.
332. Weissberger, A., LuValle, J. E., Thomas, D. S., *J. Am. Chem. Soc.*, 65, 1934 (1943).
333. LuValle, J. E., Weissberger, A., *J. Am. Chem. Soc.*, 69, 1567, 1576 (1947).
334. Venkataraman, B., Fraenkel, G. K., *J. Am. Chem. Soc.*, 77, 2707 (1955).
335. Ihrig, J. L., Caldwell, R. G., *J. Am. Chem. Soc.*, 78, 2097 (1956).
336. Heller, H. C., *J. Am. Chem. Soc.*, 86, 5346 (1964).
337. Russell, G. A., Strom, E. T., *J. Am. Chem. Soc.*, 86, 744 (1964).
338. Dávid, É. R., Bognár, R., Rákosi, M., In the press.
339. Raghunathan, K., Rangaswami, S., Seshadri, T. R., *Indian J. Chem.*, 12, 1126 (1974).
340. Gripenberg, J., Juselius, B., *Acta Chem. Scand.*, 8, 734 (1954).
341. Cullen, W. P., Donnelly, D. M. X., Keenan, A. K., Keenan, P. J., Ramdas, A., *J. Chem. Soc. (Perkin I.)*, 1975, 1671.
342. Wong, E., *Chem. and Ind.*, 1966, 598.
343. Hayashi, T., Kawai, S., Ohno, T., Iitaka, Y., Akimoto, T., *Chem. and Pharm. Bull.*, 22, 1219 (1974).
344. Chopin, J., Dellamonica, G., *C. R. Acad. Sci. Paris (Ser. C.)*, 270, 631 (1970).
345. Marathey, M. G., *J. Univ. Poona*, 8, 76 (1956).
346. Hörhammer, L., Wagner, H., Graf, E., Farkas, L., *Chem. Ber.*, 98, 548 (1965).

INDEX

to

SYNTHESIS OF INSECT PHEROMONES AND JUVENILE HORMONES

INDEX

to

COMPOSITION OF BULGARIAN ROSE FLOWER CONCRETE

INDEX

to

CHALCONE EPOXIDES IN FLAVONOID CHEMISTRY